Environment and Archeology

Environment and Archeology

AN INTRODUCTION TO PLEISTOCENE

GEOGRAPHY BY KARL W. BUTZER

 *ALDINE* Publishing Company / Chicago

First published 1964 by
ALDINE Publishing Company
320 West Adams Street
Chicago, Illinois 60606

Library of Congress Catalog Card Number 64-21379

Designed by David Miller
Printed in the United States of America

Third printing February, 1969.

For

ELISABETH and *HELGA*

Foreword

Pleistocene geology is primarily concerned with stratigraphy and chronology. A more comprehensive study of past environments is needed, a *Pleistocene geography* concerned with the natural environment and focused on the same themes of "man and nature" that are the concern of historical and contemporary geographies. This is a field to which both the natural scientist and the archeologist should contribute—more directly and with greater enthusiasm.

The book grew out of lectures and seminars in Pleistocene or prehistoric geography given at the University of Wisconsin since 1960. Their purpose was to study the contributions of the natural sciences to Pleistocene environmental analysis, and to integrate this information with a cultural-historical perspective. Without a suitable book the widely diverse backgrounds of general students, or majors in anthropology, geography, geology, or botany, required a novel approach. Some collateral reading in elementary physical geography or geology, or in general prehistory, as the case might be, proved helpful. But the interest of the students and the peculiar fascination of interdisciplinary problems were found to transcend any technical barriers.

It seemed to me that the materials assembled could be made useful to a wider audience of students in other courses dealing with either the Pleistocene or with prehistory. In its present form this book is specifically intended as a text in Pleistocene geography for coursework in both Pleistocene geology and geomorphology, and prehistoric archeology. Possibly the book may also encourage closer relations between the natural scientists and archeologists—in the field, the laboratory, and the university.

I owe my interest in paleoclimatology to F. Kenneth Hare (King's College, London, then of McGill University). Carl Troll, Roland Brinkmann, and Paul Woldstedt (all of the University of Bonn) gave me my foundations in geomorphology and geology. My subsequent collaboration with numerous friends, colleagues, and students in the field and on the campus stimulated my enthusiasm for cultural problems. To all these and particularly to Robert Braidwood and Clark Howell of the University of Chicago, Günter Smolla of the University of Frankfurt/Main, Chester Chard, Andrew Clark, and Frederick Simoons of the University of Wisconsin, I am indebted beyond measure. The Wenner-Gren Foundation for Anthropological Research provided me with a unique opportunity to learn at two Burg Wartenstein symposia. Parts of the manuscript were read by several people, including H. B. S. Cooke (Dalhousie University), Clark Howell (University of Chicago), Philip Wagner (University of California, Davis), William Denevan, John Emlen, and Johnathan Sauer (University of Wisconsin), all of whom provided valuable criticism. Diagrams and maps were drawn by William Hess.

K. W. B.

Department of Geography,
University of Wisconsin,
Madison
January, 1964

Contents

PART IV. CONTRIBUTIONS OF THE BIOLOGICAL SCIENCES

PART V. SOME PLEISTOCENE ENVIRONMENTS OF
THE OLD WORLD

PART VI. MAN-LAND RELATIONSHIPS IN PREHISTORY

Tables

Illustrations

PART I

Introduction

Prehistoric Environment, Geography, and Ecology

INTRODUCTION

Man had lived on the earth for perhaps a million years before the first literate civilizations of the Near East appeared. This long period saw repeated changes of climate with great modifications of the natural environment. At first man was a rather minor element of the biological world. But gradually the development of social organization and technology lent increasing significance to the human species. Then, with the domestication of certain plants and animals, man achieved a unique dominance in the biological world through agriculture. This new symbiotic alliance spread over most of the world with man fundamentally responsible for widespread and significant modifications of the natural environment.

A study of the environment in prehistory involves more than a complex of interacting physical and biological elements. It adds a new dimension—time. This additional perspective includes natural changes and cultural modifications of the environment.

Methods and techniques in paleo-environmental study cover a wide range of fields including geography, geology, soil science, botany, zoölogy, meteorology—to name only a few of the natural sciences. The delicate cultural aspects of paleo-environmental work are primarily within the scope of the prehistoric archeologist. This is then an interdisciplinary field of investigation.

Much interdisciplinary work in paleo-environmental matters has of course been done in recent decades, but comprehensive studies have been disappointingly absent. Standard Pleistocene geologies such as P. Woldstedt's *Das Eiszeitalter* (1954-58), J. K. Charlesworth's *The Quaternary Era* (1957), and R. F. Flint's *Glacial and Pleistocene Geology* (1957), have devoted considerable attention to the topic,

3

but have been dominated by stratigraphic considerations and glacial geomorphology and have almost ignored the presence of man. F. E. Zeuner's *Dating the Past* (1958; 1st ed., 1946) specifically attempts to bridge the gap between the natural sciences and prehistory, but is chronologically oriented and, like its more paleo-environmental companion *The Pleistocene Period* (1959; 1st ed., 1945), is based upon pre-1945 literature. Also of relevance are compendia such as A. Laming's *La Découverte du Passé* (1952) or the synopsis *Science in Archaeology* (1963) edited by D. R. Brothwell and E. S. Higgs. While the subject matter of this book is then not necessarily new, it attempts to chart a new course in presenting a comprehensive outline of paleo-environmental study from both theoretical and applied viewpoints, followed by an appraisal of some of the inferred interrelationships between man and the environment.

If only for the sake of convenience, a field of study should have a name. Interdisciplinary research, however, borrows techniques and problems from diverse fields, seldom possessing a methodological literature. This difficulty is particularly acute in the case of paleo-environmental work focused on prehistoric man.

The words "geography" and "ecology" both express the idea of interrelationships. "Ecology," according to M. Bates (1953), is concerned with the external factors that control the survival and abundance of individuals and populations. "Geography," on the other hand, can be defined as the scientific description and interpretation of the earth as the world of man (Hartshorne 1959, pp. 21, 172). Clearly "ecology" is a matter for the biologist or anthropologist, whereas "geography" is applicable to a much wider range of work and interests by natural scientists. For this reason "Pleistocene geography" is chosen as a convenient designation which serves to emphasize both environment and man in contradistinction to "Pleistocene geology." [1]

In view of the many disciplines concerned with the Pleistocene there are many different approaches to Pleistocene geography. Basically these approaches are of three kinds:

a) Individual Pleistocene research by the natural sciences, usually carried out independently in the field or laboratory by geologists, geographers, soil scientists, botanists, zoölogists, and meteorologists. Although the range of specific goals or interests may vary greatly, most of our basic techniques and paleo-environmental data have been obtained in this way.

---

[1] As a matter of convenience the term "Pleistocene" is here used as extending to the present, and including the "Recent," "Postglacial" or "Holocene." In this way it would be synonymous with "Quaternary."

b) Interdisciplinary work by natural scientists in collaboration with archeologists, particularly in the field. Pleistocene geology, geomorphology, paleontology, and pollen analysis probably form the most common backgrounds of the individuals concerned. Generally directed toward the study of archeological sites, such interdisciplinary work is particularly valuable in that it contributes ecological as well as environmental information.

c) Paleo-anthropological work by archeologists directed toward a fuller understanding of the human ecology (see Bates, 1953) of prehistoric communities—particularly of the cultural geography and economy.

EARLY RESEARCH IN THE PLEISTOCENE

Students of the Pleistocene, whether earth or biological scientists, have contributed substantially to an understanding of past environments for over a century.

In the field of glacial geology, the first milestone was set by the work of J. Venetz, J. de Charpentier, and L. Agassiz, who established the idea of a former "Ice Age" in the Swiss Alps (1822-47). Equally significant was the proof of continental glaciation in Europe by O. Torell in 1875, and the recognition of interglacial periods by A. Penck in 1879. J. Geikie provided the first systematic treatment of the "Ice Age" in 1874, while the fundamental study of the geographers A. Penck and E. Brückner (*Die Alpen im Eiszeitalter*) in 1909 marks the beginning of the modern era in Pleistocene geology.[2]

The history of botanical contributions to our understanding of Pleistocene and Postglacial climatic history begins with the macro-botanical work of J. Steenstrup in 1841 and A. Grisebach in 1844. A few decades later pollen analysis permitted the first systematic regional interpretations of A. G. Nathorst (Sweden) in 1870, A. Blytt (Norway) in 1876 and E. Engler (Germany) in 1879. Comprehensive studies by C. A. Weber and L. Von Post in 1906 and 1916 respectively had a similar impact on paleobotany as did A. Penck and Brückner in their field.[3]

Paleontological work did not lag far behind the advances in the earth sciences and paleobotany, and studies by L. Ruetimeyer (1862) on the animal remains of the Swiss lake dwellings began an era of ecologically-oriented paleontological work.

---

[2] Discussions of the historical development of Pleistocene geology are provided by Woldstedt (1954), Flint (1957), and Charlesworth (1957, with references).

[3] For general references see Firbas (1949-52, Vol. 1) and Faegri and Iversen (1964).

THE GROWTH OF INTERDISCIPLINARY PLEISTOCENE WORK

Following the establishment of Pleistocene geology, pollen analysis, and paleontology as respectable fields of scientific endeavor about 50 years ago, a later stage of development was more specifically oriented toward prehistoric man. Certainly much of the prehistoric research in France and Switzerland since about 1860 had interdisciplinary overtones, but a new pattern was probably first set by the geological-paleontological investigations of the Grimaldi caves (Boule, Cartailhac, Verneau, and de Villeneuve, 1906-19) and the Grotte de l'Observatoire at Monaco (Boule and Villeneuve, 1927). These represent the first major efforts involving trained natural scientists in direct field association with digging archeologists. Following the same tradition is the association of Elinor W. Gardner (geologist) and Gertrude Caton-Thompson (archeologist) in the Fayum and Kharga oases of Egypt (Caton-Thompson and Gardner, 1929, 1932) and the Hadramaut of southern Arabia (Caton-Thompson and Gardner 1939). A similar team, Dorothy M. A. Bate (paleontologist) and Dorothy A. E. Garrod (archeologist), excavated some of the Mt. Carmel caves of Palestine (Garrod and Bate, 1937). Equally significant during the same decade was the work of the botanists and archeologists of the British Fenland Research Committee during 1932-40 (Philips, 1951); the geological-archeological effort of the Cenozoic Research Institute at Choukoutien, China (Teilhard de Chardin, 1941, with references); the geological-archeological teamwork of H. de Terra and T. T. Paterson (1939) in India, of de Terra and H. L. Movius (1943) in Burma; and the paleobotanical work of R. Schütrumpf (1936, 1938) at A. Rust's Meiendorf site near Hamburg. Another important individual study was the pioneer cave sedimentology developed by R. Lais (1932, 1941) in Central Europe.

Following World War II geomorphological [4] and biological [5]

[4] Some of the more geomorphologically important studies include sites in sub-Saharan Africa (Cooke, 1946; Bond, 1946, 1957, 1962; Brain, 1958; Haldemann in Howell *et al.*, 1962), in the Near East and North Africa (Hey in McBurney and Hey, 1955; Wright, 1951 and in Braidwood *et al.*, 1960; Butzer, 1960b), in Europe (West in West and McBurney, 1954; Gisela Freund in Zotz, 1955; Judson in Movius and Judson, 1956; Butzer, 1963c), and in North America (Bryan and Ray, 1940; Judson, 1949, 1953a and b; Black, 1959, Black and Laughlin, 1964; Mackay *et al.*, 1961).

[5] Including botanists Walker and Godwin (in J. G. D. Clark, 1954), West (in West and McBurney 1954), Helbaek (1959, 1960a), and paleontologists Bate (in A. J. Arkell, 1949b, 1953, and in McBurney and Hey, 1955), Arambourg *et al.*, (1952), Arambourg and Balout (1952), Hooijer (1961), Elisabeth Schmid (1958), Reed (1959, 1960).

investigations of archeological sites became frequent, while the number of contributions and new techniques developed by individual natural scientists has grown tremendously.

This survey of interdisciplinary efforts over half a century is necessarily selective. But it serves to illustrate an increasing degree of interdisciplinary interest and a remarkable acceleration of activity during the last fifteen years or so. Equally symptomatic of growing interest by a wider group of people has been the establishment of an Institute of Environmental Archaeology (under the late Professor Zeuner) at the University of London, a University Sub-Department of Quaternary Research (under Prof. H. Godwin) at Cambridge, and a Geochronological Laboratory at the University of Arizona.

Analysis of the existing substantive literature shows that stratigraphy and climatic interpretation form the most general unifying theme in interdisciplinary work by natural scientists. Petrographical, mineralogical, or out-of-context osteological or vegetable identifications form a surprisingly small segment of the natural science contributions to archeological reports. The lack of distinction commonly made between stratigraphy and environment is understandable since relative dating of sites depends directly or indirectly on the succession of climatic changes. But this slight confusion is serious. Many joint studies neglect a full interpretation of the immediate environment of a site during habitation in favor of discussions of world-wide stratigraphic schemes and absolute chronology. It seems that environmental reconstruction is the higher goal of attainment. Stratigraphy and chronology are indeed important, but they have been unduly emphasized.

PLEISTOCENE GEOGRAPHY AND THE NATURAL SCIENCES IN THEORY

Although many natural scientists co-operating with prehistorians in the field, as well as a great number of individual earth scientists and biologists, are implicitly or explicitly interested in man, there is a marked reticence to engage in integration of "natural" and "cultural" data. A glance at the objectives and interests expressed in the limited methodological literature confirms this.

Methodological interest for an integrated Pleistocene geography has been greatest among geographers. A. H. Clark, in his analysis of the field of historical geography, writes as follows (1954, p. 72):

> To insist that historical geography begins where history, as opposed to prehistory, begins would assume some inherent necessity for written records in studying the past geography of an area. Archaeological reconstructions alone have sufficiently demonstrated that no such

necessity exists. The reasons for denying the validity of such a division apply with almost equal force to any other. There is, indeed, no logical date or period in time when such studies may properly be said to begin. If physical geography is something more than a summation of geological, climatological, ecological, and similar evidence, then a physical historical geography must exist, which utilizes the kind of evidence that is also studied, often in arbitrarily restricted categories, by the historical geologists, paleontologists, and paleo-climatologists. It is true that for periods before the Pleistocene and for much of that epoch, such studies either do not exist, or have been attempted only by scholars from one of these systematic fields. In practice, "dawn" for the historical geographer rarely antedates the late Pleistocene; he has shown little interest in ages devoid of human culture. In logic, however, his license as a scholar allows him to go back in time as far as he has interest and competence.

Clark further stresses that such an interest on the part of geographers has indeed been demonstrated, for example by the works of H. J. Fleure (Peake and Fleure, 1927-36) and P. Deffontaines (1930, 1933) which are devoted to a form of "prehistoric" geography. Another striking example of the geographer's contribution to a fuller understanding of prehistory is provided by the studies of C. O. Sauer on the early significance of fire (1947) and on geographical aspects of agricultural origins (1952).

From another theoretical viewpoint, the field of cultural geography (see Wagner and Mikesell, 1962, pp. 1-24) has shown distinct undercurrents which envisage the natural prehistoric or prehuman landscape as the necessary datum line from which cultural "deformations" are to be measured (Gradmann, 1906, 1936; Sauer, 1927). The natural landscape, prior to agricultural colonization, is in effect the background, and understanding it is prerequisite to a full understanding of the cultural landscape. That this goal of reconstructing the natural landscape is indeed attainable is amply illustrated by the prehistoric vegetation studies in Europe by Firbas (1949-52), Iversen (1954, 1960), Godwin (1956), and others. The natural landscape of ancient Egypt has received attention in regional studies by Passarge (1940) and Butzer (1959b). The study of physical conditions of the environment prior to first agricultural settlement is then also within the traditional interests of geographical research.

Other more general writings are confined to the possible role of natural scientists in relation to archeological investigations. The geologist's work is outlined by H. E. Wright (1957, p. 50), while W. G. Reeder (Laughlin and Reeder, 1962, pp. 106-7) describes interdisciplinary functions of the paleozoölogist.

ENVIRONMENT AND PALEO-ANTHROPOLOGY

The prehistoric archeologist has long been aware that the natural sciences provide a number of useful techniques. The very fact that specific interdisciplinary efforts have a tradition of over a half century speaks eloquently for the paleo-ecological interests of many excavators. Yet closer inspection shows that few archeologists realize precisely what the natural sciences do have to offer. Speaking as a prehistorian, R. J. Braidwood (1957b) lamented "the almost complete lack of comprehension" on the part of archeologists of (*a*) the necessity of understanding the environment as a functioning entity, before cultural interpretation can proceed, and (*b*) the full interpretative potential of non-artifactual materials. So for example, only a small fraction of excavations at prehistoric sites use the services of a geomorphologist in the field, even for a limited period of time. And although it is a common practice to have bones identified afterwards, the idea of having botanical materials studied is often as remote as having a biologist at the site. Some archeologists who do have a geomorphologist at their excavations, "employ" him as a technician expected to provide ready answers for poorly formulated questions. Corollary to such relationships is a failure on the part of the archeologist to communicate information. Such a one-way flow of information is not particularly productive in an interdisciplinary study, so that the natural scientist can hardly be "problem-oriented."

Despite this occasional lack of perceptiveness and genuine collaboration, outstanding examples of paleo-ecological interest in both practice and theory have been manifest. So, for example, J. G. D. (Grahame) Clark (1957, p. 20) insists that the archeologist wishes to obtain a complete geographical-ecological understanding of a prehistoric community—the paleo-environment, its resource potential and external limitations, and above all, the interactions of man and environment as manifested in the economic sphere. Braidwood (1957a, pp. 15-16) voices an appeal specifically directed at the natural scientist:

There is a heatrening growth of comprehension on the part of a few biological and earth scientists that specialized but fascinating problems exist jointly for them and the archeologists. But these exceptions are few . . . the few biologists and earth scientists of good will who are interested must bootleg the time they invest in projects of joint interest. As a general rule, however, biologists and earth scientists tend to side-step problems which are "culture-linked." Once the hand of man has been laid on the species of their concern, an imponderable has been introduced for them, and they seem to find the issue uncongenial.

It seems to me that in reaching for the goal, a new field, perhaps "Pleistocene ecology," might come into focus, allied to archeology (and human paleontology), but setting the archeologist somewhat more free to deal with matters of culture. This field or axis of inter-related disciplines (perhaps "Pleistocene ecology" or "paleo-environ-ment," or "Quaternary geography"—I shall not attempt to name it) would definitely include man as an element in and a factor acting upon the environmental scene.

More recently J. Desmond Clark (1960, p. 308) stated the basic need for a Pleistocene geography particularly well:

> . . . it is essential that the *environment and ecological setting* of cul-tures . . . be established as accurately as possible, for, without this knowledge, we can hardly begin to interpret the cultural evidence. It is necessary to know the nature of faunas, of vegetation and climate, of kinds and forms of raw materials, available to man and so on. Here, to a very great degree, the archaeologist must rely on workers in other disciplines—geologist, palaeontologist, ecologist, palaeobotanist, soil chemist, and geographer, to mention but a few. It is now fully apparent that unless there is teamwork with other disciplines, we cannot hope to extract more than a fraction of the evidence that in many instances our sites could yield.

Grahame Clark's paleo-ecology, if one may call it so, is clearly not intended for the natural scientist alone, but suggests total interpreta-tion by the archeologist in keeping with the natural science evidence. The approach taken in Clark's *Prehistoric Europe: the Economic Basis* (1952) and *Excavations at Star Carr* (1954) provides a good example of this. Braidwood and Desmond Clark have turned more specifically to the natural scientists. Yet both ask for more than environmental reconstruction (not chronology), namely for an applied study of the geographical setting to prehistory. If these authors be considered as spokesmen for wider anthropological circles in favor of interdis-ciplinary collaboration and a geographical-ecological approach, then the broadest scope of Pleistocene geography could be described as *environ-mental reconstruction as applied to an understanding of the ecological setting to prehistory.*

The relation of the natural sciences to anthropology has received attention in the anthropological literature. A systematic description of natural science techniques in prehistory by an archeologist was already given by L. F. Zotz in 1951, soon followed by a technical compendium of scientific methods (Laming, 1952). Since then most general texts on prehistory or archeological method have included sections or chapters of this type. A methodological analysis of the position of these studies within anthropological research is due to R. Pittioni (1961) who distinguishes several classes of auxiliary sciences:

1. Field techniques
   a) "Optional" techniques, including phosphate content of sediments, cave studies in general, particle-size analysis, organic and inorganic chemistry.
   b) "Vital" techniques, including Pleistocene and economic geology as well as pollen analysis.
2. Laboratory techniques
   a) Optional: petrography, textile studies, food-chemistry and radiocarbon dating.
   b) Vital: physical anthropology, paleontology, zoology, botany, mining engineering, metallurgy, metallography and spectral analysis.[6]

Pittioni emphasizes that each of these techniques contributes toward an understanding of the natural environment of a site or the economic activities of a prehistoric community. Among the so-called vital techniques, Pleistocene geology and pollen analysis are singled out as studies prerequisite to prehistoric interpretation and considered as "substantive branches of prehistoric research" (Pittioni, 1961, p. 21). But since their immediate object of study is only indirectly associated with man, none of these auxiliary disciplines are considered as "anthropological."

ORGANIZATION AND OBJECTIVES

To rephrase the opening words of this chapter, the purpose of this book is an analysis of the environment and its possible significance for prehistory. The name "Pleistocene geography" has been suggested for this topic which, understandably, is more a point of view than a scholarly discipline.

The first part attempts to outline a basic scheme of stratigraphy and chronology, intended as background information for the more pertinent topics dealing with prehistoric geography.

The second part deals with the significance of vegetation, soils, and geomorphology as environmental indices. This section also serves

---

[6] J. Haekel, in comments to this paper, notes that the applicability of this scheme varies according to the culture level, making such distinctions as "optional" or "vital" difficult. Some of the distinctions between "field" and "laboratory" techniques are also questionable. As Haekel indicates, the list is not quite complete.

as an introduction to the soil and geomorphic processes so fundamental
to paleo-environmental work. A further chapter discusses modern mammalian distributions, both in their relationship to the environment and
their significance as a food resource for prehistoric man.

Part III attempts a systematic account of Pleistocene sediments
and methods for their study. The terminal chapter focuses this information on the geomorphological investigation of archeological sites. Part
IV follows with a briefer outline of biological contributions to environmental reconstruction.

Although none of the methods in Parts III and IV are likely to
be applied by anthropologists, they may provide the student of
prehistory with an outline of the more relevant paleo-environmental
techniques, as well as an understanding of their possible interpretation. This should facilitate collaboration between archeologists and
the natural scientists in the field or laboratory.

The regional reconstructions of Part V give examples of current
realizations and limitations. The emphasis on Europe, the Mediterranean lands, and northern Africa reflects the range of field experience of the writer. Much information is available concerning Late
Pleistocene environments in North America but it requires the attention of a specialist.

The final section on man-land relationships, also confined to the
Old World, brings examples of the geographical setting to different
stages of prehistory. It is hoped that these examples will speak for
themselves, as they are far less susceptible to error than the connecting
thread of cultural evolution. The implicit sketch of prehistory is not
intended for the anthropologist or archeologist, but for the reader
from other disciplines. The discussions of certain cultural problems
in a geographical perspective may outweigh the many probable short-
comings of Part VI by stimulating further and more critical and effective treatment.

2

Pleistocene Stratigraphy

THE PLACE OF THE PLEISTOCENE WITHIN THE GEOLOGICAL
RECORD

The perspective of time is equally as important to the culture historian as to the geologist, but concept and dimension differ tremendously for the two disciplines. The Quaternary period, embracing the total time span of the human species, represents the very end of geological history—an interval of perhaps two million years within a total five billion years of earth history. In fact the Quaternary accounts for only 0.5 per cent of the time that has lapsed since the first appearance of the trilobites during the Cambrian, some 500 million years ago. On the other hand, "man the tool-maker" existed for as much as two million years, only 5,000 of which fall within the outer circumference of historical time. Consequently almost all of the Quaternary represents "prehistory"—for most culture historians a dark age including over 99.5 per cent of man's existence.

Beyond the pale of history, time becomes a relative concept only, dealt with by approximate methods of stratigraphic and "absolute" dating, and with the philosophy of the geologist rather than of the historian. Absolute dating techniques have provided some local chronologies for the last 40,000-50,000 years, and are now suggesting broad approximations for the total time elapsed during the Quaternary. But most of our knowledge of "time" is confined to relative information derived by stratigraphic techniques, i.e., pertaining to regional or world-wide sequences of natural events such as climatic or biologic changes. It is important then, to distinguish between relative stratigraphy and so-called absolute chronology.

The position of the Quaternary within the standard geologic

TABLE 1
STANDARD GEOLOGICAL COLUMN
(with the Approximate Duration of the Eras)

CENOZOIC
(60-70 mill. yrs.)

Quaternary	{Holocene (synonyms: Recent, Postglacial)
	Pleistocene
	Pliocene
	Miocene
Tertiary	Oligocene
	Eocene
	Paleocene

MESOZOIC
(160-170 mill. yrs.)

Cretaceous
Jurassic
Triassic

PALEOZOIC
(360-380 mill. yrs.)

Permian
Upper Carboniferous (Pennsylvanian)
Lower Carboniferous (Mississippian)
Devonian
Silurian (Gotlandian)
Ordovician
Cambrian

PROTEROZOIC
(at least 2,000 mill. yrs.)

---

column is shown in Table 1. Opinions vary as to whether the Quaternary should be classified as an era (e.g. the Mesozoic), as a period (e.g., the Cretaceous), or an epoch (e.g., the Pliocene). Some authors would even abandon the name Quaternary in favor of considering all of the post-Pliocene as Pleistocene (Flint, 1957, pp. 282-284). Even though the Holocene (equivalent to Recent or Postglacial) is probably nothing more than a warm interval within the Pleistocene "Ice Age," it is decidedly more convenient to maintain a distinctive name for the last 10,000 years—if only to avoid confusion. But for the sake of convenience, unless otherwise specified, the general term Pleistocene will be here used synonomously with Quaternary.

The Pleistocene is an unusual period in earth history. It is not only broadly contemporary with the existence of man, but was witness to one of the rare spasms of extensive and recurrent glaciation affecting the planet. Although very brief by geologic standards, the Pleistocene was marked by numerous, violent changes of climate and environment, so that its over-all effect on the earth's surface was much greater than its duration would suggest. Equally striking have been the effects of the accompanying environmental changes on mammalian (Kurtén, 1959a) and perhaps human (Robinson, 1963) evolution.

THE "NORMAL" CLIMATE OF GEOLOGICAL TIME

Throughout the greater part of earth history world climates were warmer and less differentiated than they are today (see Nairn, 1961; Schwarzbach, 1961). Permanent ice was apparently quite absent and higher latitudes were by no means frigid zones. There is good reason to believe that the position of the geomagnetic poles (and presumably of the geographical poles) has changed constantly in the past, while differential movements between the various continents are difficult to disprove (Opdyke and Runcorn, 1959; Nairn and Thorley, 1961, with references). Such changes make interpretation of paleoclimatic features of the Paleozoic and Mesozoic rather difficult. But for the comparatively recent Tertiary period there is abundant evidence that the poles have been approximately at their present position. Apart from the absence of significantly different geomagnetic data, biological distributions suggest latitudinal orientations much like those of today. The *isoflors* of the older Tertiary are already remarkably arranged in broadly concentric circles about the present North Pole (Chaney, 1940; Axelrod, 1960), while the world distribution of corals during the Tertiary and Cretaceous is almost symmetrical about the modern equator (Schwarzbach, 1961).

As a comparatively well-understood example of warmer conditions, the Eocene floral record of the northern hemisphere can be divided into three major latitudinal belts (Chaney, 1940; Axelrod, 1960) (Fig. 1):

a) The planetary belt north of 50° latitude was dominated by the Arcto-tertiary forest, composed predominantly of *Sequoia* species,

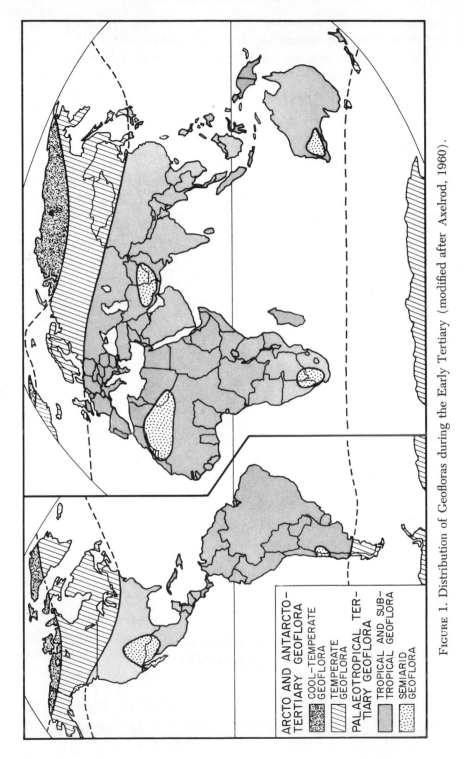

FIGURE 1. Distribution of Geofloras during the Early Tertiary (modified after Axelrod, 1960).

with pine, fir, spruce, willow, birch and elm. This coniferous-type forest is estimated to have enjoyed a mean annual temperature of 10° C., with Januaries in the range of 2°-4°, Julies 18°-21° C. A more cool-temperate facies was present in higher latitudes, north of about 70° latitude.

b) In middle latitudes, a subtropical evergreen association of the *Nipa* palm with numerous tropical oaks covered the sites of the modern deciduous or boreal forest belts, while coral growth was possible in the oceans at the same latitude. Semiarid floras were evolving on the western sides of the continents, in lower-middle latitudes.

c) In lower latitudes the presence of typical tropical forests is verified. Tropical and subtropical floras are not subdivided in Figure 1.

From this example it can be deduced that the isotherms of the present temperate zone were displaced poleward by some 15°-20° of latitude. Equatorial temperatures were not necessarily greater, so that the difference is probably more a matter of reduction of the temperature gradient between pole and equator. This small latitudinal gradient, coupled with the lower general relief common to large parts of the geological record, may be related to frequent evidence of widespread aridity in middle latitudes. Such evidence may in part, however, be a result of slow adaptation of plant life to continental conditions, something only achieved in the Mesozoic.

Although climatic distribution was still latitudinal and seasonal in character, the geography and character of climate was quite distinct from that of today, and even more so from that of the aberrant glacial phases of the Pleistocene. This condition of greater warmth and limited differentiation was called the "normal climate of geological time" by C. E. P. Brooks (1949).

ICE AGES OF THE EARLIER GEOLOGICAL RECORD

The warm conditions prevailing during most of earth history were periodically interrupted by aberrant glacial periods or Ice Ages, recorded by a wide range of geological deposits indicating the presence of great ice masses on several continents.

The first widely recognized Ice Age, the Infra-Cambrian or Eo-Cambrian, is located in the Proterozoic-Paleozoic transition zone. Exact correlation of deposits is impossible, and the duration of the successive stages is unknown. But glacial deposits are widespread in southern Africa, Brazil, and Australia (see L. C. King, 1961, with references) as well as in Greenland, Scandinavia, and the Arctic regions (see Schwarzbach, 1961, with references).

The second major Ice Age, the Permocarboniferous, is a better-defined phonomenon (see Schove *et al.*, 1958; L. C. King, 1961, with references). Major continental glaciations affected parts of eastern South America, southern Africa, India, and Australia during the later Carboniferous, circumstances best explained by a common origin in a primeval Antarctic continent then lying adjacent to the now-dispersed southern hemisphere land masses. More localized glacial features are recorded in the same areas in Upper Permian strata. There may, in all, have been five major glacial complexes during the Permocarboniferous, covering a minimum of ten million years.

HIGHER LATITUDE COOLING DURING THE CENOZOIC

The "normal" climate prevailing since the close of the Permo-carboniferous Ice Age underwent temporary oscillations during the Mesozoic and older Tertiary (e.g., see Emiliani, 1956, 1961). But a distinctive downward trend of temperatures, heralding the Pleistocene, was first evident during the Miocene.

Illustrations of the magnitude of this cooling are provided by a number of paleobotanical and paleozoölogical studies. The following mean temperatures have been suggested for northwestern Europe (Woldstedt, 1954, pp. 8-9; Schwarzbach, 1961) (Fig. 2):

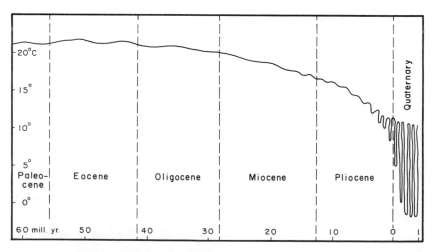

FIGURE 2.

Generalized curve of mean annual temperatures in Central Europe during the Tertiary and Pleistocene (modified after Woldstedt, 1954). The time-scale of the Pleistocene is strongly exaggerated.

Pliocene	14°–10° C.
Miocene	19°–16° C.
Oligocene	20°–18° C.
Eocene	22°–20° C.

They are based upon a number of British, French, and German floras. The present annual mean of these areas is about 9°-10° C. In other words approximately modern conditions had been reached by the close of the Pliocene, recorded by a progressive change from lowland tropical rain forest to temperate forest (Dorf, 1955). A similar trend is apparent in the western United States, between latitudes 40° and 50° (Dorf, 1955):

Pliocene	8°– 5° C.
Miocene	14°– 9° C.
Oligocene	18°–14° C.
Eocene	25°–18° C.
Paleocene	14.5° C.
Late Cretaceous	20° C.

On the nearby Pacific coast of North America, Durham (1950) estimated February marine temperature for the same latitudes as follows, basing himself on paleozoölogical evidence:

Recent	10° C.
Pliocene	12° C.
Miocene	18°–11° C.
Oligocene	20°–18.5° C.
Eocene	25°–18.5° C.

Although these studies also reveal oscillations super-imposed upon the over-all downward trend, temperature fluctuations during most of the Tertiary—as recorded by deep-sea cores—were of long duration and limited amplitude (Emiliani, 1961).

With the beginning of the Pleistocene, a series of brief but intense cold spasms, already heralded by oscillations of increasing amplitude in the later Pliocene, carried the planet into a phase of intense changes of physical environment. Each of the major cold spasms carried world temperatures several degrees below the present mean, and led to migrations and modifications of floras on a continental scale. And at least the last three cold-climate complexes were accompanied by continental glaciations, negative fluctuations of world sea level in a range of 100-150 m., and significant faunal modifications. Compared with the 270 million years elapsed since the Permocarboniferous, the Pleistocene was indeed an abnormal period.

THE PLIO-PLEISTOCENE BOUNDARY

Few of the stratigraphic problems of the Pleistocene are as difficult as a satisfactory delimitation of the boundary between the Pliocene and Pleistocene. Until 1948 the first of the four conventional Pleistocene glaciations was accepted as the base of the Quaternary. At the International Geological Congress in London, during that year, it was widely thought that the continental Villafranchian (with characteristic mammalian fauna) and the marine Calabrian (with the first paleontological evidence of cooler climate) should be added to the Pleistocene (Oakley, et al., 1950). These units, best represented in Italy, had previously been referred to the late Pliocene. There was good reason to consider the Villafranchian stage as Pleistocene since it includes biological evidence of cold climate or at least of temporary cold intervals. Whether or not such early cold phases were accompanied by extensive glaciations remains unknown. But from present knowledge the Villafranchian spans a long period of strongly fluctuating climate which is ultimately responsible for the glacial spasms which mark the climax, rather than the beginning, of the Pleistocene Ice Age.

Three criteria have been suggested for the delimitation of the new Plio-Pleistocene boundary between the Villafranchian and the Upper Pliocene: (a) tectonics, (b) the appearance of new forms of animal life, and (c) first evidence of major climatic deterioration (see the useful review by Howell, 1959b). Tectonic disconformities have on occasion proved helpful, particularly in highly disturbed areas such as East Africa. But such "breaks" in the stratigraphic record are not confined to the Plio-Pleistocene boundary, so limiting their application. The faunal criterion has limitations as well, since the first appearance of the modern genera—elephant (*Archidiskodon*), wild cattle (*Bos*), true horse (*Equus*) and camel (*Camelus*)—was not contemporaneous everywhere. In middle latitudes, wherever long sedimentary sequences are available, paleoclimatic evidence has so far proven most satisfactory. Examples are provided by the immigration of northern mollusca into the Mediterranean, or the abrupt decimation of tropical elements among the flora and fauna of certain Dutch and English beds. Acceptable Plio-Pleistocene boundaries have since been drawn in a number of Old World countries, although it is probable that a good deal of time-stratigraphic discrepancy remains from place to place.

CONTINENTAL STRATIGRAPHY OF MID-LATITUDE EUROPE

An outline of the stratigraphic sequence of Pleistocene events can be obtained by comparative evaluation of reliable and fairly complete local sequences. Unfortunately few such sequences exist, and much of what is widely held as fundamental is in fact dubious or unclear.

At present, potential stratigraphic sequences are known from several major areas: (*a*) the Alpine zone and northwestern Europe, (*b*) the Mediterranean Sea and Morocco, (*c*) eastern and southern Africa, (*d*) the India-Pakistan borderlands, (*e*) the Irrawaddy Valley of northern Burma, (*f*) the Hwang-ho Basin of China, (*g*) Java, (*h*) the Atlantic coastal region of the United States, and (*i*) the Gulf Coast-Mississippi Valley area. In addition, the deep seas of several oceanic areas have provided valuable information of their own. For the purpose of this study, discussion can be limited to a selection of such stratigraphic columns as now seem most representative of world-wide stratigraphic units. There is little question that the European area is still most fundamental for continental stratigraphy, the Mediterranean region (including the Atlantic coast of Morocco), for marine stratigraphy.

Temperate Europe—(*a*) the British Isles, (*b*) the Netherlands, northern Germany and Denmark, and (*c*) the Alpine region with southern Germany—provides fortunate interdigitation of successive glacial deposits with marine or continental beds characterized by distinctive faunas or floras. Although none of these sequences is quite independent or complete, reliable correlations are generally, although not always, possible. Table 2 attempts to sketch the most diagnostic phenomena of each of these three regions, with a suggested nomenclature for wider application. The table is basically arranged with rock-stratigraphic units correlated under headings of "warm" and "cold," and ultimately as a time-stratigraphic sequence. The "cold" intervals later than the Cromerian are either "glacials" or "stadials," the "warm" intervals, "interglacials" or "interstadials." [1]

[1] There is no general agreement as to whether, for example, the Riss and Elster complexes represent two or four glacials, depending upon evaluation of the intervening warm phases. If the Würm interstadial fluctuations be used as guides, the Cortonian and Ohe would merit interglacial rather than interstadial status. As a result, there may be as many as seven or as few as four major glacials, so that terminologies referring to glacials as "first" or "fourth" are apt to promote confusion and are no longer used by Pleistocene geologists.

TABLE 2
Basic Stratigraphy of Mid-latitude Europe

Climatic Oscillation	British Isles [*]	Netherlands Northern Germany Denmark [†]	Alpine Zone and Southern Germany [‡]	Stratigraphic Unit [§]	
Warm	Post-glacial	Postglacial	Postglacial	Holocene	
Cold	Hessle Till	Weichsel Till	Würm Moraines	Würm	
Warm	Ipswich Beds	Eem Beds	Stuttgart Travertine	Eem	
Cold	Hunstanton Till	Warthe Till	Jungriss Moraines		Warthe
Warm		Ohe Beds		Riss Complex	Ohe
Cold	Gipping Till	Saale (Rehburg and Drenthe) Till	*Altriss* Moraines		Saale
Warm	Hoxne Beds	Holstein Beds	Steinheim *Antiquus* Gravels	Holstein	
Cold	Lowestoft Till	Elster Till	(Glaciofluvial Gravel)		Elster (II)
Warm	Corton Sands		Mauer Sands	Elster Complex	Cortonian
Cold	Cromer Till and North Sea Drift		Younger *Deckenschotter*		(Elster 1)
Warm	Cromer Forest Bed	Sterksel Series		Cromerian	
Cold	Weybourne Crag	Menapian	Older *Deckenschotter*		Menapian
Warm		Kedischem Series — Waalian		Kedischem Complex	Waalian
Cold	Chilles-ford Crag	Eburonian	(Glaciofluvial Gravels)		Eburonian
Warm	Norwich Crag	Tegelen Series	Erpfingen Beds	Tiglian	

Climatic Oscillation	British Isles [°]	Netherlands Northern Germany Denmark [†]	Alpine Zone and Southern Germany [‡]	Stratigraphic Unit [§]
Mainly Cold	Red Crag Series — Butley New-bourne Oakley Walton	Praetiglian Complex		Villafranchian (in restricted (sense)
Warm	Coralline Crag	Scaldisian Beds		(Pliocene)

[°] The British sequence follows West (1955, 1956, 1961) and West and Donner (1956) for the glacial and interglacial deposits; and Boswell (1952) and W. B. R. King (1955, with earlier references), for the Crag sequence.

[†] The continental northwest European glacial sequence largely follows Wold-stedt (1958, with references), except for the Ohe interval, a long-term interstadial or interglacial of cool-temperate climate (Van der Brelie, 1955) which is now gaining widespread recognition (e.g., Paas, 1962). The earlier Pleistocene sequence is confined to the Netherlands and the northern Rhineland and is adapted from Van der Vlerk and Florschütz (1953), Pannekoek (1956), and Zagwijn (1960).

[‡] The Alpine-South German sequence is much in need of revision, and is here adapted from a tentative evaluation by Müller-Beck (1957), in its turn partly based upon Graul (1955). The Stuttgart, Steinheim, and Mauer beds are emerging as significant horizons (for details see Reiff, 1955; Adam, 1953, 1954; excellent summaries of Steinheim and Mauer are given by Howell, 1960). The relations of the pre-Riss glaciofluvial and *Deckenschotter* ("Plateau gravels") complex to what have been called the Mindel, Günz, and Donau (Danube) glaciations are by no means clear, and require detailed field reinvestigation. The suggested correlation of these gravels is therefore tentative. The Leffe sequence of the southern Alpine foothills (Venzo, 1955, with earlier references) requires systematic reworking, and is disregarded here. On the other hand the sequence developed for Carpathian Poland by W. Szafer and M. Klimaszewski since 1945 (Szafer, 1953, 1954) appears quite promising.

[§] Obviously none of these sequences are ideal for purposes of nomenclature, and rather than adopt a rigid, regional terminology, the names proposed are selected by the criteria of accurate stratigraphic implication and greatest familiarity. German terms are used in the nominative form, which may serve both the purpose of noun and adjective in that language. Anglicized adjectival forms such as "Hol-steinian" or "Elsterian" are just as ill-chosen as "Wisconsinan" or "Sangamonian" would be. "Cortonian" and "Cromerian" are, however, commonly used in that form while the anglicized adjective "Tiglian" has been adopted by Netherlands authors from the place name Tegelen. "Menapian" and "Eburonian" are derived from Latin tribal names and suited to this adjectival form. Lastly, Villafranchian is here suggested in the restricted sense to include the time range covered by the Mount Perrier, Villaroya, St. Vallier, and upper Val d'Arno beds (Movius, 1949; Viret, 1954; Brinkmann, 1956; Remy, 1958; Kurtén, 1960b). Many authors prefer to include the Tiglian, and others would even include the Kedischem and Cro-merian in the Villafranchian.

Earlier cold phases were probably not accompanied by continental glaciations, so that the terms "glacial" and "interglacial" are of dubious application in the early Pleistocene.[2]

That these earlier cold phases were indeed cold can be readily seen from the European biological record where each successive cold period eliminated part of the local flora and fauna.[3]

No attempt is made here to discuss the zones of the Würm and Holocene, which are considered in chapters 18 and 28. Absolute chronology is treated in chapter 3.

COASTAL STRATIGRAPHY OF THE MEDITERRANEAN SEA AND MOROCCO

Although terminology derived from the Mediterranean sequence is frequently used in attempts at world-wide correlation in distant parts of the Old and New World (e.g., see Woldstedt, 1960a, 1962a), objective correlation of local sequences is difficult even within the Mediterranean. The basis of correlation is the world-wide fluctuation of ocean level reflecting the growth and wastage of the continental glaciers in North America and Eurasia (see chap. 14). In tectonically undisturbed areas sequences of high sea levels (transgressions) were, in part, a result of partial deglaciation during warm phases of the Pleistocene. Mainly as a result of long-term changes in the morphology of the earth's crust, these higher levels appear to be temporary stages superimposed upon the over-all lowering of world sea level evident since late Pliocene times. There is reason to believe that regional altimetric correlation is possible between tectonically stable areas. But Table 3 is more tentative and of less general utility than the European continental sequence outlined in Table 2.

Three sequences, two in the western Mediterranean Basin, one on the Atlantic coast of Morocco, are presented in Table 3. The data

---

[2] More general designations such as the German *Kaltzeit* (cold phase) and *Warmzeit* (warm phase) would be more suitable than the current improvisations.

[3] According to Kurtén (1960a) only 7 per cent of the mammalian species of the Tegelen faunas are recent, whereas already 31 per cent of the Cromerian and 53 per cent of the Cortonian are. The floral decimations are at least equally impressive: the Cromer Forest Bed flora (Duigan, 1963, with earlier references) contains only 5 per cent extinct or exotic (tropical) species; the Tegelen beds (Vlerk and Florschütz, 1953), 41 per cent; the Upper Pliocene Reuver beds, 79 per cent. The Tegelen-age Schwanheim beds (Baas, 1932) have 28 per cent extinct or exotic species, the nearby Upper Pliocene Frankfurt beds (Mädler, 1939), 83 per cent. Similar observations were made by Szafer (1954) at Mižerna, and Huba and Krosčienko in southern Poland. Much of the outright extinction of species and genera may not have been a result of environmental change, but over a half of the floral species in question survive in warmer areas today.

consist of alternating marine deposits and continental beds or series. The older marine deposits were largely laid down at considerable depth, and almost universal deformation gives them little or no altimetric significance. The Calabrian beds, for example, commonly occur to levels of up to 300 meters or more. Units accompanied by elevation values, on the other hand, refer to direct shoreline features, generally substantiated by coastal deposits with molluscan faunas. The continental beds, distinguished by parentheses, are usually interdigited with the marine sequence. In part they pertain to deposition accompanying cooler or moister climates; in part, also, they include coastal accumulations of water and wind-borne materials related to sea levels lower than today (regressions). With such a range of features a strict distinction between rock and time-stratigraphic units is impossible. The Italian terminology has very wide application and may be suggested for the basic stratigraphic sequence.

Although the designations "cold" and "warm" have been included in Table 3, European correlations can only be suggested for part of the column. Direct relationships with the North Atlantic deep-sea sequence discussed in Chapter 3 are equally problematical. Despite the theoretical limitations (discussed in chapter 14) and the stratigraphic uncertainties, Pleistocene coastal stratigraphy is a valuable chronological tool of sorts. This is particularly the case in the later Pleistocene where association of continental deposits with transgressions or regressions may be crucial in establishing local stratigraphies.

PLEISTOCENE STAGES

In concluding this outline of the basic stratigraphical (as opposed to chronological) problems of the Quaternary, the question of Pleistocene stages must still be raised. Table 4 presents some of the views on Pleistocene subdivisions. Understandably, Pleistocene subdivision is not an arbitrary matter and has in the past been made on both climatic and faunal arguments. The various limits given in Table 4 each have faunal significance in Europe. According to Thenius (1962) and Howell (1964) the fourfold division (middle column, Table 4) into Upper, Middle, Lower, and Basal stages provides the maximum number of distinctive faunal and floral units. A distinction between Basal and Lower Pleistocene is also supported by other criteria. So for example, the australopithecine hominids of the Basal Pleistocene contrast with the new genus *Homo* widespread over the Old World

TABLE 3
Coastal Stratigraphy in the Mediterranean Area
and in Western Morocco
(Shoreline Levels Given with Respect to Modern Sea Level; Continental Series
in Parentheses)

Climatic Oscillation	Italy [*]	Majorca [†]	Morocco [‡]	Tentative Correlation
Warm	Versilian +2 m.	+4, +2 m.	Mellahian +2 m.	Holocene
Cold	(Pontinian)	(Regression)	(Soltanian)	Würm
Warm	? Tyrrhenian III	+0.5 to 2.5 m	Ouljien +5 to 8 m.	Eem
Cold		(Minor Regression)		
Warm	Tyrrhenian II +2 to +11 m.	+2 to +12 m.	Kebibatian +15 to 20 m.	} Riss Complex
Cold	(Nomentanan)	(Regression)	(Tensiftian)	
Warm		+4 to 5 m.		Transitional Holstein/Riss
Warm	+16 to 20 m.	+16 to 19 m.		
Warm	Tyrrhenian I +24 to +32 m.	+23 to + 34	Anfatian +25 to 34 m.	} Holstein
Cold	(Flaminian)	(Regression)	(Amirian)	Elster Complex
Cold	Milazzian II ⎫ Later Sicilian		Regressive Maarifian (+40 to 45 m.?)	
Warm	Milazzian I ⎭	+50, +62 m.	Maarifian +55 to 60 m.	Cromerian
Cold	(Cassian)		(Saletian)	
Warm	⎫ Early Sicilian	(+72 m.?)		
Cold	⎭	+110 m.	Messaoudian +90 to 100 m.	
Warm	Emilian		(Regregian)	
Cold	Calabrian		(Moulouyian)	Villafranchian
Cold	Calabrian		Upper Moghrebian	

during the Lower Pleistocene. Similarly the Basal Pleistocene, as reaching up to the base of the Cromerian, would include the great complex of cold and warm phases prior to the first, major continental glaciation. Stage designations are quite useful for broad temporal identification and the Basal-Lower-Middle-Upper subdivisions as defined by Howell (1964) will be used below as time (rather than lithological) units. "Late Pleistocene" will be used specifically for the Würm, while "early" and "later" Pleistocene will be employed in a general way only.

° After Blanc (1957), Castany and Ottmann (1957), Gigout (1962), and Selli (1962)—each with references. Both the Tyrrhenian I and II have several altimetric positions, many of which are not due to differential uplift. Consequently only the range of apparently undeformed shoreline levels is indicated. There may be a Tyrrhenian III at +2 m., contemporary with a similar shoreline of post-Eem age in southern France (Bonifay and Mars, 1959) and Mallorca. But this has not yet been stratigraphically demonstrated in Italy. In none of these areas has the exact stratigraphy of the +16 to 20 m. shoreline—at the end of the Tyrrhenian I or at the beginning of the Tyrrhenian II—been adequately demonstrated. Possibly there were short stands at these approximate levels at both times. The character and significance of Selli's Milazzian II has not yet been established. The term Milazzian was informally vindicated for application to a massive marine sequence in northeastern Italy by the participants at the Wenner-Gren Symposium, "Early Man and Pleistocene Stratigraphy in the Circum-Mediterranean regions," Burg Wartenstein, July, 1960 (published in *Quaternaria*, Vol. 6, 1962).

† After Butzer and Cuerda (1962a, 1962b) and Butzer (1962).

‡ After Biberson (1961a), Choubert (1962), Arambourg (1962), and Gigout (1960). The fauna of the upper, estuarine beds of the Moghrebian is distinctly Villafranchian despite the controversial status of the Moghrebian as such. The Kebibatian (= Harounian = Rabatian) transgression is placed before the Tensiftian by Gigout (1960), after it by Biberson (1961a). But unequivocal stratigraphic sections are lacking. The position of the Ouljian as either Tyrrhenian II (Gigout, 1960, 1962) or III (Biberson, 1961a; Choubert, 1962) is much in dispute. Possibly the stage requires subdivision as has proved possible on Mallorca.

TABLE 4
PLEISTOCENE STAGES ACCORDING TO DIFFERENT AUTHORS

Stratigraphic Unit	Second Inqua Congress (Leningrad, 1932)	Woldstedt (1954), Fink (1960), Thenius (1962), Howell (1964)	Lüttig (1959)	Howell (1960), Woldstedt (1962b)	Kurtén (1960)
Würm / Eem	Upper Pleistocene	Upper Pleistocene	Upper Pleistocene	Upper Pleistocene	Upper Pleistocene
Riss Complex / Holstein	Middle Pleistocene	Middle Pleistocene	Middle Pleistocene	Middle Pleistocene	Middle Pleistocene
Elster Complex / Cromerian / Menapian	Lower Pleistocene	Lower Pleistocene	Lower Pleistocene (Erfurt Stage)	Lower Pleistocene	Middle Pleistocene
Waalian / Eburonian / Tiglian / Villafranchian	Pliocene	Basal Pleistocene *	(Aachen Stage)	Lower Pleistocene	Lower Pleistocene

* The term *Basal Pleistocene* is employed by Howell (1959b) as the logical equivalent for the corresponding German *Ältest Pleistozän*. Howell (1964) would set the Lower-Basal Pleistocene boundary at the base of the Cromerian, since the Menapian ("Günz") is so inadequately known.

Dating
and Absolute Chronology

3

INTRODUCTION

Chronology, although not the central theme of this study, is a most important aspect of Pleistocene research. The details of late Pleistocene and Holocene stratigraphy have been clarified by absolute dating as much as by the more conventional methods of stratigraphic research. Similarly the duration of the Pleistocene and the later Tertiary have been made more tangible by isotopic dating. Consequently both the techniques of "absolute" dating and present information on Pleistocene chronology complement the available stratigraphic information. And both provide the perspective necessary for an effective study of Pleistocene geography.

The various techniques of isotopic dating as well as the problem of "dating" by the "radiation curve" are discussed in a non-technical manner. The available data are subsequently applied to the broad lines of late Cenozoic stratigraphy and to the details of the later Pleistocene.

RADIOCARBON (C ^{14}) DATING

Radiocarbon dating today provides almost the entire structure of geologic and prehistoric chronology for the last 70,000 years. In application since 1949, methods have been rapidly improved so that a part of the techniques and dates outlined by Libby (1955), in the one existing comprehensive study, are already obsolete. The physical background of radiocarbon dating has more recently been reviewed by Aitken (1961, pp. 88-99).

The basic principle in radiocarbon age determination is that cosmic radiation produces a small fraction of the radioactive carbon isotope C^{14} in the atmosphere. Biological assimilation of carbon, in the form of carbon dioxide, also includes a certain fraction of the C^{14} isotope. This is then present in the cellular structure of all organic creatures, plant or animal. Similarly water bodies absorb atmospheric CO_2, which is exchanged between the atmosphere and hydrosphere, so that inorganic as well as organic sedimentation of carbonates includes a definite ratio of C^{14} to C^{12}.

Immediately after absorption of this carbon isotope, directly by plants, indirectly by animals through the intermediate agency of plant tissue, C^{14} begins to disintegrate. The rate of beta ray emission is such as to reduce radioactivity to a half after about 5,730 years, the so-called "half-life" period. Thereafter the rate of decay slows down and diminishes exponentially. Sensitive geiger counters can trace this radioactivity and so enable a determination of the stage of disintegration of the isotope present. This would theoretically determine the age of the isotope, and indirectly of the organism of which it forms a part.

As a consequence of this fortuitous isotope, all organic materials such as charcoal, wood, peat, charred antler and bone, hair, hide, leaves, nuts, soil humus, organic lake and swamp beds, freshwater limestones, and spring tufas or travertines can, theoretically at least, be measured for radioactivity and hence age. This is the essence of radiocarbon dating. The potential of radioactive dating is not unlimited, however.

The theoretical dating span of C^{14} is limited to about 40,000-50,000 years, since radioactivity is not measurable with accuracy beyond that time. Fortunately, Haring et al. (1958) were able to apply artificial isotopic enrichment to samples exceeding 40,000 years in age. Although the increased effect of contamination by modern carbon is, in practice, considerable, the span of dating possibility is extended to about 70,000 years. This appears to be the outer time range of the C^{14} technique. Only the Groningen Laboratory of the Netherlands is so far capable of dating beyond 40,000 years.

SOURCES OF ERROR IN RADIOCARBON DATING

Errors of three kinds reduce the absolute dating value of the technique: (a) statistical-mechanical errors, (b) errors pertaining to the C^{14} level of the sample itself, and (c) errors related to laboratory storage, preparation, and measurement. These facts may be outlined briefly.

a) A statistical-mechanical error is present as a result of the random, rather than uniform, disintegration of radioactive carbon. This is expressed in the date by a plus-or-minus value in years (e.g., 6,240 ± 320 yrs.). The expression conveys that the chances are 67 per cent that the value lies between the stated extremes (e.g., between 5,920 and 6,560 years), and 96 per cent that the value lies within twice that amplitude (e.g., between 5,600 and 6,880 years). This statistical error can be reduced by increasing the time of measurement. It is of no great concern, however, as the practical sources of error inherent to the sample itself are far more serious.

b) Sources of error in the C^{14} content of a sample may be a result of (1) past fluctuations of the C^{14} concentration of the C^{14} exchange reservoir; (2) unequal C^{14} concentration in different materials; and (3) subsequent contamination of samples *in situ*.

1) Fluctuations in cosmic radiation with time may produce slight differences in the C^{14} equilibrium of atmosphere, hydrosphere, and biosphere. Kulp and Volchok (1953) indicated that C^{14} dates compared with independent thorium-230 disintegration rates gave no evidence of appreciable cosmic ray flux within the last 30,000 years. Rosholt *et al.* (1961), by comparisons with the independent protactinium-231/thorium-230 ratio, gave further reason to assume that this time span can be extended to 60,000 years. Willis, Tauber, and Münnich (1960) showed from *Sequoia* tests that fluctuations of cosmic radiation have been slight but rather regular over the last 1,300 years. Ralph and Stuckenrath (1960), however, suggested that appreciable minor fluctuations may have occurred, basing themselves on discrepancies between C^{14} and historical dates for Egyptian materials. Since the C^{14} dates are not really consistent in this case, sample contamination may also be involved.

The addition of "old" carbon to the atmosphere through burning of fossil fuels (since about 1850) is of no direct effect on geologic or prehistoric samples. However, many dating laboratories employed recently-grown wood as a measure of C^{14} exchange activity in the past (see Suess, 1955). The dates published by some laboratories are consequently several hundred years too young. Increased production of C^{14} by H-bomb tests raised the radiocarbon activity of recently grown plants by 25 per cent between 1954 and 1959 (Broecker and Olson, 1960). Although this is not of immediate significance, the penetration of strontium-90 in percolating rain waters presents a serious menace through potential contamination of soil and sediments to considerable depth. These and other errors in the C^{14} concentration of the exchange reservoir have been discussed and evaluated by Aitken (1961, pp. 101-10).

2) Addition of radioactively "dead" carbon to a sample poses a considerable, although frequently determinable, error. Mollusca or submerged aquatic plants add a certain proportion of ancient carbonates derived from old rocks to their tissue. In this way the radioactivity will be too low, the indicated age too great (Deevey et al., 1954). Some modern molluscs have given dates of up to a millennium or more. Fresh-water limestones are generally suspect. Another source of dead carbon is coal or bitumen derived from organic products most frequently of Paleozoic age. Bitumen, on first appearance, does not look unlike charcoal. Since it was widely dispersed in later prehistoric times as a cherished adhesive, bitumen contamination of occupation floors and hearths is a real problem.

Different sample materials do not always provide consistent dates. Charcoal, peat, and well-preserved wood are commonly thought to provide the most reliable dates. Münnich (1957) discussed the value of bone and antler, both charred and uncharred, for dating purposes, while De Vries et al. (1958) and Rubin et al. (1963) considered the same problem for shell. However, Movius (1960) cites an example where charcoal, ash, and burnt and unburnt bone gave rather consistent results. The possibilities of dating freshwater limestones are considered by Münnich and Vogel (1959), of "fossil" water, by Brinkmann et al. (1960).

3) Geobiochemical contamination of samples *in situ* is the worst and most common offender in C^{14} work. Soil processes penetrate to considerable depths in soil and sediment, whereby humic acids, other organic decay products, and fresh calcium carbonate are carried down to considerable depths by percolating waters. Similarly, modern soil humification by roots and soil organisms in a more shallow zone is equally serious. Various cleansing techniques are employed by some laboratories, but such contamination cannot be fully avoided by simple removal of humus and certainly cannot be estimated or foreseen with any accuracy. The best results have so far been obtained by treatment with both hydrochloric acid and sodium hydroxide. Nevertheless, wherever dead carbon can be excluded, a varying degree of contamination *in situ* must be assumed so that most C^{14} dates will be too young. Pedological investigation is strongly recommended for any profile from which samples are removed for C^{14} dating. Equally important is care-

ful analysis and determination of the material to be "run." This should also be specified in publication.

c) In addition to the many sources of inaccuracy already discussed, laboratory processing has introduced a number of further undesirables.

So for example, the half-life of C^{14} once calculated at 5,570 years, was remeasured to be about 5,760 years by the National Bureau of Standards in 1961. Godwin, in a letter to *Nature* (v. 195, no. 4845, 1962, p. 984), suggests use of 5730 ± 40 years as a mean of three new determinations. Published dates may be converted by multiplying them by 1.03.

Early C^{14} work measured radioactivity of solid carbon, a technique discontinued since about 1955 in favor of more efficient procedures involving less risk of current radioactive contamination. Most widely used are gas proportional counters, for which the carbon is converted into carbon dioxide (CO_2), and less frequently, acetylene (C_2H_2) or methane (CH_4). The various techniques of measurement are well discussed by Aitken (1961, p. 110-16).

In addition to the problems of different half-life assumptions, variable efficiency of radiocarbon counters, and variance of results stemming from different techniques there is the problem of preparatory cleansing of samples. The use of hydrochloric acid or sodium hydroxide or both produces appreciable differences varying by as much as 10 per cent or more. Differences of 20 per cent or more were obtained between some "preliminary" and "final" dates (after special treatment for recent humus contamination) by the Groningen laboratory in the 30,000-and-more time range. In other words the available dates, running into many thousands, are of variable reliability. So far the unpleasant but necessary reappraisal of dates has not been formally undertaken. Many disciplines will benefit when and if such a survey is made. Publications should always refer to radiocarbon dates by laboratory and number so that readers may have a ready reference to check on.

In retrospect, then, radiocarbon dates are "absolute" only in a qualified way. An isolated date should be regarded with caution, and cross-dating by use of different materials is suggested wherever possible. Equally important are dates from younger and older levels, where possible, so that internal consistency may be tested. As yet, however, the high cost of such dating only permits processing of a sufficiently great number of samples in rare cases.

A discussion of sample size and sampling is given by Broecker and Kulp (1956), while the significance of radio-carbon dating for archeology is reviewed by Barker (1958) and for Pleistocene stratigraphy, by Rubin (1963). Current theoretical and applied developments in this field since 1959 are best found in the *American Journal of Science, Radiocarbon Supplement*.

POTASSIUM-ARGON DATING

Another method of isotopic dating, applicable to a time range of several million years employs the isotope potassium-40 which disintegrates into the heavy gas argon-40. The principles of dating are analogous to those of radiocarbon, whereby the ratio K^{40}/A^{40} indicates the degree of decay and hence age, using a half-life value of 1,330 million years. The materials accessible are restricted to potassium-rich minerals of volcanic origin. Evernden *et al.* (1957a, 1957b) have somewhat refined the dating applicability by determining the preparation required to remove absorbed atmospheric argon on the crystal surfaces of the minerals used for dating purposes. Results obtained to date were suggestive and interesting (see the review by Gentner and Lippolt, 1963) and have recently proved to be rather significant in reassessing the absolute duration of the Pleistocene (see Hay, 1963; Evernden and Curtis, 1964).

Bed I of Olduvai, Tanganyika, which contains some of the earliest human occupation sites, has been dated by a large number of carefully screened and mutually consistent K^{40}/A^{40} determinations. The basal part of Bed I is approximately 1.9 million years old, the top part 1.5 million years. A sample from the Villafranchian site of Valros, France, yielded an age of 1.6 million. This all suggests a Plio-Pleistocene boundary age closer to 2 million than to 1 million years.

Potassium-argon dates of younger materials (Evernden and Curtis, 1964) are partly controversial. Some of the Italian materials selected for a premature correlation of glaciations in Europe and North America are stratigraphically uncertain. Similarly the existing series of radiocarbon dates available for the late Pleistocene pluvial deposits in Tanganyika, Angola, and South Africa (see Howell and Clark, 1963, and discussion; J. D. Clark, 1963) are partly at variance with the potassium-argon determinations.

THORIUM-PROTACTINIUM DATING

The decay of uranium (U^{238} and U^{234}) in ocean waters is attended by the formation of daughter elements, protactinium (Pa^{231}) and thorium (Th^{230}), which are scavenged by particles settling at the bottom (Rosholt *et al.* 1961). The half-lives of Pa^{231} and Th^{230} are 32,000 and 75,000 years, respectively. Being produced by the same element, their ratio should be unaffected by the concentration of uranium in sea water and should be a function of time only, independent of changes in geological conditions. Rosholt *et al.* believe the elements are very resistant to post-depositional diffusion within a sediment. Unfortunately the technique is limited to marine sediments.

Although there appears to be no reason to believe that the accuracy of Pa^{231}/Th^{230} is better than that of radiocarbon, the method promises to extend the time span accessible to detailed isotopic dating by 100,000 years. A fair number of deep-sea cores have already been dated, providing valuable information on ocean surface temperature changes in a time range of 175,000 years. The dates obtained so far are moderately, although not entirely consistent, tending to diverge badly after about 125,000 years.

THE PROBLEM OF MILANKOVITCH'S "RADIATION CURVE"

Through much of the archeological and even the geological literature the basic concept of Pleistocene chronology is defined by so-called absolute dates obtained from a so-called radiation curve. This curve was originally outlined by M. Milankovitch on the basis of astronomical theory since 1920 and was elaborated in a number of later articles (1941, with earlier references).

The basic concept is one of constant total solar radiation with variations in time of the latitudinal and seasonal distributions. The background is provided by certain periodic changes of the axis and orbit of the earth, changes which obviously did not begin with the Pleistocene. For one, the angle of the ecliptic, i.e., of the earth's axis to its orbit, varies between 65°24' and 68°21' in a period varying from approximately 38,000 to 45,000 years. Secondly there is an around-the-year shift of the date of perihelion, the day when sun and earth are closest, in a period varying from 16,000 to 26,000 years. At present, perihelion occurs on about January 2. Lastly there is an obscure variation in the eccentricity of the earth, i.e., of the degree of deviation of the earth's orbit from a true circle to an ellipsoid. The period of this poorly understood astronomic variable is uncertain, and may lie between 77,000 and 103,000 years. The results, in the main, amount to (a) moderate changes in seasonal contrast between summer and winter, and (b) very modest changes in the radiation received alternately by the northern and southern hemispheres. This is the astronomical background of the radiation curve. Its tenets have been critically reviewed by Carpenter (1955).

Direct chronological implications were attached to the radiation curve by a number of interesting but questionable climatological assumptions. The relatively minor latitudinal temperature variations were presumed to trigger off a number of changes which, after a retardation of some millennia, were supposedly responsible for the alternations of glacial and interglacial periods. Wundt (1933) emphasized that once glacier accumulation had begun in latitude 65°N., the albedo or reflection of the snow would provide a powerful self-perpetuation or "feed-back" mechanism. Further climatologic refinements were carried out by Wundt (1944), but have been sharply criticized from the meteorological standpoint by Berg (1949). Through the elaborate presentations of Soergel (1937) and his student, Zeuner (1958, 1959), a hypothetical glaciation curve or chronology, built on the foundation of the radiation curve, found its way into the core of chronological thought. Geologists such as Woldstedt (1929, 1954) and Flint (1957; 1st ed., 1947) evaluated the "curve" in the light of geological evidence and found it unsatisfactory. Strong evidence favors the synchronous nature of climatic changes and oscillations on both the northern and southern hemispheres, in conflict with the basic requirements of the "astronomical theory." Equally disconcerting have been the wide range of interpretive variations by different authors who successfully "fitted" the curve oscillations to any number of glacial or interglacial phases.

Despite the almost general reservation of Pleistocene stratigraphers and meteorologists today, there has been no lack of attempts to revive the "curve"—e.g., Van Woerkom (1953) attempted to modify the curve itself, and Emiliani and Geiss (1957) or Fairbridge (1961) have attempted to reconcile the "curve" and the geological evidence. An objectively dated deep-sea core temperature profile by Rosholt et al. (1961), discussed in detail below, does indeed show possibilities of background significance of the "curve" for Pleistocene temperature variations. But there is a lack of convincing data on the quantitative significance of the radiation curve for the world heat-balance, whether or not these fluctuations really are of paleoclimatic importance. Without a complete analysis of the theory from an astronomical and meteorological [1] point of view, recurrent attempts at curve comparison remain without adequate physical foundation. Present information is insufficient to prove or disprove the value of the astronomical radiation curve, and considerably more evidence must be available before a reliable and satisfactory analysis can be made. Great caution must be exercised in the meantime, and it is not scientifically possible to use the curve for any dating purposes.

OTHER METHODS OF ABSOLUTE DATING

Absolute dating is not confined to isotopic dating. Absolute chronological information has also been obtained by geological methods such as varve counting (see chap. 11), by tree-ring analysis or dendrochronology (see chap. 16), and by pottery dating techniques such as magnetic and thermoluminescent dating (Aitken, 1961, pp. 121-55; Kennedy and Knopff, 1960). Most of these techniques have only had application to the last few millennia. In a much greater time range, extrapolated fluorine dating of bone (see chap. 7) and the evolutionary concept of longevity and half-life of mammalian and molluscan species (Kurtén, 1959a, 1960a, 1960b) have provided interesting although tentative information.

ABSOLUTE DATING APPLIED TO PLEISTOCENE STRATIGRAPHY

The broad stratigraphic units of the Pleistocene outlined in Tables 2-4 become more meaningful in the light of absolute dating. Some of the boundaries for which information is available may be discussed briefly.

The Pleistocene-Holocene boundary.—The first absolute date calculated for the Pleistocene-Holocene boundary was the varve count of De Geer (1940), namely 7912 B.C. A large number of C[14] dates, published or compiled in a great variety of sources, suggest that the date possibly lies closer to 10,500 years before the present (B.P.).

---

[1] It is interesting that no meteorologist or climatologist at the World Meteorological Organization—UNESCO Symposium "Changes of Climate," Rome, October, 1961 (*Arid Zone Research*, Vol. 20, 1963), seriously considered the astronomical radiation curve.

Godwin *et al.* (1957) use a boundary value of about 8300 B.C.
(10,300 B.P.).[2]

The Eem-Würm boundary.—The transition from last interglacial
to last glacial is at the outer limits of C[14] dating by the artificial
enrichment technique. C[14] dates of very early Würm horizons (Andersen *et al.*, 1960; De Vries and Dreimanis, 1960) now suggest the close
of the Eem may be set at about 75,000 B.P. Interpolation of Pa-Th
dates in oceanic paleotemperature curves suggests about 65,000 B.P.
for the beginning of the last major cold-climate phase (Rosholt *et al.*,
1961).

Chronology of the Eem, the Riss Complex, and the Holstein.—
Beyond the Eem-Würm boundary absolute chronology suffers from
both a lack of sufficient and reliable dates as well as from the uncertainties of stratigraphic correlation.

The most detailed record of major temperature fluctuations during
the later Pleistocene is provided by the record of ocean surface
water paleotemperatures preserved in deep-sea sediments. However,
the available data are subject to stratigraphic interpretation since
detailed absolute dating of continental stratigraphy is limited to the
last 70,000 years. The ecological aspects of ocean water paleotemperatures are considered in chapter 17, and Table 5 below only gives an

TABLE 5

STRATIGRAPHY AND CHRONOLOGY OF NORTH ATLANTIC
DEEP-SEA CORE FAUNAL ZONES

Faunal Zone (Ericson et al., 1961)	Duration in Years (Ericson et al.)	Duration in Years (Rosholt et al., 1961)	Isotopic Temperature Deviations in ° C (Emiliani, 1955a)
Z (Warm)	11,000	10,000	+1 to —1
Y (Cold)	50,000	55,000	—2.5 to —5
X (Warm)	35,000	35,000	+1 to —2.5
W (Cold)	20,000	30,000	—2.5 to —5
V (Warm)	110,000	45,000	+0.5 to —3.5
U (Cold)	?	?	as much as —5

[2] Most C[14] dates are quoted with B.P. rather than B.C. values. For practical
purposes B.P. values are readily converted to years B.C. in the 10,000 to 70,000 year
time range by subtracting 2,000 years. For younger periods, however, subtraction
of the generally accepted "zero" date 1950 A.D. is bothersome, and the concurrent
use of B.P. and B.C. values is little short of confusing. A compromise solution of
quoting B.P. values for Pleistocene dates (older than about 10,000 years) and B.C.
or A.D. values for Holocene dates (younger than 10,000 years) will be adopted here.

outline of the basic data. The faunal zones of Ericson *et al.* (1961) have been partly dated by 37 radiocarbon determinations in 10 cores, while the time span beyond 38,000 years is extrapolated. The paleo-temperature curve of Rosholt *et al.* (1961) is largely dated by Pa-Th but extrapolated beyond 150,000 years.

Beyond question, zone Z represents the Holocene and Y the Würm. Earlier correlations are only speculative, however. Zone W has been variously interpreted as "Riss" (Rosholt *et al.*, 1961; Ericson, 1961), as an early Würm stadial (Ericson, 1961), or as "Riss II (Warthe)" (Olausson, 1961a and b). Interpretations of X, V, and U vary accordingly. In view of the continental stratigraphy adopted in Table 2, Zone W could conceivably represent the Warthe; Zone U, the Saale; and Zone V, the intervening interstadial or interglacial—the Ohe. Admitting this tentative correlation, the Eem interglacial may have begun about 100,000 B.P. and the Warthe glaciation, about 130,000 B.P. The preceding warm interval would then have begun before 175,000 B.P.

The Holstein interglacial has generally been approximated at a quarter million years old by conventional geological estimates. Richter (1958) has constructed a chronological curve obtained from rates of fluorine increase in various bone beds, fixed at one end by C[14] dates, at the other by lead-helium isotopic dating of the Miocene. The Holstein is dated at about 240,000 B.P. on this curve. Kurtén (1960b), on the other hand, uses a statistical analysis of mammalian and molluscan evolutionary rates and extinctions to arrive at a similar date of 230,000 B.P. for what are certainly Holstein faunas. A date of 250,000 ± 25,000 B.P. seems a reasonable assumption for the Holstein interglacial. This would substantiate the interpretation that the cold phases at about 200,000 and 115,000 B.P. represent the Saale and Warthe respectively (Table 6).

Chronology of earlier Pleistocene events.—Prior to the Holstein, available absolute dates diverge considerably. There are no good dates available for either the Elster or Kedischem complexes.[3] The Cromerian is assessed at about 640,000 B.P. by Richter (1958), at 480,000 B.P. by Kurtén (1960b). Kurtén (1960a) further estimates that the Elster Complex was approximately as long as the totality of post-

---

[3] The stratigraphy of the Pleistocene volcanic deposits of the Rome area dated by K-A (Evernden and Curtis, 1964) is rather uncertain. A K-A date of 370,000 years for the younger Main Terrace of the Rhine, near Andernach, is erroneously cited as Elster. The Main Terrace is, however, stratigraphically older than the Elster, being equivalent to the Kedischem series (see Paas, 1962, with references).

Elster time. A date of at least 500,000 years may apply to the Cromerian.

Earlier dates suggested by Kurtén (1960b) are 600,000 B.P. for the Tiglian (1,500,000 B.P. after Richter, 1958), and 1,300,000 B.P. for the Plio-Pleistocene boundary. The recent K-A dates provide a more detailed background for this earlier period (see Evernden and Curtis, 1964).

TABLE 6

STRATIGRAPHY AND CHRONOLOGY OF THE PLEISTOCENE
(With Approximate Date for Beginning of Units)

Holocene (10,300 B.P.)

Pleistocene	Upper	Würm Eem	(70,000 B.P.) (90,000-100,000 B.P.)
	Middle	Warthe Ohe Saale Holstein	(120,000-130,000 B.P.) (at least 200,000 B.P.) (at least 275,000 B.P.)
	Lower	Elster (II) Cortonian (Elster I) Cromerian	 (at least 500,000 B.P.)
	Basal	Menapian Waalian Eburonian Tiglian Villafranchian	 (about 2 million B.P.)

PART II

Vegetation, Soils and Geomorphology as Environmental Indices

4

The
Zonal Concept

INTRODUCTION

Paleo-environmental interpretation is based largely on evidence provided by geomorphologic features, soils, animal, and plant remains. An archeological site in a loess embankment may, for example, show evidence of former soil-frost phenomena and fossil humus horizons, while excavation may produce bone of mammoth and reindeer with pollen of herbaceous plants. Or, a Pleistocene geologist studying ancient lake beds in a dry subtropical area may find fossilized bones of fish, crocodile, and hippopotamus with various mollusca and traces of different woods. In either case consideration of all classes of evidence is desirable. Yet the question arises, what environmental significance do the plant or animal remains carry? Under what conditions would the sediments or soils form? If answers can be obtained for these queries, further questions arise. Do the various lines of evidence produce convergent results, and if so, does the ecological pattern so obtained have a modern counterpart?

None of the physical and biological data that can be gleaned from a site or exposure speaks for itself. Recognition and identification of phenomena must be followed up by careful interpretation of each line of evidence. Only then can the investigator be reasonably certain that his over-all ecological picture is representative and sufficiently clear. As a consequence proper understanding of the features and materials commonly found in ancient contexts is vital. And the ultimate key to paleo-ecology is provided by modern distributions of similar features.

Geomorphic evidence may indicate that a site was located by a stream or lake, on a windy plain with conspicuous soil-frost or with waterlogging. This evidence of the *local habitat* or *setting* may be complemented by soil-frost phenomena restricted to certain polar climates today. This would suggest that the *regional environment* was a tundra. The wind-borne plant pollen found in the sediment might corroborate the latter evidence, whereas fossilized leaves, stems, or mosses would add more to our understanding of the immediate local scene. In other words, paleo-environmental interpretation requires knowledge of both the setting and regional environment, evidence that can be obtained only by familiarity with modern processes and distributions.

Fortunately, the elements of the natural environment generally show some order in their location and occurrence on the continents. The most important single distribution affecting the face of the earth is climate. Since all living things require warmth and moisture in varying degree, they ultimately reflect resources primarily controlled by climate. In a broad way the distribution of various species of plants or animals is related to the zonation of climate. In fact, one of the basic principles of vegetation or plant geography is that climatic control is a primary factor determining the general character of world vegetation belts. Animals, unlike plants, can adapt themselves more readily to climatic conditions and often migrate seasonally to avoid unfavorable food or thermal conditions. But in a general way the animal world, when seen as a complex of organisms ranging from bacteria and mollusca to birds and mammals, also shows recognizable associations related to climatic zonation.

Vegetation and microorganisms are two of the factors influencing the character of soil development in a given area. Climate directly plays an active role in soil development by thermally controlling the rate of chemical reactions. In fact climate makes such reactions possible in the first place by supplying the necessary water by means of which chemical alteration takes place. Overlooking the nature of the bedrock and the peculiarities of relief and surface configuration, many of the processes of local soil development can, in varying degree, also be related to climate.

Many geomorphic processes are essentially a product of the same factors responsible for soil development. These are the external forces that sculpture and modify features resulting from bedrock lithology or tectonic structure. Although the broad lines of soil mineralogy or of surface morphology are frequently dominated by bedrock materials and past tectonic activity, the actual modifications underway at any one time are either directly or indirectly controlled by climate. A detailed soil map will reflect an infinity of minor factors, whereas soil types over very large regions show unmistakable analogies. Similarly the surface configuration of the earth shows no latitudinal pattern; yet in its details, regional sculpturing becomes individualistic and discernible.

Broad distributions of biological or physical associations which show latitudinal zonation—ultimately as a response to climate—are called *zonal.* The equatorial rainforest or the podsolic soils of the coniferous forest belt are examples of such zonal distributions. *Intra-zonal* features reflect both local factors, such as poor drainage, and regional climate. On the other hand, associations occurring in any latitudinal belt, such as do shore-line forms or tectonic activity, are *azonal.*

The elements of the natural environment are invariably related to both zonal and azonal factors, as Table 7 indicates. Each of these phenomena is interrelated, and the interdependence becomes more versatile as one moves from vegetation to geomorphic processes

TABLE 7
RELATIONSHIPS OF ZONAL AND AZONAL FACTORS

Zonal Factors	Phenomenon	Azonal Factors
Temperature Moisture Radiation Soils	Vegetation	Mineral nutrients Drainage and relief Other edaphic factors
Temperature Moisture Vegetation	Animal Life	Drainage and relief Population density Predators and parasites
Temperature Moisture Vegetation Microfauna Geomorphic Processes	Soils	Bedrock lithology Drainage and relief
Temperature Moisture Vegetation Soils Fauna	Morphogenesis	Tectonic structure Bedrock lithology Drainage and relief

(*morphogenesis*), while the importance of climate diminishes in that same order.

The zonal concept is fundamental for the purpose of this study. Characteristic features commonly occur in "fossil" form in prehistoric contexts, in which case they may provide a key to the former regional environment. Unfortunately the impression of homogeneity readily conveyed by discussion of such large units is misleading, and it is difficult to avoid overgeneralization and oversimplification in a brief review of the pertinent aspects of zonal vegetation, soils, and morpho-genesis. Later chapters emphasizing local settings should to some extent restore the balance between generalization and complexity.

VEGETATION AND CLIMATE

Certain basic requirements to the plant world are a direct function of regional climate: radiation, temperature, and moisture (Cain, 1944; Aario and Janus, 1958; Eyre, 1963).

The chemical life of a plant consists of absorption of water and certain minerals from the soil followed by *photosynthesis* whereby water, minerals, and atmospheric carbon dioxide are combined to form plant tissue. Radiation is a primary source of energy for photosynthesis while the rate of chemical reaction as such increases rapidly with temperature. Water is essential as a raw material in molecular structure and a basic agent in the vital processes of the plant. Consequently the length and intensity of the growing season, as determined by available light, warmth, and water, is a major control of plant life. Another complex determining factor is provided by absolute temperature toleration and optimal temperature ranges.

The free passage and assimilation of soil moisture, the rate of photosynthesis, and the eventual water loss of the plant by transpiration are intimately associated with temperature. Optimal temperatures for these processes and reactions vary by plants. So do the toleration limits. Few plants tolerate temperatures above 40° C., and no higher plants tolerate values of 50° C. Excepting a few arctic plants which may not tolerate maximal temperatures as low as 4° C., most plants do not have significantly different upper toleration limits. Greatest differentiation occurs among the minimum temperatures. Many tropical species cease to grow when temperatures drop to 10° C., while temperate species stop growing at temperatures between 0° C. and 5° C. Many tropical species die at temperatures below 5° C. or at the freezing point, so that the complete absence of frost is important for plant distribution. Many plant families seem to tolerate frost of varying intensity or duration by dormancy. Since plants do not have direct physiological protective devices against heat or cold such as thick bark or the like, adaptability is a matter of the organic chemistry of individual species.

Plants do, however, have distinct adaptations to moisture conditions. *Xerophytic* plants are adapted to chronic drought by devices effecting a reduction of evaporation, greater water storage, and improved root efficiency. Small or needle-like leaves, in part replaced by thorns or scales, reduce evaporation just as do reduced surface area, slick bark, waxy surfaces, or fewer pores. *Hygrophytic* plants are adapted to optimal moisture conditions by broad, thin leaves (providing a maximum assimilation surface with a minimum of material) and thin bark. *Tropophytes* are adapted to alternating dry and wet seasons.

Consequently a particular climatic belt will tend to favor a certain association of plants, grasses, shrubs, and trees known as a *plant formation* or as the *climatic climax vegetation*. These are the highest types of vegetation that can develop under the different aspects of climate, and that are in equilibrium with that climate. Obviously climates change, however, and according to Mason (1936) climate is the only significant variable which can stimulate the migration of plant associations. As climatic change is not local, movements of vegetation tend to show a regional parallelism. From North America and Europe we do indeed know of a dramatic succession of floras moving poleward during the recession of the continental glaciers. Such changes of environment suggest that the plant formations are to some degree temporary features and that they may be complicated by the presence of relict species. Such relicts are valuable evidence for changes in the past.

Factors other than climate do play a part, not so much in determining the large-scale patterns, but in creating innumerable local variations which reflect soil factors such as texture, temperature, moisture, chemistry, available nutrients, and humus type. Well-developed, fertile soils will for example, support a more luxuriant vegetation with different or more species of plants, than thin soils with limited plant nutrients. Similarly, groundwater available along rivers or lakes may permit local growth of fringing or *galeria* woodlands in otherwise arid or semiarid country. Natural drainage, topography, and slope are also important, so much so in fact that a climatic climax community will be limited to well-drained lands with gentle slopes and undisturbed by man.

WEATHERING AND SOIL DEVELOPMENT

Fundamental to understanding the relationship of climate and soil development is the process of *weathering* and its latitudinal variations (see Cotton, 1949; Thornbury, 1954; Louis, 1960). Weathering refers to the disintegration and decomposition of exposed rock under the direct influence of the elements. It is prerequisite to, and simultaneously a major process of soil development. Weathering may be chemical or physical.

One form of chemical weathering is *solution,* whereby soluble salts or calcareous constituents are dissolved and washed away or *leached.* Many salts such as sodas, chlorides, or sulfates can be simply washed out. Calcium carbonate, the basic constituent of limestone, is altered by carbonic acid derived from carbon dioxide dissolved in rainwater. The alteration product, a bicarbonate, is quite soluble in water and is responsible for the chemical decomposition of limestone.

Almost all other rocks can be altered and weakened by *hydrolysis,* whereby percolating waters partially dissociate into differently charged ions that break up minerals into their corresponding bases and acids. In this manner feldspars, silicates, micas, etc. are disintegrated, rendering the rock softer and weaker. Only quartz and some heavy minerals are not generally affected by this agency. Then also, contact with oxygen molecules leads to the *oxidation* of iron, manganese, and aluminum into weaker alteration products.

Each of these agencies requires heat and water, suggesting that chemical weathering will be most intense in the humid tropics and to a certain extent also in humid temperate lands. Arid zones and cold seasons or cold climates severely reduce chemical weathering so that the arctic and desert regions enjoy very little of it.

Mechanical agents break up the bedrock into smaller units more liable to chemical attack. Frost is undoubtedly the most important of these forces. Water on freezing increases its volume by 9 per cent. When this increase occurs in water held in crevices, fissures, or pores, complex forces and strains work upon the bounding rock surfaces and may eventually shatter the mineral structure. In loose materials with more than 2 per cent fine particles, freeze-and-thaw of water induces volume changes and relative displacements, together with lateral movements on slopes. On thawing such materials lose much of their cohesion and become more susceptible to erosion by wind or water. The presence of permanently frozen subsoil (*permafrost*) is linked with frost-heaving, also a potent mechanical agent.

Temperature variations may produce mechanical disintegration without passing below the freezing point. Strong daily insolation and rapid nightly cooling in dry regions leads to rapid expansion or contraction of rock surfaces, creating a differential with the interior. Particularly in the case of coarse-grained rocks of variable mineralogy, such as granites, differential expansion seems to produce microfractures and so leads to disintegration. All mechanical processes due to temperature variation are included under the designation *thermoclastic weathering*.

Seasonal changes in humidity can produce contraction of finer materials by dehydration (polygonal cleavage or contraction cracks). Certain clay minerals can expand or contract by several per cent of their volume under influence of moisture changes, and alternate wetting and drying will tend to split up rocks with a high clay content. Many of the alteration products resulting from chemical weathering exert mechanical pressures, so for example the decomposition of feldspars gives an increased volume of clay products. The various geomorphic processes may also aid mechanical weathering by surface impact or friction. Final sources of mechanical weathering are the pressures exerted by the roots of plants and trees, i.e., biological agents. The latter also include incidental items such as burrowing animals.

Summing up then, the processes of weathering are basically related to the latitudinal distribution of solar energy and the semi-latitudinal alignments of precipitation belts.

Soil development involves not only weathering but also biochemical processes directly associated with vegetation and microfauna. These biochemical agencies can be dismissed more briefly as they merely imply an intensification of the chemical processes discussed above. Lower plants such as algae, lichens, fungi, and mosses produce biochemical alteration of the immediate surface materials on which they settle. Removal of nutrients from the incipient soil and return of only selected minerals, bases, or acids by leaf or needle-fall have effects similar to hydrolysis. Particularly important here are the carbonic and humic acids of biological origin. Plants also accelerate evaporation from the soil, slowing down the process of solution and leaching. Roots effect an exchange of minerals between the upper and lower soil, while the vegetation itself breaks the impact of the external elements. The kind of humus present, which is determined by the vegetation, may accelerate or slow down decomposition in the soil. A host of bacteria and microbes—whose activity is controlled by the environment—and numerous insects, including beetles and earthworms, are also chemically active.

ZONAL SOILS

As soil development involves bedrock alteration it cannot show nearly as much zonal arrangement as plant associations, which are independent and spontaneous. Consequently azonal components dominate in all but mature and well-drained soils. In fact, the climax whereby a soil will ultimately reflect its climate and vegetation rather than its parent material is an ideal case that is never realized. But even immature soils already reflect to some degree the climate and vegetation type under which they developed. Most striking to the eye is the soil color, which often gives significant information on the physical and chemical agencies involved. Gray or blackish colors most frequently reflect humus conditions, yellowish or reddish shades may reflect chemical alteration. Only in a few cases is the soil color of mature soils directly determined by the parent material. Similarly the classes and kinds of humus, soil fauna, chemical reaction, and soil texture often permit identification of zonal factors before a mature soil profile has been developed.

Although the properties of poorly drained soils of swampy areas, alluvial soils of river valleys, and stony soils of eroded slopes diverge widely within a region, these azonal or intrazonal soils are still affected by many basically similar weathering processes. Even moderately mature alluvial soils show marked latitudinal differentiation. It is, then, possible to identify large-scale patterns in world soil distribution known as *zonal soils* or *great soil groups* (Glinka, 1927; Kellogg, 1941; Ganssen, 1957). These also show some similarity to the world's climatic provinces. But not all soils are mature, and changes in soil development reflecting climatic change may result in soil-forming agencies insufficiently intense to alter older, more mature soils. As a result relict soils of various kinds are significant in almost all latitudinal belts.

Zonal and even intrazonal soils can, with due caution, provide information on regional climate, and buried or relict soils (*paleosols*) can provide a clue to former environments. It may happen that the properties of soil profiles recognized in archeological or geological contexts will permit deductions almost as valuable as those derived from paleobotanical evidence.

EXTERNAL GEOMORPHIC PROCESSES AS A FUNCTION OF CLIMATE

Those geomorphic processes responsible for sculpturing the earth's crust are commonly known as external or *gradational* agencies. They include the work of running water, ice, and wind and are closely linked with weathering and soil development. Bedrock differences, structure, relief, and topography pose obvious limitations (Büdel, 1963) to zonal characterization of the earth's landforms. But within different climatic areas the gradational agents are balanced differently and show basic, recognizable patterns which ultimately produce distinctive surficial modifications of the crust. As a result several authors such as Büdel (1950a, 1963) and Cailleux and Tricart (1955) have defined *climatic-geomorphologic zones* in which certain forms of weathering, erosion, sedimentation, and landform sculpture are typical. Erosional features or sediments pertaining to specific climatic types are more commonly preserved in a fossil context than are soils or biological evidence. Consequently the record of former gradational processes is also fundamental for paleo-environmental work.

NATURAL REGIONS

Most, but not all of the major plant formations, zonal soil groups, and climatic-geomorphologic zones show an approximate overlap with certain first-order climatic provinces. Obviously the phenomena of the earth's surface form a continuum in which regions and boundaries are invariably arbitrary. But with due reservation certain large-scale *natural regions* can be identified, even though their number and limits will vary from author to author.

The basic regions employed in this study are adapted from the climatic classification of W. Koeppen, described in many elementary texts in physical geography or climatology (for example, Trewartha *et al.*, 1961; Strahler, 1960). The following oversimplified but nevertheless useful regions can be recognized. The terminology employs the familiar designation of vegetation types, with climatic overtones:

Vegetation types

a) Polar glaciers (Koeppen symbol [1] *EF*)
b) Polar tundras (*ET*)
c) Subarctic or boreal forests (*Dc, Dd*)
d) Continental forests (*Da, Db*)
e) Temperate woodlands (*Cbf*)
f) Dry subtropical woodlands (*Cs*)
g) Moist subtropical woodlands (*Caf, Caw*)
h) Grasslands (*BS*)
i) Deserts (*BW*)
j) Tropical woodland and savanna (*Aw*)
k) Tropical rain forest (*Af, Am*)

The distribution and location of these climatic regions is shown in Figure 3. Characteristic features of the vegetation, soils, and geomorphologic processes are discussed in subsequent chapters.

---

[1] The Koeppen symbols, with minor modifications by Trewartha (1961), are defined as follows:

A—Tropical forest climates: coolest month average temperature above 18° C.
B—Dry climates, defined by a linear relationship employing mean annual temperature, annual rainfall, and season of rainfall concentration. Subdivisions include a semi-arid or steppe-grassland climate (*BS*) and an arid or desert climate (*BW*).
C—Mesothermal forest climates: coldest month above 0° C. but below 18° C.; warmest month above 10° C.
D—Microthermal forest climates: coldest month below 0° C.; warmest month above 10° C.
E—Polar climates: warmest month below 10° C., including *ET*—Tundra climate with warmest month below 10° C. but above 0° C., and *EF*—Perpetual frost with all months below 0° C.
a—Warmest month above 22° C.
b—Warmest month below 22° C., but at least four months above 10° C.
c—One to three months above 10° C.
d—One to three months above 10° C., but coldest month below —38° C.
h—Hot and dry: all months above 0° C.
k—Cold and dry: at least one month below 0° C.
f—Moisture distributed evenly throughout the year.
s—Dry season in summer.
w—Dry season in winter.

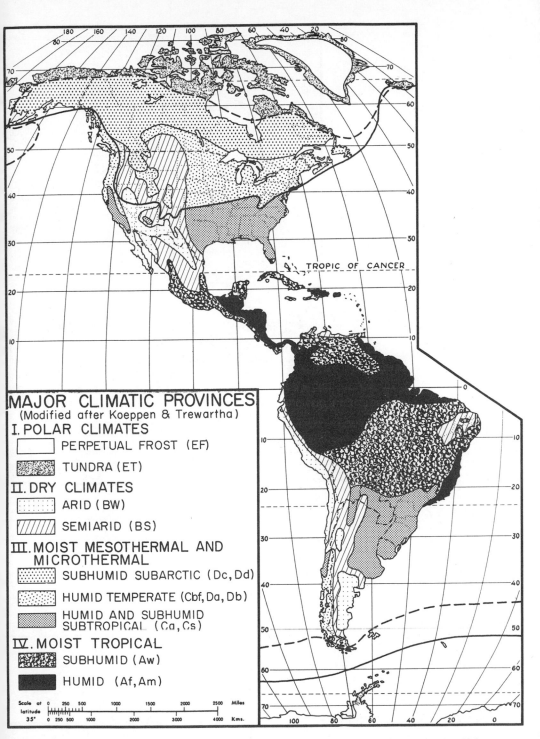

FIGURE 3. Major climatic provinces (modified after W. Koeppen and R. Geiger [*Klima der Welt*, 2d ed., 1953, Darmstadt: J. Perthes] and G. T. Trewartha *et al.* [1961]).

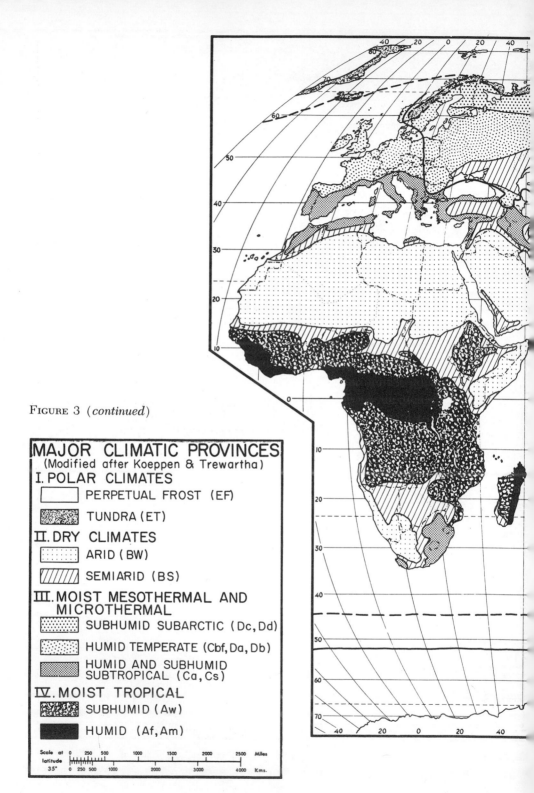

Figure 3 (*continued*)

MAJOR CLIMATIC PROVINCES
(Modified after Koeppen & Trewartha)

I. POLAR CLIMATES
PERPETUAL FROST (EF)
TUNDRA (ET)

II. DRY CLIMATES
ARID (BW)
SEMIARID (BS)

III. MOIST MESOTHERMAL AND MICROTHERMAL
SUBHUMID SUBARCTIC (Dc, Dd)
HUMID TEMPERATE (Cbf, Da, Db)
HUMID AND SUBHUMID SUBTROPICAL (Ca, Cs)

IV. MOIST TROPICAL
SUBHUMID (Aw)
HUMID (Af, Am)

Scale at latitude 35°
0 250 500 1000 1500 2000 2500 Miles
0 250 500 1000 2000 3000 4000 Kms.

54

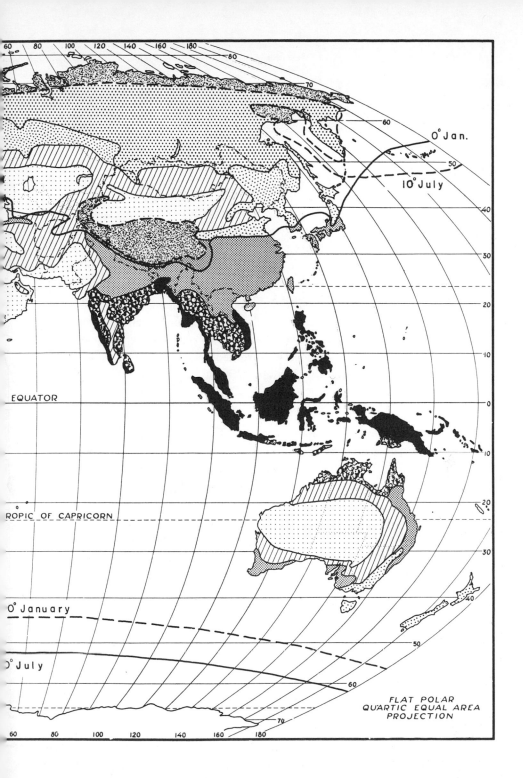

60 80 100 120 140 160 180

80

70

60

0° Jan.

50

10° July

40

30

20

10

EQUATOR

0

10

ROPIC OF CAPRICORN

20

30

40

0° January

50

)° July

60

FLAT POLAR
QUARTIC EQUAL AREA
PROJECTION

70

60 80 100 120 140 160 180

5

Vegetation
and Climate

The world distribution and major classes of vegetation are shown in Figure 4 and are discussed below in relation to climate. A useful comprehensive outline of vegetation and plant geography is given by Eyre (1963). Ecological requirements and adaptations are more specifically considered by Walter (1960).

POLAR AND ALPINE VEGETATION

Some characteristics of climate.—The polar regions beyond the limits of tree growth are affected by a harsh, cold climate. In a general way, winters are cold and long (10-12 months of the year) and average temperatures of the warmest month commonly lie below 10° C. The frost-free season is everywhere less than 50 days and may be non-existent. Most of the treeless polar tundras have a permanently frozen subsoil (*permafrost*), never affected by the summer thaw which is limited to the uppermost part of the ground.

In the broad belt of open country lying between the northern woodlands and the perennial ice fields, the brief summer vegetative period of one to four weeks is far from benign. Nightly temperatures of −1° to +5° C. alternate with daytime values of 7°-12° C., while killing frosts are possible at any time. The remaining months of the year do not permit vegetative growth since temperatures remain well below 0° C., and strong, cold and dry winds sweep the surface. Although the snowcover generally lasts more than seven or eight months, the snowcover itself is shallow and frequently incomplete, therefore offering little insulation.

As a consequence, frost may penetrate to depths of tens or even hundreds of meters, and the winter blizzards rapidly desiccate any exposed vegetation. Intense physiological drought is the result of

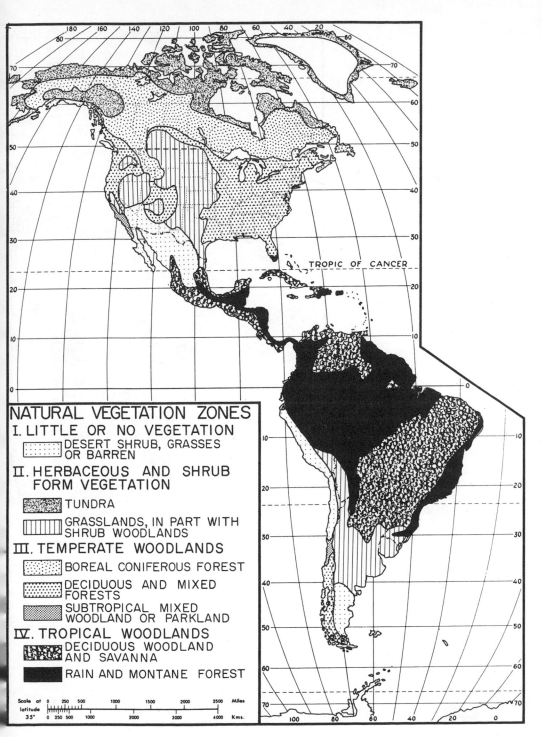

FIGURE 4. Natural vegetation zones.

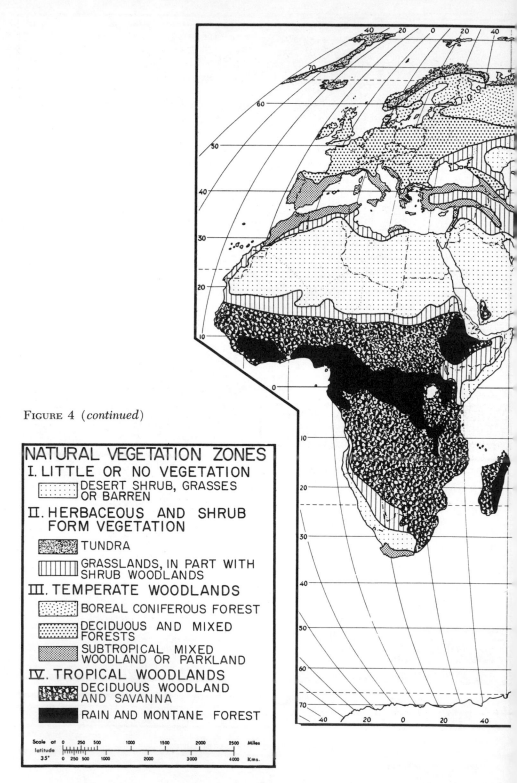

FIGURE 4 (*continued*)

NATURAL VEGETATION ZONES

I. LITTLE OR NO VEGETATION
- DESERT SHRUB, GRASSES OR BARREN

II. HERBACEOUS AND SHRUB FORM VEGETATION
- TUNDRA
- GRASSLANDS, IN PART WITH SHRUB WOODLANDS

III. TEMPERATE WOODLANDS
- BOREAL CONIFEROUS FOREST
- DECIDUOUS AND MIXED FORESTS
- SUBTROPICAL MIXED WOODLAND OR PARKLAND

IV. TROPICAL WOODLANDS
- DECIDUOUS WOODLAND AND SAVANNA
- RAIN AND MONTANE FOREST

Scale at latitude 35°

0 250 500 1000 1500 2000 2500 Miles

0 250 500 1000 2000 3000 4000 Kms.

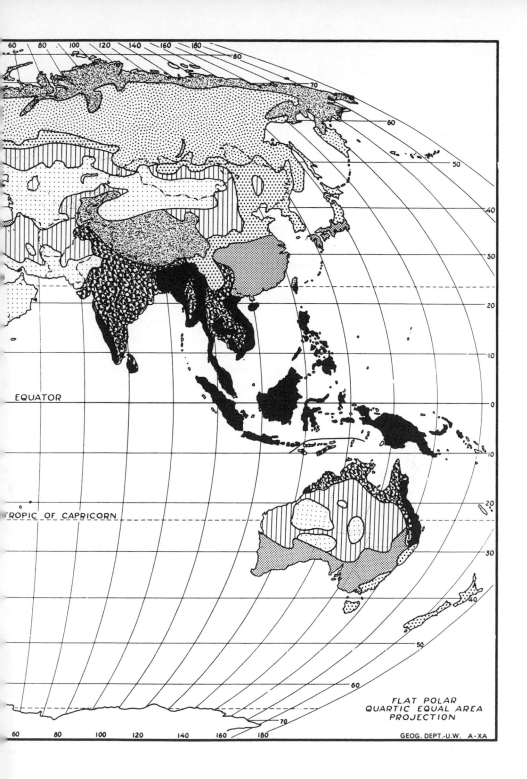

EQUATOR

TROPIC OF CAPRICORN

FLAT POLAR
QUARTIC EQUAL AREA
PROJECTION

GEOG. DEPT.-U.W. A-XA

transpiration from plant tissues at a time when water replacement through the frozen soil, roots, and stems is impossible. Similarly, cold-air drainage into lower-lying areas may create particularly cold microhabitats. Waterlogged soils have a similar effect since evaporation of soil moisture results in considerable heat loss from the soil, while the water insulates the permafrost of the subsoil. Another aspect of the microclimate concerns the lowest 30 cm. of the atmosphere in which normal air mixing is at a minimum. Nightly frosts in summertime may be twice as frequent at the surface than at the standard climatic observation level of 1.5 m. During the day, however, temperatures are 5° C. or more higher at the surface than at 1.5 m. Frost-tolerant plants of dwarf size can best utilize such a micro-environment.

According to Eyre (1963, p. 98 f.) the absence of tree growth in the polar regions reflects several factors, among them winter frost, winter winds, short growing season, and permafrost. At their equatorward margins, wind force and the shallowness of unfrozen soil are thought to be most significant, while at very high latitudes the growing season is not sufficiently long. Whatever the local cause of tree absence, a tundra vegetation of grasses, sedges, lichens, and mosses replaces the forests of middle latitudes.

High mountain areas in many parts of the world range into the *alpine zone,* above the altitudinal tree-line. Permafrost is seldom present and temperature regimes vary strongly with latitude. So for example, there is no winter season in the tropical highlands and instead, temperature oscillations between night and day may result in regular night frosts. In middle latitude highlands thermal patterns resemble those of the polar lands more closely. Although snowcover is more effective and snowfalls are considerable, tree growth is again impeded by very high wind speeds and, probably to a lesser extent, by insufficient opportunity for photosynthesis. The alpine meadows, then, are remarkably similar to the polar tundras both in physiognomy and vegetation composition.

Several subzones of decreasing climatic severity may be recognized within the polar regions. These include:

a) The ice caps of Greenland, Antarctica, and several other areas such as Spitsbergen, Ellesmere, and Baffin Islands;
b) The high arctic barrens;
c) The herbaceous tundra (in the strict sense); and
d) The transitional forest-tundra.

The vegetation of the last three will be discussed in a little more detail.

The high arctic barrens.—In many high arctic areas vegetation is limited to a discontinuous scatter of mosses, sedges, or lichens, with much bare ground in between. There is no vegetative mat, sod, or turf, and large areas support no plant growth at all. Such desert or semidesert-type conditions prevail on the Canadian Arctic Islands, in the unglaciated parts of northern Greenland and Spitsbergen, on the Soviet Arctic Islands, and on the Taimyr Peninsula.

The herbaceous tundra.—The more typical tundra vegetation, with its comparative luxuriance of plant growth and a continuous, hummocky sod, fringes the northern littorals of North America and Eurasia. Various grasses and sedges (*Carex* spp.) are probably dominant under natural conditions, with a substantial under-story of lichens (such as the reindeer "moss," *Cladonia rangiferina,* as well as the genera *Centraria, Stereocaulon,* etc.) and mosses of the genus *Polytrichum* (Walter, 1954, p. 150 f.; Eyre, 1963, p. 96 f.). A great variety of flowering plants is also present—including several genera such as the mountain avens (*Dryas* spp.), saxifrages (*Saxifraga* spp.), and gentians (*Gentiana* spp.)—which are more or less confined to polar and alpine environments. Creeping shrubs such as the dwarf willows (*Salix polaris, S. herbacea, S. reticulata*) and dwarf birch (*Betula nana*) are not uncommon, particularly on sheltered slopes and along streams.

Widespread within the herbaceous tundra are poorly drained plains, often with brackish or salty waters. These are areas of bog vegetation, with cotton grass (*Eriophorum vaginatum*), various sedges, bog moss (*Sphagnum* spp.), and at times, a number of salt-tolerating grasses and shrubs.

The forest-tundra.—On its equatorward margins the tundra belt grades imperceptibly into continental forests as riverside brush becomes more conspicuous, and higher forms begin to replace the mosses and lichens on the better-drained soils. A stage of what is often described as low-brush tundra is finally succeeded by terrain with lightly stocked tree groves or river thickets of birch (*Betula*), spruce (*Picea*) and larch (*Larix*). Tundra bogs are still common and extensive in water-logged areas, while upland surfaces are frequently bare. This fluid transitional zone is known as the forest-tundra. The so-called tree-line marks the complex zone where individual trees of the sporadic stands of brush no longer attain more than dwarf size (i.e., maximum heights of 1 m.).

The polar and alpine "tree-line."—The reconstructed position of the tree-line during various Pleistocene or Holocene periods has commonly been used for paleoclimatic interpretations. So for example, Koeppen's boundary between tundra and forest climates (*ET* and *D* or *C*) was designed to approximate the tree-line by the 10° C. July isotherm. In the northern hemisphere, the polar tree-line today generally lies somewhere between the July isotherms of 10° and 12° C., depending on the maritime or continental character of the climate.[1]

Unfortunately the tree-line is neither a "line" nor a true climatic boundary. Instead it is a transitional belt marked by different tree species in different areas. Tree growth is largely determined by exposition, relief, and surface drainage—all of which create specific microhabitats in terms of wind force, air-drainage, snowcover, soil-temperatures, soil-moisture and depth of annual thaw. There is then increasing doubt that the polar or alpine tree-lines are a simple function of the macroclimate. In fact there is no question that the tree-line would be located far poleward if summer air temperatures were the only limiting factor.

The position of a Pleistocene tree-line is, then, not simply equivalent to a particular monthly isotherm. In lieu of anything better the somewhat accidental correspondence to mid-summer isotherms of 10°-12° C. cannot be overlooked, but must still be considered with caution.

FORESTS OF MIDDLE LATITUDES

Forest classes and climate types.—Trees are sometimes classified on the basis of appearance and physiognomy. They fall into either the broadleaf or needle-leaf (coniferous) class, and may be evergreen or deciduous. Consequently the following types of forest are generally recognized:

    a)   Broadleaf evergreen,
    b)   Broadleaf deciduous,
    c)   Coniferous evergreen,
    d)   Coniferous deciduous, and
    e)   Mixed evergreen and deciduous.

---

[1] Nordenskjiöld and Mecking (1928) have in fact attempted to give an empirical climatic definition for the tree-line using the formula $W = 9 - 0.1\ K$, where W = mean temperature of the warmest month (in °C.) and K = mean temperature of the coldest month. South of the polar tree-line W is thought to be greater than the right-hand side of the expression. A more recent attempt by Hare (1954) to apply the potential evapotranspiration concept of Thornthwaite is also of interest.

Broadleaf evergreen species are confined to the tropics and subtropics while rather unusual coniferous deciduous woodlands are important in northeastern Siberia where the dahurian larch (*Larix dahurica*) forms the dominant tree type. Within the extra-tropical and subtropical woodlands there does not appear to be any all too apparent logical order for the occurrence of the physiognomic forest types. Despite a certain over-all dominance of evergreen conifers in the cool, continental climates, and of mixed or broadleaf deciduous woodlands in the more temperate maritime zones, there are many important exceptions. Consequently, certain characteristic species of limited areal occurrence must also be emphasized in describing broad vegetational groups corresponding to certain climatic environments.

Four major *climatic* provinces may be identified in the middle latitude woodlands. In summary form these can be outlined as follows.

a) *The Subhumid Subarctic.* The extreme continental climates of Koeppen's *Dc* and *Dd* provinces have extremely cold winters and cool summers (warmest month average 12°-15° C.), excessive annual ranges of temperature (July-January differences of 40°-65° C.), and a brief growing season of one to three months. Although the winters are comparatively dry the snowcover lasts five to nine months and rivers remain icebound for about the same length of time. Permafrost is widespread. Confined to the northern hemisphere, these climates have a forest vegetation of northern or *boreal* conifers.

b) *The Humid Temperate Zone.* A maritime or oceanic type, corresponding to Koeppen's *Cbf* province, is commonly distinguished from an interior or continental climate (Koeppen's *Da, Db*).

The maritime variety is generally found on the western margins of the continents in middle latitudes. Winters are mild (coldest month 2°-10° C.), summers are warm (warmest month 15°-19° C.), and the growing season lasts five to ten months. Although snow does fall, there is no durable snowcover.

The continental climates with interior and east coast situations are harsher, with cold winters (coldest month −2° to −14° C.) and warm to hot summers (warmest month 16°-22° C.). The growing season lasts four or five months. There is a significant snowcover, amounting to one to four months.

Almost any combination of temperate trees may be found within the humid temperate climates, ranging from deciduous hardwoods to warmth-loving, cold-tolerating conifers. Deciduous or mixed broadleaf-coniferous forests are, however, most common.

c) *The Humid Subtropics.* The eastern continental margins of lower mid-latitudes fall within the *Ca* climate province of Koeppen. Winters are mild (coldest month 2°-10° C.), summers hot (warmest month 23°-30° C.), with a long growing season of seven to twelve months. There is no snowcover. Moisture is abundant at all seasons, particularly in summer. In southern China and northeastern Australia this environment has favored a subtropical or tropical, broadleaved evergreen forest. In east-central South America a grassland vegetation prevailed in pre-European times which poses an ecological enigma. In the southeastern United States temperate mixed or coniferous forests are dominant today, presumably as a result of human interference rather than climatic opportunity. Nevertheless the species present are remarkably less thermophile than those of other humid subtropical climates, largely as a consequence of sporadic but exceptionally severe spells of winter cold (to —10° or —15° C.) in the southeastern states.

d) The Subhumid Subtropics with Dry Summers. On the western sides of the continents, lower middle latitudes enjoy a transitional climate with distinctly dry summers. These are mediterranean-type climates (*Cs* of Koeppen,) with mild winters (coldest month 5°-12° C.), with warm to hot summers (15°-25° C.), and very rare snow or frost. Vegetation growth, although impeded by lack of water much of the time, is possible for nine to twelve months of the year. The vegetation is composed of warmth-loving, subtropical evergreens with some deciduous species. Tree growth is clearly marginal in some of the dry mediterranean borderlands.

In a very generalized manner the *vegetational* aspects of the middle latitude woodlands can be discussed under three topical headings:

a) The boreal coniferous forests,
b) The deciduous and mixed forests, and
c) The subtropical woodlands and parklands.

The boreal coniferous forests.—The boreal forests of Canada and northern Eurasia represent a comparatively uniform vegetation type. Densely packed conifers of a limited number of species offer little opportunity for undergrowth or grass sod. Instead the moderately high stands (seldom as much as 20-30 m. tall) of forest are difficult to penetrate.

In northern Eurasia the core of the boreal forests is regionally dominated by species such as the European spruce (*Picea excelsa*) and its Siberian relative (*P. obovata*), by the cembran pine (*Pinus cembra*), and the deciduous European and Siberian larches (*Larix decidua, L. sibirica*). In regions transitional to the temperate forests of Europe, Scots pine (*Pinus silvestris*), white fir (*Abies alba*) and broadleaved species such as the goat willow (*Salix caprea*) and Eurasian aspen (*Populus tremula*) are characteristic. In the forest-tundra certain deciduous species such as willow, birch and aspen again assume more importance. Tundra bogs and barren uplands are common in the northern parts of the boreal forest, particularly in central and eastern Siberia.

The Canadian boreal forest is similar to that of northern Eurasia, except that deciduous conifers are less common and the dominant species are different. White and black spruce (*Picea glauca* and *P. mariana*), balsam fir (*Abies balsamea*), tamarack (*Larix laricina*), and jack pine (*Pinus banksiana*) are the characteristic forms.

Similar forests form the subalpine zone of many middle latitude highlands.

The peculiar adaptation of conifers to the subhumid subarctic lands is generally thought to be related to two factors (Eyre, 1963, p. 47f.). Needle-shaped leaves strongly reduce water-loss by transpiration during the winter, a time of severe drought stress as a result of persistent dry and cold winds. A second asset is provided by permanent leaves capable of immediate photosynthesis whenever sufficient warmth is available, without having first to grow a new set of leaves in the late spring. Evergreen species can then make the most of a short growing season. However, in the extreme situations of the forest-tundra and of eastern Siberia, very slow-growing deciduous species are even more drought resistant in the winter time. This is thought to account for the larch woodlands of eastern Siberia and for the prominence of certain deciduous forms in the forest-tundra in general.

The deciduous and mixed forests.—The forests of more temperate mid-latitude regions are extremely complex in their distribution, but are locally rather uniform. Dense, mixed rain forests thrive on the ultra-maritime uplands of southern Chile, Tasmania, and southern New Zealand. The world's tallest forests are found along the Pacific coast of Canada and the United States. These include conifers such as the coastal redwood (*Sequoia sempervirens*) and Douglas fir (*Pseudotsuga taxifolia*). Elsewhere in the eastern United States, Europe, and central eastern Asia, deciduous or mixed deciduous forests are dominant. Evergreens are here largely confined to the higher country and to areas of poorer soil. A few words may therefore be devoted to the broadleaf woodlands of middle latitudes that shed their foliage in winter.

In contrast to the coniferous forest, the elements of the deciduous forest are more widely spaced since most of them require much light. The tree crowns are dense so that little undergrowth is commonly present. These woodlands were originally easy to penetrate and frequently interrupted by glades or areas of fewer trees. Instead of the dense needle litter that floors the boreal forest, there is a discontinuous growth of herbaceous plants.

Among the characteristic European species on rich, well-drained soils are beech (*Fagus silvatica*) and ash (*Fraxinus excelsior*). The pedunculate oak (*Quercus robur*) favors moister lowlands, with alder (*Alnus glutinosa*), aspen (*Populus nigra*), and willow (*Salix fragilis*) characteristic of riverine situations. The sessile oak (*Quercus petraea*) and birch (*Betula pendula*) thrive on shallow, poorer soils. Other members of this association are the hazel (*Corylus avellana*), elm (*Ulmus campestris*), lime (*Tilia cordata*), sycamore (*Acer platanoides*, *A. pseudoplatanus*), hornbeam (*Carpinus betulus*), and yew (*Taxus baccata*). Many of these species have played important roles in the forest history of Europe as preserved in the pollen record (see Firbas, 1949-50; Walter, 1954). Other species, generally more diverse, are dominant in the deciduous woodlands of North America. Oak, maple (*Acer* spp.), and hickory (*Carya* spp.) are leading genera there.

The subtropical woodlands and parklands.—Of the two major subtropical woodland types, one is found in the mediterranean, summer-dry climates of the world, the other in southern Japan and China.

The woodlands of the summer-dry subtropics have been largely replaced today by scrub growth or thorn. The natural vegetative cover was very probably a dry, open forest of broadleaved and needle-leaved evergreen species. In the lowland areas of the Mediterranean basin the live oak (*Quercus ilex*) is universal, and the umbrella pine (*Pinus pinea*), Aleppo pine (*P. halepensis*), and maritime pine (*P. pinaster*) are common. The scrubby growth of leathery or thorn-leaved evergreens—constituting the xerophytic maquis or garrigue of today—probably once formed the undergrowth, particularly in areas of thin or poor soils. All of these species are adapted to the often severe summer drought, but there is no need to shed leaves during the warm, moist winters.

In the upland areas of the Mediterranean, the characteristic submediterranean forms include the black pine (*Pinus nigra*) and a number of deciduous oaks (*Quercus pubescens, Q. cerris*), the chestnut (*Castanea sativa*), the ash-elm (*Fraxinus ornus*) and a dogwood (*Cornus mas*). These species are adapted to cooler winters, and may extend into temperate Europe in favorable warm-dry situations.

Finally, along the dry margins of the subhumid subtropics, the dry Mediterranean woodlands thin out into parklands with groves or scattered stands of increasingly scrublike dry forest. The intervening areas are occupied by garrigue and herbaceous plants. This stage marks the transition to the dry lands.

The moist subtropical woodlands of southern Japan and China can be discussed more briefly. These broadleaved evergreen forests form a unique transition between the temperate deciduous woodlands and the tropical forests. Numerous species of evergreen oak and magnolias (*Magnoliaceae*) dominate, with a dense undergrowth of shrubs and small trees, as well as several woody climbers (Eyre, 1963, pp. 84-85.)

VEGETATION OF DRY LANDS

Climatic aspects.—An outstanding natural delimitation of the dry lands is given by the *grassland-forest boundary*. The limits set to tree growth as a result of aridity are in many ways comparable in complexity to those of the polar tree-line, although the boundary is probably more sharply defined. Nowhere is the natural appearance of the grassland-forest boundary preserved today, since human activity (cultivation, herding, fire) and natural interference (grazing, natural fires) have everywhere caused significant modifications. In particular, there is reason to believe that many peripheral grasslands in middle latitudes and much of the tropical savanna would be forested under "natural" conditions. However this may be, the climatic controls are in major part a matter of rainfall (amount, seasonality, reliability, frequency, intensity) and evaporation (temperature, cloudiness, wind speed). Severe sporadic droughts may carry more significance than typical averages. Microclimatic features and frost play a more subordinate role. Edaphic features such as soil moisture, soil water retention properties, and the like are significant. The presence of perennial or seasonal groundwater in depressions or along rivers and lakeshores may account for isolated tree stands or fringing, galeria forests.

The convergence of toleration limits and climatic controls is difficult to express quantitatively. In a very rough way the simple and unsophisticated formulas used to delimit Koeppen's dry B climates (see Trewartha, 1954) offer an approximation of the grassland-forest boundary. This limit is expressed by $p = 2t$ (for winter-dry climates), or by $p = 2t + 28$ (for summer-dry climates) where $p =$ annual precipitation in centimeters, $t =$ mean annual temperature (°C.).[2]

Within the dry climates there is of course an infinite gradation of moisture. The distinction of arid and semiarid climates is significant from all ecological points of view, although no simple climatic criteria other than Koeppen's will be cited for the purpose of subdivision.[3] The native vegetation belts ranging from prairie or steppe through more arid forms of grassland to semidesert scrub and barren desert speak adequately for themselves.

Climatic elements other than rainfall are also of significance in the dry lands. Temperature contrasts between day and night (12°-20° C.) and between summer and winter (10°-20° C. in lower latitudes, 20°-30° C. in higher latitudes) are exaggerated as a result of low atmospheric humidity. And the middle latitude dry lands of the northern hemisphere (north of about 35° N.) experience very cold winters, with mean cold month temperatures well below the freezing point. This implies that plant growth is impeded during the winter as a result of cold, during other parts of the year as a result of drought. It is consequently useful to distinguish the "cold" dry climates of middle latitudes (BWk, BSk in Koeppen's classification) from the "hot" dry climates of lower latitudes (BWh, BSh). Even in the hot deserts sporadic frosts occur as far equatorward as the tropics of Cancer and Capricorn. Since dry lands extend through fifty-five degrees of latitude on either side of the equator it is impossible to give representative temperature means here.

---

[2] Despite their mechanical complexity, empirical formulas by Thornthwaite (1948) provide no significant improvement on Koeppen's results, either in theory or practice. Calculations of the numbers of dry versus humid months per year were made by Lauer (1952) for the tropics and by Jätzold (1960) for North America, and the correspondence of certain critical values with vegetation belts is remarkable, considering the simple basic assumptions. A complicated but physically sound formula by Paterson (1956) sets the grassland-forest boundary at

$$\frac{V}{A} \cdot R \cdot \frac{P.G.}{12} = 25,$$

where $V =$ mean temperature of warmest month (° C.), $A =$ mean annual range of temperature (°C.), $R =$ ratio of annual radiation at the pole to that of the location in question, $P =$ mean annual precipitation (in cm.), $G =$ length of the growing season (in months).

[3] The boundary between Koeppen's arid BW and semiarid BS climates is given by $p = t$ (for winter-dry climates), $p = t + 14$ (for summer-dry climates) with p and t defined as before.

Grassland, prairie, and steppe.—The interdigitation of forest and open country is complex in the middle latitude grasslands of North America ("prairies") and Eurasia ("steppe"). But the grassland vegetation itself is comparatively uniform. The moister parts have a continuous sod of tall grasses exceeding a meter in height. This luxuriant herbaceous vegetation with its dense root network is destroyed in winter, and its decay provides the soil with rich mineral nutrients. In the drier belts shorter bunch grasses, without a continuous sod, dominate, although the root network under the exposed soil is equally dense. Maximum moisture is available in spring and early summer, and there may also be a secondary rainfall maximum in the autumn. But by late summer drought conditions are severe, and the vegetation is parched and frequently dormant.

A similar vegetation sequence exists in the subtropical *pampas* of South America, although low latitude grasslands are usually different in physiognomy. They are commonly dominated by semidesert grasses with a scattering of deciduous thorny shrubs or low trees. The xerophytic grasses and deciduous shrubs flourish during the two to five month-long summer rainy season, but lie dormant for most of the remaining year. The tropical grasslands consequently provide an environment somewhat different from that of the middle latitude steppes or prairies.

The desert margins.—The peripheral belt of the semiarid climates and the adjacent desert margins provide a number of intermediate biozones bridging the gap between the bunch grasses or thorn-scrub grasslands and the barren desert wastes. It is here that the dry steppe, the desert steppe and semidesert are found. The herbaceous component of these associations is small in comparison to the evergreen or deciduous thorn shrubs and the spiny, pulpy drought-resistant succulents. Hairy-leaved shrubs of the genus *Artemisia* are particularly characteristic in North America (sage brush) and Eurasia (wormwoods). Individual plants are commonly scattered and non-contiguous, and despite the deep and complex rooting systems the soil is not enmeshed in a continuous root turf as in the true grasslands. As the wet season progressively decreases in length from about two months to brief periods following sporadic rains, the spacing of individual plants becomes ever greater. Drainage lines and areas with groundwater near the surface are conspicuously favored. Finally, as the desert interiors are approached, even these edaphically favored patches of episodic life give out.

TROPICAL VEGETATION

Climatic characteristics.—Climatically, the moist tropics are generally subdivided into the hyper-humid equatorial or monsoon climates (Koeppen's *Af, Am*) and the seasonally wet-and-dry tropical climates (*Aw*).

The greater part of humid equatorial regions (*Af* climates) experience no marked dry season and are quite wet for ten months or more. Monthly temperatures average about 20°-28° C. all year. In the monsoon climates (*Am*) there is a distinct dry season, but the rainy season is sufficiently long and intense to provide sufficient moisture for growth the whole year through.

In the subhumid tropics wet summers alternate with dry winters (*Aw* climates). The dry season lasts some three to seven months, with maximum heat occurring just before the onset of the rainy season (daytime temperatures 28°-36° C., night time temperatures 15°-20° C.). Temperatures are lower and more uniform during the rainy season (24°-27° C.).

Whereas the evergreen forest of the humid tropics is of the most luxuriant and dense kind, that of the wet-and-dry topics is adapted to seasonal drought and shows a progressive gradation from the equatorial rainforest to the grassland margins. It is dominated by deciduous woodlands and savanna.

Tropical rain and montane forests.—The rain forest and its analogous counterpart, the montane tropical forest, is composed of hygrophytic, evergreen, broadleaved forms. Several layers of trees, their canopies forming successive stories within the forest, may reach 50 m. in height. Lianas and other climbing plants are plentiful, while undergrowth and herbaceous vegetation are practically absent. The ground is often bare except for occasional fresh leaves.

When the tree canopy is incomplete, however, and light penetrates to the floor, a dense, impenetrable undergrowth is commonly present. This is typical for regions with a moderately effective dry season. A number of deciduous trees begin to appear, and a transitional semi-evergreen or even semideciduous, mixed forest results.

Tropical Woodland and Savanna.—The lighter, tropophytic vegetation of the subhumid tropics falls into two phases, a woodland and a parkland or savanna phase. Where dominantly woodland, the plant cover grades from mixed tropical forests to deciduous woodland or thorn forest, with an increasing amount of open landscape with both trees and grasses. In the savanna phase grasslands with interspersed, isolated trees or groups of trees occupy the broad belt between the rain forest and the steppe. Tall, coarse grasses (one to two meters high) with scattered evergreen and deciduous trees occur where the rainy season persists seven to nine months of the year. Shorter, finer grasses set among groves of deciduous thorny trees are found where the rainy season lasts five to six months (Lauer, 1952). It is widely held that savannas of this kind were originally limited to areas with impeded drainage. The present widespread distribution of parkland vegetation is possibly a result of frequent dry-season burning as well as over-grazing—both activities a result of human interference (Richards, 1952; Eyre, 1963). But since the word "savanna" is the only commonly recognized name for this belt, "savanna" will be used in a more general sense in the subsequent text.

6

Soil
Processes and
Soil Types

Although it is not yet possible to give an accurate map of world soils, the general lines of regional soil development are understood (Fig. 5). The major processes involved in the genesis of soils are. discussed below with relation to the over-all physical environment. Characteristic soil types are outlined on this basis (Figs. 6-8). Paleosols are frequently used as paleoclimatic indicators so that an understanding of analogous modern soils is vital.

SOIL PROFILES AND HORIZONS

A *soil* may be defined as a zone of weathering, comprising mineral and intermixed organic matter, directly overlying unweathered parent material. Soil *types* are chiefly identified on the basis of profile, humus, texture, structure, carbonate content, and micromorphology. Before attempting to discuss zonal soil types, some of the essential soil processes or features will be discussed below. Further consideration of soil properties, particularly as observed in the field, is given in chapter 10.

The *profile* of a soil, seen in vertical section, consists of several subdivisions or horizons, often recognizable on the basis of color. The three major horizon classes are successively known from top to bottom as *A, B,* and *C*-horizons. The uppermost, *A*-horizon is commonly characterized by an admixture of decomposed or partly decomposed organic matter, the soil *humus*. Many *A*-horizons are also a result of washing out (*eluviation*) of certain fine minerals and humic matter. The *B*-horizon commonly refers to the deeply weathered subsoil, devoid of humus, but with a concentration of fine textured material derived from chemical alteration of the parent material. The

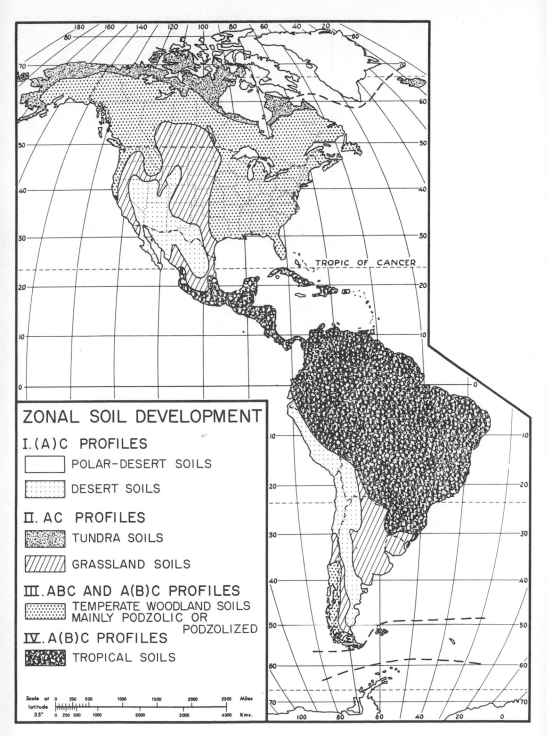

FIGURE 5. Zonal soil development.

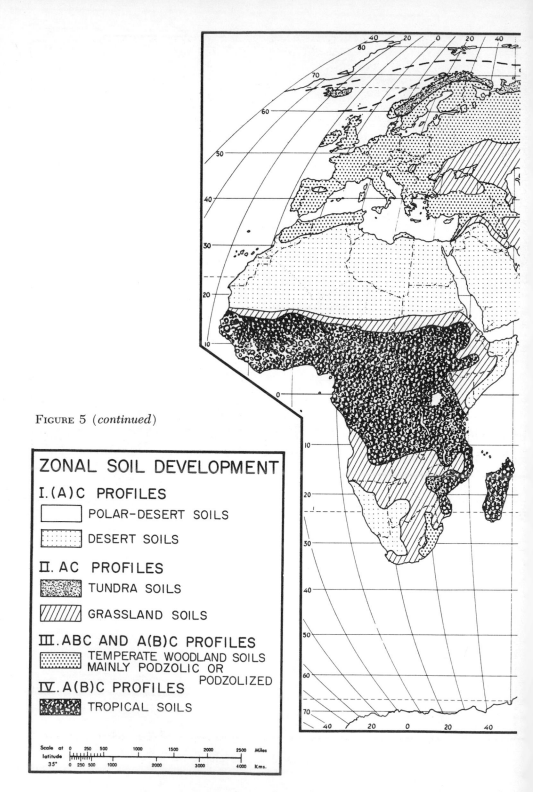

FIGURE 5 (*continued*)

ZONAL SOIL DEVELOPMENT

I.(A)C PROFILES

POLAR-DESERT SOILS

DESERT SOILS

II. AC PROFILES

TUNDRA SOILS

GRASSLAND SOILS

III.ABC AND A(B)C PROFILES

TEMPERATE WOODLAND SOILS
MAINLY PODZOLIC OR
PODZOLIZED

IV. A(B)C PROFILES

TROPICAL SOILS

Scale at 0   250   500   1000   1500   2000   2500   Miles
latitude
35°   0 250 500   1000   2000   3000   4000   Kms.

74

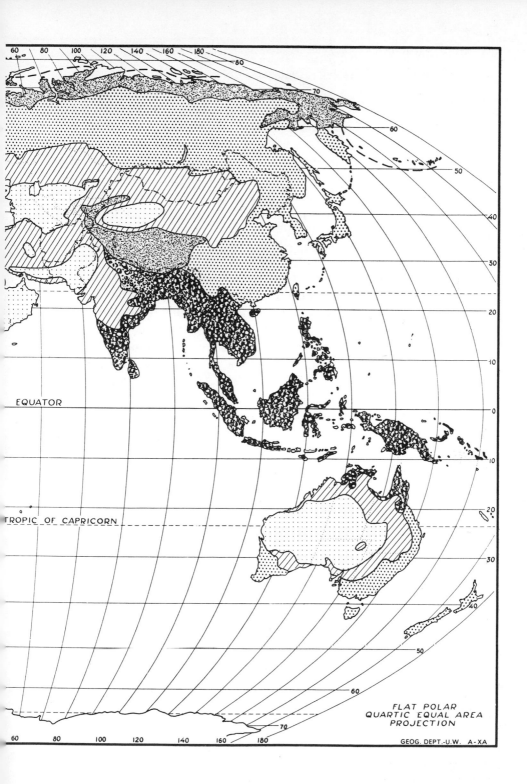

EQUATOR

TROPIC OF CAPRICORN

FLAT POLAR
QUARTIC EQUAL AREA
PROJECTION

GEOG. DEPT.-U.W. A-XA

B-horizon may also be a zone of accumulation or *illuviation* for minerals or humus washed in from an overlying, eluvial A-horizon. The C-horizon includes the more or less unaltered parent material, which may vary from unconsolidated sediment to resistant rock.

These major soil horizons may or may not occur simultaneously in one soil profile. Frequently horizons may show subdivisions of various kinds, and other, less common horizons may occur in addition to any of the above. Since the profile type of a soil is a major criterion for soil classification, the more important subhorizons are described below.[1]

A-horizons:

A_{00}—undecomposed surface leaf litter (litter horizon);

A_0—partly decomposed leaf litter (fermentation horizon);

A_1—humic mineral soil, not noticeably eluviated (humus horizon):

A_{2e}—mineral soil largely eluviated of clay, iron, and aluminum compounds, with little or no humus present; frequently the eluviation is sufficiently intense to bleach the soil (eluvial horizon);

(A)—("A-bracket") poorly-developed organic horizon of shallow, often stoney soils, found directly over C-horizon; excludes presence of other A-horizons (incipient A-horizon).

B-horizons:

(B)—("B-bracket") chemically weathered and discolored zone of finer texture than the parent material, but without humus and illuvial materials; precludes existence of an A_2-horizon (color B-horizon);

B_h—illuvial horizon with humic matter, clay minerals, and iron compounds derived from an A_2-horizon (illuvial humus horizon);

B_s—illuvial horizon enriched with sesquioxides of iron (Fe_2O_3) and aluminum (Al_2O_3) from the A_2-horizon; although a B_h-horizon may or may not occur when an A_{2e} is present, a B_s is indispensable (illuvial sesquioxide horizon);

---

[1] Needless to say the symbols used by different authors vary somewhat. The letter designations used here follow the rather general system of Franz (1960, pp. 213-18).

> $A(B)$—transitional horizon with chemical weathering and primary humus enrichment;

BC or $(B)C$—transitional horizon with visible but incomplete physical and chemical weathering.

C-horizons:

> C_1—partially disintegrated parent material with some evidence of oxidation;
>
> C_2—intact parent material;
>
> D—underlying bedrock not related to the parent material of the soil.

Other Horizons:

> Ca—horizon of diffuse lime precipitate or zone of calcareous nodules, concretions, or crusts found as A/Ca, $(B)/Ca$, C/Ca or as a well developed, distinct Ca-horizon just above the C-horizon (carbonate horizon);
>
> Sa—halite ($NaCl$) or gypsum ($CaSO_4.2H_2O$) accumulation (salt horizon);
>
> Fe—iron hydroxide ($3 Fe_2 O_3. H_2O$) accretion layer (oxide horizon); in the case of tropical soils Fe or Al is used to designate hardpan concentrations dominated by either iron or aluminum sesquioxides;
>
> P—seasonally waterlogged horizon of mottled reddish and grayish color resulting from seasonal alternations of oxidation and reduction (pseudo-gley horizon);
>
> G—groundwater horizon with chemical reduction or alternating reduction and oxidation (gley horizon);
>
> E—eroded soil sediment; may be used as a suffix such as $(B)E$ to indicate material from an eroded (B)-horizon.

Some of the broad classes of soil types are commonly based on profile types. Ignoring the groundwater soils, four more important groups can be identified: $(A)C$, AC, $A(B)C$, and ABC. These are genetic types that are primarily related to vegetation, intensity of chemical weathering, and precipitation-evaporation ratio.

The $(A)C$ soils fall into two classes. Firstly, they include the immature, shallow, incipient soils present in all climatic zones. These may be a result of recent surface erosion or, less commonly, recent deposition, with insufficient time elapsed for soil development. So, for example, $(A)C$ *lithosols* may be a permanent feature on steep slopes. The zonal soils of the arctic barrens and lower latitude deserts do not develop past the $(A)C$ stage as a result of limited chemical weathering and organic matter. Such zonal soils of $(A)C$ type reflect a quasi-absence of soil development.

AC soils are commonly found in semiarid or subpolar climates where organic material and biochemical activity are abundant, but where chemical alteration of parent material is impeded by insufficient moisture or low temperatures. Carbonate horizons are frequently found in the semiarid soils of middle and lower latitudes.

$A(B)C$ soils develop when a rich organic environment is combined with intensive chemical weathering. Eluviation and illuviation may be more or less negligible for a number of reasons related to the nutrient cycle, water balance, or parent material of the soil. Carbonate horizons form if a dry season is present. Soils with color B-horizons are most common in the subtropical and tropical woodlands as well as in regions of temperate broadleaved forests.

ABC-type soils reflect intensive chemical alteration in acidic environments as a result of vegetation type, parent material, or climate. Although most commonly associated with coniferous forests, ABC soils have a limited occurrence in the humid tropics.

The $A(B)C$ and ABC soils are, then, essentially woodland soils, in contradistinction to the $(A)C$ or AC soils of the world's deserts, grasslands, and tundras. Although groundwater modifications and immature soils are common variables to contend with, this basic classification is useful in evaluating paleosols. It can be sufficiently refined to be of considerable paleo-environmental value.

NUTRIENT CYCLE, pH, AND HUMUS

Organic plant matter and microfauna are important for the genesis of all soils, but are often crucial in the development of woodland soils.

Although the parent material of a soil provides the raw material for the nutrient cycle, the plant residues themselves are a product of the vegetation. Plant communities demanding large quantities of mineral nutrients from the soil remove potassium, calcium, magnesium, and ammonia which is then employed in building plant tissue. Ultimately these plant products are returned to the soil and partly incorporated as humus. Such a soil will probably have an alkaline or slightly acid reaction (pH value over 6) as a result of at least partial saturation with bases such as potassium or calcium carbonate (K_2CO_3, $CaCO_3$).

More modest plant species incorporate few minerals into their structures and do not afterward provide the soil with nutrient-rich residues. This paucity of bases leads to a rather acidic environment (pH under 6).

The nutrients and pH values of a soil are important for the microfauna which in its turn helps determine the humus type and soil structure.

If a soil is moderately well saturated with bases and is also not too acidic, a rich fauna of earthworms and beetles is commonly present. Through repeated ingestion and excretion by earthworms, the organic materials are completely reduced to amorphous humic acids in chemical association with iron compounds and clay minerals. The resulting clay-humus complex has few identifiable plant tissues, and the organic and mineral components cannot be microscopically separated. This optimal humus type, derived from earthworm excreta, is known as *mull* or *mild humus* (see Kubiena, 1953, p. 38ff.). A-horizons with mull humus commonly have a shallow A_{00}-horizon over an A_1, without A_0 or A_{2e}-horizons. Mull humus is largely confined to soils with $A(B)C$ profiles and the more favored AC soils.

On the other extreme, soils with few nutrients and rather acidic environments have few microorganisms, mainly fungi and mites. Organic materials are broken down physically but not chemically, and plant structures are readily identified with use of a hand lens. The resulting inert residues are not chemically integrated with the mineral soil, so that deep A_{00} and A_0-horizons may form, commonly over A_2-horizons with little or no intervening A_1 horizon. This inert, poorly decomposed humus is known as *raw humus* or *mor*. It is typically associated with $(A)C$ and ABC soils.

An important intermediate type of humus is known as *moder*. It develops when there is some base-saturation with mildly acidic or alkaline conditions, or when an earthworm microfauna is precluded by seasonal drought. Instead the fauna is dominated by beetles, and plant remains are chewed up and combined with organic excreta, but only loosely intermixed with mineral grains. The texture of moder is loose and crumbly, and plant structures can be identified microscopically. The upper soil profile is dominantly a combination of A_{00}, A_0, and A_1 horizons, and moder humus is usually associated with certain AC and $A(B)C$-type soils in drier locations or on bedrock with limited base nutrients.

PODSOLIZATION, CALCIFICATION, AND
LATERIZATION

The plant communities favoring the development of soils with raw humus and little or no base saturation are, in the main, coniferous forests. The needle litter provides few nutrients and percolating rain waters combine with the fermenting, resinous needles and become strongly acidic. The resulting environment is unattractive to most microorganisms and chemical breakdown is slow and incomplete. The acid solutions of penetrating water leach away any soluble bases, and further proceed to break down the clay minerals present. These may be eluviated in an unaltered state or decomposed with selective removal of the iron and aluminum sesquioxides. Of the three major components of most clays (two sesquioxides and silica), the silica molecules are released more slowly. A noticeable horizon of eluviation (A_{2e}), frequently of bleached color, marks this process of *podsolization.* The sesquioxides and other eluviated materials accumulate in the B-horizon whose reddish or yellowish hues contrast with the white or light gray color of the A_{2e}-horizon. This, then, is the genesis of the ABC-type soils.

Not all coniferous forests are associated with extreme podsolization as described above. Pervious sandy soils and species such as the pine provide optimal conditions for podsolization; denser soils and nutrient-demanding conifers such as spruce may retard podsolization. In such cases the A_{2e}-horizon is brownish and retains a good part of its intact clays as well as of its disassociated sesquioxides. These intermediate soils are called *podsolic* in contrast to the more extreme *podsols* with bleached A_{2e}-horizons. Soils of the ABC-podsolic group are not restricted to coniferous forest, but may also be found under broadleaved forests in wet localities on pervious or nutrient-poor soils.

Soil *calcification* is the converse of podsolization. Base saturation is high or complete, and leaching, even of the soluble salts, is limited or absent. Seasonal drought or over-all semiaridity favor calcification by limiting the amount of percolating rain water. The subsoil is often permanently dry, so that leached carbonates are soon precipitated at moderate depths as the soil water evaporates. Similarly, the dry season may stimulate upward migration of lime-charged soil-moisture by capillary action. As this water evaporates, accumulation again follows. The result is carbonate enrichment within the subsoil in the form of carbonate horizons.

Dry soil conditions, however, are only a part of the mechanism of calcification, at least in subhumid or semiarid regions. Without the intervention of the soil humus, occasional protracted rains would easily dissolve the carbonates of many grassland soils. Grasses, largely by virtue of their exceedingly fine, dense, and deep rooting network, provide the greatest quantity of nutrient-rich organic matter to the soil. This and the favorable alkaline environment attracts a teeming microfauna which in turn helps maintain a rich humus type. In this way limited losses through leaching can be compensated for indefinitely.

Most of the semiarid *AC* soils are carbonate soils, and *A(B)C* soils developed on limestone bedrock under subhumid environments commonly show lime accumulation as well. Soils with carbonate enrichment (*pedocals*) are frequently distinguished from *pedalfers,* with podsolization or intensive carbonate leaching (Marbut, 1936). Although precipitation exceeds evaporation in many areas of pedalfer soils, water-balance is not the only factor dominating their genesis. Consequently the pedocal-pedalfer limit does not provide an unqualified index of environmental conditions. Nevertheless, podsolization and calcification are two types of soil process that are of great interest in the study of paleosols.

Laterization is the process leading to hardpan formation in tropical soils. The intensive chemical weathering of the humid tropics leads to breakdown of clay minerals, with selective release of colloidal silica (SiO_2). This mobile silica is leached downward, leading to a relative enrichment of sesquioxides in the intermediate layers of the soil. These initial processes appear to be common to most tropical woodland soils, and the term *latozation* is sometimes generally applied for intensive weathering with desilicification and sesquioxide concentration. In many latozolic soils the sesquioxides form immobile concretions, and partial desilicification may ensue. Such *lateritic* horizons with concretions or massive concentrations of sesquioxides may be several meters deep, and have been known to reach thicknesses of well over 10 m. As long as they remain in the subsoil true hardpans do not develop. But when lateritic horizons are exposed at the surface by erosion, particularly in regions of pronounced seasonal drought, irreversible crystallization follows and a durable crust is formed. Concretions may also be concentrated into another form of crust by extended erosion of the unconsolidated soil aggregates. Both of these ferruginous crusts are commonly known as *laterite.*

The significance of laterites and lateritic soils is still not established to general satisfaction. Fossil laterites are known from tropical deserts, and some laterities of the subhumid tropics also appear to be fossil. In the traditional view, however, laterization was thought to be a characteristic of all mature soils of the seasonally-humid tropics. In fact, the sesquioxide accumulation was thought to be similar to carbonate concentration in semiarid soils, with upward movement by capillary action during the dry season. Field and laboratory studies by W. L. Kubiena (1954a, 1957) suggest a somewhat different genesis however. Kubiena found that laterization is at least as common in the humid tropics as in the savanna regions, and that, apart from the process of induration, laterization is only possible in permanently moist subsoils. But since laterites exposed and hardened at the surface are known best, an erroneous impression of their distribution and origin is readily possible. In fact, laterization is at least as common within bedrock and parent material as in the soil zone proper. Consequently, Kubiena considers the process as a typical form of tropical petrefaction rather than of soil development. Its prerequisites appear to be the presence of perennial soil moisture and high temperatures (see also Mohr and Van Baren, 1954; G. D. Smith et al., 1960, p. 238f.).

ARCTIC SOIL TYPES [2]

Soil development in the polar regions is generally impeded by a harsh climate as well as by the potent, ubiquitous erosional forces in the geomorphic sphere (see Chapter 7). In view of the wide extent of polar environments during much of the Pleistocene, the soils of the Arctic will be considered in some detail.

The high arctic barrens.—Within the high arctic wastes, soil development is evidently at a minimum. Biochemical agencies and chemical weathering are almost non-existent in this inhospitable environment. The snowcover is scanty or absent during most of the dry winters, a result of very low vapor content in cold air. Consequently frost-weathering acts on the surface rock during much of the year, producing great masses of debris ranging in size from

---

[2] Although there are several major soil classifications in use, most of these are basically similar and can be readily compared, with exception of a recent revision proposed by the U. S. Soil Survey (G. D. Smith et al., 1960). The classification adopted here is that of Kubiena (1953), which is followed by soil scientists and geologists in many European countries. The text in question has been published in English, German, and Spanish, while the principles have already been introduced to archeologists by Cornwall (1958, chaps. 7-9). Apart from these practical aspects Kubiena's system, with its accompanying detailed soil descriptions, is invaluable for pedological field work and for the study of fossil soils.

crude rock to medium-grained silts. The presence of permanently frozen subsoil at a few decimeters depth aids in mechanical breakdown of the bedrock surface. However the wind, unimpeded by vegetation, sweeps away the silt and fine sand produced by mechanical weathering. The over-all effect is that any incipient soil development is permanently hampered by persistent removal of any fine materials by wind or water. The climax or zonal soil is a lithosol of $(A)C$ type, known as an arctic *ramark* (Fig. 6a) (Kubiena, 1953). A discontinuous veneer of raw humus is present over a physically disintegrated C_1-horizon some 25-80 cm. in depth, and largely corresponding to the zone of seasonal thaw and frost-heaving.

The tundra.—The herbaceous tundra provides a more favorable environment for soil development than the arctic barrens. A reasonably complete vegetative mat ensures some rudimentary form of biochemical activity and furthermore helps protect fine mineral grains from deflation by wind. A more durable and effective snowcover also reduces frost-weathering at the surface, although frost-heaving over permafrost is prominent.

Although lithosols occur over wide areas affected by intensive erosion, the greater part of the landscape has both vegetation and soil cover. Drainage is characteristically poor, however, as a result of permafrost and widespread gentle relief. For this reason swamp and

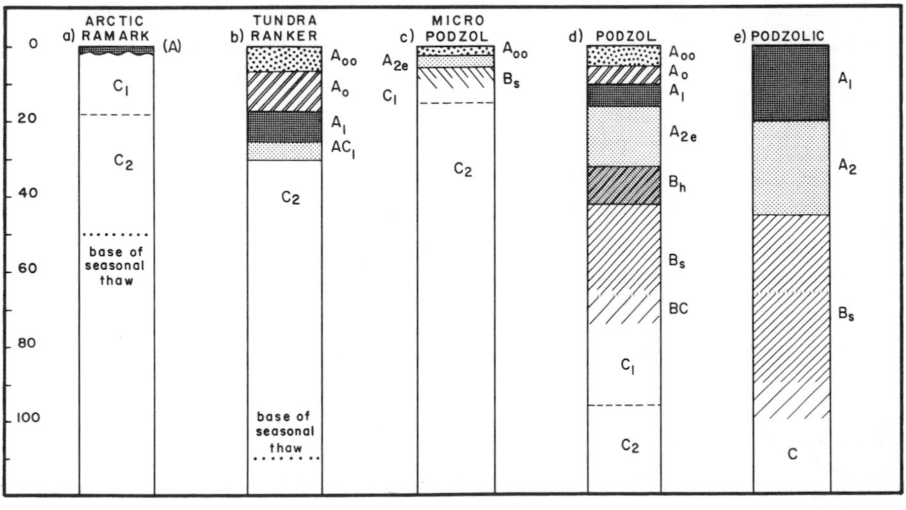

FIGURE 6.
Some higher latitude soil profiles.

groundwater soils are probably most common. Such semiterrestrial soils frequently have a shallow A-horizon over a gley zone extending down to the base of the seasonal thaw. Permanently oozing with water, the subsoil is not aerated; it is characterized by reduction and sulfide formation which gives the G-horizon a pale gray color.

In the case of better-drained terrain, a climax-type soil of AC-profile develops in response to a rich but nutrient-poor herbaceous vegetation. The microfauna is limited, and decomposition or organic materials is slow and incomplete producing raw or moder humus types. Base saturation is very low, reaction acidic. An AC-soil with such features belongs to the *ranker* class of Kubiena (1953), and the most typical soil of the tundra is a tundra ranker (see also Tedrow and Harries, 1960). Due to the high water absorption of the humus and the almost bacterialess, acidic soil environment, boggy conditions are common, leading to a net accumulation of organic matter in the form of peat. In the better-drained tundra rankers a little leaching of iron compounds may lead to sesquioxide or humus-staining on the surface of rocks in the transitional AC_1 horizon (Fig. 6b).

The forest-tundra.—Conditions in the forest-tundra transitional belt are in good part similar to those of the herbaceous tundra. Gley, peat, and ranker soils are common. In areas of higher vegetation, however, podsolization may be more advanced, with minute but none-theless typical eluvial and illuvial horizons. The resulting A_{00}-A_{2e}-B_s-C_1 horizon is that of a diminutive or micropodsol as shown in Figure 6c (Kubiena, 1953). In locations with unconsolidated bedrock a deeper BC-horizon will occur, in areas with a tundra mat, a deeper A-horizon.

Alpine soils.—The soils of high mountain regions show many similarities to those of the arctic. Lithosols are, of course, more widespread as a result of rough terrain, and as a corollary, swamp and groundwater soils less common. Various classes of rankers probably form the most typical soil type on gentler sloping surfaces, at least in middle latitudes.

FOREST SOILS OF HIGHER AND MIDDLE LATITUDES

The soils of the temperate and cold, continental woodlands are the product of moderate to considerable chemical weathering during warm to hot summers of one to five months duration. Moisture is available most of the time, and there is no climatic impediment to biochemical activity.

Forest soils of *ABC* or *A(B)C*-type occur as climax type in well-drained areas, although immature *AC*-profiles are frequent on moderate to steeply sloping surfaces and on very resistant bedrock. Such immature soils may be highly base-saturated and calcified in the case of carbonate parent materials (*rendzinas*), or they may be acidic pedalfers of the ranker group.

The equally widespread groundwater soils deserve brief mention as well. Soils subjected to seasonal waterlogging are known as *pseudo-gleys.* The subsoil is subjected to limited reduction of iron to its various derivatives while water-saturated, followed by extensive oxidation as the soil dries. The resulting iron and manganese oxides are concentrated in the form of stains, stripes, and concretions of varying size and shape but usually of yellowish or orange color, set in a background of gray. The gray tones of pseudo-gley subsoils are more commonly a result of local iron removal than of the presence of reduced iron derivatives. Gley soils are permanently located in the groundwater zone. Gley horizons are therefore characterized by reduction horizons which, depending on the iron compounds present, have dull gray to grayish green shades. The zone of fluctuating groundwater table undergoes alternating reduction and oxidation, and has many similarities with mottled pseudo-gley horizons, although the products of reduction are more significant.

The boreal forests.—Frost-weathering is important wherever bedrock is exposed in the boreal forest belt. Similarly, soil-frost phenomena are widespread, particularly where permafrost prevails. The dominant factor of soil development is chemical however. During the months when the soil zone has thawed, water percolates freely through the needle litter and partly-decomposed raw humus, passing through the mineral soil below. Meltwater is plentiful in the spring and in summer in the wet season, although rainfall is a little irregular and of some intensity. This favors repeated, rapid percolation. Thus, in combination with the unfavorable nutrient cycle, podsolization is active. The climax *podsols* have humic horizons at the surface, followed below by a more or less bleached, eluvial A_{2e}-horizons consisting largely of resistant minerals (mainly quartz) in the sand-and-silt size. The illuvial B-horizon has a light-brown or yellowish-brown zone of redeposited aluminum and iron sesquioxides (B_s). There may also be a dark, shallow, intermediate zone with leached clays and humus in addition to iron sesquioxide (B_h) (Fig. 6d). The B_h-horizon may form a hardpan, especially beneath cultivated soils.

Podsols are also found under coniferous woodland, particularly on highly pervious subsoils within the marine temperate climates. *Podsolic soils,* with partly-eluviated A_{2e}-horizons, generally show little bleaching and have no B_h (Fig. 6e). These intermediate soils are widespread under coniferous woodland, even within the boreal forests, wherever the nutrient cycle is better. They may also occur on pervious soils in wet localities under deciduous vegetation.

Bog soils and gleys are very extensive in the boreal forest belt, while tundra enclaves are typical in permafrost areas.

The deciduous forests.—Although podsolic soils are not rare under deciduous hardwoods, true $A(B)C$ profiles are more characteristic.

A protracted warm season, with equalized distribution of moisture, provides an opportunity for moderate but prolonged chemical activity. Organic matter rich in base-nutrients is provided by the more demanding, deep-rooted species. All this favors a rich microfauna, and biochemical activity is equally vigorous. The leaf litter is effectively decomposed and distributed through a fairly deep, dark-brown A_1-horizon of mull-type humus (Fig. 7a). The brown color of the deep (B)-horizon is predominantly a result of sesquioxide coatings on the mineral grains (but without apparent illuviation), or of chemical alteration forming clay minerals and oxides while obliterating original rock structure. Such brown forest soils or *braunerdes* (Kubiena, 1953) show complex intergrading with similar podsolic profiles.

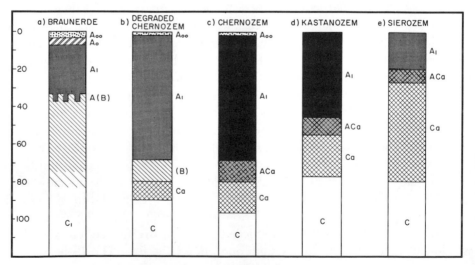

Figure 7.
Some middle latitude soil profiles.

MID-LATITUDE GRASSLAND SOILS

The soils of the middle latitude grasslands are distinct from other semiarid and arid soils in view of their exceptionally rich humus. Climatically, these regions all experience cold winters (Koeppen's *BSk* climates), so that vegetation is dormant for several months of the year due to cold, during which time little or no biochemical activity takes place. The repeated annual growth provides the soil with considerable quantities of nutrient-rich organic matter every autumn. These nutritious grasses have an exceptionally intricate and deep rooting system. Subsequent decomposition is primarily performed by earthworms, producing a mull humus. But since decay is slow, a considerable accumulation of humus takes place to depths of one meter or more. The soil is frozen in winter, and percolating waters are limited by droughty conditions in mid-summer. Leaching is therefore limited and lime accumulations are commonly found between the *A* and *C*-horizons. Chemical weathering is not sufficient to develop a (*B*)-horizon. A general profile is then A_1-*Ca*-*C* (Figs. 7*c*-*e*). Carbonate horizons are absent in areas with non-basic, silicate rocks leading to formation of ranker-type soils.

The *AC*-soil profiles of Figure 7 illustrate the most important mid-latitude grassland soils. Under optimal conditions the black *chernozems* (Kubiena, 1953) develop particularly deep, humic A_1-horizons. On the woodland margins there may be leached *AC*-type *prairie soils* of the pedalfer group, or *degraded chernozems* with shallow (*B*)-horizons, with or without some evidence of podsolization (Kubiena, 1953). Degraded chernozems with A_1-(*B*)-*Ca*-*C*-horizons (Fig 7*b*) are commonly found in Europe wherever forests have invaded former grasslands, partly as a response to climatic change.

On the drier margins the chernozems grade over into less humic soils with shallower A_1-horizons but greater carbonate accumulation. These include the chestnut soils or *kastanozems* (Fig. 7*d*), the brown soils or *burozems*, and finally the gray semidesert soils or *sierozems* (Fig. 7*e*) (Kubiena, 1953).

OTHER SEMIARID AND ARID SOILS

The lower-latitude grasslands do not experience winter cold, but vegetation is dormant and biochemical activity low as a result of seasonal drought. The rapid decay during the hot, summer rainy season together with a vegetation type producing limited organic matter, lowers the humus content of the soil. Furthermore, tropical grasses are largely poor in mineral nutrients. Consequently many tropical *AC*-profiles are not impressive.

An exception to this are the *tirs* or tirsified soils (synonyms: regur, black cotton soils, tropical black earths, margalitic soils) (Mohr and Van Baren, 1954; Kubiena, 1957; Klinge, 1960) mainly found in seasonally-waterlogged locales on both margins of the lower-latitude dry belt and extending well into the seasonally-humid tropics. Boggy conditions prevail during the rainy season, mainly over impervious bedrock or clayey subsoil. A dense mull humus is typical, the reaction alkaline. Although remarkably black when wet, the A_1-horizon, commonly 15-60 cm. deep, is light gray when dry. The color is apparently not due to high organic content but rather to some property of the base-saturated clay-humus colloids. The A_1-horizon swells up when wet and contracts strongly when dry, with dehydration cracks penetrating to its base. The clay-humus dispersal through such fissures probably reflects mechanical diffusion rather than the activity of soil microorganisms. Deep *P* or *G*-horizons commonly underlie the *A*, indicating groundwater oxidation and reduction. Also, rather massive *Ca*-horizons may frequently underlie the A_1. Despite their superficial resemblance to chernozems, the tirsified soils are distinctive of seasonally wet climates, experiencing hot dry seasons with air temperatures at some time exceeding 38° C. Yet their peculiar textural properties and relationship to groundwater conditions rule them out as true zonal soils. They appear to be significant as paleosols in some subtropical arid regions (e.g., Morocco and the Sahara).

With little chemical weathering and no vegetation the arid deserts proper allow very limited soil development, so that $(A)C_1$ lithosols are most characteristic. This is Kubiena's *yerma* or desert soil class. Areas without external drainage have widespread subsoil concentrations, or surface crusts, or precipitates of halite ($NaCl$), gypsum ($CaSO_4$), or calcium carbonate ($CaCO_3$). This is understandable since any solubles carried by the ephemeral waters will be left behind in the wake of evaporation. Subsurface *Sa* or *Ca*-horizons are also common in well-drained soils since any available soil moisture will be attracted to the surface by capillary action.

SUBTROPICAL WOODLAND SOILS

Mediterranean soils.—The summer-dry subtropics are a transitional belt in many ways, and the soil pattern is generally rather complex. Only in the Mediterranean Basin are the common soil processes and soil distributions better understood.

Chemical and biochemical weathering are at a low level of intensity as a result of the coincidence between low winter temperatures and rainy season. Soil development is painfully slow, and on fresh limestone bedrock or other unconsolidated calcareous materials, *AC*-type rendzina soils seem to represent the post-Pleistocene climax soil (Kubiena, 1954b, 1963; Butzer, 1963a, with remarks by Kubiena). On silicate rocks, with low base status, semi-arid southern or *meridional braunerdes* (Fig. 8*a*) seem to be the climax type. In contrast, the "typical" red soils of the Mediterranean region no longer develop on fresh surfaces. Various instances of fossil, Pleistocene red soils of this type have been demonstrated (Klinge, 1958; Fränzle, 1959b; Butzer and Cuerda, 1962a; Butzer, 1963c, 1964a), and it is now widely accepted that the red soils at the surface are relict, i.e., also paleosols (Durand, 1959). They are in approximate equilibrium with their environment but will not form afresh.

These conspicuous Mediterranean paleosols deserve some attention, since they are closely related to tropical soils, and since similar paleosols of Pleistocene age are found in other middle latitude areas.

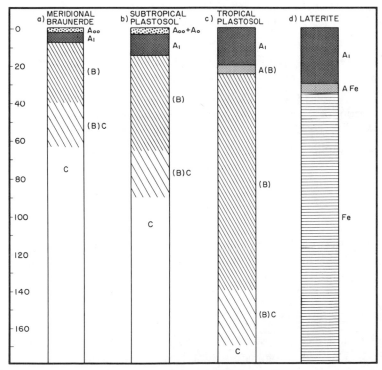

FIGURE 8.
Some lower latitude soil profiles.

The most common is the *terra rossa* developed on calcareous parent material. This soil has a shallow A_1-horizon over a deep, red, clayey (*B*)-horizon weathered from the limestone bedrock. The brilliant color is due to the presence of anhydrous iron such as hematite (Fe_2O_3) and goethite ($FeO.OH$), presumably derived from the hydrated limonitic form ($2\ Fe_2O_3.H_2O$) through extreme desiccation during a hot dry season (Kubiena, 1953; Klinge, 1958). On the other hand the iron compounds are found dispersed within colloidal silica (SiO_2) liberated during breakdown of clay minerals by intensive weathering. There is a little leaching of colloidal silica with relative accumulation of iron. This presumes an alternation of warm-moist and hot-dry conditions, so that the terra rossas are typical products of warm, seasonally-humid climates. The anhydrous iron compounds (which do not take up water upon wetting) are stable, so that these red soils are almost irreversible after a change of climatic environment. Although terra rossas are quite decalcified during formation, they have generally been subject to secondary calcification in drier parts of the Mediterranean region today. Also, as a consequence of Pleistocene geomorphic agents and more recent anthropic interference, most terra rossas are today found as soil sediments, and only rarely can the (*B*)-horizon be traced to the *C* by an intact sequence of (*B*)*C* and C_1-horizons.

On the cooler margins of the Mediterranean Basin, as well as at higher elevations, the terra rossas are replaced by reddish-yellow *terra fuscas*, the products of equally effective weathering but without anhydration of the iron compounds. Analogous soil types on non-calcareous bedrock are *rotlehms* and *braunlehms* (Kubiena, 1953). A general profile type applicable to most of these relict, subtropical *plastosols* (plastic as opposed to friable products of intensive weathering) is given in Figure 8*b*.

The humid subtropical woodlands.—The soils of the humid subtropical woodlands are little understood, except for those found in the southeastern United States where intensively weathered reddish and yellow podsolic soils are dominant, although rotlehms and braunlehms are widespread too.

TROPICAL WOODLAND SOILS

The most characteristic soil development of the seasonally-humid tropics is a *rotlehm*, dominated by anhydrous iron. In contrast, *braunlehms* with limonitic iron are found under perhumid rainforests (Kubiena, 1957). Although some latozation and even laterization may be evident, these soils are essentially plastosols (Fig. 8c). The A_1-horizon commonly has a fair amount of organic matter, and no A_{2e}-horizons are present. Any lateritic concretions present in the (B)-horizon are not crystallized, and the colloidal silica—derived from clay mineral decomposition and re-solution of crystallized SiO_2—is only moderately leached, hence the plasticity. Clays constitute over 25 per cent of the (B)-horizon. Base saturation is comparatively low, the pH acidic. These tropical plastosols (largely equivalent to the Udox class of Smith *et. al.*, 1960) only differ from the subtropical plastosols in their intensity of development and depth of profile.

Within the savanna belt rotlehms vie with *latosolic,* i.e., friable and non-plastic, *roterde* soils (Kubiena, 1953, 1957) showing considerable silica depletion and very low base saturation. Basic profiles are similar however. Also common in the savanna are tirsified soils in areas of seasonally impeded drainage. Exposed lateritic crusts, frequently under attack by water erosion, help complicate the soils pattern. Soil stripping on all slopes, with redeposition on the flat savanna plains, is probably the most extensive of all these phenomena. The over-all result is that rotlehms or roterdes are more commonly found as derived sediments than as soil profiles *in situ.* Such (B)E profiles may attain depths of 30 meters or more.

In the rain forest, groundwater soils are widespread, but their systematics are poorly understood. In many cases humic A-horizons overlie deep, mottled, gleylike beds with lateritic concretions or semi-continuous sesquioxide precipitates. Most of these horizons appear to be incipient laterites (Fig. 8d) rather than true oxidation and reduction zones. Some true podsols with peaty A-horizons are known, but most of the equatorial podsols are found in better-drained situations on base-poor, pervious parent material. Fresh alluvium in the valleys and widespread soil slumping on slopes further reduce the occurrence of the climax braunlehms. Redeposited soil sediments are again widespread and (B)E-horizons may attain remarkable thicknesses of 50-75 m. over wide areas and several hundred meters in exceptional cases.

VEGETATION AND SOIL DEVELOPMENT

The basic relationships and characteristics of climate vegetation and soil development are summarized in Table 8.

TABLE 8

CLIMATE, VEGETATION, AND SOIL DEVELOPMENT

Koeppen Climate	Vegetation Type	Soil Profile	Dominant Soil Process	Characteristic Soil Types (not including ground-water soils or paleosols)
EF, ET	High arctic barrens	(A)C	Mechanical weathering	Arctic ramark
ET	Herbaceous tundra	AC	Humification	Tundra ranker
ET, Dd	Forest-tundra	AC, ABC	Humification, some podsolization	Ranker, micropodsol
Dc, Dd	Boreal needleleaved, evergreen and deciduous forest	ABC	Podsolization	Podsols, podsolics
Cbf, Da, Db	Mid-latitude broad-leaved deciduous and mixed coniferous-deciduous forests	A(B)C, ABC	Deep weathering and moderate podsolization	Braunerde, podsolics
BSk	Mid-latitude grasslands	AC	Humification, calcification	Chernozem, kastanozem, burozem, sierozem

Cs	Dry subtropical, broad-leaved and needle-leaved evergreen woodland	*AC, A(B)C*	Humification, calcification	Rendzina, meridional braunerde
Caf	Moist subtropical, broadleaved evergreen woodland	*ABC*	Podsolization and deep weathering	Podsolics
BWh	Low latitude desert and desert shrub	*(A)C*	Mechanical weathering	Yermas
BSh	Low latitude grasslands	*AC*	Humification, calcification	(Tirsified soils)
Aw, Caw	Tropical broadleaved deciduous woodland and savanna	*A(B)C*	Deep weathering, laterozation, laterization	Rotlehm, roterde, laterite (tirsified soils)
Af, Am	Tropical broadleaved evergreen and semi-evergreen forest	*A(B)C*	Deep weathering, laterozation, laterization	Braunlehm, laterite

7

Glacial
and Periglacial
Geomorphology

GLACIERS PAST AND PRESENT

Depending on material culture, human habitation of the earth has different environmental limitations. Even today, despite extensive exploration and research on the Greenland and Antarctic ice caps, permanent setttlement in glaciated areas remains impossible or at least uneconomical. So too in the past, the glaciated surface of the earth was certainly not inhabited by early man. Consequently the former extent of permanent snow and ice is important for setting certain limits to the possible distribution of peoples and cultures.

Glaciers past and present are at least equally significant in understanding climate. So, for example, Koeppen's perpetual frost climate (*EF*) has always been at least co-extensive with the continental ice caps. Similarly in mountain areas the altitude of the snowline—that critical limit above which more snow falls than can melt—gives a coarse approximation for mean annual temperatures somewhere below the freezing point (0° C.). Pleistocene snowline elevations differing from those of today may allow broad estimates of local temperature change. In general, the different extent of former and modern glaciers provides a valuable quantitative criterion for latitudinal and altitudinal shifts of climatic boundaries. Since glacier location is influenced by moisture sources and the direction of prevailing winds, the presence of Pleistocene glaciers may also provide information about the general circulation of the atmosphere. Finally, glaciers may provide pertinent stratigraphic data to permit identification of glacial or interglacial epochs, either locally or on a much larger scale through melt water deposits and through the world-wide oscillations of sea level accompanying the growth and wastage of continental glaciers.

The following summary discussion of glacial geomorphology outlines some of the more relevant data systematically treated elsewhere
by R. von Klebelsberg (1948-49, Vol. 1), P. Woldstedt (1954), J. K.
Charlesworth (1957, Vol. I), R. F. Flint (1957), and J. Tricart (1963).
A tentative review of paleoclimatic applications of snowline data
is also given.

GLACIER REGIMEN AND MOVEMENT

Although observed summer temperatures at the margins of permanent ice fields are often quite close to the freezing point, temperature alone does not determine glacier location. Certain thermal
conditions are, of course, prerequisite, but equally important is the
relation of snowfall to annual ice wastage (*ablation*) by melting and
direct evaporation (*sublimation*). Both temperature and solar radiation are mainly responsible for the rate of ablation, but glaciers may
develop in cool areas with heavy snowfall and yet be absent in colder
but drier regions. Once formed, however, glaciers create a microclimate of their own. They reflect radiation (increased *albedo*), lower
the summer temperatures by contact and radiative cooling, and so
lead to significant temperature *inversions* in the lower atmosphere, i.e.,
a cold skin of air underlying warmer air above. Such inversions often
extend far beyond the ice margins. The larger the glacier the greater
the environmental modification, and the resulting rigor of the climate
is often out of all proportion to the basic thermal character of the
region.

Ice fields that form where snowfall exceeds annual ablation are
the result of compaction and structural alteration from snow to ice.
The density of fresh snow is in the order of 0.15-0.16. After settling,
removal of part of the pore space, and recrystallization, the stage of
granular snow or *firn* (with densities of 0.5-0.8) is attained. Repeated
melting and refreezing, aided by further compaction under pressure
of overlying firn and snow leads to complete impermeability to air
and densities exceeding 0.82. This is defined as *ice*, which is capable of
plastic flow. The resulting ice masses may form either *mountain, valley,*
or *piedmont* glaciers in rough highland terrain, or *ice caps* in areas
of smoother topography.

Two major forms of ice movement are *gravity flow,* important in
the ice streams of mountain country, and *extrusion flow,* dominant
in ice caps and continental glaciers. The last process is based upon
differential pressures reflecting differential thickness of ice, whereby

plastic flow results at the base of parts subjected to greater pressures. In the case of the mountain glacier, movement is directed downhill and makes use of existing topographic channels. The ice cap, on the other hand, expands outward in radial fashion, largely independent of topography. Mountain glaciers advance until ablation exceeds the ice supply from higher elevations. Ice cap expansion ceases when wastage balances accumulation or supply in the source areas. In the latter case several factors may be involved: increasing radiation and higher temperatures in lower latitudes, scanty snowfall in drier continental interiors or high arctic regions, and finally, geographical phenomena like the termination of ice at the sea coast.

The annual balance of accumulation versus ablation varies, so that ice margins and ice thicknesses fluctuate. These variations of regimen are less noticeable in continental glaciers than they are in mountain ice streams whose tongues may oscillate considerably. Movements are twofold, so that waning may be accompanied by *backwasting*, i.e., retreat of the front, and *downwasting*, or reduction in ice thickness.

DEVELOPMENT OF MOUNTAIN, VALLEY, AND PIEDMONT GLACIERS

Although permanent ice covers only 10 per cent of the world land surface today, it extended over 32 per cent at the time of maximum Pleistocene glaciation (Fig. 9). Apart from the areal significance of glacial phenomena, moving ice is also the most powerful agent of erosion and deposition. The rather conspicuous effects of Pleistocene glaciation are apparent both on the broad continental plains of higher latitudes, as well as in diverse highland regions at all latitudes.

Snow accumulation in mountain country is greatest wherever snowdrifts can build up in valley-heads and other hollows in the lee of the major snow-bringing winds. Such snowbanks may persist for weeks or months after the snow has melted elsewhere, particularly when they are at least partially in the shade of higher mountain ridges. Such semipermanent snow fields already exert a peculiar geomorphic influence during the summer season, especially through intensified frost-weathering along the receding snow margins, gravity movements under the snow and firn banks, and removal of debris by meltwaters. This process of *nivation* may produce broad, shallow dimples on gentle slopes or more recessed forms in rugged terrain (Cotton, 1942).

If snow fields persist over several years and evolve to larger ice masses, erosional niches created in the valley-head area will grow

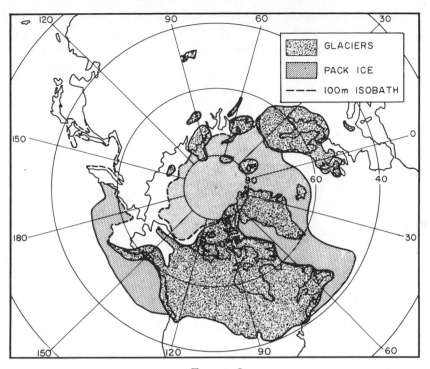

FIGURE 9.
Maximum late Pleistocene glaciation of the Northern
Hemisphere (simplified after Flint, 1957,
Frenzel, 1959-60, and others).

through further headward backweathering by freeze-and-thaw as
well as by scour beneath the moving ice. Further recession of the
steep back face or *headwall* will increase snow accumulation by
favoring drifting and avalanching, and reduce ablation by increasing
the amount of shade. The ice basin itself will be overdeepened a little
by subglacial abrasion and plucking, and broadened by scour and
quarrying of lateral rock faces. Such loosened rock is embedded and
carried within, on top of, or below the ice. The deeply recessed form
that results is known as a *cirque,* the *floor* of which is commonly
separated from the downstream valley by a gentle rise or *threshold.*
The formative ice is called a mountain or cirque glacier.

Cirque glaciation imparts an individualistic appearance to a highland area. Mature cirques in adjacent basins will cut back the divid-
ing ridges to sawtooth or *serrate ridges,* and reduce radial peaks to
jagged, frost-sharpened horns. After deglaciation, whatever its cause,

the cirque glaciers leave an amphitheater-like depression, with aprons of loose rock or talus embanked against the headwall, and frequently also a cirque lake or *tarn* in the center of the basin. The totality of such mountain sculpture by ice is known as *alpine topography* (Fig. 10).

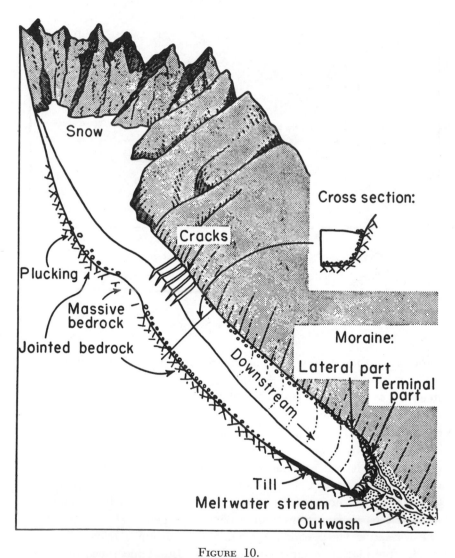

FIGURE 10.
Features related to an alpine glacier (from Longwell and Flint, 1955, with kind permission of J. Wiley & Sons, New York).

Cirque growth may lead to coalescence of several small glaciers, and the enlarged source area may permit downvalley advance of the resulting ice tongue. Such valley glaciers modify existing stream valleys by cutting deep, broad floors flanked by oversteepened cliff faces. These U-shaped or trough valleys are commonly several hundred meters deep in the case of mature glaciers, and are conspicuous hallmarks of *valley glaciation*. Towards the terminus of the ice, debris accumulation may take the form of frontal ridges or *end moraines*, as subglacial *groundmoraines*, or as side or *lateral moraines* which extend back through much of the glacial valley. Coalescing ice tongues may also leave intermediate ridges of rock and dirt known as *medial moraines*. The meltwater deposits of sand and gravel stream-laid ahead of the ice terminus are known as *outwash* (Fig. 10).

On occasion valley glaciation may be sufficiently extensive so that ice tongues descend through the mountain valleys right out onto the foothill region where they may spread out to form *piedmont glaciers*. Mountain glaciation may also grow to the dimensions of a mountain ice sheet, whereby all but a few protruding horns or *nunataks* are submerged.

DEVELOPMENT OF CONTINENTAL GLACIERS

Two large continental glaciations on Greenland (Fig. 11) and Antarctica still provide living examples of the dimensions which the Pleistocene continental glaciers of North America and northern Eurasia once had. Many smaller ice caps on Iceland and several Arctic islands provide firsthand information on processes at work at the ice margins.

An attempt to sketch the development and nourishment of the two extinct continental glaciers has been made by Flint, and the example of the Scandinavian ice sheet (1957, pp. 366-71) can be used here. The Scandinavian ice sheet had its origins as a mountain and valley glaciation in the Scandinavian mountains (crestline elevations 1,200-2,500 m.). With the intensification of glacial climatic conditions the highland glaciation developed into a piedmont glaciation, spreading out eastward over Sweden, but abutting onto deep coastal waters to the west where the ice terminated as a result of rapid terminal loss of ice through iceberg calving over the open, comparatively warm North Atlantic. Further development of a mountain ice sheet was followed by progressive eastward and then southward expansion into and ultimately across the shallow Baltic Sea. The resulting ice sheet

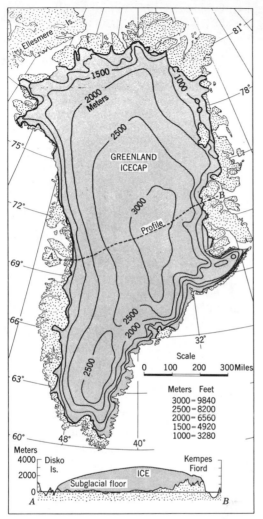

FIGURE 11.
The Greenland ice sheet (after Bauer, 1955, from A. N. Strahler, 1960, with kind permission of J. Wiley & Sons, New York).

(Fig. 12) maintained symmetry of profile by shifting the radial axis of ice outflow from the mountain crests to a point some 400 km. further east. During the glacial maximum, an ice sheet attaining a maximum thickness of 2,500-3,000 m. (Gutenberg, 1941; Niskanen, 1943; Weertmen, 1961) was nourished by moist air masses from the west and southwest, and to a lesser extent also from the south and southeast.

The erosion of a continental glacier is concentrated in its central area where soil is stripped off, hills are rounded, and bedrock gouged out in deep grooves often extending in the former direction of ice movement. In the more peripheral regions deposition of a variable mantle of groundmoraine tends to mask existing irregularities of the topography. And ahead of the ice great sheets of meltwater sweep down broad drainage channels every summer, carrying masses of sand and gravel that eventually remain behind as outwash. After deglaciation, knobby ridges of end moraines, often a kilometer or more wide and with a relief of twenty to thirty meters, extend across the countryside for thousands of kilometers to mark the former ice front. Although analogous to the depositional features of mountain or valley glaciers, the moraines and outwash of continental glaciers differ greatly in terms of thickness and extent.

The major features of ice-sheet deposition are summarized in Fig. 13. Characteristic of glacial bed proper are a lack of horizontal bedding or stratification, and an absence of sorting according to size of the heterogeneous soil products, sand, gravel, and boulders that constitute the *till.* The *glaciofluvial* or meltwater beds ahead of the former ice are stratified through successive horizontal accumulation of materials and are frequently sorted out into dominantly sandy or pebbly beds.

A final feature of interest in the case of continental glaciation is direction of ice movement. This can be reconstructed from directions of scratches, grooves, or streamline eroded bedrock in areas of dominant scour. Elsewhere the same purpose is served by the orientation of individual stones or till masses in longitudinal ridges known as

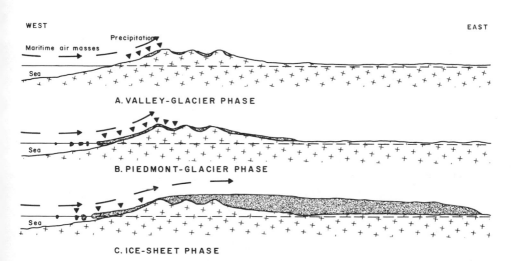

FIGURE 12.
Probable development of the Scandinavian ice sheet (redrawn from Flint, 1957, with kind permission of J. Wiley & Sons, New York). Not to scale.

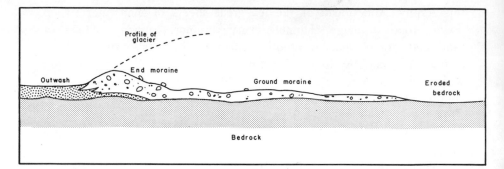

FIGURE 13.
Deposits related to a continental glacier (modified after Longwell and
Flint, 1955). Not to scale.

drumlins. Another method of study is devoted to the dispersal of
specific rock indicators derived from localized bedrock areas (Richter,
1956; West and Donner, 1956; Arnemann and Wright, 1959). Such
techniques may permit location of the initial stages of glacier development or the paths of ice movement to certain marginal areas during
different glaciations. Such information is pertinent for an understanding of the associated climatic patterns.

IMPLICATIONS OF THE CLIMATIC SNOWLINE

A controversial although conditionally useful index of climatic
change is provided by altitudinal displacement of the snowline in
highland areas with contemporary and Pleistocene glaciation. In
the case of existing cirque and valley glaciers the modern local snowline can be determined for each glacier in a number of ways, each
only approximate. The Kurowski method employs the median elevation of the glacier, the Höfer method the mean elevation between the
serrate ridges above and the tongue end of the glacier below. Another
method employs the elevation at which the contours of the glacier
change from a concave form upstream to a convex form downstream.
Each of these techniques, which can also be applied from topographic
maps, is inaccurate in varying degree depending on the peculiar bedrock topography.[1] Most dependable are field observations on the lower
limit of unmelted firn found on the glacier surface at the end of the

---

[1] The orographic snowline obtained by averaging the altitude of all perennial
snowbanks on a mountain range is of no value for comparison with Pleistocene data,
mainly because geomorphic records do not provide comparable information.

summer ablation season. This limit separates areas of net accumulation and net wastage for each individual glacier.

Exposure to radiation and precipitation-bringing winds causes the local snowline to vary considerably, particularly on the northern and southern sides of a mountain range. To offset these local topographic and orographic effects a mean value can be obtained from the total of local snowline values from a region. This is known as the *climatic snowline.*

Mean annual and summer temperatures at the climatic snowline vary considerably according to latitude (mainly as a result of radiation) and humidity. In a broad way, mean annual temperatures range from 0° to +1° C. in tropical mountains to about −5° C. in middle latitude mountains. Mean summer temperatures (June to August) vary even more strongly in the range of 0° to +4° C. in middle latitudes. Discussions of snowline temperatures are provided by Koeppen (1920), Ahlmann (1924), and Troll (1956).

The local snowline of a former mountain glacier can be determined more accurately than that of an existing one. The cirque floor median level may be at or above the local snowline so that the lowest cirque floor of a group of formerly contemporary cirque glaciers will generally give a ± 50 m. approximation of the local snowline. Employing the top of the headwall and the end moraine, Höfer's method is also occasionally used to determine Pleistocene snowlines. Median cirque floor levels are preferable, however, and can also be used to estimate regional or climatic snowlines.

If identical criteria are (and can be) employed to determine both the modern and Pleistocene snowline of an area, the difference or *snowline depression* is of some importance. The snowline depression of the Würm glaciation generally varies between 600 and 1,400 m., depending on latitude and on maritime or interior location. This would imply a local altitudinal depression of the over-all climatic zonation by about the same value. Temperature is probably the foremost variable, but changes in radiation, particularly as influenced by cloud cover, changes in precipitation amount, ratio of snowfall to total precipitation, seasonal distribution of precipitation, etc. may all be involved. Different mountain topography at different elevations may also play a conspicuous although more local role. Consequently, the common practice to single out temperature as *the* variable involved in snowline depression is unfortunate.

Quantitative estimates of temperature changes responsible for snowline depressions—with the optimistic provision that all other factors remain constant—are made by use of the modern temperature decrease with increasing elevation, the local *lapse rate*. This lapse rate is different within different mountain ranges at different seasons (Koeppen, 1920, Ahlmann, 1924; Baker, 1944; Weischet, 1954; Miller, 1955) and is not identical with lapse rates measured in the free air above nearby lowland stations. Whereas the average lapse rate of the free air is now commonly estimated at 0.55°-0.6° C. per 100 m., empirical surface observations within mountain ranges suggest that average values of 0.6°-0.7° C./100 m. are more representative. This type of information is largely lacking in many areas affected by Pleistocene highland glaciation so that many published estimates of the sort are speculative. Equally disturbing is the fact that, even if we could assume that temperature was the only variable, local Pleistocene lapse rates need not have been identical to those of today. Mortensen (1952, 1957) and Flohn (1953) have made a good case for widespread, semipermanent temperature inversions in the lower atmosphere between the Scandinavian ice sheet and the Alpine mountain glaciation as a result of the secondary cooling effects of the ice. There is reason to believe that such phenomena were common elsewhere as well. Absolute use of snowline depression values for Pleistocene temperature reconstructions is, then, not justified, at least unless supporting, convergent data are available through other methods of investigation.

With more qualified use, however, snowline depression values do contribute towards an understanding of climatic change. So for example, unequal regional or local snowline depressions beg explanations. Equally important is the realization that, averaged out by latitude, Pleistocene snowline depression values have been remarkably uniform at all latitudes on both the northern and southern hemisphere (Klute, 1928; Büdel, 1953; Mortensen, 1957). Radiocarbon data is gradually accumulating to prove that the glaciers in question were also contemporary, at least on the time scale of $x . 10^3$ years. This world-wide parallelism of glaciation strongly supports the idea of contemporaneousness of cold or warm climates in both hemispheres. And without a significant change in the water balance of the atmosphere, only a general, world-wide lowering of temperature can explain adequately a more or less similar snowline depression in all latitudinal belts.

CONCEPTS IN PERIGLACIAL GEOMORPHOLOGY

During the Pleistocene glaciations much of Europe and North America experienced polar or subpolar climates with tundra vegetation and permafrost. The European tundras witnessed a succession of remarkable cultures during the Würm glacial, so raising questions about the nature of the environment encountered by late Pleistocene man in these areas. The geomorphic processes of the polar and subpolar world are among the most striking of any, and deserve as much attention as the related vegetation and soils. The totality of information available on the physical environment of the tundras and permafrost lands may permit full interpretation of fossil phenomena, as well as an understanding of the ancient landscape in terms of modern counterparts.

The term *periglacial* is commonly used to describe a group of geomorphic processes dominant in non-glaciated polar and subpolar regions. The use of the concept periglacial is a loose one, however. Some authors include any cold-climate phenomena at all, others exclude all but those processes related to permafrost, while others still delimit the periglacial "cycle" areally to the lands between the glaciers and the polar or alpine tree-lines. An environmental definition of "the periglacial" would be most useful as this circumvents the necessity of subdividing between "periglacial" and other "cold-climate" phenomena, or of following the unfortunate practice of equating periglacial and cold-climate processes. Use of the word periglacial will here be confined to the group of processes peculiar to certain environments:

a) The high arctic barrens;

b) The herbaceous tundra, with or without permafrost;

c) The forest-tundra and coniferous forests with widespread permafrost.

The approximate modern extent of these zones on the northern hemisphere is shown in Figure 14.

The subsequent section will deal with those cold-climate phenomena which occur frequently in one or more of these regions. Less attention is paid to such features which are either rare or which are not commonly preserved in the fossil state. Unlike glacial geomorphology, periglacial environments have not been the subject of readily accessible, comprehensive studies. The specialized literature may be

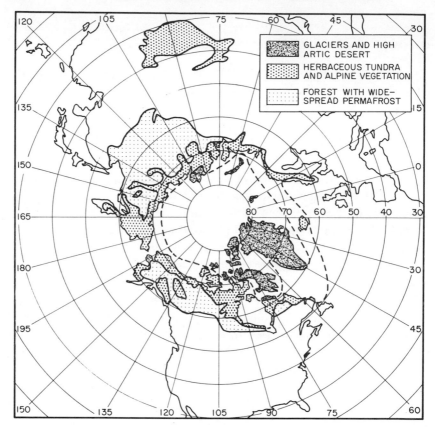

FIGURE 14.
Contemporary extent of glacial and periglacial environments
on the Northern Hemisphere.

consulted for general reference (Troll, 1944, 1947, 1948; H. T. U.
Smith, 1949: Büdel, 1950a, 1953, 1963; Peltier, 1950; Tricart, 1963;
Corbel, 1961). A final section will attempt an areal synthesis.

COLD-CLIMATE PHENOMENA

Permafrost.—Permanently frozen subsoil or bedrock accounts for
at least 25 per cent of the world's land surface (Black, 1954; R. J. E.
Brown, 1960), and is most common in continental areas with long,
severely cold winters with brief summers. This belt has been divided
into "continuous," "discontinuous," and "sporadic" permafrost zones
(Fig. 15). The base of modern permafrost reaches 600 m. in parts
of Siberia and 500 m. in North America. The surface horizon subjected

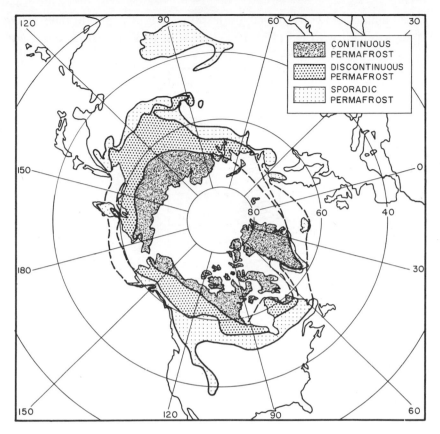

FIGURE 15.
Contemporary extent of permafrost belts on the northern hemisphere
(after Black, 1954, Brown, 1960, Frenzel, 1959, and others).

to annual thaw may range from several centimeters to several meters in depth. This active layer is a zone of considerable geomorphic activity.

Although there is no very close relationship between permafrost distribution and air temperature (Brown, 1960), continuous and discontinuous permafrost are found only in areas with mean annual temperatures below 0° C. (Black, 1954). The areal extent of permafrost, however, is not necessarily co-extensive with all frost-weathering and soil-frost phenomena. Many characteristic cold-climate features are not indicative of any thermal limit and may be found in any area with frost, although the more frequent, larger, and distinctive phenomena are concentrated where frosts are more common.

Ice wedges.—Perhaps the most typical morphological feature of frost climates are vertical wedges in soil or sediment that in their active state are filled with ice (Fig. 16). Typically some 1 to 5 m. deep, and

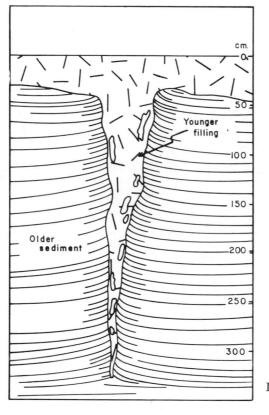

FIGURE 16.
Ice-wedge cast. To scale.

with a surface width of 30 to 50 cm., these *ice wedges* may range from a few millimeters to as much as 10 m. in width, and up to 10 m. in depth. The cracks are often found in groups intersecting at obtuse angles at distances of 20-30 m. (in extreme cases to 5 km.) to form giant polygonal networks. The centers of the polygons so formed may be either depressed or upraised in relation to the marginal cracks. The difference in height can be as much as 1.5 m. In the more frequent low-centered variety the strata in contact with the ice wedge commonly bend upward, as opposed to downward in the high-centered. Small embankments run parallel to the cracks. The low-centered type may possibly be more typical of swampy terrain, the high-centered of better drained land.

The origin of ice wedges remains controversial. One theory (Leffingwell, 1919; Black, 1954) holds that the crevices are initiated by periodic cracking of sediments as a result of rapid, extreme falls in temperature. During the melt season the fissure is filled with water derived from the supersaturated thawed parts of adjacent beds. When this water freezes on the interior crack surfaces, the increase in volume due to freezing leads to cryostatic pressures that widen the fissure. If the ice wedge does not melt out during the summer, the feature may widen from year to year. Empirical observations tend to support this hypothesis.

Another body of theory (Taber, 1943; Dücker, 1951; Dylik, 1952; Schenk, 1955) accounts for the growth and persistence of these frost cracks—which may be minute originally—by capillary movement of soil moisture from the comparatively warm, adjacent sediments to the dehydrating surface of the crevice walls. Here moisture is said to be precipitated in the form of ice crystals perpendicular to the wall. Such ice needles would grow as long as soil moisture is available, partially reinforced by dew from outside. Cryostatic pressure would continually widen the original crack until the sediments are dehydrated.

The growth of ice wedges is a function of time, sediment type, and subsoil temperature ranges. Wedges hardly, if ever, grow in the sporadic permafrost zone today, while their growth approximates 0.5 to 1.5 mm. annually in the continuous permafrost zone of northern Alaska (Black, 1954). The width of ice wedges can therefore be used to approximate the time involved in their genesis, and thereby provide an estimate of the minimum duration of corresponding climatic conditions. Although it had been thought that the depth of the ice wedge indicates the depth of the summer ablation zone, wedges seldom attain the base of the active layer in sandy or stony sediments, yet they do reach and may penetrate beyond it in fine beds (Popov, 1955; see also Büdel, 1961).

Ice wedges are found only in the permafrost zone today. In Eurasia larger, typical wedges, often forming giant polygons, are found in the poorly drained tundras and to a limited extent in the swampy parts of the forest-tundra. In the latter environment such features occur only on peaty or fine-grained, homogeneous sediments (Frenzel, 1959-60, Vol. 1, p. 75 ff.). Only coarse-grained, clastic materials seem to be affected in the permafrost tundra and the high arctic barrens. In the permafrost forest belt ice wedges are sporadic and found only on similar sediments as in the forest-tundra. They are small and do not form characteristic networks. The ice wedge is then a strict indicator of permafrost, probably indicative of at least former association with the continuous or discontinuous belts. On this basis it is believed that the former presence of ice wedges indicates mean annual temperatures of below 0° or even —5° C. at the time of formation (see Poser, 1948; Mortensen, 1952; Black, 1954; R. J. E. Brown, 1960). Further environmental localization can be made in the arctic barrens and tundra for all sediment types and in the case of highly organic or fine-grained beds also in swampy or tundra enclaves of the boreal forest. Preserved in fossil form, ice wedges are a very specific environmental criterion.

With the gradual disappearance of the ice after climatic amelioration, the crack would be filled with surface wash or slump material, and so be able to preserve its outline. Such fillings of loam, sand, loess, etc., are known as *ice-wedge casts*. Casts are comparatively frequent in former permafrost areas and can be identified in section by distortion of adjacent strata, and the vertical orientation of elongate stones found within the heterogeneous filling. Distortion is absent in the case of fillings produced by decomposed roots or contraction fissures due to dehydration of fine sediments.

Frost cracks or miniature ice-wedge fillings, seldom exceeding 15-20 cm. in length, are relatively common in unconsolidated materials. They form through simple freezing or through dehydration in fine silts, with subsequent filling by needle ice. They are not necessarily associated with permafrost.

Stone rings.—On a very much smaller scale soil frost may produce ground patterns of a different kind and dimension. These are circular rings or small polygonal structures marked by sorting of materials into fine and coarse classes. On flat ground, stone rings are most common, surrounding centers of finer material. Earth rings or geometrically arranged earth hummocks may also contrast with adjacent coarse materials. With gradients of 4 per cent or more, slope movements may elongate such stone rings into nets or garlands, which on steep slopes degenerate to stone stripes running perpendicular to the contours (Troll, 1944; Washburn, 1956). A certain proportion of vertically-oriented stones is another hallmark of such patterned ground. The diameter of stone rings may vary from 10-30 cm. in the case of areas with a dominance of daily freeze-and-thaw, to a few meters in areas with protracted seasonal frost or permafrost.

The coarse, clastic materials of stone rings are largely due to frost-weathering, and the sorting is a result of soil-frost expansion followed by differential contraction among rock and soil particles of varying particle size, mass, and cohesion. Repeated soil frosts of moderate intensity can explain stone rings adequately. The modern distribution of actively developing patterned ground in Alaska (Hopkins *et al.*, 1955) and Eurasia (Frenzel, 1959, p. 80 ff.) shows that although found most frequently in tundra areas, stone rings are not uncommon throughout the boreal forests. Williams (1961) suggests an equatorward limit in the form of the mean annual isotherm of $+3°$ C. for all but the largest features, for which he adopts $+1°$ C.

Occasional fossil, stone polygons (e.g., Wortmann, 1956), or the more common fossil stone stripes, are therefore not always indicative of a particular environmental situation. In fact Hastenrath (1960) has been able to show that occurrence of patterned ground within a considerable range of climatic possibilities is determined above all by the character of the vegetation mat.

Involutions.—Another cold-climate phenomenon takes the form of closely folded, highly crumpled laminae of fine-grained sediments, commonly segregated as to color. The resulting pockets or linear contortions are usually found within one or two meters of the surface, and show vertical orientation. Such pocket soils or *involutions* are a common fossil feature (Fig. 17) in regions once affected by cold Pleistocene climates.

Evidence from the modern arctic of exactly analogous phenomena

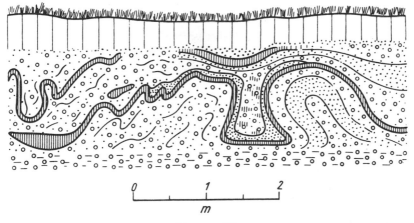

FIGURE 17.
Fossil involutions (after Steeger, 1944, from H. Weber, 1958, with kind permission of B. G. Teubner, Verlagsgesellschaft, Leipzig). The sediments have been intensely folded and partially sorted into fine (dark) and coarse (stippled) laminae through Pleistocene soil frost processes. To scale.

has not been fully satisfactory since numerous churning or contorting processes occur there (see Hopkins and Sigafoos, 1950; Frenzel, 1959, p. 78-80). Small, often temporary forms similar to the Pleistocene features have been observed developing in the temperate forest zone today (e.g., Fries *et al.*, 1961).

The most widely accepted theory of development (Steeger, 1944; Schenk, 1955) calls for the presence of permafrost. When, in the autumn, the active layer permanently refreezes, the supersaturated beds are trapped between two impermeable layers and subject to complex and intense hydrostatic pressures. Differential expansion of fine and coarse-grained beds may complicate the process. Vertical or horizontal contortions ensue, with frequent segregation of silt bands as a result of frost-sorting. Obviously the above process could take place on impermeable substrata other than permafrost. Others (see Tricart, 1963) consider convective currents, due to density differences of water during the freezing process, as a likely explanation for the distortions often found in quite homogeneous sediments. The base of the thaw zone (if we accept the presence of permafrost as a pre-requisite) will be at 0° C., whereas the water in the saturated ooze near the surface will be several degrees warmer during periods of insolation. Since water achieves its maximum density at +4° C., turbulence is set up within the thawed layer.

Fossil involutions are generally found in association with ice-wedge casts so that they are above all a permafrost indicator. But by themselves they must be considered inconclusive, particularly where there is any possibility of horizontal movements of soils and regolith, even on very gently sloping surfaces. Involutions are sometimes referred to as *cryoturbations,* although the term cryoturbation is also widely used to include patterned ground phenomena.

Other cold-climate indicators involve slope deposits partly related to gravity action.

Solifluction.—Solifluction in its strict sense refers to slow, almost imperceptible soil flow under the influence of gravity, i.e., a general downslope displacement of masses of soil and rubble saturated with water. It is common in areas with permafrost, which provides an impermeable substratum under an active layer of saturated soil (Büdel, 1944, 1961). Analogous conditions are provided in springtime where some subsoil is still frozen without intervention of permafrost. Tricart (1963) emphasizes that an impermeable substratum is not necessary. Instead, he considers that the fundamental mechanism proceeds in two stages. Firstly, freezing breaks the colloidal structure of silts and clays, so that they lose their cohesion when thaw sets in. The thawing material has a high water capacity and the abundance of seepage water provides a lubricated ooze capable of mass movement on even gentle slopes. In fact, C. Schott (1931) showed that solifluction still occurs in warm-temperate climates today, depending on lithological conditions.

Movement by solifluction is slow and irregular, varying from a few centimeters to a few decimeters per year. Solifluction materials are unstratified and locally unsorted, quite angular, and commonly occur in smooth, extensive sheets (*congeliturbate mantles*) not confined to topographic channels but rather covering broad slopes to a depth of two to three meters, possibly grading down into stream valleys below. When solifluction materials overlie the parent strata, various stages between intact, deformed, and removed or reoriented bedrock can be observed (Fig. 18). Solifluction sheets proper display a crude sorting into lenses or pockets of finer and coarser materials as a result of differential velocity according to particle mass. How-

FIGURE 18.
Coarse Pleistocene solifluction deposits. The angular limestone slabs are set in a loamy matrix, oriented downslope, in part grading into intact bedrock. Sorted and contorted lenses also occur.
To scale.

ever, coarse blocks may be found at random in finer beds. In practice, many solifluction deposits are badly contorted and consequently similar to involutions. In fact, solifluction and involutions have indistinguishable transitional forms.

Practically all slope deposits on inclinations of less than 25 to 30 per cent in middle latitudes are considered to be "fossil" and of Pleistocene age. They often contain blocks transported many miles across areas now forested. Most of the finer materials are, however, derived from local slope bedrock. Glacial deposits are often reworked by solifluction and hence foreign stones may be common at times. Also, the borders between till and solifluction are sometimes obscure.

Solifluction on slopes without vegetation is much more rapid, and the deposits have less relief than features resulting from solifluction under a vegetative mat. The second process is slower and may develop distinct surface forms on more symmetrical slopes. Such features, known as *terrassettes,* are the result of accumulations or overturning of sod. Terrassettes may follow the contours or have a lobate, tongue-like configuration. In conclusion, treeless situations are generally necessary for solifluction, but not permafrost. Nevertheless, the greater part of the low-angle slope deposits in western Europe is probably due to solifluction over permafrost.

Solifluction phenomena cannot be used to delimit the permafrost zone in marginal areas. There are many gradations between true fossil solifluction phenomena and superficially similar but water-laid colluvial deposits in the subtropics (see Butzer, 1964b), and slumping of lubricated soil on slopes may produce analogous features.

Block Streams.—Numerous coarse deposits of chaotic masses can be found localized in valleys and extending as mantles on slopes of 5-45 per cent '(Büdel, 1944; Tricart, 1963). Many such *block streams* are simply eluviated fans of coarse congeliturbate material due to solifluction. Other block streams are coarse by origin, having formed below extensive rock outcrops. Block stream movement has often been observed well below the tree-line, and modern distributions in Eurasia show a concentration in the forest permafrost zone and cold, mountainous country (Frenzel, 1959-60, Vol. 1, pp. 82-86).

Sorted Talus (*Éboulis ordonnés, grèzes litées*).—Another common fossil feature, due to frost-shattering on slopes and subsequent down-hill sliding of materials, are the beds of sorted talus often found on slopes of less than 17 per cent but occurring at angles of as much as 60 per cent. Their inclination decreases noticeably downslope. The beds show distinct alternations of fine and coarse materials, invariably quite unrolled and angular, with the coarse beds well stratified and containing little or no interstitial materials (Fig. 19) (Tricart, 1963).

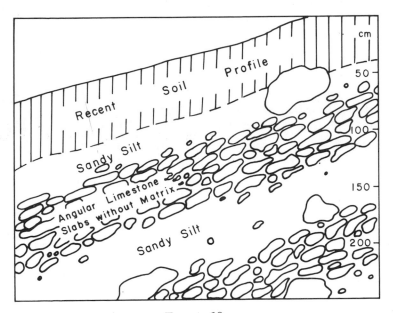

FIGURE 19.
Pleistocene *éboulis ordonnés*. To scale.

The individual beds may have thicknesses ranging from 5 to 50 cm. The coarse particles are thought to accumulate during the first thaws of spring, by sliding over still-frozen soil. Thereafter, solifluction is responsible for transportation and deposition of fines over the coarser bed (Tricart, 1956a). Permafrost is obviously not a prerequisite, and the modern distribution of these phenomena in Eurasia indicates that they occur at least as frequently outside as inside of the permafrost or tundra belts.

Other Cold-Climate Phenomena. Many additional cold-climate processes could be enumerated here, but most of these carry less paleo-environmental importance. So, for example, the large mushrooms of ice or mud known as *pingoes* have only been found occasionally in fossil form (e.g., Mückenhausen, 1960, with references). The remaining circular ridges of dirt may be as much as several hundred meters in diameter, and are mainly found over permafrost. Only small pingoes of 10-15 m. diameter and up to 2 m. high are known from outside the permafrost zone (Frenzel, 1959, pp. 88-90, Fig. 13).

Another widely cited cold-climate phenomenon is the so-called *asymmetric valley,* which in cross-section has a gentle slope on one side, a steep slope on the other. The various hypotheses for development of asymmetric valleys have been discussed by Maarleveld (1951) and Ollier and Thomasson (1957), and there can be no doubt that only some of these forms are unequivocally related to specific cold-climate processes.

Cryoplanational or *goletz terraces* are more or less horizontal surfaces cut into the bedrock of mountainous terrain by frost-weathering and solifluction (Tricart, 1963; Frenzel, 1959-60, Vol. 1, pp. 82-85). Such features show no relationship to bedrock structure or stream valleys. They appear to form only within the permafrost or tundra zones today, but have been recognized in fossil form in western Europe.

Features due to stream and wind action will be discussed further below.

A SYNTHESIS OF PERIGLACIAL GEOMORPHOLOGY

The high arctic barrens.—The geomorphic processes of the extreme periglacial environment of the rocky wastes of the high arctic have been described most effectively by Büdel (1950a, 1960, 1961, 1963). Among the basic prerequisites to landform evolution are:

a) Little or no vegetation, so that geomorphic processes are in no way impeded by a plant cover.

b) Permafrost, with an active layer of only 20-80 cm. depth. The permafrost is an agency of deep mechanical weathering, particularly at the base of the active layer where soil frost and massive ice in rock joints and cracks produce abundant, fresh rock rubble every summer.

c) Lack of groundwater percolation due to the presence of impermeable permafrost near the surface, and minimal evaporation, due to low temperatures (seldom over 10° C.). Consequently the summer snow meltwaters, the meltwater from the active layer, and any summer precipitation must all flow off the surface or through the supersaturated active layer.

d) Intensive frost-weathering of all exposed rock faces.

e) Extreme mobility of the active layer during the warmer season through the churning and heaving of various forms of soil frost, downhill solifluction of supersaturated ooze, and a remarkable subsurface drainage of water over the base of the active layer.

In this way the high arctic wastes provide both enormous masses of mechanically disintegrated rubble as well as potent agents for removal. In addition, the meltwaters of neighboring glaciers may add further masses of outwash.

Surface denudation of slopes proceeds through subsurface drainage and solifluction. Stone stripes or garlands are common on slopes of 3-25 per cent, and on even steeper slopes runoff drainage and solifluction combine to allow rill-cutting or slope dissection.

The major stream valleys are overloaded with detritus and are invariably underlain by ever-fresh, mechanically disintegrated bedrock. During the early summer runoff spates, stream incision is rather rapid, and broad steepsided but smooth-sloped valleys (Fig. 20) are excavated by the combined action of stream cutting and slope movements. Broad, coarse gravel beds cover the stream channel, commonly extending well back into the headwater areas. Resistant rock strata are vigorously attacked both on the valley slopes and in the stream bed, and so do not give rise to noticeable breaks in gradient.

While the waters are held in the frozen state and a snowcover is absent, deflation by wind is unimpeded and removes finer grain-size particles from the frost-rubble as well as any outwash areas present. Coarser sands are deposited in parabolic or blowout dunes, and fine dustlike materials of the loess category are usually deposited

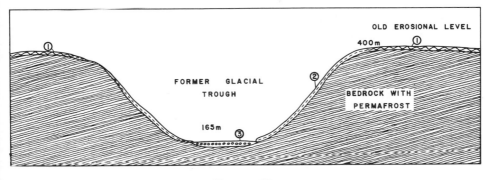

FIGURE 20.
Valley profile in the periglacial zone of Spitsbergen (generalized after Büdel, 1963). (1) cryoturbated active layer on upland surface, (2) congeliturbate mantle with subsurface drainage, (3) gravel bed of stream. The original Tertiary erosional surface, cut by a Pleistocene glacial trough, has been much modified by valley deepening and slope retreat.

as veneers or mantles possibly far distant in more vegetated zones of the tundra or forest-tundra (see chaps. 8 and 12).

The Tundras. Many of the more maritime tundras do not have permafrost, and surface frost-weathering is a little reduced by the effective mat of vegetation and a more durable snowcover in winter. Soil-frost activity and the production of debris in general is consequently less pronounced than in the barren high arctic wastes. The rate of gravity movements is severely checked by the plant cover, and this restricted (German: *gebundene,* literally "bound") solifluction leads to the formation of terrassettes or lobes perpendicular to the contours on slopes with gradients of 3 to 35 per cent. The terrassettes and vegetation in turn slow down surface runoff, reducing the potential of streams for both erosion and deposition. As a result, upstream drainage channels often deteriorate into block streams or dells choked with detritus.

Wind erosion is confined to dry river beds and block streams, although deposition of wind-borne loess from high arctic zones of deflation may be very prominent. The greatest part of the European and North American loess was accumulated under a rich herbaceous vegetation as innumerable vertical root zones indicate; in fact, the vertical cleavage of loess has been attributed to such root structure.

The alpine zone above the tree-line and below the snowline conforms in many ways to the various physical attributes of the true tundra, and in part to that of the high arctic wastes. Frost-weathering, various soil-frost mechanisms, and solifluction are present, although less intense than in the polar world, and adapted to terrain largely in steep or moderate slope.

The permafrost forests.—The forest-tundra and, even more so, the coniferous forest belts with widespread permafrost are in all ways a transitional part of the periglacial zone. Frost-weathering, cryoturbation, solifluction, surface denudation, stream cutting and deposition, and even some aeolian processes are admittedly still in effect. But all forms of geomorphic activity are rather subdued in both spatial and temporal dimensions, particularly as a result of the protective vegetation and winter snowcover.

Synthesis of periglacial geomorphology.—Following Troll (1948) and Büdel (1950a, 1963) the peculiar group of formative agents at work in the periglacial zone are summarized by the following:

a) Frost-weathering, including disintegration of surface rock by frost action in joints and fissures, the attack of bedrock by ice-wedging, etc.

b) Congeliturbation, the total of soil-frost activity through bedrock disintegration, soil churning and heaving, particularly in the active layer over permafrost.

c) Solifluction, the slow flow of the water-saturated mantle of soil and loose rock by gravity and frost-action, aided by subsurface water drainage.

d) Stream incision and gravel deposition, as a result of accelerated seasonal runoff and overloading with materials derived from frost-weathering, congeliturbation, and solifluction.

e) Deflation and deposition by wind.

f) Slope retreat and surface denudation by the total of these processes.

8

Humid,
Arid and Tropical
Geomorphology

STREAM EROSION AND DEPOSITION

Glacial erosion is probably the most powerful individual agent of gradation, but the work of running water is certainly the most universal. Before attempting to synthesize the geomorphic processes of the non-polar world, a simplified outline of "normal" stream erosion and deposition may be of use to the general reader.

The residual mantle produced through mechanical and chemical weathering of the earth's crust may be subsequently attacked in a number of ways. The direct mechanical impact of raindrops on unprotected surfaces is the smallest unit of erosion by water. It is remarkably potent in cultivated fields and a prime agent in man-induced soil erosion. Elsewhere, under natural conditions, *raindrop erosion* and mud-spattering are important wherever rainfall is heavy and irregular and the vegetative mat incomplete. The next step is corrasion through shallow, poorly-defined rivulets following channels of temporary drainage. These may transport both suspended mud and a certain amount of sand. Under more extreme conditions, thin sheets of water may spread out over much of the surface, moving within the vegetation. Such *sheetfloods* may, in the course of time, contribute to an appreciable lowering of the general surface (three-dimensional or areal *denudation*). All of these mechanical effects of rainwash are intensified and accelerated on steeper slopes where they are aided by gravity in a number of ways, so favoring *slope retreat.*

Rainwash is also important as a chemical agent of denudation, acting through rapid solution of salts and carbonates, and surface corrosion of loose or intact rock. An appreciable amount of material may thus be carried in solution. Equally important is solution and corrosion by percolating waters which pass on through the ground-water before they eventually reach the stream network.

Streams are fed by intermittent surface runoff after rains, and protracted underground percolation through seepage or springs. They may be permanent, or otherwise seasonal or even sporadic, depending upon the climate and, possibly, local factors. Stream transport accounts for a *load* of:

   a) Chemical solvents carried in solution;

   b) Clays, silts, and fine sands carried in suspension;

   c) Coarse sands and small pebbles alternately pushed and flipped along the stream bed through irregular saltation; and

   d) Pebbles and cobbles rolled and pushed along by simple traction.

Since the specific gravity of most rocks in the earth's crust varies at about 2.6-2.7, size is the major factor determining mode of transportation at a given stream velocity. Although rapidly-moving clear water will occasionally tear away loose particles from the stream bed or banks, mechanical stream erosion is mainly performed *by the load* through simple abrasion. The greater the load, the greater the capacity for stream cutting. The greater the turbulence and total velocity of the waters, the greater the transport capacity and the greater the erosive force. Stream erosion leads to downcutting of the stream bed by vertical incision, and to undercutting of its banks by lateral erosion. The upper ends of a stream or its tributaries may also work their way backwards by headward erosion. The major local effect of stream erosion is *dissection* (essentially two-dimensional or linear) as opposed to surface denudation and slope retreat by rainwash and allied phenomena.

Materials that have been transported are ultimately laid down. Such stream deposition or alluviation ensues when the total water velocity decreases, thereby reducing the transport capacity. The coarse load is deposited first, followed by the fines. There commonly are well-defined zones within a stream system where effective velocities are greater or less. So for example water movement is faster near the bottom of the stream near its center, than out near its banks. Further, stream gradients are greatest in the headwater area, so that turbulent and eddying motions of the water are most violent there. As the gradient decreases downstream the turbulent energy and total velocity of the stream is reduced, even though the usual increase in volume, as a result of tributary convergence, leads to an increase in net downstream velocity or laminar flow. But effective velocity, in terms of transport capacity, is usually reduced in the downstream parts. Generally speaking, the regions of predominant erosion or deposition within a river fluctuate in the course of the year. Almost all streams are affected by strong seasonal variations of discharge, either in response to rainfall maxima, a spring snowmelt, or to pronounced seasonality of evaporation. Erosion is generally most effective during the onset and height of the runoff maxima, deposition most widespread during the period of subsiding water level. If surface runoff and stream discharge maxima are particularly violent, a stream system will be affected by correspondingly greater erosion and deposition.

The lower courses of most well-developed streams are situated in low-lying level country, and seasonal variations of discharge may lead to regular or sporadic inundations of the surrounding flats. Such *floodplains* prone to flooding are the areas of most characteristic stream deposition or *alluviation*. The aggradation proceeds by bed-load sedimentation along the bed of the slowly shifting channel as well as by release of the suspended load by bank overflow.

The various features of the floodplain are significant for an understanding of prehistoric settlement in river valleys. In the case of sluggish rivers, the actual river bed is accompanied by banks or *levees* which tend to lie a few meters above the general elevation of the periodically inundated alluvial flats. The lowest ground is frequently found on the outlying alluvial flats where surface or groundwater may be present throughout the year (*backswamps*). The gradual decrease in elevation from the river banks to the outer limits of the floodplain are a result of the heavier, coarser materials being deposited in the area of swiftly moving water, at the bottom or margins of the meandering low-water stream channel. The slower flood waters only carry finer materials to the margins of the floodplain, so that these smaller-sized particles can only raise the level of the land at a slower rate. Hence the higher-lying banks or levees of many larger rivers. Levees, alluvial flats, and backswamps have always had a direct functional significance for river valley settlement by both food-collectors and agricultural populations.

For a more detailed account of fluvial activity the reader may consult such standard texts as Thornbury (1954), Dury (1959), Louis (1960) and Sparks (1960), or more specialized studies of stream behavior by Horton (1945), Mackin (1948) and Leopold *et al.* (1964).

HUMID ZONE GEOMORPHOLOGY

General features.—The external geomorphic forces responsible for landscape sculpture in humid, temperate environments are far better understood than those of the periglacial zone (see, Büdel, 1950a; Cailleux and Tricart, 1955). Mechanical and chemical weathering are both moderately significant since winters are cool or cold, and considerable moisture is available. The only important gradational agent is running water, aided by localized gravity movements. This is the climatic-geomorphic province which W. M. Davis' "normal cycle of erosion" seeks to describe. Vegetation cover, except for the mediterranean regions, is characterized by closed woodlands providing considerable protection for the soil. Consequently soil profiles and weathering zones are well developed and only subject to serious erosion when man removes the tree cover. Geomorphic processes are of moderate intensity and the dynamism of periglacial sculpture is absent. Instead surface denudation is limited under the natural plant cover, and soil profiles are deep.

It is therefore not surprising that "fossil" features of Pleistocene vintage have suffered little erosion and only moderate weathering. In fact, ancient glacial deposits and erosional features are rather well preserved. Where not obscured by subsequent deposition, even early Pleistocene glacial forms are commonly recognizable. In contrast to the periglacial zone, the limits of the former continental glaciers can be reconstructed with accuracy in the humid-temperate zone. Equally important is the excellent preservation of glacial-age cold-climate phenomena.

Within the humid-temperate zone there are moderate differences between the temperate-continental forests, with seasonal frosts and winter snowcover, and the marine-temperate woodlands with only occasional frosts and no durable snowcover. Differences also exist between the humid and subhumid subtropics.

The continental-temperate forest zone.—The cool-temperate *Da* and *Db* climates are subject to long, often severe winters. Frosts are of some duration and intensity, penetrating to as much as a meter or more into the soil or bedrock. Late winter or spring thaws lead to a marked seasonality of stream discharge, and larger rivers develop extensive flood-plains. Mechanical weathering of any exposed rock, moderate stream dissection of slopes exceeding 25-35 per cent, and gradual, grain-by-grain denudation of slope surfaces all provide a moderate load of fine and coarse materials for the rivers. As a result, stream erosion and deposition are of some significance although in no way comparable to that of the periglacial zone. Gravity movements only assume primary importance in areas of steep slopes exceeding 60 per cent.

"Fossil" features are not only preserved but often dominate the landscape. Particularly impressive is the disrupting effect of glacial deposition and erosion on drainage. Widespread swampy conditions and innumerable lakes within the boreal forest may reflect the local inefficiency of modern fluvial activity in providing an effective integrated drainage network.

The temperate-marine woodland zone.—In the warm-temperate *Cbf* climates winters are mild and frost-action limited. As the winter snowfalls are sporadic and ephemeral, there is no period of seasonal thaw. Rainfall is distributed rather evenly throughout the year, and is of less intensity and greater frequency than in the continental interiors. Stream discharge is consequently marked by only moderate seasonal fluctuations and is generally ineffective in moving coarser materials. The complete mat of vegetation remains effective even in winter, so restraining surface rainwash and stream dissection. As a result, soil mantles are deep and fluvial sculpture is almost at a standstill wherever deforestation and agricultural misuse have not accelerated soil erosion.

The moist subtropical woodland zone.—In moist subtropical regions such as the *Caf* climates of China and the southeastern United States, winter frosts are also of only limited importance. But the seasonality of rainfall may be pronounced, and individual downpours are of considerable intensity, favoring rainwash and rill-wash. Chemical weathering is intensified by high summer temperatures, and by the coincidence of maximum warmth and moisture. Soil stripping is important and stream erosion and deposition are active, so that in general both denudation and dissection are comparatively great, with corresponding deposition on lower slopes and in the lower stream valleys. Understandably, less is known of "fossil" Pleistocene landforms in these zones.

Geomorphic agents comparable to those of the modern *Caf* climates appear to have been prominent in the summer-dry Mediterranean lands during several phases of the Pleistocene.

The summer-dry, subtropical woodland zone.—Frost is also a negligible factor in the summer-dry *Cs* or mediterranean-type climates today. But the degree of mechanical disintegration is partly compensated for by an incomplete mat of herbaceous vegetation, permitting weathering by means of insolational heating as well as direct soil or bedrock attack by rainwash. Seasonal desiccation of soils prepares loose, clastic material for running water to remove. Rainfall is also irregular and intense.

Vigorous soil stripping, headward erosion, and stream dissection are then theoretically possible. In practice, however, only the moister uplands with considerable moderate or steep slope are typically effected by such phenomena. Numerous exceptions are, of course, provided where land misuse is rampant, particularly in areas of soft, erodible sediments. But, depending upon the area, many or most of the features loosely ascribed to "historical" erosion (e.g., Büdel, 1950a) are in fact of Pleistocene age (Butzer, 1961c, 1964a). In brief, under natural conditions geomorphic equilibrium would be typical of the Mediterranean lands, and even under cultivation, geomorphic equilibrium is characteristic of level terrain. The Pleistocene processes of this ecozone will be described in a later chapter.

ARID ZONE GEOMORPHOLOGY

General aspects.—Among the common traits of the arid zone, in the broad sense of the word, is a dominance of mechanical over chemical weathering. The vegetative cover decreases with intensified aridity, so favoring mechanical disintegration while restricting chemical reactions. The major agents of mechanical attack are as follows (see Tricart and Cailleux, 1960-61, Vol. I, p. 70 ff. and Vol. II, p. 2 ff.):

a) Frost-weathering, favored by considerable daily and annual variation of temperature, but somewhat limited by reduced rock moisture. The fragments detached are usually small, promoting grain-by-grain disintegration. Frost is common and severe in middle latitudes, but only sporadic in lower middle latidues. It is largely absent between the two tropics (Fig. 21).

b) Thermal expansion and contraction, as a result of isolational heating and rapid cooling at night or by sudden rainfalls, which puts repeated stress on the mineral structure of exposed rock. In finer-grained, homogeneous rocks microfractures are produced and small splices are eventually detached. Granular disintegration is promoted in heterogeneous rock. Although slow, this form of thermoclastic weathering is important in dry zones without frost.

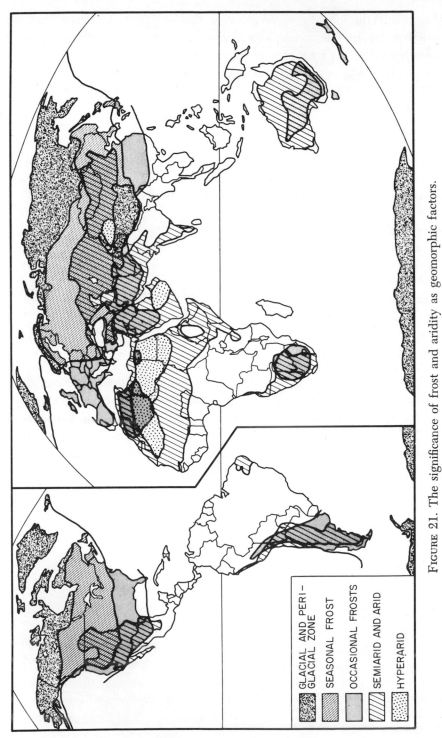

FIGURE 21. The significance of frost and aridity as geomorphic factors.

GLACIAL AND PERI-
GLACIAL ZONE

SEASONAL FROST

OCCASIONAL FROSTS

SEMIARID AND ARID

HYPERARID

c) Salt hydration (Knetsch, 1960 with references; Peel, 1960)—the expansion of anhydride salts after odd rain or dew falls as well as in response to heating.[1] Such salts are attributed to extreme dehydration of certain rock minerals. They are concentrated at or near the surface by capillary movement to the surface due to evaporation. In response to temperature oscillations and alternate wetting and drying, these salts expand and contract considerably and thereby loosen off the individual grains or slabs of material at the face of the rock.

The over-all mechanisms and effects of all three of these mechanical agents are analogous, and they are difficult to isolate. Both forms of thermoclastic weathering probably assume dominance in the middle latitude arid zone, while alternating contraction and expansion through thermal or chemical processes dominate in lower latitudes.

The products of mechanical weathering accumulate at the base of rock outcrops in the form of loose slope talus, largely as a result of gravity. Consequently slopes will tend to weather back uniformly in uniform bedrock, maintaining constant angles. Part of the debris will be removed by running water, but although evidence of periodic or sporadic water action is manifest everywhere, there frequently is insufficient fluvial activity to remove all of the coarse debris. In many areas the sparse vegetation permits denudation as well as vertical erosion, particularly in unconsolidated sediments. Fine materials may be attacked by wind erosion, and aeolian deposition may take the form of sand dunes or loess mantles. But throughout the arid zone, running water is and usually has been the major single agent of landform sculpture.

Within the arid zone the presence or absence of frost, and the amount and intensity of rainfall are responsible for differences in the kind and intensity of geomorphic activity. Consequently the mid-latitude grasslands, the marginal environments of the semidesert and, finally, the deserts proper will be considered individually. General references to arid zone geomorphology are provided by Büdel (1950a), Tricart and Cailleux (1960-61), Peel (1960) and Birot (1960).

Mid-latitude grasslands.—The sod and dense rooting network common to undisturbed mid-latitude grasslands offers effective protection against mechanical weathering. Only on steep slopes, where soils

---

[1] This is both a chemical and mechanical agent, and commonly described in the literature as a form of chemical weathering. There seems to be just as good a case for considering it a mechanical agent because of its analogies with various forms of thermoclastic weathering.

are thin and the herbaceous vegetation scarce, does frost-weathering produce accumulations of detritus. Chemical weathering is not important, although still present.

During the winter the soil is frozen to some depth and there may be a snowcover. For a brief period during the spring, conditions are favorable for rapid runoff; as any snowcover melts, and the soil is still incompletely thawed out, drainage will be concentrated at the surface with little or no percolation. The most effective erosion takes place at this time (Schmidt, 1948), which is usually also coincident with the major rainy season. Serious denudation is prevented by natural vegetation, but headward stream dissection is conspicuous in areas of poorly-consolidated sediments. Steep-sided canyons develop along the fringes of drainage lines. Without human interference, however, such erosional forms remain localized. Corresponding to the seasonality of stream discharge, most river beds are broad and sandy, although the runoff is confined to a small, shallow channel for most of the year.

Wind deflation may attack dry alluvial sands in the river bottoms, and silt-size loess of local or rather distant origin may accumulate on the upland surfaces.

The desert borderland zone.—With the sparse vegetation and lack of sod usual in the desert borderlands, mechanical weathering and erosional processes are barely impeded. Much detritus of all particle sizes is provided for removal by running water. Rainfall is seasonal or sporadic and rather intensive so that soil percolation can only account for a fraction of the water, the remainder sweeping the surface as rill-wash or as sheetfloods. But precipitation is localized and commonly of limited duration so that local spates dissipate rapidly and seldom attain well-defined channeled flow in a major drainage course. Diffuse runoff is also encouraged by scattered semidesert shrubs. This sporadic, unintegrated and brief form of fluvial activity promotes denudation rather than stream incision. In combination with the steep slopes maintained by thermoclastic weathering and salt hydration, landform sculpture favors the development of *pediments*. These semiarid forms are characterized by extensive rock-cut plains offset against the irregular fringes of original, higher surfaces by steep rock faces, often making sharp angles at their base (Fig. 22) (see Tator, 1952, for a general discussion). Only in very rough terrain is the drainage strongly channeled, developing steep-sided although

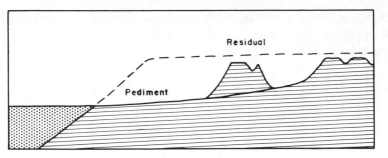

FIGURE 22.
A pediment profile. The original land surface is indicated by the
broken line. Sedimentation has been dominant in the depression
at the left.

still rather flat-floored canyons. When such gorges open onto level
plains or major stream systems, alluviation ensues as the periodic
waters spread out with reduced gradients, rapidly losing velocity.
Radial alluvial *fans* are formed in this manner.

Despite the modern significance of water action, the greater part
of the landforms of the arid zone are probably "fossil" and owe their
origin to moister climates of the Pleistocene. So for example, many
pediments of the lower-latitude arid zone are quite defunct today,
and pediment development now seems to be confined to areas having
at least sporadic frosts. Frost-action is by far the most rapid agent
of mechanical weathering, and the low latitude desert borderlands
show little talus development while cliff faces weather back at painfully slow rates. The resulting lack of coarse material for stream
transport conspicuously reduces the erosive force of running water.
Consequently semidesert landforms are similar in both low and
middle latitudes, even though the significance of Pleistocene processes
differs, and the present intensity of sculpture is much greater in
middle latitudes.

Wind erosion plays little part in slope retreat, but deflation of
fine materials from disintegrating level surfaces or alluvial plains
can be important. Shallow depressions or blowouts may be created,
and the over-all effects for denudation may be appreciable. The dust
removed may be swept through the air for hundreds of kilometers
before it is laid down in the form of loess mantles elsewhere. In
contrast, sand removal and transport is limited, and the resulting
dunes and sand sheets are seldom found far from their source. A good

part of the aeolian features of the arid zone are more or less immobile and appear to be "fossil" today. Wind deposits will be discussed in more detail in chapter 12.

The deserts.—In the hyperarid and largely barren desert interiors (Fig. 23) geomorphic processes are infinitesimally slow. The rare rainfalls are neither effective for genuine surface sculpture or true chemical weathering. Even the salt hydration of the desert border-lands becomes infrequent, and practically all landforms appear to belong to the museum of the Pleistocene.

Slow physical disintegration, occasional brief floods at long inter-vals, and the slow but everpresent deflation of fine materials by wind are characteristic. The selective removal of fines may produce surface concentrations or *pavements* of pebbles or crude rock frag-ments. Sand dunes occupy a role that is rather important areally, but not functionally.

TROPICAL GEOMORPHOLOGY

Tropical weathering.—Several general aspects of tropical weather-ing are basic to understanding geomorphic activity in the humid and subhumid tropics (for general discussions see Büdel, 1950a, 1958; Cailleux and Tricart, 1955; Birot, 1960):

a) Complete absence of frost, the most effective single agent of mechanical breakdown of rock in middle and higher latitudes.

b) Daily and seasonal temperature oscillations are moderate or negligible.

c) Complete mats of grassy vegetation or dense forest protect soil and rock surfaces from erosion, and help rule out mechanical weathering as a potent agency.

d) Considerable or excessive moisture is available part or all of the year, while temperatures are persistently high. Chemical weather-ing is correspondingly intense and effective.

As a result soil development is remarkably prominent, and smooth or moderately inclined slopes are entirely enveloped in soil or derived soil sediments of appreciable depth (Morison *et al.*, 1948; Ruxton and Berry, 1960). Crude rock fragments are seldom exposed at or near the surface. Clays and silts are the dominant particle sizes, and even coarse sands are rare since quartz is rapidly broken down in size to a fine sand component. Bedrock is only exposed on slopes steeper than 20-35 per cent in the subhumid savannas, on slopes exceeding 120-150 per cent in rainforest areas. But in view of the absence of significant mechanical weathering, slope detritus is still rather scarce. In the seasonally-dry savannas exfoliation, a gradual concentric peeling off of rock slabs, is partly a result of salt hydration. Any talus that may accumulate is rapidly decomposed as soon as it comes into contact with the soil zone.

The over-all result of this overwhelming preponderance of chemical weathering is that sand and gravel, the best tools of stream erosion, are rare in the watercourses of the tropics (Bakker, 1957). This fact is of great significance for landform sculpture.

Savanna planation.—Chemical weathering, leading to over-all surface decomposition, and insignificance of stream dissection lend a peculiar aspect to the landscapes of many tropical regions. Denudation is effective while downcutting is not, with the result that river valleys remain shallow but grow to the dimensions of great plains. These are the so-called savanna plains, commonly bounded by higher plains of similar origin from which they are separated by moderately steep, convex bedrock slopes (Fig. 23). Isolated remnants of higher ground stud the plains in the form of *inselbergs* (German for "island mountains"). The related process of savanna planation has been developed by Büdel (1958) and reviewed by Cotton (1961).

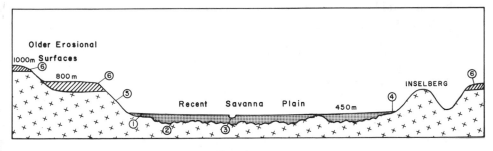

FIGURE 23.

Savanna plain in Guinea (generalized and modified after Büdel, 1963). (1) 10-30 m. clay soil or sediment, (2) base of weathered zone, (3) river channel, (4) pediment-like foot slope, (5) hillslope, (6) massive lateritic crusts on older, raised savanna plain surfaces. General vertical exaggeration 2.5x, depth of deposits strongly exaggerated.

The prerequisites to erosion are provided by a non-consolidated mantle of deeply-weathered residual products [2] which continue to form under optimal conditions of chemical alteration. Rainfall is at its world maximum of intensity in the subhumid tropics, and the violent downpours often fall on parched, hard soils. Denudation is therefore effective as clays and silts are removed. But coarse materials are lacking, so that stream beds are broad, shallow, and poorly defined as they wander across the plains, unable to cut vertically. Resistant banks of rock are not sawed through but remain prominent in the stream's profile as cataracts or waterfalls for an indefinite period of time. Streams do not then develop steeper gradients but continue to lie on the level of the plain. Excess runoff does not drain away by a network of drainage channels, but spreads out over the surface in the form of sheetfloods. The effects of such washing are extensive, gently sloping plains developing at the level of the major stream, partly by lateral planation, partly by significant washing-together of *colluvial* sediments (as opposed to channeled, alluvial stream deposits).[3] Wind deflation of fine alluvial or colluvial deposits may be of local interest during the dry season.

Remnants of analogous landforms of Tertiary age ("peneplains") are widespread in middle latitudes, together with fossil soils pertaining to tropical environments. Even during certain Pleistocene interglacials, analogous subtropical plastosols repeatedly formed in the Mediterranean region, and soil denudation and colluviation were a geomorphically significant factor at times. Savanna-like processes are therefore of considerable interest in the Pleistocene record of temperate or subtropical latitudes.

[2] It is uncertain whether or not the examples of deep soil profiles of some tropical areas cited by Büdel (1958, 1963) represent true (*B*)-horizons over gley or pseudo-gley horizons *in situ*—attaining depths of 10-30 m., with even deeper horizons showing clay mineral formation as a result of breakdown of all but quartz grains. There is reason to believe that parts of this material may have been accumulated through water action. Much remains to be clarified about the actual depth of typical tropical weathering profiles, although the outcome would not seriously affect Büdel's geomorphic arguments. Detailed local work has seldom failed to substantiate the fact that the residual mantle under such savanna plains is in fact deep, regardless of whether the material is redeposited or not.

[3] Unlike the pediments of the arid zone, savanna plantation proceeds on the surface of a residual mantle, rather than on a rock-cut platform. Such platforms are limited to the margins of savanna plains. Pediments, formed by mechanical processes taking place in climates not conducive to the destruction of rock fragments by chemical weathering, are therefore only superficially similar to savanna plains, a point demonstrated by Ruxton and Berry (1960) and Cotton (1961). Obviously the phenomenon of soil denudation (and colluviation) is not confined to the so-called savanna belt and to the humid subtropics, but common to all regions with accelerated soil erosion—particularly as a result of human disturbance of the natural equilibrium. But geologically significant deposits do not develop elsewhere today.

The rainforest zone.—The intensity of chemical weathering and the insignificance of mechanical agents are exaggerated in humid equatorial regions, both in the tropical rain and montane forests. Dense vegetation of tree type clings to steep slopes of as much as 150 per cent gradient. This, together with a less intensive rainfall, slows down surface runoff. The seasonality of rainfall is also limited and stream discharge is more uniform. It is consequently difficult to imagine that an analogous form of sheetflooding, soil denudation, and colluviation could be as prominent here as in the savanna belt. Instead, moderate fluvial activity, equally impeded by a lack of coarse bed materials, probably accounts for rather slow but different land-form sculpture.[4]

Only in rough terrain do geomorphic activities gain considerable significance. Under the influence of gravity movement, earth flows of water-saturated soil masses may periodically create slope scars under steep, forested hillsides. Tributary streams establish gully networks through headward erosion, making use of such slump scars. Coarser materials may enter the streams in this manner. As a result, fluvial dissection is greatly exaggerated in hill and mountain country of the humid tropics.

The major climatic-geomorphologic regions and features are summarized in Table 9.

[4] Although Büdel (1950a) originally considered the rainforest as a distinct climatic-geomorphic region, he no longer does so (1958, 1963). Cailleux and Tricart (1955), Tricart (1958) and Birot (1960) have maintained the more traditional division.

TABLE 9

CLIMATIC—GEOMORPHOLOGIC REGIONS AND FEATURES

Zone	Koeppen Climate	Dominant Form of Weathering	Dominant Agents of Erosion and Deposition	Type of General Erosion	Characteristic Sediments
Glacial	EF	Frost-weathering	Ice; running water	—	Moraines; coarse glaciofluvial beds
High Arctic Barrens	EF, ET	Intensive frost-weathering and permafrost	Running water, solifluction, wind	Intensive denudation and dissection	Coarse alluvial beds, gravity/soil-frost deposits, soil-frost features, dunes, loess
Tundra	ET	Intensive frost-weathering and permafrost	Running water, solifluction, wind	Denudation and dissection	
Forest with Permafrost	Dc, Dd	Frost and some chemical weathering	Running water	Dissection and denudation	Coarse alluvial beds, soil-frost features
Temperate-Continental	Da, Db, Dc	Frost and some chemical weathering	Running water	Dissection	Fine to coarse alluvial beds
Temperate-Marine	Cbf	Moderate chemical weathering	Running water	Limited dissection	Fine alluvial beds

Periglacial (High Arctic Barrens, Tundra, Forest with Permafrost)

Humid (Temperate-Continental, Temperate-Marine)

			Chemical weathering	Running water	Dissection and denudation	Alluvial and colluvial beds
Humid	Moist Subtropical	*Caf*		Running water		
	Summer-dry Subtropical	*Cs*	Limited mechanical and chemical weathering		Moderate dissection	Alluvial beds
Arid	Mid-latitude grasslands	*BSk*	Frost-weathering		Dissection	Coarse alluvial beds, loess
	Desert Margins	*BS, BW*	Thermoclastic weathering and salt hydration	Running water and wind	Denudation and dissection	Alluvial beds, dunes
	Desert	*BWh*			Denudation	Alluvial beds, dunes
Tropical	Savanna	*Aw, Caw, Am*	Intensive chemical weathering	Running water	Denudation	Fine colluvial beds
	Rainforest	*Af, Am*			Limited denudation and dissection	Fine alluvial beds

135

Mammalian and Human Distributions

THE CONCEPT OF ANIMAL REGIONS

The distribution of mammalian faunas today is of particular interest for Pleistocene geography in two ways. Firstly, most of the bone commonly preserved in ancient deposits belongs to larger mammals whose identical genera or species may still survive today. Then also, the kinds and relative abundance of game in various environments was of fundamental importance for early hunting and gathering populations.

Animals, as vegetation and soils, show peculiar distributions related to broad zonations of the natural environment. Mammals, for example, are partly adapted physiognomically to the natural vegetation of their habitats: climbers, springers, runners, breakers, burrowers, etc.

They are also adapted to the particular food and water resources provided by their environment. So for example, herbivores prefer certain combinations of grasses, shrubs, leaves, bark, roots, etc. while carnivores prey chiefly on certain plant eaters.

In considering animal distributions, zoögeographers commonly employ two different terminologies for different purposes. Zoögeographical or *animal regions* are differentiated from one another by the assemblages of mammals and birds they contain (see Darlington, 1957; George, 1962). They represent geographical localizations which are determined by physical barriers to dispersal in the course of geological history. Understandably these continental regions bear only a loose relationship to the zonations of vegetation or climate. Bioregions—reflecting the ecological conditions of the moment—have also been identified. These are superimposed on the animal regions and coincide rather closely with other zonal distributions (see Tischler, 1955; also Troll, 1950).

In the traditional zoögeographical approach, the following major animal regions are identified:

a) *Holarctic,* including Neartic (North America) and Palearctic (Eurasia, excluding India and Southeast Asia, but including North Africa) subregions;

b) *Ethiopian,* including tropical Africa and southern Arabia;

c) *Oriental,* including India, southern China, and southeastern Asia;

d) *Australian,* including Australia, New Guinea, and most of the Pacific islands;

e) *Neotropical,* including Central and South America.

major animal regions [handwritten marginal note]

Some of the more typical Palearctic animals include bear, fox, wolf, hyena, deer, ibex, sheep, wild cattle, bison, horse, camel, hare, beaver, mole and vole. Typical of the Ethiopian region are wart-hog, hippopotamus, giraffe, okapi, elephant (of the genus *Loxodonta*), rhinoceros (*Ceratotherium* and *Diceros*), zebra, gnu, baboon, gorilla, and chimpanzee. The Oriental region includes the gibbon, elephant (genus *Elephas*), rhino (genera *Rhinoceros* and *Didermoceros*), dwarf deer, tree shrews, and tarsiers among its typical species.

For our purposes the mammalian distributions of the bioregions are more useful. Most mammals, understandably, range widely and are seldom strictly confined to a single ecological habitat. Similarly, the habits of different genera or species of the same family may differ considerably. Consequently, the association of "typical" species with particular environments is a loose one.

MAMMALIAN DISTRIBUTIONS IN THE MAJOR NATURAL REGIONS

The tundra.—The modern polar regions support a specialized fauna largely adapted to conditions of extreme cold and reduced food resources lasting as much as nine to ten months a year (Tischler, 1955, p. 238 ff.). With a few exceptions the bird fauna is migratory. Even the larger endemic mammals, with the exception of the musk-ox (*Ovibos moschatus*), may all frequent the adjacent forest-tundra and boreal woodland to some degree or other during the long, snowy winter.

The ecological balance is based upon the herbivorous reindeer or caribou (*Rangifer tarandus* ssp.), rodents such as the lemming (*Lemmus* spp.) and several voles (*Microtus* spp.), the arctic hare

(*Lepus arcticus*), snowy partridge (*Lagopus* spp.), geese, and various song birds. These in their turn support endemic carnivores such as the arctic fox (*Vulpes lagopus*) or wider ranging species such as the wolf (*Canis lupus*) and ermine (*Mustela erminea*), as well as various birds of prey. In the coastal areas, seals and polar bears (*Thalarctos* spp.) obtain much or all of their nourishment from fish. All of the above animals are essentially circumpolar in the northern hemisphere, or at least were so during the Pleistocene.

During the Pleistocene the European tundra species were reinforced by great herds of now-extinct woolly mammoths (*Elephas primigenius*), less specialized open-country denizens such as the extinct *Bison priscus*, and a number of subspecies of the wild horse (*Equus caballus*). These were supplemented by smaller numbers of cold-loving species such as the extinct giant elk (*Megaceros* spp.) and woolly rhinoceros (*Tichorhinus antiquitatis*), and the saiga antelope (*Saiga tatarica*), still present in the Central Asian grasslands today. All of these animals roamed widely between the tundra and the adjacent, lighter forest belts, and sometimes into the cool grasslands.

There can be no doubt that these Pleistocene low-latitude tundras had a tremendous carrying capacity, somewhat greater than the recent, higher-latitude tundras. Human interference is probably involved in the modern paucity of gregarious herbivores in the tundra. But some environmental differences must have existed, possibly related to different drainage and radiation conditions between high and low-latitude tundras. This point has never been raised by animal ecologists, but certainly deserves attention. So for example, the extended periods of hibernal darkness in high latitudes may carry significance for some species, while intensive summer radiation in lower latitudes would favor plant growth out of proportion to the actual air temperatures.

The ecological environment of the forest-tundra is optimal in as much as cold environments are concerned. The migrating gregarious herds of the open country seek their winter refuge here where many species, faced with a deep snowcover, can augment their diets by consumption of tree shoots and bark. Arboreal groves provide windbreaks during storms, while the immediate environment provides all that the tundra otherwise offers. For the human occupant, an added hunting element of forest species is provided.

In the analogous alpine meadow environments, the marmot (*Marmota* spp.) occupies a similar ecological niche as the lemming, while the chamois (*Rupicapra rupicapra*) and certain mountain sheep take over the role of the reindeer.

The boreal forest.—The higher-latitude coniferous forests (see Tischler, 1955, p. 251 ff.) are rather dense and provide little herbaceous vegetation for gregarious herbivores. The larger herbivores are comparatively few and include the elk or moose (*Alces* spp.), deer or wapiti (*Cervus* spp.), the extinct Old World aurochs (*Bos primigenius*), and woodland bison (*Bison bonasus*).[1] Seasonally, considerable numbers of tundra reindeer range through the boreal forest, while the endemic forest reindeer are present all year. Plant, bark, and root-eating rodents, including the beaver (*Castor* spp.), various mice, rats, and rabbits, are ground-dwellers, others are climbers of one sort or other. The latter include several squirrels. The rodents provide the chief food source for carnivores or omnivores such as foxes (*Vulpes* spp.), martens (*Martes* spp.), the wolverine (*Gulo gulo*), the lynx (*Lynx* spp.), certain Holarctic bears (*Ursus* spp.), as well as buzzards and owls. Several of the carnivores also prey upon the insect and plant-eating bird life, while the omnipresent wolf and the wolverine prey upon larger herbivores as well.

During the winter most bears and many rodents hibernate, while the deer and many birds migrate south. Reindeer and elk, however, obtain sufficient nourishment from bark, dry leaves, and lichens.

All in all the variety of big game is small, and their number is limited.

The deciduous and mixed forests.—The lighter-stocked woodlands of the warm-temperate and even subtropical zones offer considerably better grazing facilities for large herbivores during all or most of the year (Tischler, 1955, pp. 223 ff. and 284 ff.). These include the red deer or wapiti, the aurochs, and the bison of the boreal forests, as well as the boar (*Sus scrofa*) and several additional deer: the white and black-tailed deer of the genus *Odocoileus* in North America, the roe deer (*Capreolus capreolus*) in Europe, and fallow deer (*Dama* spp.) in the Near Eastern area. The principal rodents and carnivores are similar to those of the boreal forest, although their number is greater corresponding to a higher carrying capacity.

---

[1] The bison, reindeer, and horse are three major genera originally present as both woodland and open-country forms, identical on the specific level. Thus even today the North American caribou has woodland and tundra forms, while the woodland form of the almost identical Eurasian reindeer seems to be almost extinct. Similarly, the wild horse of Eurasia belonged to two open-country subspecies—the western tarpan (*Equus caballus gmelini*) and the eastern Przewalski horse (*Equus caballus feral*). A rather heavy, woodland species was also apparently present (*Equus caballus silvestris*). For discussions of both horse and reindeer see Zeuner (1963, pp. 299 ff. and 112 ff.). A similar situation seems to exist for the North American and European bisons.

Mid-latitude grasslands.—The great mid-latitude grasslands and steppes until recently supported a limited variety of swift-footed, gregarious herbivores, some of which were present in exceptionally great numbers. Mainly responsible for the excellent carrying capacity are varied, rich, and nutritious grasses. First and foremost of the open-country herbivores in North America was the American bison (*Bison bison*), once totaling over 60 million animals (with grassland and woodland subspecies). Possibly equally significant in Eurasia, prior to human interference, was the wild horse of the tarpan and Przewalski subspecies. Occupying similar ecological niches in the New and Old World respectively are the pronghorn (*Antilocapra americana*) and the saiga antelope (*Saiga tatarica*). Other large herbivores are not significant in either area, although several gazelles and the central and southwest Asian onager (*Equus hemionus*) are of some interest in the Eurasian Pleistocene. All of these fast-moving open-country forms vacated the snowy plains in winter, seeking out green pastures in southerly areas.

The rodents are mainly burrowers finding protection underground from carnivores and from the cold, winter season. Certain species of voles, prairie dogs, ground squirrels, pocket gophers, hamsters, kangaroo rats and mice, as well as of the ubiquitous rabbits and hares belong to this group.

Preying upon the mammalian herbivores are the wolf, coyote (*Canis latrans*), and several smaller carnivores in the New World, and the wolf, jackal (*Canis aureus*), the East European steppe fox (*Vulpes corsac*), and several weasels (*Mustela* spp.) in the Old.

The lower latitude arid zone.—The grasslands and desert shrub areas of lower latitudes are by no means as luxuriant or attractive as those of higher latitudes, and the plant species remarkably less nutritious. The carrying capacity in terms of larger herbivores is limited, and leading Old World species include a number of swift gazelles and antelopes, the wild ass (*Equus asinus*) of northern Africa, and the wild ancestor of the dromedary (*Camelus dromedarius*)—all able to survive with little water. Here too there are numerous specialized rodents. Large carnivores in the same areas include the jackal, hyenas (*Hyaena* spp.), lion (*Panthera leo*), and leopard (*Panthera pardus*).

The tropical parklands and woodlands.—Many of the savannas and light tropical woodlands, particularly those of eastern and south-central Africa, have a high carrying capacity exceeding even that of the middle latitude grasslands. Others, such as those of West Africa or South America have less nutritious or less palatable grasses and are rather inferior. The characteristic African "savanna" fauna with its once endless herds of antelopes, gazelles, zebra, giraffe, and elephant needs little emphasis. Some species, such as the giraffe (*Giraffa camelopardalis*) and the non-mammalian ostrich (*Struthio camelus*), are thought to be open-country forms as are the zebras, antelopes, and gazelles. Others such as the African and Asian elephants and rhinos are adapted both to forest and open parkland. The rodents play an insignificant role by comparison.

Among the carnivores the great cats, including lion, leopard, tiger, and cheetah, are best known. All range through grassland and woodland.

The dense rain forests, like the boreal forests, provide little grazing, and there are few large herbivores and few carnivores (Tischler, 1955, p. 212 ff.). Instead, a great variety of insectivores, partly mammalian, take advantage of the particularly rich insect life. The few typical species of larger herbivores include the tapirs, forest buffalo, the duikers (*Cephalophus* spp.) the okapi (*Okapia johnstonii*), the chevrotain (*Tragulus* spp.), and several anthropoid apes (gorilla, chimpanzee, orangutan). Elephants were at one time relatively common, so for example the Congo dwarf form (*Loxodonta africana cyclotis*). Game resources are, however, generally sporadic and limited.

An approximate index of different carrying capacities between grassy tropical woodlands and rainforest is given by biomass statistics of hoofed mammals (ungulates) in several reserves and parks in Africa (Bourlière, 1963). In East African game reserves—without conspicuous overgrazing—the biomass of savanna woodland environments varies from 5,000 to 20,000 kg/sq km. In some overgrazed parks it exceeds 35,000 kg/sq km. On the other hand a dense rainforest environment in Ghana, the Tano Nimri forest reserve, has less than 6 kg/sq km. These statistics speak for themselves.

A few tropical genera were of considerable importance in higher latitudes during parts of the Pleistocene. Most of them were represented by extinct species, some less specialized, others adapted to rather different environments.

CULTURE, TECHNOLOGY, AND THE HUMAN RESOURCE BASE

Turning from mammalian distributions to the dispersal of the human species, cultural and technological achievements strongly determine the settlement potential of particular environments. In other words, although the non-human ancestors of man shared some sort of tropical distribution such as those of the anthropoid apes, man has progressively occupied and culturally adapted to numerous, diverse environments. From the viewpoint of prehistoric geography and ecology it is important to assess the availability and assets of different environments *at different cultural levels*. We commonly tend to interpret the implications of a particular environment for early man from a contemporary perspective. Yet for humans possessing neither fire nor clothing, middle latitudes would provide a rather marginal environment. The grassy tropical woodlands or savannas would provide a far better resource base for a general hunting economy than would the temperate forests. And the tundra was not a peripheral environment for the mighty hunting clans of the late Pleistocene.

During most of the Pleistocene the cultural-technological status of man was that of an *unspecialized food-collector*. A great variety of edible roots and plants, as well as many animal foods, were used. At first man may have confined his carnivorous attentions to smaller mammals and to birds, approaching bigger game on a more incidental, possibly scavenging basis. Later, as the archeological evidence attests, big game was hunted on a large scale, possibly eclipsing the importance of vegetable foods in many areas. By this time, in the later Lower Pleistocene, fire was in widespread use, and some sort of protective clothing was presumably worn where necessary.

The terminal stages of the Pleistocene witnessed a number of *specialized, hunter-gatherer economies* in both the Old and New World. Considerable advances were made in hunting technology, so that the great clans wreaked considerable havoc among the gregarious herbivores (see chap. 27). A certain proficiency in the making of clothing is also evident. Some hunter-gatherer groups specialized further still by exploiting fish and other sea-food resources.

By the beginning of the Holocene a new cultural and economic level of subsistence had been established in parts of the Near East, where plant and animal domestication are first recorded. Primitive agriculture led to a renewed emphasis on plant foods, although hunter-gatherer activities still continued to play some economic role in these new communities. Agriculture led to the exploitation of new niches in the environment, particularly of the soil. Soil availability, texture, fertility, and moisture rapidly became new criteria of settlement potential. And the adaptability of available seed crops and household or herd animals to new environmental conditions further influenced the dispersal and establishment of food-producing economies. Primitive mineral extraction was begun, lending some interest to regions with accessible mineral resources. With time, big game and edible wild plant foods were no longer vital to farming populations, so casting a completely different perspective on the settlement potential of different environments.

Unfortunately there is no systematic body of information concerning the human ecology of contemporary "primitive" groups.[2] Also, most of the present-day food-collecting populations have been driven into undesirable refuges, particularly in the humid tropics. Hence the optimal patterns of resource exploitation by Pleistocene food-collectors can only be inferred today (see Bartholomew and Birdsell, 1953). Similarly, cultural contact with higher economies has influenced all modern "primitive" groups to some degree. The ethnological parallels for an ecological understanding of early man are then incompletely preserved and often inadequately understood.

In the domain of the biological and physical sciences, more information is needed concerning (*a*) the animal carrying capacity of various grasses and vegetation types, (*b*) the range and dietary value of edible wild plant resources in different environments, and (*c*) the working and productivity of different soils under primitive agriculture.[3] In other words, the biological foundations for a fuller ecological study are also lacking.

The subsequent outlines of environmental resources for food-collecting and primitive agricultural economies are not more than provisional and rudimentary. Possibly they will serve to emphasize a need for further systematic work.

ENVIRONMENTAL RESOURCES FOR EARLY FOOD-COLLECTORS

The wild vegetable foods eaten by food-collecting economies are obviously most abundant in warmer latitudes, where a cold season does not impede or slow down plant growth. Long, intensive dry seasons are also undesirable. The products used vary from roots and tubers to seeds, nuts, acorns, and fruits, and the aborigines of central

[2] Good monographs exist for a number of cultures, although their emphasis is commonly upon social rather than ecological attributes. The one existing attempt at a more comprehensive study of habitat and economy (Forde, 1934) is rather incomplete and in some ways obsolete in view of more recent investigations in many parts of the world.

[3] A good example of cattle carrying capacities according to grass types in Africa is given by Rattray (1960). A valuable pioneer study on soils and primitive agriculture has been written by Nye and Greenland (1960).

Australia are known to have exploited over seventy-three plant species.[4]

In addition to these vegetable products, insects, lizards, snakes, birds, small rodents, birds' eggs, and fish may also have been eaten. In fact, primitive fishing, particularly in shallow inland waters may have been of considerable importance locally. Whether or not the fish traps used by various "primitive" groups today were known in the Pleistocene, is not established. But fish gorges and harpoons were well-known during the terminal stages of the European Pleistocene, while fish bones are archeologically verified from earlier sites. Fresh-water fishing resources are not known to vary conspicuously wherever inland waters are available. Salt-water fishing requires far greater skills, and was probably not systematically followed until the early Holocene. The equally protein-rich shell fish of the seashore, including oysters, cockles, mussels, lobsters, crabs, crayfish, and shrimp, probably already provided a valuable food resource for people with limited techno-logical skills. Bivalves, gastropods, and crabs are also available in many inland waters.

The greatest individual resource of high-calorie, protein-rich food for all the larger, hunter-gatherer populations was almost certainly animal flesh. It is here that the great regional differences in carrying capacity assume paramount importance. The hoofed mammals became the best meat provider for early man since carnivores were rarely attacked, and smaller mammals, such as rodents, provided less meat in proportion to the efforts and skill required to hunt them. It is on the big herbivores that primary attention must be focused. A review of the potential of various environments is given by Table 10 which lists ungulate biomasses recorded in a number of game and forest reserves. Biomass and carrying capacity are by no means identical, but in view of the limited information available about the latter, biomass statistics provide some sort of index of potential utilization by all resident species. Since the number of ungulate species available increases the potential resources of an environment due to fuller ex-ploitation of ecological niches, species data are included where avail-able. It is also of interest from the hunter's point of view.

It is obvious from Table 10 that the tropical savannas stand out as optimal areas. Since many savannas are thought to be artificial, resulting from human interference of former grassy, open woodlands, the potential utilization under "natural" conditions may have been less. Yet even the thorn forest has a remarkably high biomass. Con-

[4] For a very general discussion of plant utilization see Schery (1952).

TABLE 10
UNGULATE BIOMASSES OF CERTAIN ENVIRONMENTS
(From Bourlière, 1963. Data from Overgrazed Reserves Omitted.)

Vegetation Type	Locality	Species Number	Biomass (kg/km²)
Rain Forest	Ghana	3	5.6
Thorn Forest	Southern Rhodesia	15	4900
Savanna Parkland	Congo; Uganda	5-11	5950-19540
High Grass Savanna	Kenya; Transvaal	17-19	1760-16560
Low Grass Savanna	Kenya; Tanganyika	over 15	5250
Semidesert Grassland	Chad	4	83
Desert Shrub	Rio de Oro; Mauretania	2	0.3-189
Temperate Grasslands	Eurasian steppe; Great Plains		350-3000
Deciduous Forest	Scotland		*ca.* 1000
Mixed Forest	Carpathians		*ca.* 500
Tundra	Northern Canada		*ca.* 800

sequently, the tropical parklands and the middle latitude grasslands remain optimal areas. The Canadian tundra rates relatively high, but does not compare with the other open-country habitats. As suggested earlier, however, Pleistocene lower latitude tundras may have been far more suitable. The deciduous woodlands also have a noticeably high biomass. The boreal forest (no data), the tropical rain forest, and truely arid situations provide the lowest carrying capacities of all.

In summary, vegetable foods were probably optimal in the humid and subhumid tropical and subtropical climates. The relative suitability of various environments for early hunter-gatherer populations can be suggested by using the following three categories based primarily on animal food resources:

a) Optimal. The grassy, tropical deciduous woodlands and savannas; the mid-latitude grasslands; the lower latitude Pleistocene tundras.

b) Intermediate. The temperate and subtropical deciduous and mixed woodlands; the high latitude tundras.

c) Marginal. The tropical rainforest; the boreal forest; the semideserts and deserts.

ENVIRONMENTAL RESOURCES FOR PRIMITIVE AGRICULTURISTS

Primitive agriculture in prehistoric times was largely based on cereal or vegetable cultivation, and remains so even today. The following comments will then be confined entirely to relevant problems of crop-cultivation.

Early working of the soil was done with digging and planting sticks or hoes made either of wood, bone, or stone. Animal traction was not used for cultivation in prehistoric times prior to the invention of the plow. Stone tools for forest clearance were present in larger numbers in some prehistoric cultures, but most forest (and grassland) clearance appears to have been made by burning. Consequently, the immediate technological problems were not presented by vegetation clearance but in breaking up hard soils and combatting densely rooted sods. Weeding was presumably another problem to contend with in many areas.

Hard soils are most common where heavy, clayey soils are subject to seasonal drought. The first is a matter of soil texture, the second a matter of climate. Dense soils may occur almost anywhere. Seasonal drought, however, is largely confined to the arid zone and to the lighter tropical and subtropical woodlands. Forest soils are therefore not necessarily more friable than grassland soils. All areas with dry seasons of some importance will experience soil drying and hardening. As already pointed out, lateritic soils only become indurated when stripped by soil erosion and exposed at the surface. Lateritic soils still in process of development do not necessarily make primitive agriculture more difficult than non-lateritic soils.

Densely rooted sods are largely confined to the middle latitude grasslands and, to a lesser extent, to some tropical grasslands. Dense rooting is no problem in most forest locales.

If a soil can indeed be managed mechanically, the next problems are posed by available moisture, sufficient warmth, and by soil fertility.

In a general way primitive agriculture is possible in the humid tropics and subtropics most or all of the year; in the subhumid and semiarid tropics, during the summer rainy season; in the subhumid subtropics, during the moist winters; in the middle latitude grasslands, during the spring and early summer; in the temperate mixed woodlands, during the summer. The boreal forest and tundra belts have too short a growing season for any of the genetically unspecialized crops of primitive agriculturists. The arid lands were too dry without irrigation and, therefore, soon attracted communities that abandoned planting but emphasized herding, giving rise to pastoral economies in very late prehistoric times.

Soil fertility is difficult to assess as a resource problem for primitive agriculturists, even though animal dung as a fertilizing agent was and often remains unknown. In the absence of animal dung, variable periods of fallow, lasting up to thirty years or longer, help the soil to regain its natural humus content, structure, and base saturation. Some of the principal factors affecting soil fertility are as follows:

a) Humus content and type. Rich mull humus is very much more productive than a moder or raw humus, retains more moisture, and provides good aeration. Similarly the clay-humus complex in mull A_1-horizons is optimal. Chernozems, kastanozems, tirsified soils, degraded chernozems, braunerdes, podsolics, and terra rossas generally have the most favorable humus environment. Podsols, rendzinas, rankers, and tropical and desert soils commonly have little or poor humus and lack a good clay-humus complex.

b) pH and base saturation. Soil environments with an intermediate *p*H (5-8) are desirable for most crops, and base saturation reflects directly on the availability of the principal nutrients (calcium, nitrogen, phosphorus, potassium.) This is partly a matter of vegetation type and climate, and partly of bedrock. The middle-latitude grassland soils, braunerdes, and terra rossas rate best in this sense, the podsols and leached tropical soils least favorably.

c) Degree of podsolization or latozation. Podsols and latosolic soils are not only poor or lacking in the principal nutrients but often poor in some micronutrients (boron, cobalt, copper, iodine, iron, magnesium, manganese, sulphur, zinc).

d) Texture and structure. Moderately fine to fine-grained soils (silt and clay-sized particles) are preferable to those with sandy texture. They are water-retentive, less readily leached, and provide more nutrients made readily accessible to the roots. Some fine-textured soils are rather dense by nature, i.e., have a rather compact, non-porous structure. Among these are the tirsified soils, most tropical plastosols, and many groundwater soils. Other fine-textured soils, such as the temperate grassland *AC*-types or the braunerdes maintain a well-aerated so-called crumb or spongy structure through their rich, mull humus. But such soils can deteriorate rather rapidly through overuse. In fact, structural deterioration may occasionally be more important than nutrient depletion for reduction in soil fertility by overuse.

e) Local factors. A number of local intrazonal factors are also of importance for soil fertility. They include drainage, bedrock texture, and chemistry. Free-draining soils are generally desirable, as is bedrock with a high base content. Certain bedrock types may also provide too permeable or impermeable a base, or may weather extremely slowly due to high resistivity. These are all part of the great mosaic of innumerable local variations.

In overview, weighing all factors of mechanical soil cultivation and soil fertility and productivity, a few generalizations can be attempted. Probably most undesirable of all are the deserts, tundras, and boreal woodlands. Either there is no water, or an insufficiently long growing season, and the soils are poor or rudimentary. The optimal environment seems to be provided by the moist and temperate deciduous woodlands with their fertile braunderdes. The runners-up each have some negative aspects, despite an over-all positive balance. They include the temperate grasslands, the podsolic woodland soil zone, and the terra rossa lands. Regions of other grassland soils, of immature AC-type soils, and above all, the greater part of the tropics occupy an intermediate position. With exception of the humus content, which seems to be lower in the grassland soils, there seems to be no generally valid reason why tropical woodland soils should be better than tropical grassland soils when all factors are considered.[5] Nor are subtropical woodland soils inherently more suitable than temperate grassland soils when all factors are weighed.

In terms of resource potential for primitive agriculturists, the various habitats can tentatively be classified as follows:

a) *Optimal.* The warm-temperate and subtropical woodlands, and the temperate grasslands.

b) *Intermediate.* The humid, subhumid, and semiarid tropics.

c) *Marginal or unsuitable.* The deserts, semideserts, boreal woodlands, and tundras.

Contemporary population densities, despite the impact of industrialization, run remarkably parallel to these estimates of resource potential for primitive agriculture. This serves to emphasize the rather different criteria applied to the environment by hunter-gatherer populations.

[5] According to Denevan (1964) the savanna and forest regions of the northeast Bolivian lowlands and of the Llanos of the Orinoco are about equally easy to cultivate under shifting agriculture—even though the savanna soils are less productive and were probably only used when population pressure was great.

PART III

Interpretation of Pleistocene Sediments

10

Field
and Laboratory Study of
Sediments

INTRODUCTION

When investigating a sediment exposure or interpreting an archeological site with geological stratification, the earth scientist commonly studies certain features in the field while removing select samples of material for subsequent laboratory study. Part of the field study inevolves the surficial expression or morphology of the land. But detailed study of the sediments (and possible soil zones within it) is equally important. Such sedimentological work is crucial for an understanding of the depositional environment, which in its turn may be the key to understanding the local and macrosetting of an archeological site or to interpreting stratified biological remains.

The importance of carrying out morphological and sedimentological work simultaneously can hardly be stressed enough. The one is of only limited meaning without the other. The subsequent chapters are therefore devoted to a brief, systematic outline of the major Pleistocene deposits preceded by a general outline of field and laboratory techniques and interpretations. A final chapter in this group applies this information to a survey of different types of geologically stratified archeological sites.

A useful and detailed description of mechanical and chemical laboratory techniques is given by Cornwall (1958, chaps. 10-17). The various aspects of sand and gravel sedimentology are discussed in detail by Cailleux and Tricart (1963). General texts on sedimentation are strongly oriented towards marine environments and consolidated rocks, although Pettijohn (1957) also brings in general information applicable to the Pleistocene.

SEDIMENT DISPOSITION

Stratification.—The *stratification* or disposition of beds or materials is a fundamental characteristic of any deposit laid down by water, wind, ice, or mass movements. A sediment may lack defined beds or horizons, although closer inspection might show that the sand-sized particles are disposed as inconspicuous laminae or that individual pebbles are bedded, i.e., laid down on their flatter faces. Such a sediment can conveniently be called "moderately stratified," reserving the use of "unstratified" to quite unbedded deposits. When both the individual materials are aligned in parallel planes and conspicuous beds are present, "well stratified" is an appropriate designation.

Stratified beds may be classified as horizontal, inclined, cross-bedded or undulating (Fig. 24). Horizontal beds are commonly associated with standing waters, stream gravels, or water-laid sands deposited during laminar flow of uniform velocity. Sheets of aeolian sand or loess may also be horizontally stratified.

Inclined beds may be found in certain slope deposits such as in *éboulis ordonnés.* They are more common however in sand dunes, delta beds, and stream banks. Sand dunes commonly show gently inclined *backset* or *topset* bedding planes dipping to the windward with steeply inclined *foreset* beds in the lee (Fig. 25). The backset and topset beds are derived from particles rolling or bouncing up the slope, the foreset bed from particles blowing or falling down the steep lee face. Delta beds are laid down by streams into standing waters at the edge of a sea or a lake. Foreset beds are most conspicuous, although lenses of topset beds, dipping gently seaward, are frequent (Fig. 26). Seen parallel to the direction of stream movement, stream bank deposition also produces backset and topset beds inclined towards the center of the channel and commonly wedging out into alternating fine and coarse strata at the margins (Fig. 27).

Cross-bedding refers to complex patterns of discontinuous foreset beds with different inclinations, or alternating, and sometimes intergrading, foreset and topset beds. Cross-bedding results from alternations of deposition and erosion, with or without changes of velocity or direction of movement. It is confined to stream and aeolian deposits. In turbulent streams, rapid changes of local stream velocity produce localized erosional hollows which may be soon refilled by advancing foreset beds. Topset beds may be built up against raised surfaces present in the stream bed. Such alternating

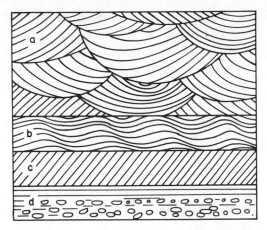

FIGURE 24.
Common types of stratification. (a) crossbedding, (b) undulated bedding, (c) inclined bedding, (d) horizontal bedding.

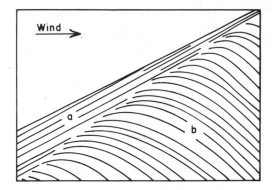

FIGURE 25.
Aeolian bedding: (a) backset, (b) foreset.

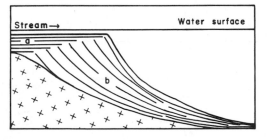

FIGURE 26.
Deltaic deposits showing (a) topset and (b) foreset beds.

horizontal and cross-bedded strata are a common product of swift, irregular flow, and may be called *current bedding*. Cross-bedded sand dunes are mainly confined to situations with several major wind components, and are rare where one wind direction is dominant.

Finally, *undulating* beds are most commonly exposed in sections perpendicular to beds with ripple marks. Only those found in stream deposits are of interest here. According to Cailleux and Tricart (1963, pp. 324 ff. and 334), undulating, ripple bedding is characteristic during phases of rapid increase in stream velocity. Beds are inclined downstream as a product of advancing sand bars. With further increase of velocity, horizontal beds are laid down by laminar flow of water. If the velocity is great enough, pebbles may also be laid down horizontally, gently inclined upstream. As the stream decelerates, following a flood peak, undulating ripple beds may form once more.

The thickness of distinctive stream beds further provides information on stream velocities (see Cailleux and Tricart, 1963, p. 334): thin, extensive beds—up to 2-5 cm. thick—are commonly laid down during periods of quiet or moderate flow; thick, localized beds or lenses—exceeding 5-10 cm. in depth—during times of violent, torrential flow.

Sorting.—The various size components of clay, silt, sand, gravel, and cobbles are seldom present in equal proportions. Strong winds will sweep up both sand and dust, depositing the coarser grades first and closer to the source of deflation. The finer particles will be carried farther. Streams will deposit coarser materials at a particular locality during periods of strong flow, while the fines are swept further downstream. During periods of gentle flow, fines may be laid down exclusively. Only glacial till is laid down without any regard to size.

Sorting as to dominant or average particle sizes may shed further light on the medium of deposition. Till commonly shows rocks of all sizes chaotically intermixed in a finer matrix. Many slope deposits are equally unsorted. Aeolian deposits are remarkably homogeneous

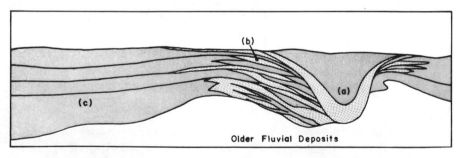

FIGURE 27.
Ancient floodplain deposits. (a) channel bed filling, (b) levee backset and topset beds, and (c) fine, mainly horizontal beds of the alluvial flats. Older fluvial beds below. Sandy beds stippled, silt and clay dark.

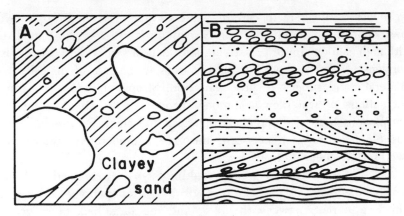

FIGURE 28.
Till (A) and fluvial (B) deposits. The till is unstratified and
unsorted while the stream beds are stratified
and sorted, and partly current-bedded.

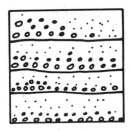

FIGURE 29.
Graded bedding.

FIGURE 30.
Pebble orientation diagram of pebbles
displaced by solifluction. Slope inclination corresponds to vector with arrow.

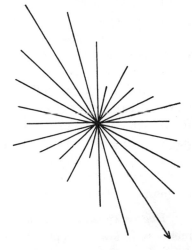

on a local scale, due to careful wind sorting. The same applies for most deposits in standing water. Stream beds are more intermediate. Although seldom unsorted, stream-laid deposits may lack distinctive horizons of clayey, sandy, or pebbly beds if the rate of deposition is moderate and subject to little variation. Strong episodic or seasonal fluctuations of waterflow commonly produce noticeable sorting into conspicuous beds of different particle size and color. On this basis it is possible to distinguish between "unsorted," "moderately sorted," and "well-sorted" beds (Fig. 28).

graded

A particular case is *graded* bedding, where a marked and progressive decrease in particle size—usually from pebbles to sand or silt—is apparent between the base and top of a bed. Such graded beds have abrupt contacts, and result from flood-level erosion followed by deposition in waters of gradually diminishing velocity (Fig. 29).

orientation

Orientation.—From a different dimension, orientation of beds or individual pebbles may also provide significant information. In the case of aeolian deposits, the orientation is given by the direction of dip of particular beds. This compass orientation is an average value for the responsible wind direction.

Pebble orientations may give equally significant information for stream, slope, coastal and glacial deposits (see Cailleux and Tricart, 1963, p. 289 ff.). During transport, individual pebbles may be rolled, in which case their major axis will be oriented perpendicularly to the direction of movement. In the case where pebbles are pushed by sliding, they tend to point nose downstream or downhill. All pebbles are affected by both kinds of movement, but the orientation of a pebble at any one time dominantly reflects either the one or the other form of motion. The *compass orientation* of the major axis of 100 pebbles in a horizon can be plotted in the form of a rose diagram (Fig. 30). The results may help determine contemporary flow direction at a point, and may permit differentiation of slope and stream deposits in marginal cases. In archeological sites this technique is equally useful for recognition of random scatters of rocks, possibly artificial, or in plotting stone patterns that may be cultural or natural.

Inclination or dip of pebbles has also been studied by Cailleux and Tricart (1963, p. 304 ff.) and others, but the results are less diagnostic (see Pettijohn, 1957, p. 250 f.).

Degree of consolidation.—Consolidation of most Pleistocene sediments is limited, except where calcareous cement is available to fill the pore spaces and interstices. Ferruginous and siliceous cements may also be present, either derived from without or through alteration of the sediment itself. The degree of consolidation attained can be described as follows:

a) *Loose.* Sample non-cohesive in both wet and dry states.

b) *Unconsolidated.* Sample cohesive but soft or pliable in wet state.

c) *Consolidated.* Sample not soft or pliable in wet state, but edges fairly brittle.

d) *Cemented.* Sample can only be broken up by use of hammer, even in wet state.

SIMPLE QUANTITATIVE ANALYSES

Sand size analysis (*wet-sieving*).—Loose, unconsolidated or semi-consolidated sediments can be readily analyzed for over-all texture or particle size either in the field or laboratory.

A set of standard brass sieves with different mesh sizes, a balance sensitive to 10 mg., a pan, a source of water, and a dispersal agent (a detergent or mild hydroxide will usually do) are required. A 100 gm. sample is weighed in the dry state and often set in solution overnight to ensure separation of the fine silts or clays from the sand grains. It is subsequently washed through the set of sieves. Each sieve component is weighed after drying (in the sun or by use of hot plate or drying oven). The difference between the cumulative totals and the original sample weight belongs to the component finer than the closest mesh sieve. The coarsest sieve normally used is one with openings of 6.0 or 6.4 mm., since coarser sieves lack accuracy. The coarser components are generally considered separately. The finest sieve that can be realistically used for simple wet-sieving is a 0.063 or 0.060 mm. mesh. Many sedimentologists prefer dry-sieving, without use of a dispersant, but employing a mechanical sieve-shaking device. Although simpler, accuracy is reduced if a considerable fine component is present.

The various size components used by sedimentologists vary, although two major classifications are rather well known. The modified Wentworth grade scale (Wentworth, 1922; see Pettijohn, 1957, p. 19) is most widely used in North America. It has the following logarithmic subdivisions:

boulders	over 256 mm.
cobbles	64-256 mm.
pebbles	2-256 mm.
sand	0.064-2 mm.
silt	0.004-0.064 mm.
clay	under 0.004 mm.

Atterberg Scale of

The non-logarithmic, modified Atterberg scale widely used in Europe has slightly different nomenclature and size units. It has become the accepted standard of the International Soil Science Society and the British Standards Institution. Fortunately the basic terms of both classifications can be used more or less interchangeably. The major classes are as follows:

cobbles	over 60 mm.
coarse pebbles	20-60 mm.
medium pebbles	6-20 mm.
fine pebbles	2-6 mm.
coarse sand	0.2-2.0 mm.
medium sand	0.06-0.2 mm.
fine sand	0.02-0.06 mm.
silt	0.002-0.02 mm.
clay	under 0.002 mm.

Angular materials coarser than sand may be classified differently, with grit (2-20 mm.) distinguished from detritus (over 20 mm.).

Depending on the importance of the gravel, sand, silt, or clay components, the textural classification of the sediment can be made according to Table 11 (after Wentworth, 1922).
There is very little standardization of textural classes however.

In the case of consolidated or cemented deposits, thin sections are commonly examined on a calibrated grid by binocular microscope. This procedure is tedious and complicated.

With a little practice it is possible to approximate sediment or soil texture in the field. A little of the material is rubbed between the fingers in the dry state, examined with a hand lens and then tested for pliability and plasticity by rolling a small quantity in moistened condition (Table 12, modified after Franz, 1960, p. 103).

Gravel Size Analyses.—Mechanical analyses of gravel size can be made using round-meshed sieves or, for components greater than 6.0

TABLE 11
Textural Classes of Sediments

Component	Percentage			Class Term
Gravel	>80			Gravel
Gravel	>sand	>10, others	>10	Sandy gravel
Sand	>gravel	>10, others	>10	Gravelly sand
Sand	>80			Sand
Sand	>silt	>10, others	>10	Silty sand
Silt	>sand	>10, others	>10	Sandy silt
Silt	>80			Silt
Silt	>clay	>10, others	>10	Clayey silt
Clay	>silt	>10, others	>10	Silty clay
Clay	>80			Clay

TABLE 12
Field Approximation of Texture
(Not Valid for Latosolic Soils)

Texture	In Dry State	Under Hand Lens	In Wet State
Clay	Fine, homogeneous and very hard; greasy appearance	No sand grains visible	Very sticky and pliable, can be rolled into wire form
Silt	Not quite homogeneous; hard	Sand grains visible	Plastic but not very pliable (no wire is formable)
Sandy Silt	Heterogeneous and somewhat brittle (clay mixed with sand)	Sand grains visible	Slightly plastic
Silty Sand	Sand grains predominant		Too friable to be rolled out on hand
Sand	Almost exclusively sand grains		Does not stain hand

or 6.4 mm., by simple measurement of major axes on graph paper. This measurement of pebble length can be used statistically or grouped according to classes. It can also be used to sort out gravel components for subsequent weighing.

In practice, gravel coarser than 6 mm. is best considered independently since much larger and rather heavy samples are needed for a representative count. The component below 6 mm. can be removed by simple dry-sieving. The coarser gravel can be simultaneously analyzed for shape while measuring.

Morphometric Gravel Analysis.—The pebble load of a stream or the detritus of a slope deposit is mechanically worn and modified in shape during transport. Material moved down a slope will be largely rough and angular in shape, whereas material carried along a stream bed for several kilometers will be smoothed and rounded. Gravel rolled across the bed will tend to be squat; gravel pushed along the bed by sliding motions will tend to be flat.

Various indices have been devised for quantitative expression of gravel shape. Most widely known are those of A. Cailleux (see Tricart and Schaeffer, 1950; and Cailleux and Tricart, 1963, p. 259 ff.).[1] Two formulas are most commonly used:

$$\text{Index of rounding} = \frac{2r \cdot 1000,}{L}$$

$$\text{Index of flattening} = \frac{(l + L),}{2E}$$

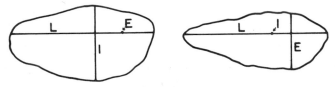

FIGURE 31.
Length, width and breadth in pebble measurement.

where r is the smallest radius of curvature on the circumference of the pebble expressed in cm., measured from the smallest, smoothed convex segment of the circumference;

[1] Other, rather different methods of analysis include those proposed by Wadell (1932) and Krumbein (1941).

l is the minor axis (width) of the pebble;

L is the major axis (length) of the pebble; and

E is the height of the pebble (Fig. 31.)

The index of rounding varies from 0 (completely angular) to 1,000 (a true sphere); the index of flattening ranges from 1 (a square cross-section) through 10 (extremely flat).

These classifications can be performed in the field and should be applied to samples of 100 pebbles, although smaller samples of 50 pebbles can be effectively used for simple comparative analyses. Marianne Blenk (1960), providing the most intensive evaluation and overview of such techniques to date, has shown that statistical improvement by use of 200 rather than 100 pebble samples is negligible. Samples must be selected from materials of similar or identical bedrock, which must be specified in the description. Pebbles should be between 2 and 10 cm. in length.

Several modifications to Cailleux's system have been suggested. Blenk (1960) has reviewed their applicability and found that none of them provide a significant improvement. An analogous but different system, however, was suggested by Lüttig (1956, also 1962). It provides (*a*) greater mechanical simplicity, reducing the time required in measurement by almost a half, and (*b*) considerably reduced error, both in terms of possible error and individualistic differences of measurement by different workers. The writer has used both techniques and considers the technical accuracy of Lüttig's index of rounding to be greater than Cailleux's. Its theoretical base is sounder and its possibilities of mechanical differentiation greater. Indices of Lüttig applied to flattening are as accurate although much simpler than Cailleux's. The Lüttig indices are as follows:

Index of rounding (ρ), expressed as per cent of smoothed, convex circumference of a pebble, obtained by careful visual estimation;

Index of flattening (π), as E/L, expressed in per cent, which may be read directly from a graph-paper chart. According to suggestions by Blenk (1960), the ratio E/l, also expressed in per cent, can be used as an auxiliary tool to express the degree of flattening.

Making use of the basic Lüttig indices, the following procedure of morphometric gravel analysis is suggested here:

a) *Mean sample value of* ρ, employing the following classes:

$$(\rho) \quad 0\text{-}10\% \text{—angular}$$
$$11\text{-}20\% \text{—subangular}$$

21-40%—subrounded

41-60%—rounded

over 60%—well rounded

b) *Homogeneity of the ρ values of the sample.* The coefficient of variation of the sample $CV = 1000\sigma/\text{mean}$, where σ is the standard deviation, can be introduced as follows:

(CV) 0-25%—very homogeneous

25-50%—homogeneous

50-75%—heterogeneous

over 75%—very heterogeneous

c) *Detrital component.* The percent of pebbles which have undergone very little transport (ρ values $\leq$ 8 per cent) provides useful information on the significance of slope or local rubble in the sediment.

d) *Transport motion.* The sample averages of E/L or E/l, or both, provide information on mechanical transport by sliding as opposed to rolling motions. The following limits may be suggested:

E/L	E/l	
under 50%	under 65%	sliding motion dominant
50-60%	65-75%	both sliding and rolling
over 60%	over 75%	rolling motion dominant

e) *Average pebble length.* The average value of L provides basic reference data for the above measurements, as well as a quantitative data on gravel size distribution.

f) *Mechanically fractured pebbles.* Originally subrounded to well rounded pebbles with fresh fractures may be counted. More often than not they imply frost-weathering, although such pebbles may in part be the result of transport or weathering *in situ.*

The lithology of pebbles considered for morphometric analysis requires a little more attention. Quartz, quartzite, chert, and flint are next to useless, since they are commonly derived from older deposits and hardly amenable to effective shape modifications during reasonably brief periods of transport. Absolute lithological uniformity of material is not required, and it is more important to differentiate according to the degree of induration of sedimentary rocks rather than to their type, e.g., limestones or sandstones. Most igneous and moderately metamorphosed rocks may be safely grouped together, as they behave rather similarly, with exception of the fissile metamorphics.

As a critical evaluation it should be remembered that morphometric gravel analyses do not provide absolute results. Rounding, for example, is a function of transport distance, and only indirectly of transport capacity or climate. Yet, angular gravels are largely confined to slope deposits and to dry stream beds of the arid zone. Rounded gravels are found in most large rivers and in the smaller rivers of humid lands in general. Surface corrosion of exposed limestone fragments may also produce rounded edges together with vermiculate ridges and pock-marks. Interpretation of a gravel analysis from a Pleistocene bed can best be made after comparative analyses of modern bed materials at the same locality. It is a comparative technique, designed to contrast past and present transport conditions in the same stream.

The homogeneity of a gravel sample is useful in understanding the regularity of stream flow and possible lateral intermixture of colluvial or slope components in the bed load. Further information on local, slope derivatives is provided by the detrital component.

The major mechanical form of pebble transport is less indicative of climate than of stream bed features. Sliding motions will be insignificant in the case of colluvial gravels, but will dominate on the beds of larger streams, particularly with strong and uniform stream velocities. Insignificant streams of dry regions can motivate considerable rolling of gravel during rare floods. A sandy stream bed will impede rolling, whereas a rocky stream bed favors it. Finally, rocks with pronounced bedding planes or fissile cleavage will flatten rather more rapidly than massive rock types.

Pebbles freshly fractured after initial stream transport may be predominantly, although never entirely, attributed to frost-action. Comparative statistics on such fractured pebbles in beds of differing age, but within the same stream valley, may allow crude approximation of comparative frost significance.

In overview, morphometric gravel analysis is by far the most significant single quantitative technique in stream sedimentology. It may permit:

a) accurate, quantitative description of sediments;

b) comparative analysis of transport capacity and, indirectly, of precipitation effectiveness;

c) insight into the mechanics of bed transport;

d) differentiation of fluvial, colluvial or slope components within heterogeneous beds; or, also, identification of the dominant transport agent in the case of dubious beds;

e) rough estimation of the comparative significance of frost.

Gravel petrography.—Hydrographic changes within a drainage basin frequently produce changes in the petrographic composition of gravels. Study of gravel petrography may therefore help determine the former dimensions of the catchment area or the hydrological significance of different tributaries within the drainage system. One or two hundred pebbles may be classified and counted out. A procedure has been described by Zeuner (1932).

FIELD DESCRIPTION OF PALEOSOLS

General.—Many Pleistocene sections expose horizons of humification or weathering well below the modern soil profile. Such buried or *fossil* soils deserve particular attention. They may have developed during periods of slow or interrupted deposition, or, they may represent a long period marked by a hiatus in the sedimentary record. Many fossil soils have been "truncated," i.e., have lost part of their upper profile through erosion.

Relict soils are the product of a somewhat different environment, but they are exposed at the surface. They may or may not show evidence of more recent pedogenesis. Most of the braunlehms and rotlehms found in temperate Europe are examples of such relict soils.

Other vestiges of ancient soil development are provided by soil *sediments*—older soil materials that have been eroded and redeposited by stream, gravity, or wind action. They may be buried or exposed at the surface, analogous to relict soils. A good number of alluvial and colluvial sediments are in fact partly derived from older, non-functional soils. Their interpretation is more difficult although possible (see Kubiena, 1954b).

The concept of ancient soils or *paleosols* includes fossil and relict soils as well as soil sediments. Each provides paleo-environmental information, so that every zone of discoloration or abnormally fine texture in a sedimentary profile should be examined for evidence of weathering *in situ* or from derived soil products. Much of the necessary analysis and a provisional interpretation can already be made in the field by the qualified earth scientist. Further laboratory studies are commonly required for final interpretation. Persons not familiar with soils can remove samples at selected vertical intervals from the top of a particular stratum downward to the "normal" material at its base. A color photo with a scale object can provide other relevant data for a specialist consulted later on.

Pertinent information in soil documentation has been outlined by Franz (1960). It includes—as far as possible—a description of both the location (including terrain, soil-moisture, climate, vegetation, and bedrock) and the soil profile. Profile description includes (*a*) soil horizons and general profile, (*b*) soil color, (*c*) texture, (*d*) carbonate content, (*e*) humus type and amount, (*f*) structure, and (*g*) concretions, stains, flecks, etc. Most of these characteristics have been discussed in chapter 6 but color, carbonate content, structure, and concretions deserve further attention here.

Soil Color.—Accurate color description is not only important for soil horizons but for archeological layers and sediments as well. The *Munsell Soil Color Charts* have rapidly attained international status and are to be recommended. Colors are compared between a quantitatively organized scheme of color chips and natural, fresh soil or sediment surfaces. Moist or dry samples may be used, although these should be specified as the results are by no means identical.

Colors diverging from those of the parent material are commonly due to soil development. Grayish to blackish colors are often produced by organic materials such as humus and charcoal. Black flecks in the *B*-horizon frequently indicate the presence of manganese oxide, a result of moderate seasonal waterlogging. Grayish or greenish horizons over parent material may indicate reduction within the permanent water table (*G*-horizon). Whitish colors indicate the presence of carbonates, gypsum (calcium sulfate), salt or bone ash (calcium phosphate). They may also record a bleached A_{2e}-horizon. Brownish to yellowish colors commonly suggest limonitic iron compounds due either to weathering in (*B*) or *P*-horizons, or to illuviation in sesquioxide horizons. On the other hand, brownish surface horizons may be the result of both humification and weathering. Lastly, reddish colors may indicate the presence of anhydrous iron or hematite in the soil profile.

In review, the depth and color of blackish or brownish surface horizons commonly reflects on the intensity of humus accumulation, while the depth and intensity of yellowish or reddish discoloration of the subsoil commonly indicate the intensity of weathering or illuviation. Color is frequently used to distinguish *A* and *B*-horizons in the field: the B-horizon must be one Munsell unit redder and one unit brighter than the A-horizon.

Carbonate Content.—Although carbonate content cannot be determined quantitatively in the field, a reasonable estimate is possible through spraying a vertical column with a 20-25 per cent solution of hydrochloric acid (HCl). In the case of a dry profile it may be preferable to wet the section first, so that released soil air does not simulate effervescence. High calcium carbonate contents are recorded by increased reaction. The following qualitative description of reaction has been suggested by Franz (1960, p. 233):

a) no reaction;
b) audible reaction only;
c) brief visible reaction;
d) conspicuous, persistent reaction;
e) strong effervescence.

Since the reaction of different aggregates in a single sample may be different (e.g., finer or coarser grained materials, concretions, oxidation stains), it is sometimes useful to check whether reactions are uniform. Differences of carbonate reaction in a sedimentary or archeological profile may help locate buried weathering horizons or occupation levels.

A representative sample fragment or two submerged in a vial with dilute HCl can provide further information. Many samples break down into their various particle size components in HCl. If this is so, the texture can be estimated with a little practice. Other samples may or may not break down, regardless of their reaction. Among the types of materials that do not break down are salts, noncalcareous silts or clays, and siliceous or ferruginous cements.

Structure.—The mineral grains and humus of soils and finer grained sediments may be combined in various ways with respect to pore space and interstices. The resulting *structure* is largely a function of humus type and the kind and amount of clay minerals and is often preserved in paleosols. Some of the major structural types (Nikiforoff, 1941; G. D. Smith *et al.*, 1960, pp. 256-57) are as follows (Fig. 32):

a) *Platelike:* geometrical arrangement into horizontal laminae or sheets. This structure is common in poorly drained soils and generally attributed to periodic presence of groundwater.

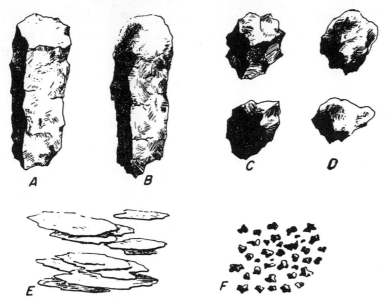

FIGURE 32.

Some major types of soil structure (from G. D. Smith *et al.*, 1960, with kind permission of the author). (a,b) prismatic and columnar, (c,d) angular and subangular blocky, (e) platy, (f) granular.

Major structural types

b) *Prismatic* or *columnar:* breaks up into columnar units with well-defined vertical faces and angular or rounded caps. This type is commonly a result of dehydration of fine materials. Salts, gypsum, or carbonates precipitates may occur on the face of such cracks. Prismatic structure is freqent in arid and semiarid soils, particularly when saline or alkaline.

c) *Block:* breaks up into variable blocklike, polyhedron-like or spheroidal aggregates, with all three dimensions of the same order of magnitude. Several important subtypes are distinguished:

1) Blocky or *polyhedral:* densely fitted, regular, geometric fragments that may be refitted, having angular or rounded vertices. This structure is common in dense, non-humic *B*-horizons, where it results from contraction of fine textured material. In other cases polyhedral structure is due to eluvial pore spaces in podsolized soils.

2) *Granular:* loosely fitted, irregular, spherical fragments with relatively little pore space and little cohesion. Found mostly in friable soils, particularly in sandy materials and moder humus horizons.

3) *Crumb:* loosely fitted, irregular, spherical fragments, conspicuously porous, and consisting mainly of earthworm excreta. It is commonly associated with mull humus, and with most woodland agricultural soils.

Dry sediments or soils generally exhibit their natural structure when plowed up, exposed in vertical sections, etc. Removal of samples by hand or pick generally leads to disintegration into the desired aggregates. Aggregate size of the individual structures varies considerably. In the case of platelike, granular, and crumb structures, the individual aggregates range from less than a millimeter to a centimeter in diameter; in the case of polyhedral structure, from less than 5 mm. to over 50 mm., in the case of prismatic structure, from under 10 mm. to over 100 mm. The dimension of structures in paleosols or fine-grained sediments may provide additional information for the soil scientist.

Concretions and staining.—*Concretions* are consolidated aggregates of rather irregular shape, with rough or jagged surfaces. They may be distinguished from smooth-surfaced, usually ellipsoidal *nodules.* Whereas nodules are usually found in bands in relation to the ground-water table, macroscopic concretions are more dispersed and may form as a result of upward or downward migration and localized concentration of salts, carbonates, and oxides of iron or manganese. Both may provide useful information, and should be recorded as to frequency, size, and constituent material.

Stains or flecks of color, mainly of iron oxides, may record seasonal or perennial waterlogging (*Fe, P,* or *G*-horizons).

Interpretation.—Field study of the features discussed above, as well as of the humus and general profile (see chap. 6), can permit tentative recognition of soil horizons and the profile type of a paleosol. Identification of the soil type is however hazardous without further laboratory study. For a discussion of paleosol identification and interpretation see Simonson (1954).

MECHANICAL ANALYSES IN THE LABORATORY

General.—Although detailed discussion of specific laboratory techniques is well beyond the scope of this book, a brief outline of the requirements and purpose of certain basic analyses will be pertinent. For a general discusion of mechanical analyses the reader is referred to Kilmer and Alexander (1949), while various methods are described by Cailleux and Tricart (1963), Cornwall (1958, chaps. 10-13) and Thun *et al.* 1955, Part II).

Pipette and hydrometer techniques for particle-size study.—The accurate determination of all particle-size components (including the fine sands, silt, and clay) is imperative for paleosol examination and may be desirable for general sedimentology as well. The two most widely used techniques are the pipette and hydrometer methods.

In both cases the materials coarser than 2 mm. are removed, and the sample dispersed in a solution by use of distilled water and a dispersant such as sodium pyrophosphate ($Na_4P_2O_7.10\ H_2O$). Contrary to the specifications of some published procedures, the organic and calcareous components should generally *not* be removed.

The pipette method requires small sample sizes (10 gm. of material under 2 mm.), a decided advantage in some cases. The components under 0.06 mm. are determined through sampling a suspension at specified depths and times by means of an inserted pipette. The coarser grades are studied by wet-sieving.

The hydrometer method is somewhat simpler and also accurate, but requires a 50 gm. sample. The grade components are determined through measurement of changing density of the suspension as the sediment settles out, the coarsest materials first. A succinct description for the general reader is given by Cornwall (1958, pp. 128-130).

Heavy mineral analysis.—The mineral components of a sandy sediment include a number of rarer and therefore often useful minerals, particularly those with a specific gravity exceeding 2.89. These are commonly rather resistant and remain statistically representative even after weathering of the sediment itself.

Heavy minerals are isolated through immersion in bromoform ($CHBr_3$), which has a specific gravity of 2.89. The "heavies" are then removed through filtering and studied by a mineralogist (see Cornwall, 1958, pp. 133-36; and Cailleux and Tricart, 1963, pp. 38-49).

The one-hundred-odd heavy minerals are in each case present in certain combinations in certain rocks only. As a result, bedrock source regions may be localized for alluvial or lacustrine sediments. Since the heavy mineral composition in different stratigraphic units is commonly distinctive, their study is sometimes vital for stratigraphic correlation over wide areas.

Quartz grain micromorphology.—Microscopic analysis of the sand-size quartz grains after removal of other materials in a sample may disclose information on the history of the individual sand particles. Cailleux (1942) and Cailleux and Tricart (1963, pp. 54-103) have shown that quartz grains transported by moving waters in streams or at the beach are commonly well-rounded in shape and glossy or polished in appearance. In contrast to such *water worn* grains, materials that have been transported by wind action are crudely rounded and characteristically dull or frosted in appearance. These are *wind worn*. *Unworn*, fresh quartz grains are fully angular and rough in shape (Fig. 33). Sand grains 0.3-1.5 mm. in diameter are most frequently used for the purpose. One or two hundred grains are classified, and the relative composition of a sample may provide information on the genesis or the derivation of the sediment.

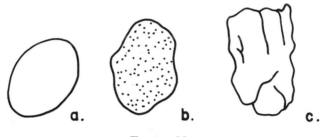

FIGURE 33.
Micromorphology of quartz sand grains: (a) water worn, (b) wind worn, and (c) unworn (modified after Cailleux and Tricart, 1963).

Quartz grain micromorphology has been overemphasized in the French sedimentological literature, and interpretations can only be made with reservation. Quartz sand is rather resistant and has commonly been modified and redeposited several times. The mystifying statistics provided by some unequivocal aeolian sands bear this out. In granite areas, where coarse quartz grit is abundant, many kilometers of stream transport are necessary to round off and polish quartz grains. Commonly this is only accomplished after several generations of transport, i.e., after repeated derivation from older deposits. The resulting spectra are therefore not too meaningful.

Even more serious are the conclusions of recent experimental work by Kuenen and Perdok (1962) that frosting of quartz grains is due only in minor degree to mechanical action. Instead chemical action by corrosive solution, or by alternate solution and deposition, are shown to be dominant, and true desert frosting is thought to be the result of alternating precipitation and evaporation of dew. In other words, only in some environments will frosting form, so that its relationship to wind abrasion is dubious.

Microscopic study of fabrics.—Examination of soil or sediment aggregates under a binocular microscope may be done either with direct light or through transmitted light in a *thin section*. Thin sections are prepared through impregnation of incoherent materials, after which a thin, transparent section is cut out and mounted in glass (see Cornwall, 1958, pp. 141-51 for preparation procedures).

Microscopic examination of samples may provide the specialist with a wealth of information on mineralogy and fabrics. The *fabric* refers to arrangement of minerals or microconcretions and to the absence or presence of colloids and precipitates in the intergranular spaces and conducting channels. Such micromorphological work has been developed by Kubiena (1938, with updating in subsequent books and articles), and is often basic in soil identification. Cornwall (1958, chap. 17) provides a brief but useful discussion.

CHEMICAL ANALYSES IN THE LABORATORY.

The sample size required for most chemical analyses in the laboratory is small, and 50 gm. will usually be adequate for general purposes. Several chemical analyses are described by Cornwall (1958, chaps. 14-16), while Jackson (1958) and Thun *et al.* (1955, Part III) provide detailed accounts of all the standard procedures. Only a few such techniques are of direct interest here.

pH values should be determined for all paleosols and for the various strata of complex stratigraphic profiles. Samples are suspended in distilled water or a potassium chloride (KCl) solution and then measured by means of a sensitive electrometer. Colorimetric tests can also be made with indicator papers or fluids, but they lack accuracy and are at best useful for tentative approximations in the field.

Absolute calcium carbonate content can be readily determined in the laboratory by a number of similar devices which measure the volume of carbon dioxide released after application of sulfuric or hydrochloric acid. Total carbonate content can also be determined by weighing sample loss after boiling with HCl and removing the solubles. The results may be valuable for recognizing weathering or secondary carbonate accumulation in a soil or section. The amount of organic matter present in the soil may be of considerable interest, but analysis is difficult and the margins of error are sizable.

Clay mineral determinations, now commonly made by differential thermal analysis (DTA), may provide information as to the source of a fine sediment or about the intensity of chemical weathering. The principle involved is that none of the major clay minerals such as illite, montmorillonite, and kaolin have identical origins. Finally, the amounts of iron and aluminum sesquioxides and of colloidal and total silica may also be determined.

In concluding, some or all of the qualitative and quantitative, mechanical, and chemical techniques discussed and evaluated here may be employed to interpret and understand the depositional environment of a sediment, the genesis of a soil, or the setting of an archeological site. The sedimentological work can only be performed by a qualified earth scientist, but it is essential that the problems, possibilities, and techniques of study be familiar to both the biologists and archeologists with an interest in Pleistocene geography.

11

Stream
and Lake Sediments

The intensity and extent of alluviation in a stream valley may vary considerably in different environments. In the arctic barrens and tundra, streams are overloaded and deposit sediments along the length of their courses. Progressive water-loss through evaporation and seepage along arid zone watercourses may also lead to alluviation. In the boreal forests large floodplains are characteristic while in the temperate and tropical woodlands, the rate and extent of downstream alluviation is comparatively limited. The savanna lands are somewhat exceptional through significant colluviation.

Seen in the perspective of time, the rate of alluviation—or the relation of downcutting to alluviation—also varies appreciably. On the annual basis, major deposition generally follows the flood-season discharge maximum. On a longer-term basis, many streams of the world also show distinct evidence of past periods of considerably greater stream alluviation. Largely responsible for this were Pleistocene climatic changes inducing major latitudinal shifts of climatic-geomorphic regions. During glacial intervals, tundra climates prevailed in many mid-latitude regions, and river cutting and alluviation were understandably accelerated. The effects remain conspicuous in the landscape today. In arid lands, shifts from drier to wetter climates led to overloading of streams with subsequent alluviation.

When a stream has accelerated its activity due to changes in sediment load, water volume, or river gradient, the moment the aberrant impetus is removed, readjustment sets in. The stream re-establishes a form of equilibrium related to its gradient and transport ability, and will frequently cut down its bed to a lower and smaller floodplain. The older floodplain becomes obsolete, and is separated from the new, functional floodplain by vertical escarpments forming *terraces*. Such alluvial terraces consist of benches, built of river deposits, remaining at the level of defunct, higher floodplains (Fig. 34).

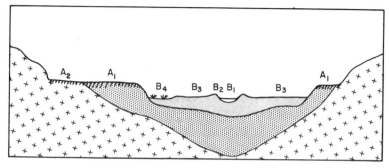

FIGURE 34.

River floodplain with terraces. (A_1) Alluvial terrace, (A_2) bed-rock bench belonging to terrace A_1, (B_1) low-water channel of modern floodplain, (B_2) levee, (B_3) alluvial flats, (B_4) back-swamp. Not to scale.

Assuming no changes of base level, the following idealized and simplified sequence may take place. At the start, the floodplain has a certain elevation and rate of deposition. Increased flood-stage discharge with greater transport ability and load will lead to (*a*) more extensive flooding and consequently enlargement of the floodplain, with undercutting of nearby hillslopes and (*b*) a higher floodplain level due to accelerated deposition. The new floodplain, across which the river migrates horizontally, is broader and higher, and characterized by deposition of more and larger-sized materials. When the volume and rate of deposition decrease to their original level, the stream will attempt to maintain its velocity—despite a decreasing volume—by shortening its course and thereby increasing the gradient. A straighter course is adopted, usually associated with a predominance of downcutting. The new floodplain will be smaller, and will be cut out as a limited section of the greater floodplain. In this way alluvial deposits are built up at various elevations and with a distinctive morphology. For general discussion of river terraces due to various origins see Cotton (1945) and Thornbury (1954, Chap. 6).

ALLUVIATION DUE TO GLACIAL ADVANCE

A spectacular Pleistocene phenomenon of higher middle latitudes was the creation and advance of continental and mountain glaciers. One impact of these glaciers was stream alluviation ahead of the ice front.

During the summer ablation period tremendous water masses leave the glacier by watercourses below, within, or on top of the ice. As these issue in front of the ice they lose velocity due to the decrease in gradient and the diffusion of waters over a broad, level area. The considerable load is then rapidly deposited ahead of the ice front and eventually concentrated along drainage lines at greater distance. In the case of continental glaciers, broad fans of outwash contrast with the more localized valley alluviation downstream from mountain glaciers. The materials are coarse—mainly sand, gravel, and cobbles—and conspicuously bedded into alternating, sorted strata of finer or coarser materials.

Glaciofluvial deposits may extend for hundreds of kilometers ahead of the ice front, forming broad floodplains conspicuous along rivers such as the Danube, Rhine, and Rhone in Europe, and the Ohio and upper Mississippi in North America. Protrusion of a glacier into the headwaters of a stream is of more than landform interest. The outwash deposits can be employed as stratigraphic markers over wide areas. The bed materials often reflect rock types not present in the modern drainage basis, a criterion useful in distinguishing periglacial alluviation from glaciofluvial deposits. Foreign rocks or minerals may of course be reworked from older glacial drift. Also the material size, stratification, sorting, or degree of water-rounding of pebbles in glaciofluvial and periglacial terraces are difficult to distinguish. In fact such deposits were often contemporary, intergrading at stream confluences. The only way then to identify glaciofluvial deposits with certainty is to associate terraces with moraines. This is possible through careful study of the geomorphology and sedimentology.

Once identified, glaciofluvial terraces may provide valuable chronological aids. Meltwaters actively deposit ahead of the ice front during both the advance and standstills of a glacier while deposition declines, sometimes to be replaced by downcutting, during glacial retreat. Consequently such terraces date glacial periods with considerable precision. Local geomorphic events, possibly relevant to a particular archeological site, may be stratigraphically associated with such a glaciofluvial terrace. This remains the principal application of glacio-fluvial terraces to prehistory since practically all of the sporadic implements or animal fossils found within them are derived from older deposits bulldozed by the glacier. No occupational levels have yet been recognized in glaciofluvial beds.

TERRACES DUE TO PERIGLACIAL ALLUVIATION

Throughout middle latitudes and at higher elevations stream basins were repeatedly subjected to the processes of the periglacial zone in the course of the Pleistocene. The immediate results, apparently, were slope denudation by solifluction and subsurface washing, so injecting great quantities of frost-weathered debris and soil into the overloaded streams (Büdel, 1944, Peltier, 1949). Reduced evaporation, stronger seasonal concentration of runoff in late spring or early summer, and no water percolation into the impermeable, frozen subsoil each increased the vigor of seasonal stream discharge. Alluviation of gravels and sands was equally accelerated, while large boulders were often transported great distances by ice floes. Most humid mid-latitude stream terraces can be attributed to periglacial alluviation. The environmental implications are clear.

Stratigraphically, periglacial stream gravels are as important as glaciofluvial deposits. Theoretically, alluviation should continue for the duration of cold climate, i.e., the time span of the glacial advance and maximum. There is, however, good reason to believe that periglacial alluviation was limited to the periods of glacial advance and, in a general way, characteristic of the early glacial intervals. So for example, the periglacial terraces of streams draining northward across Germany were overrun shortly afterward by the southward moving glacier (Soergel, 1921; Grahmann, 1955, with references). Schaefer (1950) and Fink (1962) have convincingly demonstrated this stratigraphic relationship. It is assumed that the change of climatic environment, rather than the persistance of tundra conditions, initially provided great masses of frost-weathered debris and solifluction materials. Their production was apparently reduced during the glacial standstills (Büdel, 1950b). At any rate, less material was conveyed to the streams, and these reduced their rate of deposition or ceased alluviation altogether.

Periglacial terraces are of limited importance in lower latitude highlands. They are difficult to isolate from alluviation due to increased moisture and fluvial action.

PLUVIAL ALLUVIATION IN ARID REGIONS

Pleistocene alluviation was rather important in the lower latitude arid lands. Increased cold during glacial intervals certainly did not pass unnoticed in the dry subtropics. But fluctuations of the hydrological balance—related to precipitation amount, seasonality, intensity, and the rate of evaporation—have even greater effect on stream equilibrium. The following discussion is modeled according to conditions in the Mediterranean lands and northern Africa. Interpretation of alluvial deposits in that area has been attempted by the author (Butzer, 1963b).

The dry subtropical woodlands of the Mediterranean region have no complete mat of grassy vegetation today, and much bare soil is exposed everywhere. An increase in aridity in such areas (with 500-1,000 mm. annual rainfall) would not significantly increase the area of bare soil. A trend to drier climate would only reduce the stream runoff and potential for erosion and deposition. In fact, modern Mediterranean streams originating in lowland catchment areas carry nothing but a few, irregular waterflows per year. These seldom suffice to fill the dry stream valleys or *torrents* from end to end. In other words, lowland drainage basins with little gradient are almost defunct today. The active watercourses, responsible for accelerated erosion as a result of human interference, invariably have strong gradients and obtain their waters from highland drainage basins. These cannot, therefore, be considered fully characteristic.

An increase of rainfall in the lowland Mediterranean region would lead to flood erosion capable of transporting water-saturated soils as well as ready, mechanically-disintegrated detritus. These would be carried into the drainage channels and deposited there. The stratigraphic evidence indicates that this was the case during the early glacial intervals (Butzer, 1963a). Such geomorphically significant periods of comparatively greater rainfall are known as *pluvials*. Pleistocene river terraces of small, "typical" Mediterranean torrents invariably contain much coarse material (indicating greater transport capacity) and better rolled gravel (indicating longer-distance transport than today).

In semiarid grasslands the vegetative mat is commonly composed of contiguous sod or bunch grasses providing fairly efficient soil protection. A reduction of plant cover on hillsides during drier climate would permit accelerated runoff, resulting in soil stripping and headward erosion or gullying. Deposition would be localized in the lower valleys of major rivers (Bryan, 1941; Antevs, 1952). During moister climates an increase in the vegetative mat would reduce the intensity of runoff, and fine eroded materials would soon be deposited by slowly moving waters in the upstream parts of the drainage basin, leading to general alluviation.

In the deserts, stream activity is limited today and the vegetation can do little to prevent soil-erosion. A rainfall decrease would therefore have no serious effect on the vegetative mat but would simply reduce the stream potential. An increase in rainfall would produce similar results as a change to moister climate in the Mediterranean woodlands (Cotton, 1945; Tricart and Cailleux, 1960-61, Vol. 2, p. 142 ff.; Butzer, 1963a, 1963b).

Interpretation of alluvial deposits in dry lands must be studied in relation to contemporary environments in each particular case. Greater rounding of gravel samples indicates greater transport distance and consequently, not only greater or longer waterflow or both, but also more runoff and a greater availability of moisture. Greater pebble size indicates greater erosive or transport capacity. Better stratification and moderate over-all sorting of beds may indicate perennial or seasonal, rather than episodic, flow. The polemic as to whether alluviation or downcutting indicates greater aridity or greater humidity, or whether alluviation upstream and incision downstream suggest semiaridity as opposed to aridity, or vice versa, is unnecessary. The deposits themselves reflect the conditions of deposition and tell their own story. On the basis of sediment analysis it seems that the greatest stimulus to arid zone stream alluviation is an increase in moisture, and that alluviation is a temporary result of disruption of the delicate balance of erosion and deposition through a change from one form of geomorphic equilibrium to another. Soils, residual mantles, and detritus provided by one climatic balance may, with a trend to greater or more intensive rainfall, be available for large-scale denudation and resulting alluviation of the entire stream channel.

It is symptomatic of stream deposits of northern Africa and of the Mediterranean area that terraces usually accompany the whole or most of the length of rivers, so allowing no differentiation of "erosion upstream, deposition downstream" or vice versa. Instead, the differentiation of areal from linear erosion and deposition is more significant. The fact that many coastal streams aggraded their beds even during falling sea levels suggests that absolute loads are more significant than longitudinal distribution of complementary agencies.

Detailed sediment analyses of pluvial sands and gravels may then provide good paleo-environmental evidence. Various generations of alluvial deposits may provide local relative stratigraphies, especially when found in association with prehistoric assemblages, faunas, or floras. Particularly desirable, however, is direct linkage of pluvial beds with the sequence of world sea-level fluctuations. If sufficient care is taken not to confuse the two effects, stratigraphic dating may then be extended to wider areas.

COASTAL STREAMS AND SEA LEVEL FLUCTUATIONS

Integrated stream systems drain onto a base-level, either an inland lake or sea, or the ocean. If the base-level is raised, the gradient of the lower stream is reduced together with the stream velocity and transport capacity. The theoretical result is increased deposition near the stream mouth. A gradual lowering of base-level would increase gradients and velocities and hence favor downcutting. As discussed in chapter 14, world sea level fluctuated appreciably during the Pleistocene. During the glacials sea level was 100-150 m. below that of today; during some interglacial periods, 10, 20, 30, or 50 m. and more higher. The complications for river alluviation around the world's coasts are apparently overwhelming (Fig. 35) (see Baulig, 1935; Dury, 1959, p. 79 ff; Sparks, 1960, chap. 9).

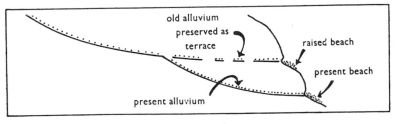

FIGURE 35.
The effect of sea-level fluctuations on stream profiles
(from G. H. Dury, 1959, with kind
permission of the author).

Larger streams with weak gradients rapidly alluviated their lower courses and left terraces of fine alluvium graded to high interglacial sea levels (see Zeuner, 1959). Then during glacial-age cold climates, mid-latitude streams alluviated in response to tundra climates or the protrusion of glaciers into the stream headwaters. Woldstedt (1952) showed that cold-climate streams resorted to downcutting downstream in response to falling sea levels. This calls for reversals of erosion or deposition, upstream or downstream, between glacials and interglacials (Fig. 36). In the case of large streams such factors are extremely

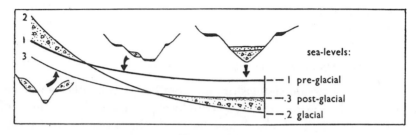

sea-levels:

– – 1 pre-glacial

– –.3 post-glacial

– –.2 glacial

FIGURE 36.
Profiles controlled by changes of sea-level and of climate
(from G. H. Dury, 1959, with kind
permission of the author).

difficult to separate. Plant and animal remains, fossil soils, or geomorphic phenomena are therefore necessary to distinguish "warm" and "cold" alluvia in some mid-latitude coastal regions.

In lower latitudes, however, pluvial rainfall during periods of falling sea level induced alluviation to well below modern sea level, even while the stream adjusted to a lower sea level. At any rate, frequent examples can be cited of coastal streams in the Mediterranean region which actively alluviated during periods of low sea level (see Butzer, 1958a, chap. 5; 1963a, 1964a).

Generally speaking, complications in lower stream courses resulting from Pleistocene sea-level fluctuations are common although interpretative difficulties are surmountable in all but the larger streams. But precise interpretation of alluvial deposits of the coastal segments of larger rivers is a most difficult geomorphic problem (e.g., the complex problem of Nile and wadi terraces in Egypt, see Butzer, 1959a, or the Mississippi terraces, see Woldstedt, 1960a).

Despite these difficulties, valuable stratigraphic information may be provided wherever alluvial deposits can be associated with high or low sea levels. Hence the Pleistocene terraces of many smaller rivers draining to the sea may be of great stratigraphic importance for correlation with the continental interiors.

CRUSTAL INSTABILITY AND STREAM ACTION

Earth movements, involving uplift or subsidence of mountains or coastal plains, tilting or other modes of crustal deformation within a stream basin, provide another possible stimulus to alluviation or downcutting. Although most geomorphic treatises of older vintage attribute river terraces to such tectonic disturbances of base-level and stream equilibrium, only a few alluvial terraces have been convincingly demonstrated to be the direct result of crustal deformation. Such alluviation must be recognized in the individual, local case, Although it is unjustified to minimize the significance of tectonic activity on stream profiles and equilibrium, it is reasonable to assume that few stream terrace sequences can be primarily attributed to local tectonic activity.

LAKE AND SWAMP BEDS

Lake and swamps beds have been laid down in standing waters and are more generally known as *lacustrine* deposits. They include:

a) evaporites, usually gypsum or salts;
b) calcareous beds, including chalk;
c) marls;
d) silts and clays;
e) sands;
f) organic deposits.

Some of the more typical physical aspects of these sedimentary facies may be outlined below.

Evaporites consist mainly of gypsum (calcium sulfate) and other salts such as sodium, magnesium and potassium chlorides or sulfates. Such beds frequently indicate desiccation or lake shrinkage—periodic shrinkage during the dry season or long-term reduction of a larger lake to a lagoon or salt pan. So for example, the Pleistocene ancestor of the modern Dead Sea deposited some 50,000 banded alternations of silts (rainy season influx) and carbonates, sulfates, or chlorides (dry season evaporites) (see Butzer, 1958a, p. 78, with references). Evaporites, with the exception of open coastal lagoons are indicative of some degree of aridity or at least of a high ratio of evaporation to precipitation.

Lacustrine chalks usually indicate perennial lakes which are not subject to very great seasonal fluctuations of oxygen content. Lacustrine chalks are common in many climatic zones. In temperate Europe they may be deposited organically by pond weeds; in dry areas such as the Sahara, inorganic precipitation is more important. Plant and animal remains are common in such beds.

Marls or calcareous silts are deposited both in lakes and swamps. The lime content may be derived through plant or inorganic agencies; the clays and silts represent soil products carried in by streams and rainwash. Common in humid and even semiarid lands, freshwater marl sedimention is commonly confined to comparatively small water bodies.

Silts and clays are generally carried into standing waters in suspension by local streams. They may occur wherever finer weathering products are available, from glacier-fed lakes in the arctic to spring-fed lakes in the Saharan oases. Lacustrine silts and clays are, however, most common in moister climates. In some cases, such as the "lacustrine loess" of the Persian Lut Desert (Hückriede, 1962), similar beds may be at least partly of aeolian origin.

Sands of lacustrine deposition are most widely found in areas with limited vegetation. Glacial meltwater streams feed sandy products to ice-margin lakes. In lower latitudes the widespread lacustrine sands of the Sahara were largely derived from sandy wadi deposits in the course of the Pleistocene. The prehistoric Chad and Fayum lakes of northern Africa are striking examples of lacustrine sands derived from direct stream influx as well as lake wave-action on local sandstone bedrock.

Organic deposits, of many different kinds and complex origins, are most common in cooler latitudes although they are not quite unknown in the tropics and subtropics. The various facies will be considered in detail further below.

INTERPRETATION OF MINERAL OR SEMIORGANIC LACUSTRINE BEDS

Simple mineral sediments, such as evaporites, marls, silts, clays, and sands, as well as semiorganic deposits, such as chalks, may be of considerable archeological or paleo-environmental interest. The direct origin of such standing waters in localities which are dry today is chiefly the result of (a) moister climate (in the arid zone), (b) poor drainage (in humid lands), or (c) a rise of sea level (in coastal areas). Sedimentation may vary considerably from place to place and is necessarily determined by local conditions. In higher middle latitudes, lacustrine beds are mainly found in poorly-drained areas of ground-moraines dating from after the retreat of the continental glaciers.

Apart from particle-size and certain chemical analyses (carbonate content, *p*H, organic matter), biological studies usually provide significant paleo-ecological information. Combined with study of any macro-remains of plant leaves, fruits, stems, or wood, the pollen spectrum offers an excellent picture of the regional setting. Pollen diagrams can be further studied from different strata to yield chronological information. Depending on the sediment, various other studies directed towards ecological interpretation of mammalian fauna, snails or mollusca, algae or diatoms, etc., may yield results of interest.

Each of these laboratory approaches provides vital complementary evidence to the more standard geomorphologic field investigation of the lacustrine sediments in a wider setting.

VARVE ANALYSIS

General.—A particular study of interest to both archeology and geochronology is that of *varves*. These are annual, graded bands of sediment laid down in glacier-fed lakes contiguous with the margins of continental glaciers. Detailed work by G. de Geer (1912, and later authors) on such annual sediment layers show that a new load of sediment enters the lake in the wake of each spring's thaw. The coarser materials (mainly silts) settle down first while the fines (clays) gradually settle during the course of the summer. In larger lakes, wave-motion may impede fine sedimentation until autumn when the lake surface freezes over. In numerous cases fine sedimentation continues under the ice throughout the winter. When coarse silts or fine sands are deposited again during the succeeding spring, a sharp contact zone is formed, so enabling clear identification of the annual increment.

Further seasonal distinctions are provided through biological evidence. The coarse springtime accretion is generally dark and rich in organic matter, while the fine summer sediment is light-colored due to calcium carbonate precipitation. The late summer and autumn sediments are dark again. Pollen examinations of the upper dark layers have shown pollen sequences according to the time of blooming, while microorganisms such as diatoms are concentrated in the light, summer segment.

The thickness of the annual deposit or varve varies from year to year depending on the course of the annual weather and its influence on the ablation of the nearby glacier. A warm year produces large varves, a cold year narrow ones. A requisite to the regular laminar sedimentation is the temperature contrast of warmer, inflowing waters and cold lake waters, whereby the sediment is distributed evenly over the lake bed. Such conditions are best met in ice-margin lakes. Attempts have been made to study annual, varve-lake evaporite sediments in lower latitudes, e.g., the Saki salt lake of the Crimea (Shostakovitch, 1936), the Dead Sea (see references in Butzer, 1958a, p. 78), and some lake beds of Kenya in East Africa (de Geer, 1934).

Teleconnection of varves.—De Geer first recognized that varve sequences were very similar between nearby lakes—within a kilometer of each other—on account of the similarity of local climate. On this basis sequences were correlated and extended in time from area to area. By following the various stands of the retreating ice front De Geer established an almost complete sequence covering 15,000 years from the late Upper Pleistocene well into historical times. This provided a true chronology whereby glacial features related to the retreat and dissipation of the European glacier could be more or less precisely dated. For example, the close of the Pleistocene was fixed by the event of the draining of the Baltic ice lake, which, according to the varves, occurred in 7912 B. C. Radiocarbon cross-dating suggests that this date may be at most a few centuries "off." During four decades De Geer's varve-chronology of Scandinavia remained an invaluable tool the significance of which for prehistory and geochronology is all too easily overlooked today.

Difficulties in the varve-chronology.—Within Fennoscandia the varve-chronology, as established by De Geer (1912, 1940) and Sauramo (1929), has in part remained a respectable body of evidence. It has been shown, however, that storms create multiple varves annually in *shallow* lakes through addition of extra influx and the stirring of sediments (Hansen, 1940). As most of the lakes south of the Fennoscandian moraines, dating about 9000 B. C., are shallow, the earlier chronology has been widely discredited. Most of the lakes north of this line, extending across south-central Sweden and southern Finland, are quite deep, and combined with Sauramo's more conservative approach to the Finnish chronology, there is little ground for serious criticism here.

The establishment of varve-chronologies outside Scandinavia, as attempted by Antevs (1925) in North America, has not been very successful. A major reason for this failure has been extrapolation of sequence segments over hundreds of miles. World-wide correlations of a frivolous type were attempted later whereby reversed seasons on the northern and southern hemispheres, or non-glacial characteristics of varves, have been simply ignored. These have discredited the varve method, and generally speaking, other techniques have now replaced the varve-chronologies everywhere except in Fennoscandia.

SPRING DEPOSITS

Although rather localized in their occurrence, many springs in limestone areas have promoted a class of particular calcareous sediments occurring in direct association with the spring or in adjacent stream beds or lacustrine basins. Two major kinds of deposit are formed by evaporation of, or precipitation in, lime-charged waters:

a) *Tufas,* formed through precipitation of cryptocrystalline calcite on growing plants, leaving an inhomogeneous, spongy, porous and often brittle rock. The stems, grass blades, and leaves are preserved as open casts, as a dense calcite replacement, or as a partial cast-filling of lime sand. The filling between the plant structures is commonly soft and very porous, consisting of cemented calcite sands.

b) *Travertines,* dense, banded cryptocrystalline calcite occurring as.dripstone in caves, or as horizontal beds within and outside of cave environments. Cave travertines are further discussed in chapter 13. The external travertines can be further subdivided into two types:

1) "True" travertines, precipitated as horizontal, undulating or bulbous bands, commonly alternating from dense calcite, crystallized with columnar structure, to porous calcite with little or no macroscopic crystalline structure.

2) Sedimentary crusts (the *croûtes zonaires* of the French authors), consisting of fine, wavy laminations of cryptocrystalline calcite. These are frequently confused with *Ca*-horizons of the soil zone.[1] Fossil crusts of this kind are widespread in the arid, semiarid, and subhumid subtropics. Their occurrence may indicate either moister or drier paleoclimates, depending on the situation. In subhumid climates with acid rocks, sedimentary crusts presumably record drier conditions. In arid or semiarid limestone areas, they probably indicate

[1] Variously called calcareous crusts, tufaceous or travertine crusts, and caliche. For detailed discussion of these controversial features in Algeria see Durand (1959, pp. 75-136); for Morocco, Gigout (1960, pp. 91-129); for the Balearic Islands, Butzer (1963b). For a general analysis, see Tricart and Cailleux (1960-61, Vol. 2, p. 147 ff.).

greater spring activity and more abundant moisture. Such travertines should preferably be associated with defunct springs or lacustrine beds when such an interpretation is made.

INTERPRETATION OF ORGANIC SEDIMENTS

Standing waters, partly closed in by plant growth and not subject to mechanical water turbulence, tend to develop an oxygen deficiency. This may be the case for deep waters with limited vertical stirring or where the water supply is either poor in mineral plant nutrients or acidic as a result of base deficiency in the catchment area. In such moderately acidic waters, organic precipitation of humic solutions known as gel mud or *dy* ("sedimentary peat") takes place. In extreme cases of oxygen and nutrient deficiency, anaerobic conditions and reduction produce ferric sulfide, hydrogen sulfide, and methane through lack of or limited oxidation of plant materials. This badly-smelling clayey humus is known as *sapropel.*

Where partly overgrown water-bodies are sufficiently well aerated and supplied with nutrients, sediments are rich in organisms such as diatoms, and the plant and animal remains are partially decomposed. The resulting gray to gray-black, occasionally brown, sediment recalls a highly humic marl, and is known as a *gyttja.*

The above forms of organic deposits are essentially lake types. Emergent plant growth along the margins of such water-bodies is limited to the shores and shallower waters. Plants with submerged roots—reeds, horsetails, and water-lilies—inhabit water to about a meter in depth. On the immediate shore, plants such as sedges and rushes are found on wet ground, but with their roots out of the water. Since the supply of dead organic matter is great in the reed bank zone, and since wave action and oxygen distribution are effectively impeded by root and stem networks, oxygen is insufficient to enable complete decomposition. Consequently, a net accumulation of organic materials progressively narrows the open water surface, and is followed by colonization of the peaty shores by swamp plants. A botanist can approximate the depth of water associated with peaty swamp deposits, and may be able to reconstruct the general ecological setting in some detail.

When such a lake has finally been reduced to a swamp, the ensuing deposition may be entirely organic, without mineral matter. This is known as *peat.* A distinction is usually applied between a *low moor,* at or under the water level, and *high moor,* above the water level.

The low moor harbors reeds, sedges, horsetails and water-tolerant arboreal species such as alder and willow. When peat accumulation rises above the groundwater table, the moisture supply is largely derived from rainwaters, which are notably lacking in nutrients. The resulting highly acidic environment leads to rapid growth of sphagnum or bog moss, heather, and cottongrass, while the deciduous trees are replaced by pine and birch. Ultimately the pines, as the last tree species, are also replaced by peat mosses.

The colonization and ultimate disappearance of innumerable late glacial lakes and swamps on the Würm-age groundmoraines of northern Germany have been systematically studied by Overbeck (1950). According to Overbeck the lacustrine sequence typically began with deposition of sands, silts, and clays in topographic depressions by the meltwater streams of the retreating continental glacier. As herbaceous vegetation recolonized the areas just abandoned by the ice, simple mineral sedimentation was gradually replaced by deposition of thick beds of *dy* or *gyttja*. Rapid increase in warmth favored a more luxuriant vegetation whereby the lakes were reduced to bogs, low moors, and eventually high moors.

The present world distribution of ancient organic beds or contemporary bogs is largely confined to (*a*) areas overrun by ice during the last glaciation, and consequently suffering from disrupted drainage, (*b*) low-lying coastal areas with a correspondingly high water table, and (*c*) poorly drained mountain localities with high rainfall. This limits the distribution of older organic deposits to higher middle latitudes, with the exception of occasional coastal or highland bogs in subtropical latitudes. More recent bogs are also widespread in the tundras.

The interpretation of organic deposits for the purposes of archeology and Pleistocene geography is only to a limited extent a matter of geomorphic investigation. Detailed analyses are mainly concerned with organic materials and are therefore performed by the biologist. On account of their acidic, anaerobic environment, which enables them to preserve most organic materials—ranging from flesh and bone to plant materials—bogs are of exceptional paleo-ecological value. Paleobotanical studies consequently provide detailed environmental and chronological information. Geomorphic investigation is confined to interpretation of the lacustrine setting, as well as to sedimentation features such as disconformities, burnings or peat cuttings in the depositional record.

12

Wind-borne
and Slope Sediments

WIND ACTION

Erosion by wind is limited to dry, loose, and fine-grained sediments, not protected by a plant cover. Under natural conditions wind erosion will be more or less limited to the arid zone and high arctic barrens, except for locally favorable areas: broad sandy beaches, and exposed stream or lake beds during low-water. Particles in the silt or fine and medium sand size (under 0.2 mm.) are carried in suspension by stronger winds. Coarse sands are moved by saltation. Such grains are picked up by local microturbulence and then deflected downwind. As they strike the surface their impact may cause them to rebound or to start saltation by other grains (Fig. 37). Wind-driven coarse sands are responsible for any and all wind abrasion of the surface. Such abrasion is limited to the lowermost meter of the atmosphere, although rarely significant above 50 cm. A secondary effect of

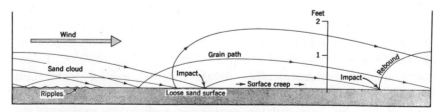

FIGURE 37.
Aeolian transport (after R. A. Bagnold from A. N.
Strahler, 1960, with kind permission of
J. Wiley & Sons, New York).

saltation is general disturbance of the surface sands which are motivated to a steady forward motion through rolling, sliding, or low saltation. This is known as surface creep.

Transport of the suspended load, consisting of silts and finer sand grades, is effected over long distances. During strong dust storms, great masses of aeolian materials may be carried over hundreds of kilometers, only to be deposited very slowly in response to decreasing wind velocities, or more rapidly by being washed down by rain. Extensive aeolian sedimentation of silt and fine sand may then occur well outside of those environments suitable for wind erosion. The coarser sands of the bed load can only move along the ground, migrating as sand ripples, ridges, or dunes. These materials will ordinarily be confined to the general source region, with exception of smaller dunes migrating from the coast or along other local sources of sand.

Corresponding to the mode of transport of the different particle sizes, wind-borne sediments may consist of striking coarse-grained sand mounds or dunes, or of smooth, extensive sheets or mantles of fine-grained materials. The morphologically conspicuous, coarse-grained types are largely confined to the world deserts and the arctic barrens, whereas the sand or dust (loess) sheets may be deposited almost anywhere, although they only retain their structure and other characteristics when laid down in open country.

The localization of aeolian features in different environments is summarized in Table 13. General discussions of wind processes are given by Bagnold (1954), Thornbury (1954, chap. 12), Flint (1957, chap. 10), Sparks (1960, chap. 11) and Tricart and Cailleux (1960-61).

TABLE 13

WIND ACTIVITY IN DIFFERENT ENVIRONMENTS

Vegetation	Wind Erosion	Wind Deposition
Desert and Arctic Barrens	Active	Dunes and sand sheets
Grassland and Tundra	Localized	Loess and sand sheets, some local dunes
Forest	None	Negligible
Littoral Zone	Localized	Local dunes and sand sheets

FEATURES OF WIND EROSION AND ABRASION

Pavement.—One of the more common forms of aeolian erosion is the gradual deflation of fine materials, leaving increasing concentrations of heavier grit, detritus, or gravel at the surface. Such a *desert pavement* or *lag deposit* forms extensive desert surfaces today—the rocky *hamadas* of disintegrating, angular bedrock and the pebbly *serirs* of deflated alluvial fans or weathered old conglomerates. On a much more local scale, buried stone concentrations in various Pleistocene deposits have frequently been identified as pavements, particularly if other evidence of aeolian action is also present.

Blow-outs.—Wind scour and deflation may locally achieve more than simple denudation. Small depressions may be repeatedly excavated in dune fields or other types of sand accumulation. Such *blow-outs* may also develop in areas with poorly consolidated bedrock, as on the Great Plains (Judson, 1950, 1953a) or in southern Africa (Flint, 1959), or even in consolidated bedrock, as in the Libyan Desert (Pfannenstiel, 1954). Whatever the origin of the desert hollow at start, or its dimensions today, a combination of chemical weathering and deflation is generally postulated for its development. Salt hydration or various forms of chemical weathering produce fine residual products in hollows where surface drainage collects and percolates or the water table is high. Solution may also have been an important auxiliary factor in limestone bedrock. Periodic or long-term drying permits repeated deflation of accumulated silt and sand, leading to steady deepening of the hollows. The dimensions of such blow-outs in the Great Plains area are rather modest—as much as a few square kilometers in size, and up to 50 m. deep. The oasis depressions of the Libyan Desert may be a thousand square kilometers or more in area, and several hundred meters deep. Despite their size the excavation of the Libyan depressions cannot be explained except through wind removal of loosened materials.

Yardangs.—Whereas blow-outs are probably more or less exclusively due to deflation, a less common but equally conspicuous abrasional form occurs in non-consolidated fine sediments. Elongated, U-shaped grooves or furrows, oriented with the prevailing wind, are separated by jagged hillocks or ridges of sand-scoured clay, silt, or fine sand. Known as *yardangs*, these forms are a product of both abrasion and deflation and may have a local relief of several meters. Uncommon in mid-latitude Pleistocene contexts, they play a prominent role in the archeology of the Sahara, where various prehistoric cultures are related to deflated and scoured fluvial, lacustrine or spring-deposited silts (Caton-Thompson and Gardner, 1932; Butzer and Hansen, 1965).

Ventifacts.—Wind does not only erode by deflating, pitting, grooving, and scouring, but also by polishing and faceting. Pebbles may be polished and faceted on one or more sides by wind-driven sand The *ventifacts* so-formed require only a few decades, given strong winds, plentiful sand, and no vegetation. Ventifacts are common in lag deposits and provide corroboration for their identification. Cailleux (1942) has shown that ventifacts are common in many European Pleistocene beds, and Cailleux and Tricart (1963, pp. 216-41) give a number of techniques for systematic analysis of ventifacts. Multifaceted ventifacts are far more common in the periglacial environment than in lower latitude deserts. Cailleux attributes this to soil-frost heaving, whereby ventifacts may be repeatedly overturned and faceted on new faces.

BED LOAD DEPOSITS: SAND DUNES

Dune types.—Dunal forms include migratory "free" dunes, whose existence is independent of topography, and "tied" dunes, related to some permanent wind obstruction. The free dunes include several types:

a) *Longitudinal* dunes or *seifs* occur in groups of long, parallel ridges, with many peaks and sags. They may be 100 km. long and over 100 m. high, lying parallel to the direction of strong winds. Their formation may be aided by local turbulence, leading to accumulation now on one side, now on the other.

b) Crescentic dunes or *barchans*, as the name implies, are crescentic in plan, the horns and steep concave slopes facing downwind (Fig. 38). Barchan dunes may attain 30 m. in height and 400 m. in width and length. They develop with unidirectional effective winds.

c) *Transverse* dunes form irregular, wavelike ridges at right angles to the effective wind direction, sometimes merging or occurring simultaneously with barchan fields. Some authors do not recognize transverse dunes as an independent type, others consider them as identical with the barchan. There are, however, several types of complex dune fields (as opposed to single dunes) of controversial

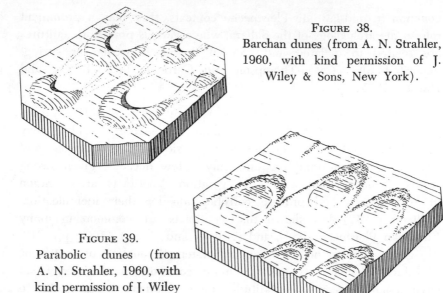

FIGURE 38.
Barchan dunes (from A. N. Strahler, 1960, with kind permission of J. Wiley & Sons, New York).

FIGURE 39.
Parabolic dunes (from A. N. Strahler, 1960, with kind permission of J. Wiley & Sons, New York).

origin that are quite distinct from merging barchan fields (see Tricart and Cailleux, 1961, Vol. 2, p. 77 ff.).

d) *Parabolic* or U-shaped dunes are superficially similar to a barchan, but are more elogated and slightly asymmetrical, with the gentle, concave slope facing windward, the steeper, convex face downwind (Fig. 39).[1] Merging parabolic dunes may form very narrow ridges running parallel with the effective winds, producing *hairpin* dunes.

The "tied" dunes include a number of types of which *lee* dunes are probably most conspicuous. Often nondescript in appearance, they develop in the lee of obstacles, frequently growing into longitudinal forms.

All of the above types belong to the class of interior or *continental* dunes. The somewhat different coastal or *littoral* types are discussed in chapter 14.

Sedimentology.—Particle-size analyses are particularly useful in distinguishing various classes of aeolian deposits. Although there is usually a concentration of coarser sand around the dune crests, the

---

[1] Discussions of parabolic dunes are conspicuously absent in some basic textbooks.

grade size of continental dune sands is remarkably uniform. Medium sands (0.06-0.2 mm.) provide 20-90 per cent of the material, and there is an almost total absence of silts or clays under 0.02 mm. (see Tricart and Cailleux, 1960-61, Vol. 2, p. 89 ff.). The constituent material is almost exclusively quartz, although a calcareous component may be present locally and rather exceptional gypsum dunes are known. Only in transitory small dunes is there, on occasion, a high silt or clay component.

In the case of fossil dunes, particularly where the morphology has been obscured or destroyed, dune and wind directions may be obtained from bedding. The compass bearing of bedding-dips determined from a number of localities gives the effective wind direction responsible for sedimentation. The *prevailing* winds may be gentle and from another direction than the *effective* winds sufficiently strong to shape the sand. The effective wind is then a storm wind that may or may not coincide with the average wind. Whereas effective wind directions can be obtained from the orientation or bedding directions of a dune, prevailing winds can be deduced from the position of a dune with respect to the source area of sand. Uniform layer-by-layer bedding suggests uniform effective wind directions, while crossbedding implies winds of variable direction. Uniformity of grain size throughout the sediment suggests that the effective winds had a relatively constant velocity, while sporadic coarse sand laminae may record periodic gales. Information on former effective winds can be compared with modern climatic records of strong winds and, if present, with recent dunes or wind-deformed vegetation.

Environmental interpretation.—Although the exact origins or development of most dune types are still controversial or uncertain, the formative environment of the major types is clear.

Mobile longitudinal, barchan and transverse dunes of moderate or great size are now limited to areas without vegetation. Localized fields of small, active dunes may move through vegetated terrain along the sandy beds of some streams in semiarid zones. But if no ready source of sand is available, these types indicate aridity and a lack of vegetation. The same applies to lee dunes.

Parabolic dunes more commonly indicate a subhumid climate with some, although sufficiently modest, herbaceous vegetation. They were once widespread in the European tundras and on the Great Plains of North America (Poser, 1950; H. T. U. Smith, 1949). They commonly form when the vegetation cover of extensive sand deposits is degraded by man or by increasing aridity (Tricart and Cailleux, 1960-61, Vol. 2, p. 76 f.).

Barchan and parabolic dunes are widely thought to indicate rather uniform effective wind directions, whereas opinions diverge in the case of longitudinal dunes. Bagnold (1954) has given good reason to believe that the typical seifs with irregular, knifelike crests form where effective winds are of different direction than the prevalent winds. Some of the simpler and smaller longitudinal dunes may however be a product of unidirectional winds.

In addition to providing information on vegetation, sand sources, and wind directions, dunes may also record effective wind velocities. So, for example, longitudinal dunes may be due to stronger winds than any of the other types. Of greater potential are the parameters governing wind speed and sand size, a relationship differing according to whether the effective winds are unidirectional or not. Studies by Poser (1950) and Dubief (1952) are of interest here, although much more experimental work is required.

SUSPENDED LOAD DEPOSITS: LOESS AND SAND SHEETS

Loess.—Loess is a pale yellowish unstratified silty sand, rich in vertical capillary structures. The material typically consists of quartz (60-70 per cent), carbonates (10-30 per cent), and clay minerals (10-20 per cent). The particle-size distribution shows a distinctive maximum in the silt and fine sand grades, with 70-95 per cent below 0.06 mm. in size and 97-99.5 per cent below 0.2 mm., i.e., nothing coarser than medium sand. For a comprehensive study see Guenther (1961).

Two classes of loess are recognized: (a) *periglacial* loess, deflated from outwash deposits (see Schönhals, 1953), from freshly exposed till, and from the rocky surfaces of the tundra and arctic barrens,[2] and (b) *desert* or continental loess, derived from desert areas. Grahmann (1932) believes it possible to distinguish the two on the basis of particle-size distribution. Periglacial loess should show a smaller grain-size range due to double selection—first sorting by meltwater streams or selective frost-weathering, followed by selective wind deflation.

---

[2] There is a remarkable concentration of fines between 0.01 and 0.1 mm. among the frost-weathered surface materials of the polar regions (Dücker, 1937). This loess-like size is readily deflated in summer, while a constant supply of materials is assured by continued frost-weathering. Apparently weathering of this type does not produce material of clay or coarse sand size.

Desert or continental loess is only wind sorted and contains more clay and medium sand particles with a less striking silt or fine sand maximum.

Pleistocene loesses, largely of the periglacial type, are rather widespread in Europe, China, the central United States as well as in the Pampas of Argentina. With a subdued topography they mantle hills and valleys to depths varying from 50 cm. to over 50 m. Much or most of this periglacial loess was laid down in the herbaceous tundra, as is suggested by little or no evidence of soil development (see Schönhals, 1951, 1953), by the contemporary snail faunas (see Prošek and Ložek, 1957), and by the rather limited pollen (see Firbas, 1949-52, Vol. 1). This does not mean that loess was never laid down in forest areas, and contemporary cases of sedimentation under woodland are indeed known (see Péwé, 1951). But it has not yet been proven that any of the extensive loess beds preserved from the Pleistocene were deposited under forest vegetation. Soil development with its leaching, humification, and biological mixing would continue to destroy the characteristic aspects so that a theoretical forest loess would normally be assimilated soon after deposition—except if the depth and rate of accumulation were excessive. The typical columnar structure and vertical cleavage of true loess is compatible with herbaceous vegetation but not with a woodland soil environment. The absence of calcified root-casts and impressions or secondary root-fillings is of interest in the same connection.

Much of the European and North American loess was subsequently redeposited on a local scale through rainwash, a feature sometimes noticeable through fine wavy laminations, lenses of fine pebbles, and horizons of stratified mollusca. These *Schwemmlöss* (German for "colluvial loess") characteristics do not however influence the over-all interpretation of periglacial loess since such washing may also have taken place during deposition in rainy weather.

Periglacial loess is also significant for stratigraphical purposes. Generally indicative of glacial phases, the loess of western and west-central Europe is mainly attributed to the glacial maxima (see Büdel, 1950b), that of the more continental parts of central and eastern Europe to the glacial advances and maxima (see Prošek and Ložek, 1957). Similarly loesses, with their buried weathering profiles, molluscan faunas, etc., have provided the greatest impetus for stratigraphic controversies concerning the details of European glacial stratigraphy.

Lastly, the periglacial loesses of several Old World areas have assumed importance in another way. Their functional coincidence with highly fertile, well-drained soils and open or lighter-stocked woodland vegetation destined the loess plains for earliest agricultural colonization in middle latitudes.

Sand sheets.—The somewhat coarser sand sheets with incoherent or subdued morphology are rather less common than loess. Included here are a variety of features comprising all classes of drifted sand, excluding dunal forms, coastal features, and specific loess deposits. Particle sizes are commonly in the silt to medium sand grade with maxima in the fine sand category (0.02-0.06 mm.). Since this is a heterogeneous intermediate class in all ways, few environmental generalizations can be made other than that a ready source of sand must have been available at not too great a distance.

SLOPE DEPOSITS

Slope deposits are due primarily to gravity movements, but are commonly aided by soil frost or rainwash. They are most common in the periglacial zone and rough mountain country. Solifluction, block streams and sorted talus, already discussed in detail in chapter 7, are probably the most significant of these processes.

Not all slope deposits are, however, a result of frost activity. The gradual accumulation of loose rock detritus on the flanks or at the foot of steep slopes of 45 per cent or more produces *talus*. The physical disintegration of crude fragments from the exposed rock face above may be largely due to frost-weathering, but this may be difficult to prove in a fossil context. Occasional *rock falls* may accelerate deposition, although the impetus to such sudden slips of slope materials may again be obscure. Slow, imperceptible movements of soil by gravity (*creep*) or by combined water action and gravity (*slope wash*) are common to most climatic zones, as are talus slopes. In the case of lubrication of clayey soil masses by excessive rains, large masses of sod or residual mantle may slip or slide down slope as *earth slips* or *earth flows*. Each of these more general forms of gravity movement is of greater significance for archeology than for Pleistocene geography so that further discussion will be confined to chapter 15.

For a more detailed account of slope sedimentation the reader is referred to any of the standard texts on geomorphology.

13

Cave Sediments

INTRODUCTION

Caves were first "discovered" for science by archeologists, and despite the enthusiasm of amateur cave explorers, caves and archeology remain almost synonomous in the public mind. The earth sciences have also shown considerable interest in caves and subterranean caverns. In fact, the various processes of groundwater solution and cave formation are a part of *karst* geomorphology (Grund, 1903; Davis, 1930. For general discussions see Birot, 1954; Thornbury, 1954, chap. 13; Louis, 1960, p. 141 ff.). Practically all true caves have developed as a result of solution in limestone, and the term "karst" refers to landscapes noticeably modified through the dissolving agency of underground waters. Karst is an intrazonal feature much in the same way as is vulcanism. Many of its processes are individualistic. And the geomorphologists who first studied cave phenomena, often in relation to archeological sites, had to interpret a set of rather peculiar sediments.

Man and animals have sought shelter in caves since the beginnings of prehistory, and some of the most interesting cultural sequences have been derived from cave sites. Almost as a by-product, biological evolution and changing geomorphic environments have also been studied successfully in cave strata. Today certain sequences of cave sediments, faunal assemblages, and pollen are as vital for Pleistocene stratigraphy as the cultural horizons are for Stone Age archeology. Cave environments and processes consequently deserve special attention.

197

CAVE ENVIRONMENTS AND SEDIMENTATION

Two major kinds of caves are distinguished: *exterior* caves and niches, and *interior* passages and caverns (Schmid, 1958, 1963; Trombe, 1952). The exterior type may vary from simple overhangs and shelters to shallow caves. Most of these have been dissolved or eroded near the water-mark by streams or wave-action at the coast. Sometimes they are produced by hollowing out of softer rock strata. Although generally found in limestone, exterior caves may also occur in other bedrock. The interior type is limited to limestone country and is mainly the result of karst activity. Underground corrosion along rock joints and bedding planes leads to enlargement by removal of dissolved material in subterranean waters. Irregular, vaulted caverns and narrow, cleft-like passages follow underground streams or natural rock fissures. Some caves of this kind extend for several kilometers, often at several levels. Locally the surface drainage may be swallowed up in sink holes, only to emerge at some distance from a hillside spring.

Cave environments are highly variable. Direct sunlight is reduced or eliminated entirely. Relative humidities are high, particularly in deep, shaded caves. Mean temperatures are lower than outside, but an almost unlimited range of possibility exists: deep caves maintain relatively constant temperatures; shallow caves may be heated by the sun in day, and cool off rapidly at night. Except at the very entrance, temperatures are usually too low for soil development, and chemical weathering is practically limited to carbonate solution. Schmid (1958) consequently distinguishes several cave environments (Fig. 40):

a) The *entrance* is located under the cliff face and is exposed to external weathering agents such as frost, rainwash, wind, and possibly sunlight. Plant life is present, soil development is possible and talus commonly falls in from the cliff face. Sediments at the entrance consequently accumulate rapidly and are rather complex in nature. Many of the rock-overhangs or *abris* of prehistory are of this type.

b) The *front part* of a cave is still effected by the external weathering agents but to a limited degree only. Rainwater may wash the floor locally, but wind activity is very subdued, ventilation limited, and temperature contrasts more restricted. Plants are generally absent, snails are few and uncommon, and soil development ceases. Talus is absent. Instead rocks fractured off the ceiling and walls of the cave

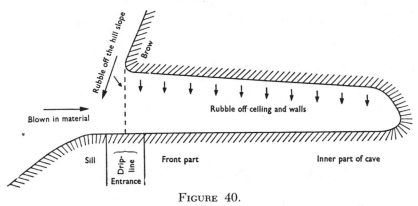

FIGURE 40.
Sedimentary environments of a cave (from E. Schmid, 1963,
with kind permission of Thames and Hudson, London).

accumulate slowly on the floor. Soil products may be washed in from outside through large joints in the cliff, and soluble limestone precipitates may accumulate on the ceiling, walls, or floor. Exterior caves and the external portions of interior caverns or passages may be listed as part of this environment. Most prehistoric cave living-floors belong here.

c) The *inner part* of the cave is permanently dark. Temperatures are practically constant all year commonly around 5°-15° C. in midlatitudes. Humidities are high. Sediment production is restricted. Habitation by men or animals is sporadic and less common.

The geological layers found in caves are therefore partly of external origin, partly internal. The extraneous materials may be washed in by rainwash, drawn in by gravity, blown in by wind, moved in through solifluction or washed through rock joints by percolating soil and groundwater. In addition man and beast may carry in a variety of inorganic objects or materials, deliberately or inadvertently. Local weathering within the cave is limited to thermoclastic agencies and solution. Oxidation is almost entirely absent so that weathered products such as "cave earths" are either extraneous or are simply the clayey residuals left after solution and removal of the carbonates constituting the bulk of the bedrock. There are then no true cave *soils,* only *sediments.*

The principal forms of mineral cave sediments therefore include (e.g., Fig. 41).

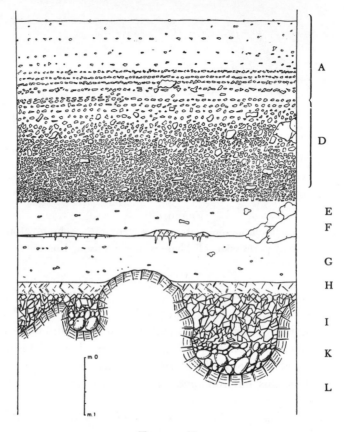

FIGURE 41.

Sedimentary profile of the Grotta Romanelli, southern Italy (from G. A. Blanc, 1921). (A-D) *éboulis secs* beds, with "cold" fauna, (E) brown earth, partly aeolian, with cold fauna, (F) discontinuous stalagmitic layer, (G) reddish earth, partly aeolian, (H) dripstone and flowstone, (I) limestone detritus with "warm" fauna, (K) beach conglomerate of Tyrrhenian II stage, (L) limestone bedrock.

    a) Extraneous mineral sediments or materials introduced from the outside by water, wind, gravity action, man or animals;

    b) Limestone detritus derived from mechanical or chemical attack on the walls and ceiling of the cave;

    c) Limestone precipitates derived from solution of limestone products;

    d) Residual products mainly clay minerals, derived from the dissolved limestone.

In addition to these more general, geological strata, Schmid (1958, 1963) distinguishes further biological horizons:

1) Fossil layers: animal bones, carcasses, feces, etc. included naturally within a sediment;

2) Archeological layers: the occurrence of individual proofs of human presence with or without fossil remains, but little or no alteration of the sediment;

3) Cultural layers: sediments strongly influenced by human activities such as fire and toolmaking, and with many imported objects such as stones, bones, shells, plant matter, etc.

Major attention will here be devoted to mineral sediments. Unfortunately the exact interpretation of such deposits still leaves much to be desired. Systematic analyses were introduced by R. Lais (1932, 1941) and followed up by Freund (in Zotz, 1955), Bonifay (1956), Schmid (1958), and Vértes (1959). Yet there still is little or no comparative material on cave microclimates, contemporary cave sedimentation processes, or on differences within different parts of a single cave or between caves in different regional environments. Much of the outline given here must be considered as tentative. It is only an attempt to sketch and discuss the information available.

LIMESTONE DETRITUS

Limestone fragments are separated from the ceiling or walls either by corrosion and solution (chemical weathering) or by thermoclastic fracturing (mechanical weathering).

a) Chemical Agencies. Subsurface waters contained atmospheric CO_2 or humic acids in solution, and therefore act corrosively on limestone bedrock. Passing through joints, bedding planes, and fissures a certain amount of calcium carbonate is dissolved and carried away in solution, while minute quantities of residual clay or sand are washed out. The cracks are gradually enlarged until, one by one, corroded fragments of rock break off and fall to the floor. Rocks derived in this fashion are superficially corroded, have somewhat rounded edges, and are generally embedded in residual clays, coarse calcite sand, or crystalline carbonate precipitates (travertines). Both Lais (1941) and Bonifay (1956) consider coarse calcite sand (0.2-2.0 mm.) as primarily due to chemical decomposition.

Production of limestone detritus by chemical agencies is limited to environments that are at least moderately moist and either temperate or warm.

b) *Mechanical Agencies.* Thermoclastic weathering may be effective as a result of expansion and contraction following rapid temperature changes in abris or cave entrances, or in the interior of inhabited caves as a result of fires. Frost-weathering is far more significant in the front part and entrance of a cave. With even a little percolating moisture, ice forms in joints and fissures, creating pressures due to increased volume. Repeated freeze and thaw will lead to physical disintegration of superficial rock fragments which drop to the floor. Known as *éboulis secs* (French for, literally, "dry talus") such detritus is sharp-edged, angular, uncorroded, and often flattish in shape. When washed, the faces and rims look quite fresh, unlike those of other talus. The characteristic size range is that of grit 2-5 mm. in length (Lais, 1941; Bonifay, 1956), although coarse detritus and large tabular blocks are very common in the resulting formations.

Although deposition may take place either when the waters are frozen or after thawing, the breccia-like sediments so formed are usually—although not necessarily—unconsolidated and porous, lacking a matrix of fines. *Éboulis secs* are almost mutually exclusive with travertines.

It is generally accepted that typical *éboulis secs*, as defined above, are mainly due to frost-weathering. A more specific climatic interpretation is difficult however. Repeated, strong, penetrating frosts will probably be most effective in producing larger quantities of *éboulis secs*, whereas long protracted frost periods, or frequent, ineffective freeze-and-thaw alternations will be less productive. Subtropical and tropical climates with little or no severe frost are definitely excluded, whereas persistently cold high arctic climates would provide little opportunity for thaw. Another variable is introduced by the degree of water saturation of the rock. Even though frost-weathering is effective on cliff faces in western Europe today, *éboulis secs* are comparatively rare in Holocene cave deposits of Central Europe (Lais, 1941) and France (Movius, 1960, reply comments), presumably as a result of the reduced temperature amplitude of cave environments. Although *éboulis secs*, by argument, do not demand extremely cold conditions, they will presumably be most favored by a cold-temperate climate, not too dry, but with appreciable daily and seasonal temperature ranges.

In general, the concentration of *éboulis secs* in Würm-age cave horizons speaks its own story for the case of temperate Europe (Lais, 1941; Movius, 1960, reply comments). But interpretation must proceed with due caution as too little quantitative work has been done on frost-shattering of intact limestones.

LIMESTONE PRECIPITATES: TRAVERTINE

Waters percolating through the joints of limestone bedrock will inevitably acquire some dissolved calcium carbonate through corrosion and solution. This effect is most evident when (*a*) soil and vegetation are present at the surface over the cave, so increasing the acidity and CO_2 content of the water, and (*b*) when abundant water percolates through into the cave. This water may drip from the ceiling or flow over the cave floor. The distance, speed, and amount of water percolation will determine the degree of saturation of the waters leaving the ceiling, and rapidity or likelihood of precipitation of the dissolved lime salts will depend on temperature, humidity, ventilation, and carbon dioxide content of the cave air (Cornwall, 1958, pp. 35-36). It is therefore not surprising that the resulting precipitates show a considerable range of variation. For example, both slow evaporation of saturated waters and rapid evaporation of unsaturated waters may produce dense precipitates, while very rapid evaporation of saturated waters may only produce an unconsolidated calcareous grit.

The general class of deposits is grouped as *travertine*, and occurs as:

a) *Dripstone*, including icicle-like forms hanging from the ceiling (*stalactites*), upward-growing *stalagmites*, and *columns* in such cases where stalactites and stalagmites have merged.

b) *Flowstone*, including a variety of horizontal beds ranging from hard, translucent, banded, or vertically crystallized strata to soft, opaque chalky, gritty, or clayey deposits. Flowstone may assume bizarre shapes or spread in fine, laminated crusts or veneers. Depending on the amount of embedded clay, oxides, sand, and organic deposits, colors may range from clear to white and yellowish-brown or even reddish-yellow.

Horizons of flowstone or fractured dripstone are comparatively frequent in the Pleistocene beds of many mid-latitude caves, and travertines are also known as surface deposits in some subtropical areas. Whenever carbonate precipitation is important in a cave, clastic deposits on the floor may be cemented into resistant *breccias*.

Precise paleoclimatic interpretation of fossil travertine strata is again difficult. Protracted frost will, of course, impede solution processes; severe cold will limit vegetation at the surface and reduce the CO_2 content of the waters; extreme aridity will not provide the requisite water. Consequently travertines pre-eminently suggest a temperate or warm climate and a humid or subhumid moisture regime. In arid and semiarid regions, caves without modern dripstone formation will, by fair judgment, produce such features only with an increase of moisture. In contemporary humid environments, however, the same implication of "wetter climate" becomes highly debatable. Consequently the only reasonable deductions possible from fossil travertine horizons found in caves of temperate mid-latitudes are that climate was fairly moist and not subarctic in character.

RESIDUAL CLAYS AND EXTRANEOUS SEDIMENTS

The commonest deposits of most caves are soft, moist, plastic cave earths, mainly of silt or clay size, but frequently containing coarser inclusions. The calcareous component of such earthy deposits is sometimes rather small. Yet, even in the deep interiors of dark caverns and passages, only a part of this material is a local residual from dissolved limestone. Foreign materials from the surface trickle in through cracks and crevices, even where washing, blowing, or sliding of sediments from the entrance is excluded. Kerekes (1951) calculated the residual materials to be expected by solution of limestones corresponding to the volume of certain central European caves. In each case the non-calcareous sediment present was greater than the calculated residual materials. Obviously much foreign matter had been intermixed.

Residual clays may be more or less uncontaminated when directly embedded in travertine during its formation. Aluminum silicates are most common, although many minerals are present including a certain amount of limonitic iron.

Wind-borne loess or sands are probably the most important extraneous sediments. They are either deposited directly at the entrance or in the fore-part of the cave, or washed in through the entrance or through the overlying rock. When caves lie at river-level in valley gorges, stream deposition may take place. Elsewhere subterranean waterflow may carry foreign sediments far within a cave. And solifluction may induce sliding of extraneous material into a cave from the entrance (see Black, 1959). The interpretive value of such complex extraneous mineral sediments necessarily lies in their association with processes outside.

Materials introduced naturally through the cave entrance generally reflect on the external environment at the time a particular stratum was formed. Thus, loess deposition or a stream terrace may be correlated and used for interpretation. In the case of materials washed through the walls or ceiling, older sediments or paleosols may be derived from the surface above. As a result, such materials are suspect.

ORGANIC DEPOSITS

Biological deposits may assume considerable importance in caves once occupied by cave bears, cave hyenas, and cave lions, or in caves frequented by owls or bat colonies. Birds and bats leave masses of dung, while the feces of the larger mammals may also be very considerable in amount. The bones and other tissues of small mammals, particularly rodents, may be added to the osteological remains of their carnivorous hunters. And repeatedly, the carcasses of dead mammals partially decompose and are added to the accumulating sediment. In addition to this animal matter, plant parts adhering to the animals, or excreted through the intestinal tract, are added to the "fossil layer."

Decomposition of these biological remains produces various compounds, most important of which are the reddish-brown phosphate beds corresponding to many fossil layers in middle latitudes. Schmid (1958) emphasizes that these have, on occasion, been confused with climatically significant mineral sediments. Humic acids may also be derived from decomposition of excreta and carcasses.

Human occupation, even in cultural layers, is not evidenced by a similar intensity of organic accumulation. Instead, a great deal of mineral ash, partly decomposed or charred plant matter, and foreign rock are introduced.

Plant materials are carried in by man and animals and, together with wind-blown pollen grains, are remarkably well preserved, even in the subtropics (e.g., the Cueva del Toll, Catalonia, Donner and Kurtén, 1958). Bone preservation is also good in the calcareous, alkaline sedimentary environment. Snail faunas, where present, are also well preserved in most environments (e.g. the Haua Fteah Cave, Cyrenaica, Hey, 1957).

SPECIAL SEDIMENTARY ANALYSES

A few specialized sedimentological techniques deserve brief mention here in addition to the more standard techniques (particle size, carbonate content, clay minerals, heavy minerals, etc.). Both Lais (1941) and Bonifay (1956) have devised mechanical analyses to help estimate the relative importance of mechanical and chemical weathering. According to Lais, the sample components of coarse sand size are weighed in comparison to the detrital materials 5-10 mm. in size. The work can be simply performed by sieving, the results expressed in diagrammatic form with relative percentages by weight. Bonifay outlined a more complicated although not necessarily better technique for mechanical separation. He further suggested quantification of frost-fractured pebbles and chemically corroded detritus. Specialized techniques were also developed by Brain (1958) for study of the South African australopithecine deposits.

Another technique, so far mainly applied to cave sediments, is trace element analysis (see Sokoloff and Carter, 1952; Martin *et al.*, 1961; Sabels, 1960). The presence or absence of certain minor elements is thought to express humid and warm or cool climates as the case may be. However, the physical reasoning of this method has yet to be clarified. Other objections can also be raised in view of the heterogeneous sources of cave sediments and the limited alteration *in situ.*

A last specialized cave sediment technique is the so-called phosphate method (see Schmid, 1958). Its purpose is to determine the phosphate content of various strata. Schmid cautions that phosphate content varies according to the size and number of the cave inhabitants and the rate of mineral sedimentation, so that phosphate contents do not provide a simple correlation with the frequency or importance of animal or human occupation.

CONCLUSIONS

Cave sediment analysis by the earth scientist, in collaboration with biologists, can provide good paleo-environmental evidence. The existing general body of comparative information on cave sedimentation leaves much to be desired, although certain basic patterns can be identified and tentatively interpreted. Chemical solution as an erosional and a depositional agency is of interest just as much as is mechanical weathering leading to the production of *éboulis secs.* Study of extraneous sediments may help identify external geomorphic processes at the time. Add to this the ecological interpretation of the fauna and flora, and it is evident how a careful cave study can, at times, provide a cornerstone to a regional understanding of the Pleistocene.

Due caution must, however, be maintained in generalizations about cave sedimentation. Apart from a lack of quantitative-empirical evidence on actual processes, complications may arise. That which may hold for one microclimatic environment in one cave or in a part of a cave, need not apply elsewhere. Similarly, cave sedimentation may gradually alter the local microhabitat by reducing the size of the entrance or by leading to collapse of the ceiling, so changing the patterns of cave drainage, etc. Possible results include different ventilation, temperature ranges, and relative humidities. And lastly, it is impossible to assess fully the possible impacts of man. Artificial modifications aimed at greater temperature comfort may have altered the microclimate. Fires possibly affected the rate of thermoclastic weathering of the overhanging parts of the ceiling. And, finally, the organic acids derived from human occupation may have induced leaching of underlying stratigraphic horizons.

14

Coastal Phenomena
and Sea Level Fluctuations

Coastal phenomena give little information on local climate, except in the case of mangrove swamps or coral reefs. Mangroves are largely confined to the humid and subhumid tropics, while coral reefs are restricted to warm seas with water temperatures never dropping below 18° C. Coasts, developed entirely as a result of inorganic processes, show some, although minor features of zonal character. But generally speaking the significance of Pleistocene coastal phenomena lies in somewhat different spheres.

For one, the Pleistocene experienced a series of remarkably rapid fluctuations of world sea level—from a maximum of about 180-250 m. higher than that of today to a minimum of about 150 m. lower. The stratigraphy of these oscillations was already outlined in Table 3, chapter 2. Application of sea-level stages, some of them world-wide, has largely been stratigraphic. Excellent possibilities for correlating continental sequences with glacial or interglacial phases are provided, and cold or warm molluscan faunas in beach deposits may contribute direct paleo-ecological evidence.

The other contribution is more topographical in nature. The location of the coastal zone varied considerably in areas of gentle gradients, and land bridges were periodically opened, so for example, permitting the settlement of the Americas and Australia by late Pleistocene man. Numerous other archeological applications are also of interest here.

This chapter consequently diverges from the pattern of chapters 11-13 in presenting data on Pleistocene sea-level variation and on fossil coastal forms—partly stratigraphic, partly topographic and environmental in application. Unless otherwise stated, reference is to marine coasts (rather than to lakes or non-outlet inland seas).

MECHANISMS OF WORLD SEA LEVEL FLUCTUATIONS

Two major factors are involved in the complex pattern of Pleistocene sea level. The over-all trend has been downward, ever since the later Pliocene when sea levels were apparently found in the range from +180 to +250 m. Quite possibly these values are misleading since slow, epeirogenic uplift on a continental scale and local tectonic displacements have all obscured the record. But the Pliocene generally conformed to a transgressive phase in geological history, leaving marine deposits well inland of the present coasts in most parts of the world. Whatever its true dimensions a general lowering of sea level is admitted for the Pleistocene, and this is attributed to possible changes in the water-holding capacity of the great oceanic basins (Baulig, 1935; Zeuner, 1952, 1959; Valentin, 1952). Such fluctuations of sea level may have been responsible for a good part of the shoreline changes evident in the geological past.

A number of violent, rapid oscillations were superimposed upon the downward trend. These short-term features had a range of at least 150 m., and are attributed to actual changes in the amount of ocean waters resulting from alternating glaciation and deglaciation of the northern hemisphere continents. They are designated as *glacio-eustatic* fluctuations.

The range of possible glacio-eustatic sea levels depends on the calculation of (a) how much water is still retained in the solid state in Greenland, Antarctica, and other smaller glaciated areas, and (b) how much more water was held in the glaciers existing during the various Pleistocene glaciations. For general treatment and a discussion of the problem of isostatic adjustment see Flint (1957, p. 258 ff.).

Ablation of the existing ice caps and mountain glaciers would provide a considerable volume of water to the oceans. Various estimates prior to 1955 (see Valentin, 1952, with references) were first superseded after the results of the French Polar Expeditions to Greenland (1948-49) determined the thickness of the Greenland ice cap. Based on these results and guess estimates for the Antarctic, Bauer (1955) set the possible rise at +54 m. Preliminary reports from the International Geophysical Year expeditions to Antarctica (1958-59) indicated that the thickness of the Antarctic ice cap had been previously underestimated. The rise in sea level has now been estimated at 66 m. (Thiel, 1962).

Allowing complete deglaciation during the earlier Pleistocene warm intervals, glacial-eustasy alone could never explain the high sea levels of the Pliocene or earlier Pleistocene. On the contrary, there is as yet no proof that the Greenland and Antarctic ice sheets were appreciably smaller at any time during the Pleistocene. It is consequently unproven that even the modest higher sea levels of the later Pleistocene were primarily a result of greater ablation of existing ice caps.

Turning to the negative side of the glacio-eustatic ledger, estimates of theoretical sea-level lowering depend on accurate calculation of the volume of the Pleistocene ice sheets.

Although the areal extent of the defunct Würm-Wisconsin glaciers is accurately known, the extent of former glaciation in Greenland, Antarctica, and several smaller highland areas is difficult to assess. Whereas sources of error are presumably small in the case of the Würm, they may be rather more appreciable in the case of older glaciations outside of North America and Europe about which we know next to nothing.

The average thickness of the former continental glaciers is more controversial. Estimates vary strongly, although current calculations of 1,400 m. for the Scandinavian glacier and 2,000 m. for the North American glacier carry some degree of conviction. Donn *et al.* (1962) arrive at slightly higher values by assuming these glaciers had thickness-area ratios comparable to those of existing ice sheets. None of the estimates for thicknesses of pre-Würm glaciers are based on direct geophysical or geomorphical evidence, and can only be rated as reasonable assumptions.

As a result, estimates of glacial sea levels vary considerably. For the Würm-Wisconsin maximum Valentin (1952) gives a value of —95 to —100 m.; Woldstedt (1954, p. 293), —90 to —100 m.; Donn *et al.* (1962), —115 to —134 m. For the maximal, pre-Würm glaciation (Riss complex?) Valentin (1952) and Woldstedt (1954) suggest —115 to —120 m.; Donn *et al.* (1962), —137 to —159 m. There are a great number of submerged shoreline features that can be freely correlated with any one of these values, but they do not prove the reliability of the one or the other. It should be realized that precise estimates are impossible at present, and a general estimate of —100 to —150 m. is quite sufficient for all practical purposes. Greater precision would be misleading, both theoretically and in specific application, since any local area may have since been effected by small or large tectonic movements.

In overview, the positive or negative trends of Pleistocene sea-level fluctuations can be understood by means of both ocean volume and glacio-eustatic changes, but neither of these mechanisms carries a meaningful absolute value. Instead, the stratigraphy of high and low Pleistocene sea levels is a relative one, and even where altitudinal correlations appear to be possible they do not necessarily have a theoretical explanation.

EVIDENCE OF HIGH PLEISTOCENE SHORELINES

General.—The high Pleistocene shorelines forming the basis for glacio-eustatic stratigraphy can best be understood by means of con-temporary coastal geomorphology. Numerous classifications of shore-lines or coastal types have been made. That of Guilcher (1954, p. 41 f.) is possibly the most simple and useful. Guilcher recognizes four groups of littoral forms:

a) Cliffs with rocky platforms;
b) Sandy beaches with coastal dunes;
c) Tidal marshes, stream estuaries, and deltas;
d) Coral reefs.

Each of these phenomena can and has been recognized in the fossil state. With the exception of coral reefs and tidal marshes most of these features may be found both on lake and seashores. But the lakeshore phenomena are, in general, only poorly developed, and the subsequent discussion is focused on sea coasts. For further descriptions see Cotton ·(1949, p. 396 ff.), Valentin (1952), Guilcher (1954), Thornbury (1954, chap. 17), Sparks (1960, chap. 8), and Butzer (1962).

Cliff coasts.—One of the most common coastal types is the cliff coast, marked by a cliff, a basal notch or knick-point at the water-mark, and a sand and pebble-strewn abrasional platform at its foot. The *cliff* may have a gradient anywhere from 30 per cent to an almost vertical face, and its height may vary from 3 m. to 50 m. or more. Wave erosion at the water-mark continually undercuts the cliff and thereby widens the platform. Overhangs may be created at the *notch* and *sea-caves* excavated by mechanical abrasion in rocks with pro-nounced structure or differential resistance, by mechanical and chemical attack of homogeneous limestones. Repeated collapse of undercut cliff sections will periodically destroy the notch or individual sea-caves, but their distinctive association with the high water-mark (in the case of the open ocean) or mean sea level (in the sea or lakes with little or no tidal amplitude) remains clear. In some cases the cliff may plunge directly to well below sea level without an abrasional platform and only a small notch at the high water-mark (Fig. 42a). In areas with rather heavy surf, the water-mark may be located away from the foot of the cliff, somewhere on the platform. Both of these divergent situations may also be a result of sea-level fluctuations or relative movements of the land.

The *wave-cut platform* itself commonly has a gentle gradient, and may attain a width of several hundred meters or more. The materials eroded at the cliff base are sooner or later swept out by the undertow and deposited as a *wave-built terrace* at the seaward edge of the abrasional platform (Fig. 42b).

A shoreline dominated by cliffs and abrasional platforms is commonly interrupted by prominent headlands and by coastal indentations with sandy beaches. The headlands may have plunging cliffs, they may also be fronted by small islets or *stacks*—resistant erosional remnants of the retreating cliff face.

Abandoned sea cliffs and marine terraces are among the best known vestiges of higher shorelines. Notches and sea-caves may still be recognizable and may allow precise determination of the former high water-mark (see Zeuner, 1961). Approximate mean sea level can then be obtained by deducting half the local tidal amplitude from this value. Where notches are unavailable, lines of holes produced by rock-boring organisms may be substituted. Marine beds are seldom preserved *on* abrasional platforms, except where rough seas are rare. They may however, be preserved on the wave-built platform. In the case of cliff coasts caution should therefore be applied when using marine beds to determine former sea levels.

Nip and shingle-beach coasts.—Not all contemporary or fossil coastal forms can be grouped as either cliff or sandy beach types. Many coastal sectors, for example, exhibit an incipient cliff or *nip*, with a face in the order of 0.5-2 m. in height. This nip is incised into a moderately sloping marine platform with a veneer of beach sands and gravels (Fig. 42c). Many of the fossiliferous marine sediments of the Mediterranean Sea pertain to former nip coasts. If the nip can be identified, sea-level determination can be made with a fair degree of accuracy.

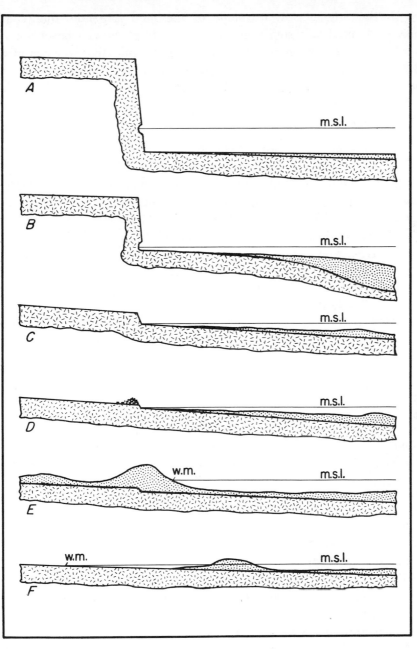

FIGURE 42.

Coastal profile types. (A) plunging cliff coast, (B) cliff coast with notch, wave-cut and depositional platforms, (C) nip coast, (D) shingle-beach coast, (E) sand-ridge coast, (F) bar-and-lagoon coast. wm = watermark.

If the original seaward slope of the land is gentle, the "cliff" may be limited to a step some decimeters high. Marine beach sands mask the platform on which coarse blocks and other wave-eroded detritus or gravel are thrown up and accumulated as a *shingle* beach or ridge in the rear of the nip by high seas (Fig. 42*d*). Shingle ridges may also develop as exceptional *storm beaches* above nip or low cliff coasts.

Sandy beaches.—Sandy beaches develop in gently sloping, shallow-water bays interrupting cliff coasts, or elsewhere they may be found fringing low-lying coastal plains. In some instances such low, sandy, shallow-water coasts develop broad sandy beaches fringed by semi-aeolian sand ridges or coastal dunes to the landward (Fig. 42*e*).

When gradients are extremely gentle, a coastal type develops with wave-action barely affecting the immediate shoreline. Instead, waves break, erode, and deposit offshore, so forming submarine or offshore sand bars (Fig. 42*f*). These are separated from dry land by a shallow-water zone, a lagoon, or a tidal marsh, possibly characterized by mixed marine and continental deposition. If the bar becomes large enough, the coast may develop a semi-aeolian beach ridge or a dune cordon. Such sandy beach features are often difficult to distinguish in the fossil state.

Former sea level in the case of the bar-and-lagoon coast lies somewhere between the level of the lagoon floor and the mean elevation of the offshore bar. It can only be precisely determined by examination of the lagoonal sediments: the altitude of the transition between aquatic-lagoonal and terrestrial facies in the center of the former lagoon closely approximates former mean sea level (Zeuner, 1961). Exact sea-level determinations are difficult for other sandy shoreline features.

Marine-littoral sediments.—Sands and gravels are among the most common sediments of the marine-littoral environment. Coarse sands, sometimes with a scattering of pebbles, are commonly found on the submerged platforms of sandy beaches or nip coasts. Moderately stratified, they commonly occur as topset beds inclined at 5 to 10 per cent or more seaward. Molluscan shells may be present, and if so, they seldom show the broken edges and badly scoured surfaces usually found with derived shell in coastal dunes or semi-aeolian beach deposits. The pebbles of the sandy beach are well-rounded, rather flat, and homogeneous. Various aspects of beach sand sedimentology are outlined by Shepard and Young (1961).

Pebbly beach deposits, with little or no sandy matrix, are probably characteristic for the abrasional platforms of cliff coasts. Rounding indices are very high and homogeneous except where detritus is in plentiful supply at the shoreline. Flattish pebbles are usual except in potholes carved into the platform. Pothole churning produces more spheroidal shapes. Pebble size varies from beach to beach according to the bedrock and the roughness of the sea during stormy weather. Beds are stratified, sometimes with comparatively steep inclinations.

The possible environmental information provided by fossil faunas contained in such sediments will be discussed in chapter 17.

Coastal dunes.—Coastal dunes are common along many modern sandy beaches. A classification proposed by H. T. U. Smith (1954) includes the four major continental dune types (parabolic, barchan, transverse, and longitudinal) and the nondescript beach foredunes that lie adjacent and parallel to the shore forming mounds up to 3 m. high. Shepard and Young (1961) have discussed various sedimentological criteria for distinguishing between beach and littoral dune sands.

Estuarine and deltaic features.—Deposition at the mouths of rivers may be rather significant. It may take the form of foreset-bedded deltas built out into a lake or into the sea, particularly in areas with little or no tidal variation. In areas of marked tidal amplitude, broad tidal marshes may develop along the river banks near the mouth with mixed fluvial-marine or estuarine deposition.

In Pleistocene contexts, the surface of uneroded estuarine beds gives a fair estimate of the high water-mark (Zeuner, 1961). In the case of delta formations, sea-level approximation may be possible when the uppermost sediments are formed by very gently inclined topset beds.

Coral reefs.—Coral reefs are limited to tropical salt waters, with a salinity of 2.7-4.0 per cent, with temperatures never dropping below 18° C. or exceeding 36° C. Light requirements restrict major coral growth to the upper 25 m. of the water, and growth is usually impossible at depths greater than 60 m. Nourishment for the reef-growing organisms is obtained from the open sea, so that the reef grows seaward, extending up to about mean sea level. Coral is absent near the mouths of muddy streams or larger rivers in general, partly due to the presence of fresh water, partly due to reduced light.

The shorelines built by coral reefs may take the form of: (*a*) *fringing* reefs, attached directly to the shore as platforms; (*b*) *barrier* reefs, separated from the shore by a flat-floored lagoon of variable width; or (c) *atolls,* "islands" consisting of more or less circular reefs enclosing a lagoon, but without a land surface inside.

Some of the more important general features of modern coral coasts include (Fig. 43):

1) The steep external slope, formed of both coral and talus, often dropping off for many decameters with gradients as much as 100 per cent;

2) The reef crest adjacent to the external slope, partly constructed of coral-building algae, partly of detrital coralline sand, and usually attaining about mean sea level, although sand ridges may be higher;

3) The reef surface itself, composed of both dead and living coral, often several hundred meters wide, extending no higher than mean low-water; and

4) The lagoon, if present, with a sandy floor, interrupted by sporadic coral growths reaching up to the mean low-water mark.

Since fossil coral reefs are rather widespread and conspicuous in lower latitudes, they provide valuable information both on shoreline levels as well as on the local marine environment.

EVIDENCE OF SUBMERGED PLEISTOCENE SHORELINES

Submerged shorelines.—The coastal types discussed above can be used to recognize most high Pleistocene shorelines, generally of interglacial date. They may also record higher sea levels of the Holocene.

Field evidence for "submerged" shorelines, pertaining to glacial-age regressions of world sea level, is a little different. Well-developed

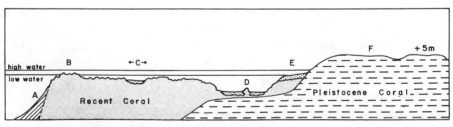

FIGURE 43.
A fringing coral reef. (A) Talus slope, (B) reef crest, (C) reef surface, (D) lagoon, (E) sandy beach, (F) high Pleistocene interglacial reef. Not to scale.

cliff coasts and other extensive beach platforms can be recognized as extended platforms with marginal steps or ridges in the submarine topography. Submerged offshore bar-and-lagoon or coral reef topography may also be identifiable from good hydrographic maps. Submerged fluvial phenomena such as stream deposits, estuarine beds, and deltas may also be traced onto shallow marine shelves or may be tapped in bore profiles below modern coastal plains.

Generally speaking however, little detailed evidence is available on submerged shorelines to date. Even where such shorelines have been indisputably recognized, correlations with particular regressions are difficult or impossible. Stratigraphically more important is the indirect evidence of regressions provided by wind-borne sediments of the coastal zone.

Aeolianites.—Coastal dunes functionally attached to sandy beaches play only a subordinate role in the Pleistocene. Far more important are the subtype of consolidated *regressional* dunes, generally called *aeolianite*. These are widespread in lower and lower-middle latitude littoral zones, and were blown up from freshly exposed marine sediments during the regressions of world sea level accompanying the advance of continental glaciers. They consequently provide valuable stratigraphic information when present in relation to fossil shorelines or continental deposits.

Two major arguments support the fact that well-developed aeolianites specifically pertain to marine regressions rather than to sandy shorelines in equilibrium. For one part, they are most often submerged well below modern sea level, on the other hand they frequently occur along coasts that have no exposed beach sands today. Detailed discussion of some Mediterranean aeolianites is given by Butzer (1962, 1963b).

Aeolianites developed in typical aeolian facies may be found either as (*a*) steeply inclined, uniformly bedded dunes of transverse type embanked against coastal cliffs with typical seaward dip values of 40-60 per cent, and landward dip values of 60-80 per cent, or (*b*) free longitudinal dunes of subdued morphology on coastal plains, where they may form littoral cordons—the relief of one dunal generation may be in the order of 5-25 m. while slopes are gentle, and seldom exceed 25 per cent,—or (*c*) undulating sand sheets with subdued topography of longitudinal affinities, concentrated in the face and lee of minor surface irregularities. These sheets are found beyond the rims of coastal cliffs and well inland on coastal plains or level uplands.

The constituents of aeolianite are mainly limesands, overwhelmingly derived from the rubble of calcareous marine organisms. In areas of bedrock other than limestone the importance of quartz and other minerals may jump from less than 1 per cent to as much as 90 per cent.

Grain size distributions of the typical coastal facies of aeolianite include a 70 per cent coarse sand (0.2-2.0 mm.) component, while in aeolianites of interior facies this proportion may be reduced to an average of 40 per cent. Clay and fine silt (up to 0.006 mm.) components almost always account for 5-15 per cent. Grain size characteristics of continental dunes are quite distinct: coarse sand components are small, while medium sands (0.06-0.2 mm.) average 20-90 per cent (over double that of aeolianites), and there is an almost complete absense of any component under 0.003 mm. Littoral and continental dunes are then both morphologically and sedimentologically distinct.

Such aeolianites are largely indicative of a marine regression actually in progress, for once regression ceases or a renewed rise in sea level occurs, no new sands are exposed to deflation and consequently sedimentary stops (Wright, 1962a). Interruptions of aeolianite deposition may indicate world-wide halts or oscillations of the continental glaciers. Aeolianite deposition will more or less cease when the maximum of a glacial regression has been attained. True aeolianites are therefore stratigraphically equivalent to the phases of glacial advances much in the same way as periglacial terraces.

Paleo-ecological information may also be available. Poor or absent stratification is usually associated with frequent calcified roots or rootcasts of shrubs or conifers. Such aeolianites were probably deposited under vegetation, there intermingling with the needle litter derived from coniferous woodlands. Unbedded littoral dunes form in this fashion on the Balearic Islands today. On the other hand well-bedded coastal plain or interior aeolianites without root-casts are suggestive of sparse vegetation and prevailing aridity. Further paleoclimatic information may be derived from bedding directions, as in the case of continental dunes.

Other evidence of glacial regressions.—During the glacial regressions, continental processes were responsible for erosion or deposition in areas subsequently submerged. Valleys cut by streams or glaciers may now be drowned, forming inlets known as rias or fiords. Stream or glacier deposits may also be submerged, possibly forming islands of peculiar shape. Such drowned deposits may be of considerable stratigraphic importance.

GLACIO-EUSTATIC STRATIGRAPHY

Even the best glacio-eustatic stratigraphy, that of the Mediterranean Basin and western Morocco (Table 3), is not without controversy or problems. Promising sequences also exist along the
Gulf-Atlantic coastal plain of the U.S.A., in southern Australia, and on
the North Sea coasts of Europe. Useful summaries and tentative
correlations of these particular areas have been given by Woldstedt
(1958, 1960a, 1960b, 1962a) and Richards (1962), while Fairbridge
(1961) and McFarlan (1963) have prepared compilations of radiocarbon data for sea-level fluctuations during the last 15,000 years or so
(Fig. 44). Seen objectively however, the possibilities of world-wide
correlation have not been fully explored.

Numerous difficulties exist, even though Pleistocene sea-level
fluctuations were a world-wide phenomenon. Local tectonic activity
has hopelessly complicated the basic picture of eustatic sea levels in
some coastal sectors. In those regions overrun by the continental
glaciations, compression of the earth's crust under the weight of ice
has been matched by isostatic uplift since deglaciation. And elsewhere,
slow continental-scale epeirogenic uplift or downwarping has spread
the altimetric range of eustatic sea levels over a wider amplitude
than was originally the case. Particularly the Sicilian and Calabrian
stages are difficult to employ on the basis of elevation. World-wide
correlation of the Eemian high sea levels may however be feasible
in tectonically stable areas.

The stratigraphic value of glacial-eustatic sea-level fluctuations
plainly does not yet lie in world-wide altitudinal correlation of high
Pleistocene shorelines. The only fact of general applicability is that

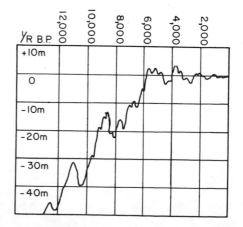

FIGURE 44.
Curve of Holocene sea-level
changes (simplified after Fairbridge, 1961).

the Elster, Riss, and Würm glaciations corresponded to major regressions, while the intervening interglacials experienced sea levels at least as high as the present. Excellent local sequences can theoretically be constructed upon these premises. But prior to the Eem there is little possibility so far of specific correlation with higher-latitude continental stratigraphy. And prior to the Cromerian there is little certainty as to whether the glacials corresponded to regressions or the interglacials to transgressions.

Nonetheless, Pleistocene shorelines are significant from a number of perspectives. Firstly, the world-wide rhythm of glacial regressions and interglacial transgressions—at least during the second half of the Pleistocene—provides an invaluable stratigraphic guide to fixing local relative continental stratigraphies. Then again, local sequences of higher sea levels and intervening regressions can be established as regional stratigraphic horizons. Some coastal deposits like coral, aeolianite, or molluscan faunas may provide direct paleoclimatic information. And lastly, the topographic significance of Pleistocene sea levels for the distribution of human settlement and the paths of human dispersal need hardly be stressed.

15

Geomorphological
Study
of Archeological Sites

GEOLOGIC CLASSES OF ARCHEOLOGICAL SITES

Introduction.—Archeological sites, depending on the cultural time range involved, may represent former houses, villages, or towns, they may pertain to temporary or seasonal camps, or to kill or butchering sites. Other sites may have little or no ecological meaning, but consist only of scattered artifactual material, possibly redeposited within a river terrace. Sites dating from historical or late prehistoric times are commonly found at the surface, possibly buried under cultural debris or a little blown dust, and altered by a weak modern soil profile. Many sites of all time ranges are found exposed at the surface. A great number of prehistoric sites, however, are found in direct geologic context, within or underneath sediments deposited by some geomorphic agency.

For the archeologist a "stratified" site is one with distinct archeological horizons, with or without a geologic context. The term "surface" site might be used to describe a variety of things, such as an archeologically unstratified surface-find or even an ancient open-air encampment—as opposed to cave site—now buried by a meter or two of loess or marl. From the archeologist's point of view then, sites may be classified according to their cultural-ecological meaning, or by digging criteria. The earth scientist, interested in providing a stratigraphic date or a geographical-ecological meaning for a site, would naturally use different criteria of classification.

"Stratified" and "surface" sites.—The most interesting kind of archeological site for the earth scientist is one found in a direct geologic context, i.e., geologically stratified or geologically *in situ*. This

221

should not imply that the cultural materials have not been derived, only that their present location is geologically circumscribed. For the sake of convenience "stratified" will here be used in this geologic sense only. "Surface" site will be restricted to materials found at the surface, without geologic context.

According to the basic geomorphological situation or the type of deposits involved, archeological sites can be geologically classified as follows:

a) Alluvial sites: artifacts, fossils, occupational floors and the like found within former stream deposits.

b) Lacustrine sites: archeological materials found in former lake beds, in ancient bogs, swamps, or spring deposits.

c) Aeolian sites: archeological materials found in or under wind-borne sand or loess, or found in relation to features resulting from deflation or wind scour.

d) Slope sites: archeological materials found within or under deposits due to mass movements motivated by gravity action, including congeliturbate beds, slope wash, or talus.

e) Cave sites: archeological materials found in caves with some form of geologic or archeological stratigraphy.

f) Coastal sites: archeological materials found in direct relation to erosional or depositional phenomena associated with former coastlines.

g) Surface sites: the great mass of scattered archeological materials and sites found at the surface, with little possibility of direct association with any geomorphic event.[1]

Identification of the depositional medium contemporary with or subsequent to an archeological site is vital to the earth scientist. The specific relation of a cultural horizon to a geomorphic event can provide direct paleo-environmental information. This local environmental setting may in turn be stratigraphically linked to regional or world-wide changes of climate. Both environmental reconstruction and dating of sites or occupation levels may then be possible through geomorphological investigation.

---

[1] In many cases sites can definitely be associated with two different geologic categories, e.g., cave sites found along former shorelines. A further category could also be set up for volcanic sites buried by lava or ash falls. Since vulcanism is not an external geomorphic agent and lacks zonal or geographical meaning, no class of volcanic sites is employed. Aeolian features such as volcanic ash falls can be conveniently classified as such.

Pleistocene and Holocene sites.—The oft-heard statement that only pre-Holocene sites have geologic context is not completely true. Numerous late prehistoric sites have been found in swamp or cave deposits or have been buried by aeolian sediments. On the other hand there are countless pre-Holocene surface sites, some of them still recognizable as occupation sites. Although there are more sites with meaningful geologic contexts in the Pleistocene (*sensu strictu*) than there are in the Holocene, many late prehistoric and even historical sites are buried by sediments of greater interest than most archeologists would suppose.

A distinction of greater validity between Pleistocene and Holocene sites concerns an understanding of the original topography. A completely different perspective is required in studying a Pleistocene site. The great changes of climate and environment introduced rather different local settings in many areas: shifts of stream channels, valleys swept by glacial meltwaters, swamps or lakes that no longer exist, loess plains where forests prevail today, shorelines well inland. Many geologically stratified sites were once part of valley floors that remain as dissected terraces high above the present stream. The environment and topography of post-Pleistocene sites has changed in degree only. One has little difficulty in envisaging the site in its setting, a factor of more than psychological advantage.

ALLUVIAL SITES

Alluvial sites rank second only to cave sites in the early history of archeological excavations. Excavations or borings in river valleys have frequently struck alluvial sands or gravels of various ages containing animal remains or human artifacts. Natural exposures in terrace faces have also revealed archeological materials. Many such sites have little more to offer than sporadic, water-rolled stone implements and possibly a little bone of dubious association. Other sites, however, may represent occupation floors with rich associations of undisturbed tools and fossils. Interpretation of such sites can, with due effort, be carried to a satisfactory stage of environmental and stratigraphic understanding.

The periglacial stream terraces of the Old World were probably first studied by Paleolithic archeologists, and the well-known Somme River succession of northern France was established as a sequence of intergraded solifluction beds, loesses, and periglacial stream deposits (Breuil and Koslowski, 1931-32). Once assumed to be the framework of Paleolithic cultural stratigraphy, many of the sites in question are of limited importance since they were mainly collections of derived artifacts rather than occupation floors. Of far greater significance today are well-studied sites such as that of Salzgitter-Lebenstedt, near Braunschweig, Germany, situated along the banks of a late Pleistocene tundra stream at the base of a slope affected by solifluction (Tode *et al.*, 1953). The Middle Pleistocene site of Markkleeberg, near Leipzig, was similarly located in periglacial gravels of a northward flowing stream subsequently overrun by the Saale moraines (Grahmann, 1955).

The pluvial terraces of the arid zone have played a significant role archeologically in both the Old and New World, even in rather late prehistoric times. The twin sites of Torralba and Ambrona, in the Spanish province of Soria, were situated on the marshy floodplain margins of a stream valley during a moist, cold phase of the Lower Pleistocene (Howell *et al.*, 1963; Lynch *et al.*, 1964). In a drier environment, the terminal Paleolithic cultures ("Sebilian") of Kom Ombo, Egypt, were concentrated along the river banks of several defunct Nile branches (Butzer and Hansen, 1965).

Swanscombe is an example of a significant site associated with downstream valley alluviation during a high, Middle Pleistocene sea level (see Howell, 1960). The site was occupied on a Thames floodplain almost 30 m. above that of the present. Although not wholly undisturbed by stream redeposition, the contemporaneousness of the human and animal fossils was established by fluorine tests.

Geomorphological investigation of alluvial sites should concentrate on two aspects of detailed work, apart from the more general question of external correlations and regional setting:

a) Have the materials been derived? Cornwall (1958, pp. 23-24) raises the problem that archeological objects may be carried into a stream bed by floodwaters or abandoned on the floodplain by man. In either case implements could be part of deposits reworked several times through shifting stream channels. Consequently, Cornwall suggests that a "rolled" artifact need not be derived from deposits older than one which is unabraded. The difference in condition could be entirely due to the distance traveled before once more coming to rest. Since animal bones are far less resistant, Cornwall believes that they will rarely survive redeposition, so that the relation of fossils to artifacts in alluvial beds raises a serious problem. If the artifacts are quite unworn, bone and tools may be strictly contemporary. If the tools are water worn, however, it is reasonably certain that a considerable time distance separates them (Cornwall, 1958, p. 24).

Some alluvial sites clearly represent occupation floors that are *in situ* in every way, with no question that the entire cultural assemblage is contemporary. Even here the excavator or the geomorphologist can contribute information by making orientation studies of tools, bones, and the like, to see whether some reorientation has taken place through stream action. Careful attention should also be given to possible water wear on artifacts or fossils. The natural mineral sediments in the cultural layer may also provide information whether running water affected the site during occupation or only afterwards.

When a site does not constitute a clearly defined cultural floor, derivation problems may be more serious. Stream rolling of fossils produces noticeably worn joints. Rolling of stone implements can be recognized in different degrees. Sharp, fresh edges suggest little or no water wear. Sharp edges that are smooth or blunt to the touch should be checked with a hand lens. The edges may show minute rounding while scratches may be evident on the faces. Such an artifact is probably *water worn*. If the edges are conspicuously bluntened, sometimes beyond recognition, the implement is clearly *rolled*. In the case of dubious assemblages, a representative sample should be analyzed by an improvised classification of wear characteristics. If the assemblage is not largely homogeneous, caution should be exerted. Gravel analyses applied to all apparently unworked stone may show that a part of the rock present was deliberately fractured or is foreign to the bed load of the stream. Implement orientation and finally, sedimentological study of the mineral beds should permit an opinion as to the significance of the site.

b) What part of the stream valley was occupied? Equally as important as derivation and redeposition is the topographic location of a site within the former floodplain. Sedimentological studies should establish whether the occupation floor was located on the backset beds of the river bank, in the intercalated backset and topset beds of the levee, or out on the alluvial flats. Particle sizes and sorting should reveal whether stream flow was strongly seasonal or uniform, whether the waters were fast or slow-moving, what their direction was, and finally, what conditions of waterflow ultimately overcame and buried the site?

All in all, in the ideal case, stream terrace sequences—with archeological assemblages in geologic context or in place on the surface, with surface paleosols or derived soil sediments at the base of terrace alluvium—can be of exceptional interest for both the prehistorian and earth scientist.

LACUSTRINE SITES

Prehistoric settlement was common around the banks of lakes. So for example, the early Holocene site of Star Carr, Yorkshire, was situated next to a now extinct lake, and subsequently buried by bog deposits (J. G. D. Clark, 1954). In the Fayum depression of northern Egypt, high Nile floods were responsible for the creation and maintenance of several late Pleistocene and Holocene lakes (Caton-Thompson and Gardner, 1929, 1934). Various Paleolithic and Neolithic populations occupied the fringe vegetation of these lakes, leaving cultural and animal remains along the former shorelines or within the sands of the beaches. At the Lower Pleistocene site of Ternifine, western Algeria, a rich fauna with skeletal remains of the hominine *Atlanthropus (Homo) mauritanicus* is exposed in clays and spring deposits of a former lacustrine basin (Arambourg, 1955). And last but not least are the *Zinjanthropus* and "pre-Zinj" sites found in mixed lacustrine and volcanic ash beds of Bed I, at Olduvai Gorge, Tanganyika, dating from the Basal Pleistocene (Hay, 1963). These examples are all related to pluvial climate.

In higher-latitude Europe, lacustrine beds were mainly found in poorly-drained groundmoraine areas abandoned by the continental glacier. So for example, the Lower Palaeolithic occupation level at Hoxne, near Ipswich, is located in clayey silts of Holstein interglacial age. The beds record a former lake within a depression in Elster till (West and McBurney, 1954). The interesting Middle Paleolithic spear of Lehringen, near Hannover, was found with an intact elephant skeleton in lacustrine marls of Eem interglacial age, overlying the Saale groundmoraine (Adam, 1951).

Swamp and bog deposits, some of them postdating sites, have long enjoyed considerable archeological interest in northern Europe. They have produced potsherds, plowshares, house or village foundations, and even fully intact corpses.

The general environmental setting of lacustrine beds may be a task for both the earth scientist and the biologist. Why, for example, was a lake or swamp there in the first place? The more detailed geomorphological site investigation revolves around its association with the lake or swamp in question: how was the site located in relation to this lake, did the lake exist at the time, was it shallow or deep, seasonal or perennial, was the site flooded soon after occupation? Sedimentological investigation may contribute in many ways to a full understanding of both the local and regional setting.

AEOLIAN SITES

Specific archeological associations with aeolian features are mainly of three kinds:

a) Occupation floors or scattered artifacts found under or on top of sand dunes;

b) Archeological materials found under, within, between, or on the surface of loess;

c) Archeological materials exposed by wind deflation or scour.

One of the best examples of an archeological site related to a complex sequence of stream and wind erosion and deposition is the Holocene San Jon site of eastern New Mexico (Judson, 1953a). Most of the terminal Pleistocene Sebilian cultures of the Kom Ombo plain, Egypt, were deflated and are now partly found on yardangs scoured out of old Nile deposits (Butzer and Hansen, 1965).

In the late Pleistocene innumerable loess sites from central and eastern Europe are examples of occupation during or after loess sedimentation. Possibly among the most famous are the Moravian Upper Paleolithic stations of Předmost (see Prošek and Ložek, 1957, with references) and Unter-Wisternitz (Dolni Vestoniče) (Klima, 1954; Brandtner, 1956).

Geomorphological investigation of aeolian sites is primarily concerned with whether aeolian activity was contemporary with occupation, and whether it preceded or followed occupation. Evidences of soil development in the stratigraphic profile are important, and other indications of sedimentary breaks may be obtained from vertical curves of particle sizes, carbonate, or humus content. With due caution pollen studies may be possible in the humic horizons of an aeolian profile. In general, the exact stratigraphic correlation of sediments and archeological levels can almost always be determined, and careful examination may possibly reveal both the contemporary environmental setting of the site as well as the changing environmental patterns of the period.

SLOPE SITES

A large number of late Pleistocene sites in Europe and Holocene sites in the modern arctic have been seriously affected by slope solifluction or cryoturbation of artifacts and fossils, leading to disruptions of archeological stratigraphy. Other gravity movements in non-arctic regions may also be significant for sites. The various "slope sites" *sensu lato* require more detailed attention.

a) Sites subsequently buried by solifluction can be studied by means of pebble orientation and morphometric gravel analyses. So for example, at Salzgitter-Lebenstedt (Tode *et al.*, 1953) orientation studies in a complex stratigraphic sequence at the base of a slope determined the varying amounts of lateral downslope movement caused by solifluction as well as the fluvial sedimentation related to stream bedding. Gravel analyses can be applied to determine comparative indices of flattening between the weathered coarse source material still *in situ* and similar materials which have suffered short solifluid transport. Transported detritus is slightly flattened because of dominantly sliding motions. Repeated frost-splitting during transport also increases the angularity of the sample. By combining both techniques at Salzgitter-Lebenstedt, it was possible not only to define the physical conditions contemporary with the cultural horizon, but also to determine the position of the site in the climatic stratigraphy of the Würm.

Another application of solifluction phenomena to archeology are the "stone lines" found running perpendicular to moderate slopes in many former tundra regions. Most of these are nothing but fossil stone stripes, a patterned ground phenomenon.

b) Sites disturbed by solifluction or involutions during or after deposition may show complex vertical and horizontal movements of artifactual materials—bedded in sediments of differing density and grain size, with different rates of frost-penetration and frost-heaving. Organic and mineral matter in particular tend to behave differently. As a result, horizons of fossils and artifacts may be mixed or even inverted. A surface site may also be distributed through many decimeters of soil, so giving the impression of a long-term site with geologic context, or even of complex archeological stratigraphy. The difficulties involved in interpreting the late prehistoric Eskimo site at Engigstciak, Yukon Territory, Canada (Mackay *et al.*, 1961) illustrate this well. Any indication of contortion or other non-horizontal disturbances should be carefully studied for possible effects of cryoturbation.

c) Slope and gravity phenomena of middle and lower latitudes may effect archeological sites in different ways. They carry little or no environmental significance but are nonetheless important. Some of the more common categories can be enumerated:

1) Talus accumulation and rock falls have buried or destroyed many a site located near steep cliffs or under former rock overhangs. There are few stratigraphic or environmental problems here.

2) Creep and slope wash often lead to accumulations on or at the foot of even moderate slopes (over 8 per cent). In this way scattered artifacts may be found in geologic contexts with no reason other than subsequent mass movement. Many *Schwemmlöss* beds contain former surface tools embedded during redeposition by slope wash.

3) Pseudo-stratigraphic situations can be produced by earth slips or earth flows, the notorious south German site of Lengfeld, near Regensburg, being a case in point. Three so-called cultural levels of final Paleolithic aspect proved to be nothing but a random collection of Paleolithic, Mesolithic, and Neolithic surface materials stratified by three successive earth slips in late prehistoric times (see Zotz, 1956). Geomorphic investigation of such a site would have saved the original excavator both money and disrepute.

4) Related to problems of surface materials buried by slope redeposition is the widespread occurrence of Middle Paleolithic implements several decimeters within the soils of tropical Africa. This is attributed to activity of micro-organisms, particularly ants and termites, which inadvertently displace such artifacts from the surface to the base of the biologically active subsoil (J. D. Clark, 1960). Similar phenomena have been observed in England, although Cornwall (1958, p. 53) emphasizes that relative stratigraphic order is always preserved. Burrowing animals may also disturb archeological context (Marx and Reed, 1957).

5) Another problem of some relationship to gravity movements and redeposition is the possibility that implements may "sink" into well-lubricated, unconsolidated beds. This form of movement is not confined to swamp or lake beds but can apparently occur in river floodplains as well. So for example, Predynastic potsherds occur at the base of the somewhat older Nile Valley mud. Sandford (1934, pp. 107-8) believes they migrated downward through gravity action.

6) Finally, volcanic lavas or ash, although not necessarily

gravity pheonomena, may be mentioned at this point. They have stratigraphic value at best and need no further discussion.

CAVE SITES

Cave sites and associated sediments have been considered in detail in chapter 13. The only point of further interest requiring comment is the type of use made of caves by early man. In all but the rarest cases, occupation was limited to the fore-parts or entrance area of a cave. Deep interior caverns were widely used for ritualistic or artistic purposes in some areas, but such damp, lightless vaults would hardly have proved attractive for dwelling purposes. If certain modern ethnological analogies have bearing on Paleolithic cave-dwellers, it may be mentioned that the Australian aborigines of the northern Lake Eyre area, the Shoshones of the Great Basin and the Kalahari Bushmen are all known to have occupied caves or overhangs on occasion. In each case leaves, branches, grass, moss, bark, etc. were used to line the walls. Together with the use of fire this emphasizes that cave microhabitats were actually modified by man during occupation, possibly sufficiently so as to affect the geomorphic environment. This question needs further checking in the field.

Cave sites have assumed importance at many times and in many areas, ranging from the australopithecine caves of South Africa to the crevice breccias of Peking, from the Upper Paleolithic caves of southern France and adjacent Spain to the terminal Pleistocene cave cultures of the southwestern U.S.A. It would be superfluous to give specific examples here.

COASTAL SITES

Fluctuating Pleistocene sea levels are obviously of more than passing interest for archeology. For one, they were a physical reality for prehistoric man to cope with, although not in any dramatic way such as "watching the waters rise" (e.g., Pfannenstiel, 1944). Shorelines have always set limits to the habitable earth, especially during the Pleistocene when large coastal areas were alternately submerged or emerged. Glacial regressions provided land links between islands and continents, a factor of fundamental importance for Paleolithic migrations. The natural distribution of insular floras and faunas was also partly the result of glacial regressions which allowed temporary passage over exposed continental shelves. Finally, shoreline stages may permit stratigraphic dating of coastal sites.

Man has often been attracted to the coast as an economic milieu, so that there are specific coastal sites related to modern or Pleistocene shorelines. In other cases man has also occupied caves abandoned by the sea during glacial regressions.

Coastal sites may consist of (*a*) occupation sites located in former sea-caves, (*b*) occupation sites located on former beaches and often incorporated into marine or aeolian sediments, and (*c*) transient occupations of a littoral zone, recorded by scattered artifactual materials in geological context or found at the surface of coastal erosional features. In other cases, marine transgressions destroyed former continental sites and reworked their artifactual materials, embedding these in beach deposits.

Foremost among coastal sites are former sea-caves, usually occupied during regression from a particular shoreline, and occasionally submerged anew during a subsequent transgression. To mention only one example, the renowned cultural sequence of Sidi Abderrahman near Casablanca (Biberson, 1961a, 1961b) is largely preserved within infillings of what were a number of ancient sea-caves. Methods of study are in part similar to those of cave sites in general, in part they involve gravel or paleontological studies of marine beds as well as mechanical analyses of aeolianite strata.

A number of important surface occupation sites may be found adjacent to former shorelines. These belong to *strandloper*-type cultures devoted to sea-food consumption. It is possible, although difficult to prove, that comparatively rich archeological assemblages found but little rolled within marine sediments of the beach platform may belong to an immediate shoreline settlement of analogous type. Stratigraphic dating possibilities are again excellent at such localities, although environmental aspects are more difficult to reconstruct. Organic materials, apart from shell and bone, are most likely to be absent.

Scattered artifacts found in coastal deposits should be regarded with caution. They may be derived from destruction of interior sites by marine transgression, so that the marine sediments in question only provide a chronologically younger limit or *terminus ante quem*. In the case of scattered surface implements, as opposed to concentrated, occupational sites on the surface, the shoreline itself more often than not only serves as a *terminus post quem*.

SURFACE SITES

Last but not least either in significance or interest, are the great mass of surface finds—scattered implements or true occupation sites— not found within or under geologic deposits. Geologists engaged in archeologic-geomorphic work generally shrug their shoulders at surface sites, with the implicit observation that there is nothing for them to do here. Admittedly, in terms of chronology, a time span of anywhere from the present to the Würm or the Paleozoic may be all that is indicated.

However, even such *termini post quem* can often be of importance. A site located on last glacial till is probably of Holocene age. An example that such information is not useless is provided by seven Acheulian-type bifaces found at the surface near Tocra, Cyrenaica, in 1943. Investigation at the site indicated that these implements of pre-Würm appearance were found on top of Würm-age pluvial gravels (McBurney and Hey, 1955, pp. 172-74), suggesting possible human interference.

Chronology is, however, far from being the only point of interest. The geographic setting of surface sites can, in part, be successfully studied by geomorphic methods. Siting with relation to regional landforms can be particularly significant for archeological surveys. When the typical geomorphic situation of certain occupation sites is understood, regional landforms can be evaluated as to their possible role in the pattern of prehistoric settlement. A case in point is the Neolithic-Predynastic archeological "gap" between Upper and Lower Egypt, which is in fact accidental rather than cultural: any sites within this area have either been buried by Nile alluvium or drifting sands, or destroyed by expansion of the cultivated land (W. Kaiser, 1961; Butzer, 1960b, 1961b).

The geographic setting and environmental evaluation of a site should also be attempted by study of outside evidence from contemporary neighboring sites, or by biological investigation of organic remains obtained from the site itself.

Obviously there are no fixed rules for geomorphological work applied to surface sites. It is here that the personal intuition, improvisation, and interest of the earth scientist begins to be decisive, and the problems to be solved or formulated must grow out of discussion with the archeologist. Depending upon physical and human factors, the problems involved will vary from country to country or culture to culture. To recognize the problems in the first place the geomorphologist much have some familiarity with archeology and must actively exchange ideas and notions with the anthropologist. In other words, the "straight" geologist with little direct interest in the cultural aspects of a site cannot fully apply himself to problems which can only be formulated in interdisciplinary discussion.

GEOMORPHOLOGY, SURFICIAL GEOLOGY, AND ARCHEOLOGICAL SITES

Through study of the geomorphology and sediments of a site the earth scientist may be able to:

a) Reconstruct the local habitat or setting of a site, including

1) terrain type and geographic location with respect to terrain features;
2) water resources, if available, and whether permanent or not;
3) ground water conditions and possibilities of flooding.

b) Reconstruct the regional environment—preferably with contributions from the biological sciences.

c) Establish a local stratigraphy that may be integrated into the chronology of a wider area.

Specific relationships of sites to particular geomorphic situations or Pleistocene deposits may also be of value in archeological surveying, either in the field or through use of aerial photographs or geologic maps.

The field work and environmental interpretation involved can only be undertaken by a qualified earth scientist. But the archeologist must also understand something of what the geomorphologist or Pleistocene geologist can do and what he is about. This is essential if there is to be any profitable interdisciplinary discussion. The archeologist need not become a field geomorphologist, but it is vital that the archeologist can understand the full implications of the earth scientist's findings. In many a report archeological and earth science evidence remains quite unintegrated and of correspondingly limited value. Possibly this chapter will be of some use, in connection with the preceding section, in outlining principles and possibilities of such geomorphological investigation, so helping to sponsor the necessary synthesis of cultural and physical data.

PART IV

Contributions of the Biological Sciences

16

Palynology and Paleobotany

Pollen analysis or palynology is by far the major botanical technique in paleo-ecological work, although examination of plant macro-remains, where available, is equally vital. The results achieved by palynology are truly spectacular in their detail, interpretive value, and record of rapid time-change when compared, for example, with geomorphic investigation. But palynology may be limited both areally—for want of suitable sediments—and temporally—through poor representation in certain strata. It is consequently only one of several major fields of study and an excellent source of complementary evidence in sedimentological work. Comprehensive studies of theoretical palynology and its application have been made by Erdtmann (1954), Firbas (1949-52, Vol. I), Faegri and Iversen (1964), Overbeck (1950), and Felix (1961).

The basic principle of pollen analysis is that most wind-pollinated trees, shrubs, and grasses emanate pollen in great quantities. The particle size of pollen is in the order of 0.01-0.1 mm., and the absolute weight less than 10^{-9} grams. Consequently, pollen grains are readily removed by wind and widely dispersed in the lower atmosphere where the grains are carried in suspension. Distances of 100-250 km. are readily crossed by traveling pollen, and grains may be found up to several kilometers in the lower atmosphere. Pollen density is greatest at elevations of 200 to 500 meters above the ground, and the density remains appreciable to elevations of 2 km. Pollen accumulations in any one locality will therefore provide a regional rather than a local cross-section of the pollen-emanating plants present.

The annual pollen "rain" in a vegetated area amounts to several thousand grains per square centimeter. A part of this pollen may be preserved indefinitely if oxidation is limited or absent, particularly in dense, poorly aerated sediments or in acidic environments such as provided by bogs or many lake beds. Year after year stratified laminae of sediments, including a small cross-section of the year's pollen such as is preserved, may be laid down under various conditions at a number of localities. Each of these sediments, then, preserves its own chronological and environmental record.

Of great importance to the botanist is the fact that the pollens of different plants are quite individualistic and can in many cases be identified easily as to genus (Fig. 45). On the specific level, some trees and most non-arboreal species are rather more difficult. Only in rare cases can subspecies be identified accurately, and then only with difficulty.

FIELD REMOVAL OF SAMPLES FOR POLLEN EXAMINATION

Field sample selection and removal may be carried out by earth scientists and archeologists, as well as by palynologists.

Generally speaking, organic lacustrine sediments and semi-organic beds such as marls are excellent for pollen preservation. Clays and dense silts, where not conspicuously weathered, are generally favorable. Sandy sediments are usually poor, unless dense impermeable strata "seal" the beds in question. Beds discolored by oxidation are also poor.

Samples should be removed from stratigraphically meaningful horizons or sections at vertical intervals of 5, 10, 20, or 30 centimeters as the case warrants. Some 20 cubic centimeters of material will suffice in the case of all but sands or deeply weathered sediments. The sample should be removed with great care so as to avoid contamination from the atmosphere or the removing tool, preferably after cleaning and discarding the surface layer. Short test-tubes with a cap are most convenient for storage. In the case of general pollen studies applied to non-exposed strata, such as lake or bog sediments, core borings are made employing various hand operated devices.

In the case of open sections, and as far as possible in core profiles as well, careful study should be devoted to the possible presence of sedimentary disconformities, erosional surfaces, traces of fire or peat cutting, and the like.

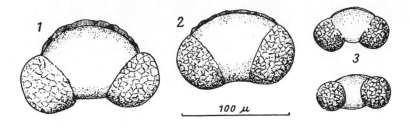

FIGURE 45.

Some pollen types (from F. Overbeck, 1950, with kind permission of the Niedersächsisches Institut für Landeskunde und Landesentwicklung, Göttingen).

Above (1) *Abies*, (2) *Picea*, (3) *Pinus;* below: (1-2) *Alnus*, (3-4) *Betula*, (5) *Corylus*, (6) *Carpinus*, (7) *Quercus*, (8-9) *Ulmus*, (10-11) *Tilia*, (12) *Fraxinus*, (13) *Salix*, (14) *Fagus*, (15) *Juglans*, (16) *Castanea*.

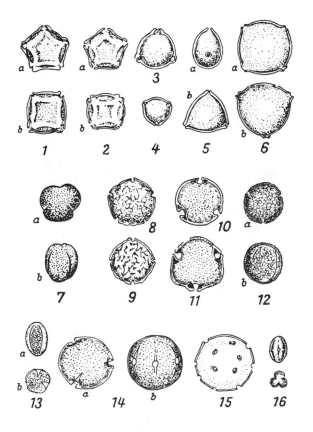

LABORATORY PREPARATION OF SAMPLES

Although the laboratory preparation and ultimate analysis of samples is strictly a task for the qualified specialist, it is useful for the persons concerned to be aware of the different results possible, depending on the method of preparation used. There is, at present, no standard method of preparation. Many authors specify their methods, others do not. Some authors have obtained pollen from certain samples by use of one technique, other authors employing another may fail to find any pollen. Some techniques are widely considered acceptable, others are frequently considered of dubious validity. Other, less frequently-mentioned but equally serious grievances, are directed against overintensive preparation of samples with massive destruction or mutilation of pollen. Since pollen has now been widely and successfully studied from rather "unorthodox," non-acidic sedimentary environments in the arid zone and humid tropics, new preparation methods have necessarily been introduced to preserve from wanton destruction such pollen as is present. The writer, not in any way qualified to evaluate these methods, cannot comment specifically on the topic. But it is highly recommended that geomorphologists and archeologists carefuly ascertain the methods whereby their samples are studied, and if need be, seek outside advice on their reliability.

Until recently the only evaluation of the problem, unfortunately not well-suited for the non-specialist, was a detailed compilation by C. A. Brown (1960). The revised text book of Faegri and Iversen (1964) consequently fills a long-felt need.

Only one, widely employed technique is briefly described here, in order to illustrate the stages of "cleaning." Three undesirable substances may be present and may be removed in the following manner:

a) Calcium carbonate is removed with cold, diluted (25 per cent) hydrochloric acid.

b) Silica is removed by letting the sample stand for 48 hours in 40 per cent concentrated hydrofluoric acid, after which the sample is washed and then heated with 10 per cent hydrochloric acid.

c) Unwanted organic matter is destroyed by first boiling in 10-15 per cent hydrogen peroxide, and then after washing, boiling the sample a second time in 10 per cent potassium hydroxide.

All three techniques may have to be applied to clays or marls, whereas only (c) may be required in the case of peat, lignite, or coal. When the various undesirables have been so removed, the final residue of pollen is mounted in glycerine jelly on a permanent slide, or suspended in liquid glycerine for immediate investigation under the microscope with 300x to 1000x magnification.

THE POLLEN SPECTRUM AND POLLEN DIAGRAM

Either 100 or 200 grains are identified, the total pollen assemblage of which is known as a *spectrum*. When samples from successive stratigraphic layers are studied, data are presented in the form of a stratigraphic *diagram* representing changing spectra through time (Fig. 46). Such pollen diagrams generally show the absolute level,

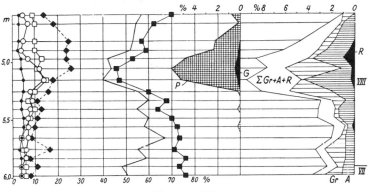

FIGURE 46.

Partial pollen diagram from Körup Sö, Denmark (after Iversen, 1949, from Walter, 1954, with kind permission of J. Iversen and of Eugen Ulmer Verlag, Stuttgart). The tree pollen symbols are as follows: dark squares, oak, plus elm and lime; drawn line, oak only; dark rhomboids, hazel; dark dots, pine; open squares, alder; open circles, birch. The NAP (on the right) include *Plantago* (P), cereals (G), grasses (Gr), *Artemisia* (A) and *Rumex* (R).

the sedimentary facies of the stratigraphic column, and the percentage of each genus with respect to the total count of arboreal pollen (AP) grains. Modern analyses invariably include a single or specified curve of the non-arboreal pollen (NAP) present, expressed as a percentage of the total AP. The pollen diagram may consist of a single composite diagram, including all of the AP, with separate recording of NAP in one or more vertical columns. Other authors prefer separate vertical columns for each pollen species (see Fig. 75).

DIFFICULTIES IN THE INTERPRETATION OF POLLEN PROFILES

The validity of the pollen spectra and diagrams is never absolute, even with proper identification. Errors are sporadically or systematically introduced by a variety of factors:

a) Differential representation of pollen due to
   1) differing surface receptivity of lakes, swamps, bogs, etc.;
   2) differential preservation of pollen under different environmental conditions.
b) Primary over or underrepresentation of species:
   1) some species are systematically overrepresented on account of excessive production: *Corylus* (hazel), *Pinus* (pine), *Alnus* (alder), and *Betula* (birch);
   2) some species tend to be present in more representative proportions: *Abies* (fir), *Carpinus* (hornbeam), *Picea* (spruce);
   3) some species are underrepresented on account of small pollen production or insect pollination: *Fagus* (beech), *Quercus* (oak), *Ulmus* (elm), *Tilia* (lime) and *Salix* (willow);
   4) some species are little or not represented on account of easily decomposed pollen: *Populus* (poplar or aspen), *Acer* (maple), *Fraxinus* (ash), *Castanea* (chestnut), *Larix* (larch), and *Juniperus* (juniper).
c) Long distance transport of pollen by wind. Pollen represented by less than 1-2 per cent of the AP spectrum may be a result of long distance transport. It is thought by some that pollen from distances exceeding 100 km. represents less than 1 per cent of the spectrum, provided there is no local source (Firbas, 1949-52, Vol. I, pp. 23-24).
d) Redeposition of pollen from older sediments.
e) Long distance transport by streams.
f) Truncated, interrupted or incomplete profiles due to
   1) fire or peat cuttings leading to destruction of sections;
   2) natural interruptions of sedimentation;
   3) lateral differences of sedimentation within the water body.

The implications of the first source of possible error above are presumably small, although no comparative material exists for an objective assessment. "Errors" introduced by (b) and (c) are rather substantial, but do not provide an objection to the use of pollen data. The palynologist is fully aware that a pollen spectrum does not provide an absolute or relative picture of forest composition. True *forest composition* can only be estimated by (1) full evaluation of available macrobotanical evidence, such as preserved leaves, leaf impressions, wood, seeds, fruits, and (2) by comparative study of the pollen spectra associated with various forest or grassland associations today. Relative *forest density* can be estimated by (1) the relative percentages of AP and NAP pollen in a diagram, and (2) by relative pollen density per unit of sediment compared with pollen density in similar sediments within the pollen diagram. In other words palynology entails considerably more than mechanical identification and enumeration of pollen. It requires that the analyst be a knowledgeable plant geographer or plant ecologist.

Lastly the possible errors introduced by factors (*d*) and (*e*) can be systematically evaluated by careful site examination. Redeposited pollen must be derived from a source whose direct accessibility should be considered. In case of question, sedimentary strata possibly affected by erosion may be checked for pollen content, if any. Disturbed profiles may be readily detected in section, although this would not be easy in the case of simple core-bore sampling.

APPLICATIONS OF POLLEN ANALYSIS

Pollen analysis may be applied to a broad range of paleo-environmental problems.

a) Reconstruction of local vegetation. Careful interpretation of contemporary pollen spectra from neighboring sites may provide a good picture of local vegetation and ecology, a technique that may be extended to particular regional settings (Firbas, 1949-52, Vol. II).

Certain floral elements are characteristic of certain environments, although most genera are distributed rather more broadly. Species identification is usually required, and just this is difficult or impossible through palynology alone. The direct paleoclimatic interpretation of many spectra is consequently limited. If species identification is possible and supported by some macrobotanical evidence, the presence of several tundra elements [1] may, for example, establish the vegetation as tundra or forest-tundra. The additional presence of steppe genera

---

[1] Some of the most common Eurasian species of indicator value (see Firbas, 1949-52, Vol. 1; Iversen, 1954; Godwin, 1956) were already discussed in Chapter 5.

such as *Artemisia, Hippophae* (sea buckthorn), and *Helianthemum* (rock rose) would contribute a further environmental note. Vegetation reconstruction is commonly based on such combinations of ecologically significant species within the over-all pollen spectrum obtained, for example, from a geological exposure or from an archeological horizon.

b) *Regional pollen maps.* Plotting of data of approximately contemporary pollen spectra over wider areas can, of course, not assume the validity of a vegetational map. But absolute "pollen maps" can be constructed, as for example carried out by Firbas (1949-52, Vol. I) for central Europe and Godwin (1956) for Britain. Such geographic patterns of pollen spectra are highly informative for environmental reconstructions (Fig. 47).

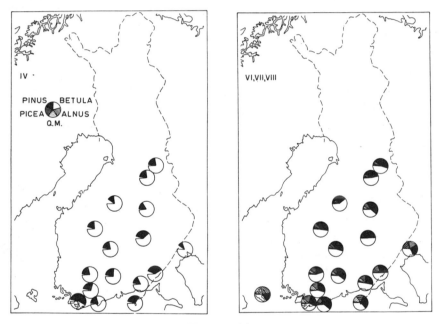

FIGURE 47.
Pollen spectrum maps of Finland during the Preboreal (left) and Atlantic/Subboreal (right), (from J. J. Donner, 1963, with kind permission of the author). The symbols show the percentage of tree pollen as explained on the left diagram, with Q. M. indicating mixed oak woodland.

c) *Climatic change.* Although with considerable qualification, it may be said that specific changes in pollen spectra with time may indicate climatic or ecological changes at a locality. However plant successions, during colonization of an area by pioneer plant communities, probably account for many of the assumed climatic changes recorded in pollen diagrams (Iversen, 1960) (Fig. 48).

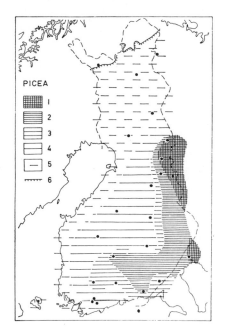

FIGURE 48.
The immigration of *Picea* into Finland, during the Boreal (1), the early Subboreal (2), the middle Subboreal (3), the late Subboreal (4), the Subatlantic (5). The barbed line (6) shows the present northern limit of *Picea abies*. Dots indicate pollen sites. (from J. J. Donner, 1963, with kind permission of the author).

d) *Stratigraphic dating.* Characteristic pollen diagrams have been described for certain interglacial periods or for the Holocene period in temperate Europe (Woldstedt, 1954, p. 220 ff). Such standard profiles are frequently used as dating tools, either within the span of a certain diagram, or as fossil assemblages referring to a particular interglacial interval. Artifactual materials in bogs can occasionally be dated according to their position within pollen profiles.

e) *Prehistoric settlement.* Forest clearance, burnings, and agricultural colonization are dramatically recorded in pollen profiles by sudden abundance of NAP, appearance of weed or cereal pollen, and the like. In fact the earliest agricultural settlements in temperate Europe frequently have been first recognized by pollen diagrams, as in the case of Denmark (Iversen, 1960) (Fig. 46).

MACROBOTANICAL REMAINS

Macrobotanical remains are usually indispensable as an auxiliary form of evidence in a palynological interpretation.

Alone, macrobotanical remains lack the statistical possibilities and completeness of the pollen spectrum. But macro-assemblages including several indicator species of a particular formation may provide good environmental information. In fact a well-preserved macroflora, such as that of the late Pleistocene volcanic ash of the Laacher See (Schweitzer, 1958), near Andernach, Germany, may well exceed a pollen spectrum in interpretive potential.

TREE-RING STUDIES

Tree-ring analysis is a botanical technique with strong analogies to varve study. The underlying principle is that non-tropical trees add an annual growth increment to their stems. Particularly in "stress" zones, along the polar and grassland tree limits, annual radial growth fluctuates widely, depending on the fluctuations of the growing season climate. In warm subhumid regions, available moisture largely controls the rate of radial growth of trees: the tree-ring of a moist year is wide, while that of a dry year is narrow or, on occasion, missing entirely. In subpolar regions rainfall is less significant since the late spring snows keep the water content of the soil sufficiently high. Instead summer, and particularly July temperatures, show the most significant correlation with radial growth.

Tree-ring studies have been almost exclusively carried out in the semiarid American southwest (Schulman, 1956), the western arctic of North America (Giddings, 1954), and the Finnish subarctic (Sirén, 1961). Despite all optimism, areal correlation of tree-ring growth is not very convincing over distances of more than 200 km. Nor are the correlation coefficients between radial growth and single variables, such as growing season precipitation or midsummer temperatures, really satisfactory. A statistically significant approach, drawing different variables into account, is in the process of development by Fritts (1963). Fritts' work has yielded excellent correlation results in detailed, local studies at the grassland tree-limit of Illinois. Such methods, applied to the classical areas of tree-ring analysis, promise to revolutionize the field and secure for it a more deserved respectability.

The major application of tree-ring studies has been directed toward chronology. The method involved is a simple teleconnection of rings from different logs, partly in archeological context. These chronological aspects, known as *dendrochronology*, have proved most useful in North America when confined to sufficiently small regions and to a time span not exceeding a millennium or so. For an outline, with references, see Bannister (1963).

The other application of tree-rings to paleoclimatology remains more controversial (see for example Bryson and Dutton, 1961), although refined mathematical analyses of all variables involved promise good results.

17

Paleontology and Paleotemperatures

Fossil bone and shell may be obtained from a number of natural and cultural sedimentary environments:

a) stream, lake, swamp and spring beds;

b) beach and estuarine beds;

c) loess and volcanic ash;

d) "fossil," "archeological," and "cultural" cave strata;

e) artificial situations such as kitchen middens, burial pits, etc. Study of such materials by paleontologists or paleozoölogists may yield data of considerable environmental and stratigraphic importance. And for the archeologist, the findings may be indispensable for proper understanding of a prehistoric site—whether the animals present were wild or domesticated, and whether the site belonged to agriculturists or food-collectors.

Yet generally speaking, paleontological data lack the precision and reliability of palynological work. Statistical samples are usually small and seldom representative of the former animal community through highly selective sedimentation, hunting, or preservation. Stratified sequences are seldom present at any one locality. Living species today commonly have wide geographic ranges and are seldom rigidly confined to any one environment. In addition, many fossil species and even whole genera are extinct today, so that their ecology is at best imperfectly understood (see Ager, 1963). Despite these qualifications paleontology is very vital for Pleistocene geography and ecology.

The following discussion will be devoted mainly to mammalian faunas, including a discussion of some characteristic Pleistocene faunas of Europe. Birds and mollusca are considered very briefly, while domesticated animals are relegated to chapter 29. Finally the paleo-environmental background to deep-sea paleotemperature work is out-lined in relation to the stratigraphic data of chapter 2.

FOSSIL PRESERVATION

Dehydrated animal bone consists of about two-thirds mineral matter and a third of organic matter. The mineral component is mainly calcium phosphate with some calcium carbonate and other salts. The organic components—including fat, citric acid, organic car-bon, nitrogen, and amino acids—are largely combined in proteins and fats such as the marrow filling the shafts of long bones (Cook, 1951; Cook and Heizer, 1952). Cornwall (1956, p. 205) indicates that soak-ing in dilute soil acids will dissolve the calcium compounds, leaving only the soft, pliable organic tissue of the bone. On the other hand, rapid oxidation of the organic matter, as can be produced by heating, converts bone to a brittle structure of light, porous mineral ash. In humid climates therefore, bones left on the surface will break down rapidly into the constituent components of carbon dioxide, water, ammonia, and mineral salts under the impact of chemical weathering.

Depending on the conditions of sedimentation or the chemical environment, rapid burial of bone or shell may preserve either the mineral or organic matter. Lacustrine, cave, or aeolian sedimentation are least likely to exert mechanical friction on bone and thus destroy it during deposition. Peat, spring deposits, cave strata, and loess con-sequently supply some of the best fossiliferous deposits. Fluvial sedi-mentation (except perhaps in the floodplain) and beach deposition take a far greater toll of destroyed bone. Yet only a small fraction of that which is buried intact is preserved for the paleontologist.

Alkaline or calcareous environments are favorable for the preserva-tion of the mineral components of bone. The organic materials are largely decomposed and carried away in solution. In this *fossilized* condition the bone is characteristically light in weight, porous and brittle. Soil waters may percolate freely through fossilized bone, carry-ing oxides and carbonates in solution. When the soil dries out, a film of mineral precipitates is left in the pore network of the bone. Eventually these spaces are refilled, and mineral replacement of bone material by calcium carbonate, sequioxides, or silicates may take place. The *mineralized* end product is considerably heavier and harder than the original bone. In an arid soil or sediment, bone may remain in the fossilized state however.

In the case of an acidic, waterlogged environment the mineral component may be largely dissolved, while various organic materials, including fleshy parts, horn, hide, hair, or wool, may be preserved. These are the conditions responsible for remarkable conservation in some bogs. Bone material is very soft under such conditions and must be removed with great care.

The intermediate case of non-calcareous, neutral, or acidic soils with permanent or seasonal aeration and oxidation is a rather common sedimentary environment. Under such circumstances all of the bone will eventually be destroyed.

A few exceptional cases of preservation of animal carcasses may be mentioned. For example, the artificially mummified animal fauna of historical Egypt (Lortet and Gaillard, 1903) is a case in which an exceptionally arid climate has helped preserve hair, hide, and bone and, aided by mummification, fleshy tissue as well. Elsewhere in the Sahara surface fossils are rare and preservation of buried bone is not exceptional. In other words, the artificial case of careful burial and mummification is not a typical sedimentary environment. The case of some Siberian and Alaskan mammoths, removed quite intact in flesh and bone from permafrost, is different. Such continuous refrigeration is an important zonal feature for carcass preservation. Other examples of exceptional conservation in petroleum-saturated beds from central Europe and California are also of interest.

METHODS OF STUDY

Field collection and preservation of fossil bone has been described by Heizer (1958). Subsequent study of fossil bone from geologic strata or archeological sites involves a number of steps (Thenius, 1961b):

a) Taxonomic identification, for which purpose skull, dentition, antlers, horn cores, and long bones are particularly useful;
b) Quantitative analysis, i.e., determination of the number of species' individuals present, for which the quantity of the most frequent diagnostic skeletal part is used;
c) Age, sex, and size composition;
d) Ecological interpretation, based on comparison of the morphology, behavior, and ecological relations for a living species, or comparative anatomical collections for an extinct species.

Animal remains, including bone and a wide range of organic

refuse pertaining to dietary habits, are invariably richest in occupation sites of man or "sedimentary" predators. The latter include the cave-dwelling bears, hyenas, lions and owls of the European Pleistocene. The prey of owls in particular includes a valuable cross-section of the local rodent population. More relevant information is provided by human occupation sites, particularly kitchen middens. Kitchen middens are probably as old as the Pleistocene, although they only assume an important role towards its close. They are most numerous along the seashore or on river banks where a molluscan and fish component could be added to the diet. These are the richest sites for mammalian or molluscan faunas.

Archeological salvage of occupation sites is increasingly concerned with the physical analysis of habitation residues. As Heizer (1960) amply illustrated, such refuse may provide invaluable information on dietary economy, settlement pattern, human activities, and environment. The paleontologist should be at the site during excavation and removal of animal bones, since only then can the context and conditions of deposition be interpreted correctly (Thenius, 1961b).

RELATIVE DATING OF BONE BY CHEMICAL ANALYSES

An oft-raised question concerns the possibility of relative or absolute dating of prehistoric bone by techniques other than isotopic analyses. The breakdown or removal of proteins or amino acids, removal of hygroscopic or hydrated water, degree of mineralization and the like have been discussed. So far, with exception of the fluorine method, it has not been possible to provide a reliable and objective method (see Cook, 1960; also Baud, 1960). The major difficulty lies in the variable conditions of the soil or sediment environment.

The so-called fluorine dating method, although a relative technique intimately associated with the peculiarities of soil water, has already provided rather useful information (Oakley, 1963). According to Richter (1958), bones must have been permanently immersed in groundwater ever since fossilization. Fluoric apatite gradually enters the bones from the groundwater and accumulates at a relatively constant rate. The absolute fluorine content depends on local groundwater conditions, and varies from place to place. The value of the method lies in the fact that the bones of an assemblage may be tested for stratigraphic equivalence since contemporary bones at one locality should normally have a comparable fluorine content. This test was largely responsible for the exposure of the Piltdown Man fraud and has proved extremely useful in assessing a number of other critical fossil assemblages (Oakley, 1963, with references).

With further study of the chemistry and physics of soil processes and fossilization, valuable advances in such chronological techniques may be expected.

GLACIAL AND INTERGLACIAL FAUNAS OF THE EUROPEAN UPPER PLEISTOCENE

The environmental significance of the European Upper Pleistocene faunas is better understood than that of any other Pleistocene fauna. Only three of the genera are extinct and two of these, the woolly mammoth and rhino, have been found more or less intact at certain localities, so that their diet and cold adaptations are well known. A half dozen further species became extinct at the close of the Pleistocene, but allied species of the same genera are still present. All in all, these Upper Pleistocene faunas can be fully evaluated in terms of their modern (or historical) environmental distributions. They are therefore an interesting case in point. For excellent syntheses see Hescheler and Kühn (1949) and Thenius (1962). Monographs on the mammoth are provided by Pfizenmayer (1939), on the reindeer by Soergel (1941) and Degerboel and Krog (1959), on the musk-ox by Soergel (1942).

The characteristic mammalian species of the interglacial (Eem) fauna are the extinct, straight-tusked woodland elephant (*Elephas* [*Palaeoloxodon*] *antiquus*), the extinct woodland rhino (*Dicerorhinus mercki*,[1] the African hippopotamus (*H. amphibius major*), the boar (*Sus scrofa*), fallow deer (*Dama dama*), and roe deer (*Capreolus capreolus*). In mid-latitude Europe these animals are rarely, if ever, found in glacial age deposits. They do however occur in the Mediterranean lands during part or all of the Würm. In addition to these species there are a few dozen mammals of the temperate and boreal woodlands also found in mid-latitude Europe during glacial periods. These include the elk (*Alces alces*), red deer (*Cervus elaphus*), aurochs (*Bos primigenius*), the woodland horses ancestral to *Equus caballus silvestris*, lynx, wild cat (*Felis silvestris*), fox (*Vulpes vulpes*), wolf, wolverine, sable (*Martes zibellina*), and brown bear (*Ursus arctos* ssp.).

The glacial (Würm) fauna is far more complex (Fig. 49). In part it includes temperate and boreal woodland forms, particularly in the southern parts of France, southeastern and southern Europe. In part it

---

[1] The correct name for Merck's rhino is *Dicerorhinus kirchbergensis*, but the more widely known form is retained here.

FIGURE 49.

Characteristic Upper Pleistocene mammals of mid-latitude Europe (from an original kindly made available by E. Thenius; see Thenius, 1962).

consists of the "typical" tundra fauna: reindeer (*Rangifer tarandus*), musk-ox (*Ovibos moschatus*), the snowshoe and arctic hares (*Lepus timidus, L. arcticus*), the mountain lemming (*Lemmus [Myodes] lemmus*), and the arctic fox (*Vulpes [Alopex] lagopus*). Alpine forms such as the steppe ibex (*Capra ibex prisca*), the chamois (*Rupicapra rupicapra*), the alpine marmot (*Marmota marmota*), and alpine vole (*Microtus nivalis*) were found well outside of their high mountain haunts.

In addition to these "expectables," a cool, mid-latitude steppe fauna was also present, ranging through Hungary into southern France (Astre, 1937; Jánossy, 1961). Included here are the saiga antelope (*Saiga tatarica*), the wild steppe horses of tarpan and Przewalski type (see Zeuner, 1963, p. 299 ff. for a useful discussion of the late Pleistocene subspecies problem), the steppe fox (*Vulpes corsac*), the steppe polecat (*Putorius putorius eversmanni*), the steppe marmot (*Marmota bobak*), the hamster (*Citellus citellus*), and a gerbil (*Allactaga saliens*).

Some of the best known "cold" elements are surprisingly enough not quite as specialized as commonly believed. These include the woolly mammoth (*Elephas [Mammonteus] primigenius*), woolly rhino (*Tichorhinus [Coelodonta] antiquitatis*), the steppe bison (*Bison priscus*), and the giant elk (*Megaceros giganteus giganteus*). Thenius (1961b) classifies these species as steppe-and-tundra forms. The woolly mammoth was a huge creature standing up to 3.5 m. tall with curved tusks as long as 4 m. It was obviously adapted against the cold with a 10 cm. layer of fat under its skin, a 10-12 cm. long woolly undercoat, and a hairy overcoat (30-70 cm. long). Stomach contents examined from well-preserved carcasses (Pavlovsky, 1956; Polutoff, 1955) suggest that grasses formed the basic diet. In its heyday, during the height of the Würm-Wisconsin, the woolly mammoth ranged from northern Spain across Eurasia into Alaska, extending eastward to the New England area and southward into Florida. The woolly rhino was not as universal, but it was also found throughout the colder parts of Eurasia. This rhino was as much as 3.5 m. in length standing 1.6 m. at the shoulder, with a fore-horn up to 1 m. long. A woolly undercoat, up to 6 cm. thick, was complemented by a long hairy overcoat, as in the case of the woolly mammoth. Less clearly adapted to cold were the steppe bison and giant elk. *Bison priscus* was probably an open country grazer, with considerable cold tolerance, occurring both on the tundra and loess steppes. The giant elk, supporting 3.5 m. broad antlers, seems to have preferred open habitats for practical reasons, but has also been found in association with interglacial woodland faunas.

The characteristic cave faunas of the European Pleistocene included the cave bear (*Ursus spelaeus*), the spotted cave hyena (*Crocuta crocuta spelaea*), and cave lion (*Felis [Panthera] leo spelaeus*). Each of these species was cold tolerant but rather intermediate in its requirements. They are not "cold" indicators by any means. Whereas the cave bear was distinct from the brown bear (*Ursus arctos*) on the specific level—probably due to isolation in western Europe during the Elster glaciation (Kurtén, 1959b)—the cave hyena and cave lion were not very much different from the living spotted hyena (Kurtén, 1957) or the now extinct lion of the Balkans.

STRATIGRAPHIC ASPECTS OF PLEISTOCENE MAMMALIAN FAUNAS

The comparatively rapid evolution of mammalian faunas during the Pleistocene (Kurtén, 1959a) is of great stratigraphic value. Particularly useful are the genetically rather differentiated elephants and rhinos of Europe. It seems that these two genera, as well as several other tundra or boreal elements, specialized only during the course of the Pleistocene (Thenius, 1961a, with references).

A few words may be devoted to the evolution and paleo-ecology of the extinct European elephants and rhinos (see Soergel, 1940, 1943; Adam, 1953, 1954, 1961; Kurtén, 1960a; Thenius, 1961a, 1962). The earliest Pleistocene elephant in Europe was the forest type *Elephas* (*Archidiskodon*) *meridionalis*. Specialization took place during the earlier part of the Elster glacial complex when the steppe or grassland form *Elephas* (*Archidiskodon*) *trogontherii* diverged from the *meridionalis* stock, and the more specialized temperate-woodland type *Elephas* (*Palaeoloxodon*) *antiquus* replaced *E. meridionalis*. During the Riss glacial complex, *E. trogontherii* specialized further into a cold steppe or tundra form, the woolly mammoth. With exception of the straight-tusked loxodon group, all of the Pleistocene elephants of Europe belonged to the curved-tusked archidiskodon or mammoth groups. Mastodonts, primarily distinguished from the true elephants on the basis of their dentition, became extinct in Europe in the Basal Pleistocene.

In the rhinocerotid family each of the Pleistocene genera in Europe were two-horned. The earliest species, *Dicerorhinus* (*Opsiceros*) *megarhinus* and *D. etruscus*, were probably intermediate, warm or warm-temperate woodland forms. A bifurcation similar to that of the elephants marked the evolution of *D. etruscus* during the Elster, with the appearance of a more specialized woodland species *D. mercki* and of the steppe form *D. hemitoechus* (Zeuner, 1935). At about the same time the rather specialized Asiatic woolly mammoth makes its first appearance in Europe.

Both the woodland elephants and rhinos evacuated mid-latitude Europe during the early Würm and became extinct in southern Europe before the end of the same glaciation—not much earlier than the final disappearance of the more northerly woolly mammoth and rhino at the close of the Würm. Table 14 summarizes the stratigraphy of the European proboscidians and rhinocerotids.

In a more general way, the European Villafranchian was characterized by a Pliocene fauna (see Thenius, 1962, with references). Despite the appearance of certain Pleistocene guide fossils, world-wide faunal affinities existed. Widespread moist, subtropical or temperate climates did not favor the development of geographical variants, and most of these extinct mammals were ecologically less specialized (Thenius, 1961a). Great faunal and floral changes accompanied the close of the Villafranchian, and the biological array of Cromer times is largely one of modern genera. Most of the Pliocene elements had disappeared when more specialized woodland and steppe forms first appeared.

At the beginning of the Upper Pleistocene the faunal picture of Europe is divided into the characteristic interglacial and glacial assemblages discussed above.

The last major faunal zone, the Holocene, is characterized by a fully modern fauna. Most of the great Pleistocene mammals such as the mammoth, woolly rhino, the steppe bison, giant elk, and cave bear died out at the close of the Pleistocene, while the musk-ox withdrew from temperate Europe, eventually becoming extinct in the Old World. Other tundra elements still persist in higher latitudes today, while the wild horses, the aurochs, and a woodland bison survived into recent centuries, when they were destroyed by man.

The problem of extinctions at the close of the Pleistocene is discussed in chapters 27 and 28 in relation to the environmental changes and hunting activity of the time.

The stratigraphy of other continental areas is less completely understood. The African faunas have been carefully synthesized by H. B. S. Cooke (1963), while Flint (1957, p. 457 ff., with references) may be consulted on the North American fauna.

TABLE 14

STRATIGRAPHY OF THE EXTINCT EUROPEAN ELEPHANTS AND RHINOS

(After Kurtén, 1960a; Adam, 1961; and Others)

Species	Villa-franchian	Tiglian	Kedischem Complex	Cromer-ian	Elster Complex	Holstein	Riss Complex	Eem	Würm
Elephas meridionalis									
Elephas antiquus									
Elephas trogontherii									
Elephas primigenius									
Dicerorhinus etruscus									
Dicerorhinus mercki									
Dicerorhinus hemitoechus									
Tichorhinus antiquitatis									

NON-MAMMALIAN FAUNAS

Despite the paleo-environmental potential of non-mammalian faunas, little systematic knowledge is available for such classes as birds, fish, mollusca, and the like. The value of non-migratory birds for understanding past climatic and vegetational changes has been demonstrated for sub-Saharan Africa by Moreau (1963). Certain larger bird genera are sufficiently numerous in archeological contexts of the late Pleistocene and Holocene so as to offer good possibilities for local environmental interpretation. Particularly well-known tundra or northern denizens in the Würm record of mid-latitude Europe include snowy partridges (*Lagopus* spp.), the snowy owl (*Nyctea scandiaca*), and the great auk (*Alca impennis*). A bibliography of bird remains in archeology is given by Dawson (1963).

Fish are also relatively scarce in the archeological record, although they may attain some importance for paleo-ecology. For references see Ryder (1963) and J. G. D. Clark (1952).

Marine mollusca have, in some areas, been studied to the same degree as mammalian faunas. But most marine mollusca are almost indifferent to their climatic environment within ranges of 30 degrees of latitude or more. Ecologically significant species are largely confined to the level of local assemblages and have less general validity than mammalian indicators. So for example the relative frequency of cold-loving species such as *Yoldia arctica*, *Saxicava arctica*, and *Tellina calcarea*, and of thermophile species such as *Lutricularia ovata*, *Gastrana fragilis*, *Mytilus lineatus*, *Lucina divaricata*, and *Haminea navicula*, may mean the difference between glacial and interglacial periods in the North Sea area (Woldstedt, 1954, p. 242). The case of the Mediterranean Sea is unique. Here the Straits of Gibraltar have on occasion admitted cold-loving or thermophile species which became locally extinct with the next climatic change. *Cyprina islandica*, *Mya truncata*, *Anomalina baltica* and *Buccinum undatum* have entered the Mediterranean Sea during some colder stages. On the other hand, thermophile faunas from the Cape Verde - Senegal area invaded the Mediterranean during the Eem interglacial, only to disappear with the onset of the last glacial. These typical "Tyrrhenian" species include *Conus testudinarius*, *Tritonidea viverrata*, *Strombus bubonius*, *Natica lactea*, *Mytilus senegalensis*, *Arca plicata*, and *Cardita senegalensis* (Cuerda, 1957).

Even fewer generalizations can be made about non-marine mollusca. Interglacial and glacial indicators are comparatively well understood in Great Britain (Sparks, 1963), central Europe (Ložek, 1955), and France (Germain, 1923), while some useful molluscan studies in the Sahara are due to Gardner (1932, 1935) and Sparks and Grove (1961). The immobility of some terrestrial snails may make them particularly suitable for statistical analyses in stratigraphic profiles. In this way they may carry both stratigraphic and ecological implications.

PALEOTEMPERATURES AND DEEP-SEA SEDIMENT
CORES

Deep-sea cores.—Sedimentation on the more level parts of the deep-sea floor is limited to very slow accumulation, consisting partly of fine organic oozes. A part of the organisms found in these sediments are calcareous skeletons of one-celled *Foraminifera*. During life, a few species of foraminifers inhabit the photosynthetic zone of the ocean's surface waters. They are consequently adapted to ocean surface temperatures which are, in their turn, in equilibrium with regional climates. After death, a part of these planktonic foraminifers accumulates on the deep-sea floor. The faunal composition will reflect environmental conditions, particularly temperature, so that deep-sea sediments may record stratigraphic successions of microfauna capable of paleo-ecological study.

Specially equipped ships can operate a so-called "piston-corer," which is able to remove thin columnar sedimentary sections of twenty meters or so in length from the sea floor. Such deep-sea cores are subsequently studied and evaluated in the laboratory. The number analyzed is now sufficiently great that sedimentary interruptions or disturbances can be recognized (Ericson *et al.*, 1961). These can be eliminated through careful micropaleontological layer-by-layer cross-correlation between cores from different localities within the same sedimentary basin. The collections of the Lamont Geological Observatory and the Swedish Deep-Sea Expedition have been evaluated and are sufficiently numerous to inspire considerable confidence (Ericson *et al.*, 1961; Olausson, 1961a, 1961b). Earlier publications are generally based on limited evidence and should be considered with caution.

Temperature evaluation.—Several different approaches have been taken to determine paleotemperatures as recorded by deep-sea cores:
   a) Identification and statistical analysis of "warm" and "cold" foraminifers;

b) Calcium carbonate content and foraminiferal productivity, which will vary according to temperature, or also in some oceanic areas, according to oceanic circulation and nutrient level (Arrhenius, 1952; Wiseman, 1954; Olausson, 1961a);

c) Ratio of the oxygen isotopes O^{18}/O^{16} employed in skeletal development of foraminifers varies according to water temperature, and may be converted into an isotopic temperature by use of appropriate equations (Emiliani, 1955a);

d) Faunal zones characterized by presence or absence of certain indicative foraminifera in faunal assemblages (Ericson *et al.* 1961; Ericson, 1961).

The optimal method of determining paleotemperatures from planktonic foraminifers has so far not been decided upon, each method having advantages and drawbacks. So, for example, an "absolute" isotopic temperature, such as may be obtained by Emiliani's technique, has been skeptically evaluated by Wiseman (1961) on the basis that several assumptions employed in the temperature equations are not established, and that modern foraminiferal behavior is too little understood. The productivity approach is a fair qualitative technique, yielding good relative results, but liable to regional complications (Olausson, 1961a). At the moment it appears that the simplest technique, with only relative temperature implications, and based upon a minimum of assumptions, may be preferable. In the author's opinion, the wealth of core data synthesized adds particular weight to the Lamont determinations (Ericson *et al.*, 1961), which will be discussed in a little detail.

Paleotemperature horizons.—For the North Atlantic region, Ericson *et al.* (1961) employ the presence or absence of the moderately thermophile species *Globorotalia menardii,* and its apparently extinct subspecies *flexuosa,* as a prime indicator of temperature conditions similar to those of the present. W. Schott (1935) had already postulated that the topmost deep-sea sediment layer with *G. menardii* represented the Holocene period. The underlying zone, without that species but characterized by higher latitude species, was thought to have been deposited during the last glacial. Ericson *et al.* (1961) calculated the number of individuals of thermophile species present per unit weight of the coarse sediment fraction greater than 0.074 mm. in diameter (mainly planktonic foraminifera). Employing such criteria several clear-cut faunal zones were established (Ericson *et al.,* 1961; Ericson,

1961), the upper three of which had already been recognized and essentially defined by W. Schott (1935):

a) Zone Z with *Globorotalia menardii* in abundance (warm);

b) Zone Y without *G. menardii* but containing species now abundant in higher latitudes (cool);

c) Zone X with *G. menardii* in abundance, together with *G. menardii flexuosa* and *Globigerina hexagona* (warm);

d) Zone W without *G. menardii* (cool);

e) Zone V with *G. menardii* and the subspecies *flexuosa* in abundance (warm);

f) Zone U without *G. menardii* (cool).

Data from 108 North Atlantic cores were used to substantiate these faunal zones. The significance of the faunal "breaks" involved is indicated by the curious phenomenon of alternate dextral and sinistral coiling of the species *Globigerina pachyderma* related by Ericson (1959) to ocean temperature conditions.

Although a correlated stratigraphic column of deep-sea paleotemperatures, based on a few select cores, was outlined by Emiliani (1955a, 1958), the world-wide correlations adopted there seem premature. Whether or not one is prepared to accept the isotopic temperature curve Emiliani has constructed, the relative fluctuations of temperature obtained by different authors correlate well, although the absolute time sequence upheld varies with the author.

Two sequences are compared in Table 5 (in chap. 3): that of Ericson *et al.* (1961) and that of Emiliani, as dated by the Pa^{231}/Th^{230} technique (Rosholt *et al.*, 1961). Correlation is good between both sequences except for the duration of zone V. It is not possible to argue for one or the other version, as the Rosholt-Emiliani curve is also extrapolated beyond 150,000 years while Ericson's curve has the advantage of a far greater selection of representative cores. In addition to the above units, Emiliani recognizes a minor warm interruption in the middle of zone Y. It was obviously not significant enough to tally in the Lamont analyses. The stratigraphic interpretation of these results is discussed in chapter 3.

PART V

Some Pleistocene Environments of the Old World

18

Mid-latitude Europe during the Late Pleistocene

INTRODUCTION

Whereas the preceding sections attempted to outline methods and theory of environmental reconstruction, the following chapters are devoted to a sketch of some Pleistocene environments. Three major aspects of Pleistocene geography appear to warrant reconstruction. These are firstly the environmental changes attendant to glaciations in higher latitudes, secondly the phenomenon of pluvial phases in lower latitudes, and thirdly environmental conditions during inter-glacial periods. Reconstructions must necessarily be selective on the basis of available information and representative situations. The late Pleistocene, in particular the Würm, provides a good example of both glacial and pluvial conditions. Spatially, the only "documented" areas are Europe, the Mediterranean borderlands, and certain parts of Africa. Our knowledge of the Pleistocene of eastern and southern Asia, Australia, and to a good extent also of the Americas, is frag-mentary beyond the margins of the Pleistocene glaciers. Even in Europe the detail and reliability of Pleistocene research is only satis-factory in a qualified way. But the available data at least permit tentative reconstruction of glacial and pluvial environments.

EXISTING RECONSTRUCTIONS OF LAST GLACIAL CLIMATIC ZONES

Serious attempts to reconstruct the geographical distribution of eco-zones in Europe during the last glacial have been made by Poser (1948, 1950), Büdel (1951a), and Frenzel (Frenzel and Troll, 1952; Frenzel, 1959-60). Their work forms the basis to the subsequent dis-cussion on late Pleistocene climatic zonation of temperate Europe.

Cold-climate phenomena are also discussed by K. H. Kaiser (1960), while Wright (1961) has reviewed much of the literature with exception of Frenzel (1959-60).

Poser's regional reconstruction (1948) is by far the most original and stimulating of the three approaches, although not all of his criteria are considered valid today. Poser attempted to delimit the southern boundary of permafrost (a very crude approximation for the —2° C. mean annual isotherm) and the position of the arctic tree-limit (an approximation for the July isotherm +10° C.). Of the three criteria he employed to determine the extent of permafrost, fossil ice wedges alone are generally considered valid. Involutions and asymmetrical valleys must be questioned, although this would not significantly alter Poser's picture on the basis of the then available information. Poser further attempts to estimate the degree of summer warmth by drawing isolines of equal depth of involutions, meant to indicate the depth of the active thaw layer. Although this assumption is open to question, the consistency of his findings suggests there may be considerable validity to the concept. It is more difficult, however, to follow Poser's arguments that the vertical depth and surface width of ice wedges is proportional to the severity of winter cold (rather than to the grain size of the sediments involved). Overlooking such details however, the primary importance of Poser's reconstruction is that the essentials are sound, even though subsequent work on periglacial phenomena in France and on palynology in Poland and Russia impel modifications in detail. Poser further attempted isobaric reconstructions of pressure distribution during the Würm maximum using the unfounded argument of the glacial anticyclone (see Matthes and Belmont, 1950). That particular theoretical sketch (Poser, 1948, Fig. 3) is then of no scientific value. A later study by Poser (1950) is devoted to a reconstruction of mean summer wind directions during the later Würm glaciation based on the alignment of fossil parabolic and longitudinal dunes (Fig. 50). This very significant reconstruction will be discussed further in chapter 22.

Büdel's reconstruction (1951a) has curiously found greatest access into the general literature, presumably on the basis of its cartographic suitability for reproduction. Yet its criteria are open to question, despite a considerable degree of intuitive accuracy. The basis of much of Büdel's analysis is a shrewd evaluation and extrapolation of data derived from modern isothermal distributions. There is no evidence that paleobotanical data was employed in either the delimitation or classification of forested areas. Büdel's attempt is not a factual

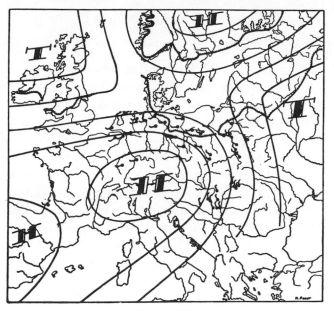

FIGURE 50.

Late glacial summer circulation in Europe (from H. Poser, 1950, with kind permission of *Erdkunde*). (H) High pressure, (T) low pressure centers. Barbed lines indicate ice margins during the full and the late glacial period. Wind arrows are based on dune orientations.

reconstruction but a hypothetical sketch, certainly interesting, but to be regarded with caution.

Frenzel (1959-60) contributed a great wealth of material on the U.S.S.R., derived from an exhaustive study of the Russian literature. The information employed is largely paleobotanical, partly paleontological, partly geomorphic. The amount of data available for Russia and western Siberia was appreciable, although it is less satisfactory for other parts of the U.S.S.R. where the reconstruction sometimes attains hypothetical character. Frenzel, however, rates the reliability of his work objectively, and does not delude the reader with unfounded covering statements. Unfortunately, Frenzel uncritically employed a hypothetical sketch of the China area by Wissmann (1938), and adopted Büdel's (1951a) reconstruction in western and southern Europe without improvement. Consequently Frenzel's *ca.* 1:21,000,000 map (1960), despite its over-all value and broad validity, is of variable reliability from region to region.

BASIC CHRONOLOGY OF THE LAST GLACIAL IN MID-LATITUDE EUROPE

Before attempting to review existing information on full glacial climatic conditions in Europe during the Würm, it is essential to emphasize the oscillating character of the ice front and the fluctuating nature of climate during the 60,000 year time span involved. A fairly good radiocarbon chronology is available for the period (Movius, 1960, with various reply comments; Gross, 1958; Andersen, 1961; Fink 1960, 1962). The basic pattern may be tentatively outlined as follows:

a) *ca. 70,000* B.C. End of the Eem Interglacial and beginning of the Würm Glacial. Formation of Scandinavian glacier. Cold climate.

b) *ca. 62,000* B.C. *and ca. 57,000* B.C. Temperate phases, known as the Amersfoort and Brörup, respectively. Of these the Brörup, lasting several millennia, merits importance as an interstadial. Temporary retreats of the ice front.

c) *ca. 56,000-28,000* B.C. First maximum phase of the *Early Würm.* Ice front south of the Baltic Sea (?). Very cold.

d) *ca. 28,000-26,000* B.C. Interval of cool-temperate climate, now commonly designated as the Paudorf interstadial, also apparent in the deep-sea core measurements of Emiliani (Rosholt *et al.*, 1961). Retreat of ice front into Scandinavia (?).

e) *ca. 26,000-14,000* B.C. *Main Würm.* Re-advance of ice front to its maximum position with greatest cold during Brandenburg stage, *ca.* 18,000 B.C. Followed by gradual retreat and halts at the Frankfurt (*ca.* 16,000 B.C.) and Pommeranian (*ca.* 14,000-15,000 B.C.) moraines. Very cold.

f) *ca. 14,000-10,000* B.C. Protracted glacier retreat of early *Late Würm* with temperate oscillation about 11,000 B.C. (Bölling). Palynologically, the interval preceding the Bölling is known as the Oldest Dryas and that between the Bolling and Alleröd, as the Older Dryas. Climate cold but warming.

g) *ca. 10,000-9,000* B.C. Temperate interstadial, known as the Alleröd. Ice margins in central Sweden and south-central Finland.

h) *9,000-8,000* B.C. Last glacial relapse or Younger Dryas. Minor readvance of ice. Cold.

Conditions to be outlined refer in a broad way to the main Würm or full glacial, as opposed to the early glacial 70,000-26,000 B.C., or the late glacial 14,000-8,000 B.C. This corresponds, more or less, to the period of maximum cold. Wright (1961) raises the objection that the very coldest phase was also the driest, and consequently unfavora-

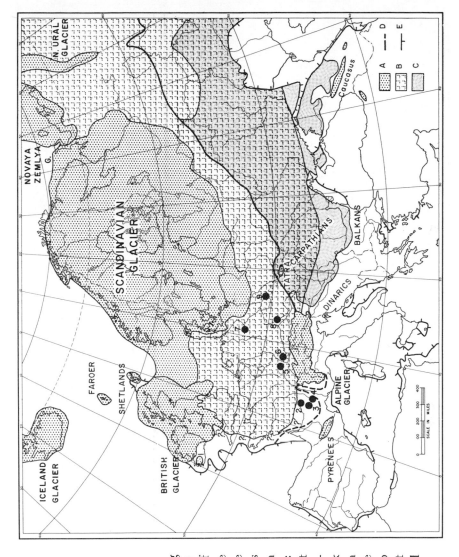

FIGURE 51.

European environments during the main Würm glacial. (A) glaciated areas, (B) extent of permafrost, (C) loess-steppe areas south of the arctic tree limit (D), (E) coastlines. Areas of smaller highland glaciation indicated by numbers on map: (1) Kerry Mtns., (2) Mont Doré, (3) Cantal, (4) Cevennes, (5) Vosges, (6) Black Forest, (7) Harz, (8) Bohemian Forest, (9) Sudeten Mtns. The Dinaric and Balkan Mtns. also had local glaciations. Tree-limit in eastern Europe after Frenzel (1960).

269

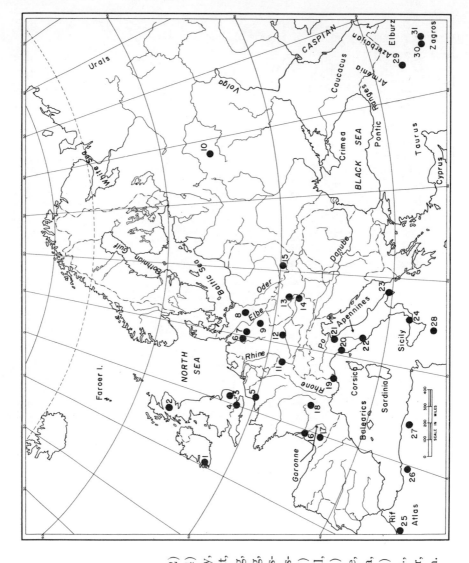

FIGURE 52.
Europe. (1) Kerry Mtns., (2)
Grampians, (3) Hoxne, (4)
Swanscombe, (5) Somme valley,
(6) Lehringen, (7) Lebenstedt,
(8) Berlin, (9) Markkleeberg,
(10) Moscow, (11) Strassburg,
(12) Mauern, (13) Unter-Wisternitz, (14) Vienna, (15) Krosčienko, (16) Bordeaux, (17)
Lourdes, (18) Massif Central,
(19) Monaco, (20) Pisa, (21)
Ravenna and Forli, (22) Rome,
(23) Otranto, (24) Messina, (26)
(25) Sidi Abderrahman, (26)
Ternifine, (27) Jurjura Mtns.,
(28) Malta, (29) Shanidar,
(30) Palegawra, (31) Marivan.

270

ble to ice wedge development. There is however, no serious discrepancy between maximum areal extent of permafrost indicators and typical climatic conditions during the full glacial. The latter probably represented a complex of moister glacial advances and drier glacial standstills or retreats—both the advances and standstills during a time of intense cold.

THE SCANDINAVIAN, BRITISH, AND ALPINE GLACIERS

At the maximum of the Würm (Brandenburg-Valdai moraines) the Scandinavian glacier attained an area of about 4,250,000 sq. km., and an average thickness of 1,900 m. (Grahmann, 1937; Niskanen, 1943). The ice sheet was centered at about 21° E., 59° N. over the Bothnian Gulf, where the maximum thickness may have amounted to 3,000 m. The ice merged with the British glacier over the North Sea (Valentin, 1957), then extended down the length of Denmark following the Elbe valley to south of Berlin, reaching farthest south in the Oder valley (about 52° N.) (Figs. 51 and 52). Beyond the Oder the ice margin recurved slowly northeastwards toward the Volga River headwaters and thence due north to the White Sea (S. A. Jakovlev, 1957, cited after Woldstedt, 1958).

The British glacier was not only considerably smaller (about 370,000 sq. km.) but also much shallower than the Scandinavian glacier. Directions of flow outwards from several major highland centers were controlled by the underlying topography. The glacier formed through the merging of several ice caps on the Scottish (Grampians and southern uplands), Welsh, and Irish highlands. All of these mountain areas are of moderate elevation (1,300 m. in Scotland, 1,000 m., in Wales and Ireland), but receive considerable precipitation (to over 2,000 mm.). Louis (1934) estimates the snowline in western Ireland at 400 m., and the general snowline depression at 1,200 m. At its greatest extent during the Würm the ice extended eastwards from Limerick across Ireland to southern Wales (about 51°30′ N.), recurving up to about Manchester and passing on to the North Sea at Hull (Charlesworth, 1957). A local glaciation existed in the Kerry Mountains (1,041 m.) of southwestern Ireland. During the late glacial, the British glacier again disintegrated into its discrete parts.

The Alpine glacier occupied an area of about 25,000 sq. km. and consisted of overgrown, coalescent valley glaciers, up to 2,000 m. thick, spreading out in a chain of small piedmont glaciers beyond the edge of the mountains (see Klebelsberg, 1948-49, Vol. II). The ice extended down to elevations of about 500 m. on the north, 200 m. on the west, and 100 m. on the south of the range. The Würm snowline elevation varied between 1,500 and 2,000 m., rising eastward and into the interior of the mountains. Snowline depressions amounted to about 1,000-1,200 m. Considering that the 1,000 km. range has crest elevations of 2,000-4,000 m. and a modern precipitation of 1,000-3,000 mm., the extent of glaciation at this latitude is not surprising. The advance of glaciers right onto the edge of the Po Valley suggests that a major source of moisture was from the south, derived from the warm waters of the Mediterranean Sea.

Further extensive glaciations existed on Iceland and the Faroer Islands, on Novaya Zemlya and adjacent parts of northern Russia, on the northern Urals, the Caucasus, and the Pyrenees.

Climatically these areas of permanent ice must have had midsummer temperatures little above the freezing point, and presumably belonged to the class of frost (*EF*) climates of Koeppen. Flohn (1953) has attempted to evaluate the paleo-climatic implications of the 1,200 m. snowline depression. Provided the lapse rates, radiation, and precipitation remained constant, the evidence possibly suggests a temperature lowering in the order of 6° C. As a test case, Flohn illustrates the example of the Faroer Islands, which today receive solid precipitation (snow) during the months December through March. A lowering of mean temperature by 5° C. would reduce the mean temperatures of November and April to below 0° C., and thereby increase the number of days with snow from 44 to 218 days per year, out of a total of 281 days with precipitation. More snow would then fall than could melt in summer, and glaciation would ensue. This value of 5° C. also tallies with Emiliani's O^{18}/O^{16} paleotemperature determinations for North Atlantic surface waters (1955a). Nonetheless snowline deductions should be considered with caution (see chap. 7).

NON-GLACIATED REGIONS OF WESTERN EUROPE

Turning to the non-glaciated areas of France and the southern British Isles, much of this region experienced both permafrost and tundra conditions during the main Würm. The 100 m. lowering of world sea level produced an important change in topography, whereby the southern North Sea, the English Channel, and much of the Atlantic continental margin were exposed. This may have affected the continentality of local climate.

Geomorphic evidence from southeastern and south-central England includes ice wedges, frost cracks, involutions, and widespread soli-fluction features (Fitzpatrick, 1956; Te Punga, 1957). This zone was certainly well within the discontinuous permafrost area, although information is not yet available from the more maritime regions of Cornwall and southern Ireland. As the mean annual temperatures range about +10° C. today, a temperature lowering of at least 12° C. is implied for southeastern England.

The pollen evidence of the Oldest Dryas, prior to the Bölling oscillation, indicates the dominance of tundra or open park-tundra vegetation (Godwin, 1956; Suggate *et al.*, 1959). NAP pollen is almost exclusive, including considerable *Artemisia* and *Thalictrum,* both indicative of at least seasonally dry soil conditions. At least as far back as the Older Dryas however, copses of dwarf and arctic willow were to be found in Cornwall and of willow and dwarf birch in Ireland (Co. Monaghan) (Godwin and Willis, 1959). This implies that even during the colder parts of the late glacial, forest-tundra occurred in southwestern Great Britain, suggesting mean July temperatures around the 10° C. mark (+10 to +14° C. today). Whether or not this was also so during the full glacial is not known.

In France, geomorphic evidence relating to Würm-age cold-climate phenomena is relatively well dispersed (Tricart, 1956a, 1956b). Unfortunately ice wedges are poorly recorded. Scattered localities with ice wedges occur through much of the northern half of the country, and a single ice wedge is recorded at Bordeaux. As there is no ready way to judge the validity of the latter evidence, the question must remain open whether or not discontinuous permafrost did extend south of latitude 46°.

Interesting comparative information is available from the glaciated highlands. For example, a number of valley glaciers existed in the Mt. Dore (1,886 m.), Cantal (1,858 m.) and Cevennes (crest elevations at 1,700 m.) mountains of the Massif Central (Boisse de Black, 1951). The Würm snowline was found at about 1,200 m.

The Pyreneen glaciation was considerably more important. Crest elevations run at 2,000-3,000 m. (Pico d'Aneto 3,404 m.), and the range enjoys 1,000-2,000 mm. precipitation. The present snowline rises from 2,500 m. in the west to 2,800 m. in the east, whereas the Würm snowline was located between 1,500 and 2,300 m. Except for small piedmont glaciers in the upper Pau and Neste valleys, glaciation was limited to valley glaciers (Nussbaum, 1928; Alimen, 1957, with refer-ences). These extended down to elevations of 500 m. on the northern flanks, to 1,000 m. on the southern flanks of the range.

Full glacial paleobotanical evidence is scanty from France. Lemée

(1954) has outlined Older Dryas pollen records from elevations at 1,100-1,350 m. in the Massif Central. NAP pollen include *Artemisia* and *Helianthemum,* two "steppe" species, although no statistics are given. The AP pollen recorded at the Cantal site is dominated by pine and dwarf birch (*Betula nana*), without oak or hazel. At Mézenc, in the mountains of Vivarais, pine is dominant with some birch, and traces of *Quercus* and *Corylus.* Lemée believes an oak-hazel, mixed deciduous woodland may have been found in the lowlands at this time. Elsewhere, on the northern flanks of the Pyrenees, considerable work has been done by Florschütz and Menéndez Amor. Published to date is only one profile from Poueyferré, near Lourdes, at 420 m. (De Vries *et al.,* 1960). Several Groningen radiocarbon dates leave no doubt as to the stratigraphic position. Twenty-four samples antedating 11,000 B.C. (and the Bölling oscillation) have AP under 10 per cent. Pinus is dominant, with traces of *Betula* in 16 samples, *Quercus* in 6, and *Corylus* in 5. *Artemisia* forms 10-25 per cent of the NAP. From this one must conclude a (mountain) tundra vegetation with scattered stands of wood at a little distance, and of mixed deciduous woods at greater distance in lower elevations. There is little likelihood that *Quercus* and *Corylus* pollen were derived from beyond the Pyrenees so that these species must have occurred somewhere in the lowlands of the Gascogne. Yet, results by Oldfield (1961) in the coastal area of Biarritz show less than 3 per cent AP for a full glacial deposit.

The exact position of the polar tree-line in France cannot be determined from this scanty information, but it probably did not lie north of the modern 20° C. July isotherm (at about 46° N. lat. in the lowlands). But further pollen studies may still reveal that forest-tundra existed in the Garonne and Rhone lowlands during the Oldest Dryas.

NON-GLACIATED REGIONS OF CENTRAL EUROPE

The Scandinavian and Alpine glaciers bordered central Europe (the Low Countries, Germany, Czechoslovakia, and Poland) on two flanks. Pinched in between two cold centers, the severe climate of this area is not surprising.

Ice wedges are common throughout (Poser, 1948; Maréchal and Maarleveld, 1950; K. H. Kaiser, 1960, Sekyra, 1960; Dylik, 1956). Discontinuous or continuous permafrost seems to have been universal, so that a mean annual temperature depression of *at least* 11° C. must be assumed for the region as a whole. Needless to say numerous other cold-climate indicators are equally frequent.

Local mountain glaciers were present on the Vosges (1,423 m.), Black Forest (1,493 m.), and the Tatra (2,663 m.), and in a more limited way on some smaller highlands such as the Harz and Sudeten ranges (data summarized by Woldstedt, 1958). The Würm snowline elevation was at 800-900 m. in the Vosges, in the Black Forest at 850-950 m., in the Tatra at 1,450-1,650 m. (2,500 today). The snowline depression of these intermediate highlands was also in the order of 1,000-1,200 m. (see maps 1 and 2 in Frenzel, 1959-60, Vol. I.). This is well out of key with the permafrost evidence, and may reflect both the presence of a surface temperature inversion (Flohn, 1953) and a reduction in precipitation due to greatly increased continentality (see also Weischet, 1954). In this connection Poser's (1948) deductions on the limited depth of the active thaw layer in the east-central Europe (70-150 cm.) are relevant.

In some of the areas close to the ice front, high arctic barrens with little or no vegetation prevailed during the maximum of the Würm (e.g., the Netherlands, Van der Hammen, 1952). Throughout the central European loess belt, and probably in other areas as well, herbaceous tundra was, however, more characteristic. Firbas (1949-52, Vol. I, pp. 294-300; 1950), and Iversen (1954) consider that a herbaceous tundra with wild grasses, sedges, herbaceous plants—and steppe indicators such as *Artemisia*—is generally indicated by Oldest Dryas pollen profiles of Germany and Denmark. *Salix herbacea* is locally present, and Firbas supposes the existence of a scrub-tundra with *Salix herbacea, S. polaris,* and *Betula nana* in the warmer Upper Rhine lowland and the Bohemian plain at about the same time. According to Frenzel (1960), the arctic tree-limit crossed the Danube at Vienna and extended across Moravia into southern Poland, where Klimaszewskii *et al.* (1950) found pollen of *Larix* sp., *Pinus silvestris,* and *P. montana* at 228 m. near Kroscienko, while pollen of *Salix reticulata, S. retusa, Betula nana,* and numerous tundra elements were found at a neighboring site in 437 m. This places the contemporary tree limit very approximately at the modern July isotherm of 19° C. suggesting a main Würm midsummer temperature depression in the order of 7°-9° C. Andersen (1961) assesses this value at 10° C. for Denmark during the full glacial. Curiously enough however, *Armeria maritima*, which does not now occur in areas with mean cold-month temperatures below —8° C., is present in contemporary Danish materials (Iversen, 1954). This would imply a maximum January temperature depression of 8° C. for Denmark. As this is not, in total, compatible with the geomorphic evidence, the limitations of indirect evidence suggest a need for caution.

SOUTHEASTERN EUROPE

The lands of southeastern Europe (Hungary, Romania, Yugoslavia, and Bulgaria) have a rather varied relief dominated by the Hungarian and Wallachian plains on the one hand, the Carpathian, Dinaric, and Balkan mountain systems on the other. The only substantial information for much of the area concerns numerous localities of limited mountain glaciation. The Carpathians (crest elevations 1,200-2,500 m.) had a Würm snowline rising from 1,550 to 2,100 m. north to south, that of the Dinaric-Balkan ranges (crest elevations 1,000-2,500 m). rose from 1,300-2,300 m. west to east.

Cold climate phenomena are only recorded from Hungary, where ice wedges occur in the northern half of the country. The exact southern limit of discontinuous permafrost is unknown but is still thought to run across southern Hungary and northern Wallachia as indicated by Poser (1948), (see Fig. 4 in Frenzel, 1959). Loess deposition was prominent in both the Hungarian and Romanian lowlands.

Pollen information is a little better. According to Serčelj (1963) a subarctic boreal forest occupied much of Slovenia in the 800-1,200 m. elevation range. It was dominated by pine, with a little birch, willow, and alder present on occasion. In Hungary an open brush woodland of *Larix decidua, Pinus cembra*, and *P. montana* occupied the foothills between 400 and 900 m. elevation, while a forest steppe, with galeria woods of pine and larch, was located in the Hungarian plain (Zólyomi, 1953). In the lower Carpathians of Romania, Pop (1957) analyzed a large number of profiles showing that pine was dominant during the full glacial, almost exclusive during drier phases, and present with spruce, oak, and hazel during moister (and slightly warmer?) phases. Charcoal of deciduous hardwoods found at various Hungarian sites as well as in northern Yugoslavia presumably dates from warmer interstadial episodes.

Information from this sector of Europe is still incomplete and does not permit any definitive reconstruction. Frenzel (1960) provides a reasonable although partly hypothetical sketch of vegetation belts.

NON-GLACIATED EUROPEAN RUSSIA

The full glacial geography of European Russia has been well investigated and is competently summarized by Frenzel (1959-60). Apart from the Scandinavian glacier in the northwest, a smaller ice cap centered over Novaya Zemlya (crest elevations 200-1,000 m.,

Würm snowline under 200 m.) invaded a small area of the Arctic coast, while a mountain glaciation enveloped the northern Urals (crest elevations 1,000-1,600 m., Würm snowline at 500-800 m.). Further east, glaciation in Siberia was limited to certain highland areas as a result of continentality and insufficient moisture. Frenzel (1959, Fig. 4, p. 102 f.) indicates that ice wedges and involutions have been found as far south as the northern shores of the Black and Caspian Seas. The southern limit of discontinuous permafrost was then probably located at about the 46th parallel where mean annual temperatures range between +8° to 10° C. today.

Three major physical belts are distinguished by Frenzel in the unglaciated parts of the country: (*a*) A broad expanse of herbaceous tundra was found north of the main Würm tree-line, which crossed east-northeastward from southern Poland to the southern Urals. *Artemisia* as well as a number of salt-tolerant plants were prominent in this vegetational association. Saline soils are not unknown over permafrost in the arctic today, although the origin of the salt is obscure. The tree-line itself was located close to the modern +19° C. isotherm for July, again suggesting a summer temperature depression of 7°-9° C. (*b*) South of the tree-line a broad belt of forest-tundra or forest steppe gave way to small woodland areas around the Carpathian foothills, on the central Russian uplands, in the Crimea and the southern Urals, and along the shores of the Caspian Sea which at this time was expanded to about twice its present size. (*c*) As a third unit, loess tundra extended over southern Russia, characterized by an association of NAP similar to that of the herbaceous tundra adjacent to the ice sheet, but with widespread loess deposition. Galeria forests, partly with coniferous species, accompanied the moister river lowlands.

The dominance of steppe and tundra through most of the country, despite the presence of a parkland vegetation with scattered arboreal tree growth, can only be explained by a dry, extremely continental climate.

FULL GLACIAL TEMPERATURE CONDITIONS

In the previous sections the approximate distribution of ice wedges, and by inference, of discontinuous or continuous permafrost, was discussed for Europe. On the existing evidence it would be unjustified to draw a precise "line" designed to represent either the permafrost or ice wedge limit. In some areas, the ice sheets set one of the few more convincing limits, for it is assumed that the insulation provided by the ice would enable heat from the earth's interior to remove permafrost conditions previously established. Consequently, the ice sheets set definite limits to the north, while the Alpine glacier apparently set a comparable limit in the south, since ice wedges have not yet been recorded from the Po Valley. Due to the variation of local climatic and soil conditions in mountain areas, there is little chance that a reliable permafrost limit could be drawn through mountainous terrain. In three major lowland areas—western France, the Hungarian Plain, and the southern Ukraine—information is far too incomplete. The extent of full glacial lowland permafrost given in Fig. 51 is therefore rather tentative.

The location of the arctic tree-line is better known, although no exact data are available from France. Information concerning altitudinal zonation of climate is generally unavailable from the highland areas. The zone between the ice front and the tree-line can, with some reliability, be placed in the tundra (ET) climates of Koeppen. It serves no obvious purpose to distinguish climatic subtypes within this ET zone, such as Poser (1948) suggests. The available evidence is insufficient, and the quantitative significance of such subdivisions would be obscure. Neither does the distinction of "frost-rubble" and loess tundra in Büdel (1951a) or Frenzel (1959-60) have any legitimate inference for either vegetation or climate. Much, if not the greater part, of this "frost-rubble tundra" was in reality clad by herbaceous vegetation.

Reviewing the values of suggested temperature depressions one can hardly avoid the conclusion that mean annual temperatures throughout the main Würm permafrost zone were in the order of 10°-12°, or more, lower than today. There is no reason to assume that these temperatures were confined to Germany between the Alpine and Scandinavian glaciers, as Poser (1948) and others have implied. In the light of evidence elsewhere it is difficult to reconcile such a value with a general planetary temperature reduction in the order of 4° C. suggested by Flohn (1953), of 5°-6° C. according to Emiliani (1955a). At the Würm tree-line, the inference for July temperature depressions is in the order of 7°-9° C., suggesting that winters rather than summers were anomalously cold.

Mortensen (1952) was probably the first to suggest the presence of a secondary cooling effect in the areas adjacent to the continental glaciers. In this way a cold air dome (or surface temperature inversion), considerably cooler than the overlying atmosphere (at 2,500 m. according to Mortensen [1952], 1,000 m. according to Flohn [1953]), would persist during much of the year. The area affected by such an inversion must have extended 1,000-1,500 km. beyond the major continental glaciers however, something not realized by either Mortensen or Flohn at the time. Modern, semipermanent analogies from the Greenland ice cap (Flohn, 1952) and the Antarctic ice sheet (Sabbagh, 1962) are convincing. Seasonally, the winter surface inversions over North America and Siberia (Willett and Sanders, 1959, Fig. 13; Flohn, 1952, Fig. 1), during well-developed high pressure or anticyclonic conditions, are easily comparable in both dimensions and mechanics to the surface cooling effects suggested for Würm-age Europe. The elevation of the temperature inversion responsible for the continental dimensions of the former European inversion must, however, have been closer to the 2,500 m. mark cited by Mortensen, rather than to the 1,000 m. elevation suggested by Flohn. It may be assumed that a semipermanent winter anticyclone, of similar intensity and depth as the modern Siberian anticyclone, was centered over Europe during the full glacial. During the greater part of the winter half-year, local surface temperatures may have been in the order of 20° C. "below normal." Averaged out for the year as a whole, this would more or less account for the available evidence.

FULL GLACIAL MOISTURE CONDITIONS

Of apparent significance for evaluation of moisture conditions in glacial Europe are the widespread loess mantles (Fig. 51) (see Frenzel, 1959, pp. 109-15) south of the polar tree-line. Accepting the presence of permafrost in most of these regions, it is difficult to weigh the effects of physiological drought due to extreme winter cold and the effects of possible climatic aridity. Widespread "steppe indicator" plants and steppe faunal elements may only indicate that the physiological processes of vegetative life were frequently interrupted in summer by freezing or near-freezing soil temperatures. Similarly, the halophytes present, capable of exerting exceptionally great osmotic pressures in the root zone, were possibly better adapted to physiological (as opposed to climatic) drought. There may certainly have been saline soils in the permafrost belt, but the salt-tolerating halophytes, the steppe indicators, and the absence of forest growth through much of the southeast European lowlands is all a part of the general problem of physiological versus climatic aridity in very cold environments. Paleobotanists have so far found no solution for it.

The available physical evidence in favor of increased aridity in middle latitude Europe is expressed in the following arguments: (a) the widely observed phenomenon that early glacial solifluction (under moister, oceanic conditions?) was frequently replaced by full glacial loess deposition (under drier, continental conditions) (Büdel, 1950b; Frenzel, 1960, p. 89 ff.; Fink, 1962); (b) the occurrence of loess steppes in areas forested today; (c) the occurrence of steppe floras and faunas in both the tundra and steppe regions; and (d) the fact that the snowline depression of the central European highlands (1,200 m.) is not "sufficient" in view of a temperature depression of at least 11° C. The question of physiological drought renders (a) to (c) inconclusive. Point (d) is open to dispute. Klein (1953) argues that the "deficient" snowline depression was a result of reduced precipitation. Klein suggested a precipitation reduction of 150 mm. for every 100 m. of difference between the observed Würm snowline, and the snowline "to be expected" by a temperature depression of, for example, 12° C. Although a part of the difference may well be due to reduced precipitation, Klein's argument as such is fallacious. A surface temperature inversion, such as postulated for Europe at the time, would have been much less evident at higher elevations, i.e., at the critical snowline altitude (Flohn, 1953).

The geomorphic processes recorded do not all support an argument for climatic aridity. The Aral and Caspian Seas stood 12 m. and 75-77 m. respectively higher than today (see Frenzel, 1960, p. 86; Butzer, 1958a, pp. 95-97). The latter overflowed into the Black Sea across the Manych depression during the early glacial, although it appears that the Caspian Sea level dropped to 26-28 m. above the present during the full glacial. The major control of Caspian Sea fluctuations today is summer temperature over the Volga drainage basin (Butzer, 1958d). Evaporation over both the watershed as well as over the sea itself was considerably reduced during the Würm, while a part of the rivers draining northward to the Baltic and White Seas were diverted southward to the Volga system. This can adequately explain the improved hydrological budget of these Asiatic lakes, but at the same time does not support the hypothesis of greater aridity. A similar argument is offered by the general alluviation of streams in what is now temperate Europe. This cold-climate aggradation, discussed in chapter 11, does not prove greater humidity but does not necessarily support greater aridity either. Thomé (1958) has convincingly illustrated the impressive summer discharge of the Rhine River during the full glacial.

The most convincing argument in favor of increased aridity is climatic. Severely reduced air temperatures over Europe necessarily brought a considerable decrease in atmospheric moisture content; reduced evaporation over the oceans (by somewhat over 20 per cent, [Flohn, 1953]) would decrease average world precipitation in general; and lastly, a cold air dome over Europe during the winter half-year would impede the passage of rain-bringing cyclonic disturbances. These theoretical arguments are convincing even though not as yet supported by sufficient empirical evidence.

THE GEOMORPHIC LANDSCAPE OF THE WÜRM TUNDRAS OF EUROPE

To complete the picture of the physical landscape of full glacial Europe—as a potential environment to man and animal—a brief sketch of geomorphic processes may be of interest.

Firstly, the general topography of the continent was altered by the glacio-eustatic sea-level lowering of 100 m., as well as by the extension of the Scandinavian and British glaciers. Not only was the land surface of these areas obliterated, but the existing drainage patterns were disrupted and new streams of glacial meltwaters complicated the hydrographic picture.

Ahead of the ice, meltwater streams deposited outwash over wide areas periodically inundated during early summer. At intervals, extensive fans of sandy deposits were alluviated along the ice margins. In central Europe these meltwaters eventually drained into the great river valleys, known as glacial spillways, which carried the diverted waters of the Vistula (Weichsel) and Oder (and during earlier glaciations, of the Elbe, Weser, and Rhine as well) westward along the front of the ice. The outwash beds were liable to wind deflation in late summer, as were also the fresh till beds gradually exposed by the ice during the glacial retreat.

Further south, rivers and streams alluviated disproportionately wide floodplains. River channels were braided and characterized by great spring to early summer floods, following the annual snow thaw. Smaller valleys ("dry valleys"), with little or no surficial stream discharge today, harbored watercourses as a result of the impermeability of the permafrost subsoil.

Between the rivers, aeolian deposition of loess was common in many of the lowlands and in topographic hollows within more rugged terrain. Frost-weathering was prominent on exposed bedrock, and solifluction processes were active on moderate and steeper slopes. Talus accumulation was rapid at the foot of rock ledges or cliffs.

Flat-lying surfaces were probably poorly drained as a result of permafrost in the subsoil.

Generally speaking, the dynamism of geomorphic processes was largely comparable to that found in the herbaceous tundra today, a background factor of some importance in evaluating the ecological setting of contemporary human cultures.

PHYSICAL CONDITIONS DURING THE INTERSTADIAL PERIODS

In a broad way the improvement of physical conditions during the many warmer spells, characterized by oscillations of the ice margins and of the vegetation zones of Europe, was at a level intermediate between contemporary and full glacial conditions. Forest-tundra, scrub, or boreal woodlands reoccupied most of the former tundra belt in a rather short time. Pollen analyses of deposits attributed to the Brörup in Denmark and the Netherlands (Andersen, 1961, with references) indicate the presence of temperate forests in those countries. Brörup interstadial beds from Unter-Wisternitz, Moravia, contained some pollen dominated by NAP (52 per cent), and pine (35 per cent), with traces of oak, alder, hazel, elm, and linden (in order of importance) (R. Schütrumpf in Brandtner 1956; see also Fink, 1962, for stratigraphic position).

Palynological evidence from the Paudorf interstadial is missing in northern Europe (Andersen, 1961), and if present in southern central Europe is stratigraphically not clearly defined. A number of undated interstadial beds may belong either to the Brörup or Paudorf. These include:

a) A peat intercalation in valley fill near Strassburg (140 m.) (Lemée 1954). Pine pollen represents 95 per cent of the pollen at the base, with birch and spruce gradually increasing to 30 per cent at the top of the profile, and oak attaining a 15 per cent maximum midway in the sequence. Hazel, alder (*Alnus glutinosa*), and willow occur sporadically, while NAP is scarce.

b) Deposits from the Mauern Caves near Steppberg, southern Germany, containing charcoal of *Pinus silvestris*, *P. cembra*, *Quercus pedunculata*, *Fraxinus exelsior*, and *Fagus silvatica* (Hofmann in Zotz, 1955), although the agency of burrowing rodents cannot be excluded.

c) Several Hungarian caves from which almost 1,000 charcoal samples of possible Paudorf age have been analyzed (Firbas and Frenzel, 1960, with references) demonstrate the presence of *Pinus silvestris, P. cembra,* and *Larix decidua* as dominant species, with smaller amounts of maple, elm, ash, oak and linden, and a single sample of beech.

Obviously the paleobotanical evidence of Würm interstadial episodes is incoherent and fragmentary. A sole exception to this is the Alleröd interval discussed in chapter 28.

The second major class of information on environmental conditions during the Würm interstadials comes from fossil soils. The correlation of such soils in Austria has been convincingly established by Fink (1962, with references to detailed section descriptions), in southern Germany by Brunnacker (1958). So-called *Nassböden* ("wet soils") frequently interrupt most loess profiles of central Europe. Such soils display humic *A*-horizons, with *G*-horizon mottling and platy structure indicative of waterlogging, and are interpreted as "humid tundra soils."

Considerably more work must obviously be done before environmental interpretation of the Würm interstadials becomes possible.

SUMMARY OF MAIN WÜRM CLIMATIC ZONATION IN EUROPE

In retrospect, the present state of knowledge on main Würm climates in mid-latitude Europe permits several tentative conclusions.

a) A frost climate, comparable to the Koeppen *EF* climates, was characteristic for three broad areas occupied by the Scandinavian, British, and Alpine glaciers. July mean temperatures certainly did not exceed +4° C., and were probably generally less than 0° C.

b) A tundra climate, comparable to the Koeppen *ET* climate, occupied much of France, most of central Europe, and the unglaciated northern parts of Russia. This broad belt simultaneously had continuous or discontinuous permafrost. This assumes a July mean under +10° to 12° C., and an annual mean under —2° C. For an unspecified locality, where the southern discontinuous permafrost and arctic tree-limit coincided (in eastern Austria and central France?), Poser (1948) suggests the following monthly temperature values in degrees Centigrade for January through December: [1]

---

[1] To obtain these values, Poser employs two assumptions, namely that in Europe today the April and October means are approximately equal to the mean annual temperature, and that the annual march of temperature approximates a sine curve. While both assumptions are reasonable for modern climatic conditions in Europe, question may be raised about their validity for colder and certainly more continental climates of the late Pleistocene.

—13 —12 —8 —2 4 8 10 8 4 —2 —8 —12

This assumes an annual mean of —2° C., a July mean of 10° C. and implicitly, an annual range of 23° C. (21°-22° C. in eastern Austria today).

c) A forest-tundra or loess-tundra belt with permafrost, possibly comparable to Koeppen's winter-dry *Dc* climates was found in Hungary, Romania, and the southern half of European Russia. At a guess, by modern analogy, July means possibly lay around the 12°-13° C. mark, with 30-40 frost-free days a year.

d) A cold-temperate forest, without permafrost and possibly comparable to Koeppen's humid *Dc* and *Db* climates, was probably first encountered along the Mediterranean borderlands and along the southern shores of the Caspian. Probably the temperature and ecological transition was rather rapid here.

These conditions appear reasonable as a reconstruction of main Würm eco-zones in mid-latitude Europe, and probably also give a fair impression of conditions during the slightly colder Riss and Elster glaciations. Prior to the late Pleistocene however, documentation of cold climate phenomena is still—and may well remain—hopelessly inadequate.

19

The Mediterranean Region during the Late Pleistocene

INTRODUCTION

Lower middle latitudes experienced considerable changes of climate during the course of the Pleistocene, although the geomorphic imprint of these paléoclimates on the landscape is less apparent than in temperate Europe. Among the reasons for limited landform sculpture is the absence of cold-climate processes except in the uplands. Lower elevations enjoyed forest vegetation throughout the Pleistocene.

Interpretation and documentation of Pleistocene features and paleoclimates in the Mediterranean lands are unfortunately incomplete. The pollen record known to date is fragmentary: a few profiles are recorded from Spain and Italy, with little or nothing elsewhere. Faunal evidence is available and may occasionally assume an important role. Geomorphic evidence is to some extent confused by features indicating greater cold in the highlands (presumably of main glacial age) and others indicating pluvial conditions in the lowlands (during the early glacial in particular). Although a rough qualitative picture of the environment may be obtained, accurate quantitative estimates of temperature or precipitation anomalies are not possible at the moment. Nor is a regional outline possible on account of the fragmentary nature of the evidence. Consequently, the discussion will be arranged topically. As comprehensive studies are lacking for the area, individual categories of evidence are often outlined in some detail.

EVIDENCE OF MOUNTAIN GLACIATION

Mountain glaciation, particularly during the maximum of the Würm was common, although areally insignificant, in most of the Mediterranean world. Practically everywhere confined to small cirque or valley glaciers, the importance of glaciation lies solely in its paleo-climatic implications.

Beginning in the west, the Iberian Peninsula experienced local glaciations, in the Cantabrian Mountains adjacent to the Bay of Biscay (crest elevations 1,500-2,600 m., Würm snowline at 1,400-1,800 m.), the Central Sierras (crest elevations 1,900-2,600 m., Würm snowline rising west to east from 1,650 to 2,000 m.), and the Sierra Nevada (to 3,478 m., Würm snowline at 2,200 m.). The snowline depression of the Cantabrian Mountains amounted to 1,000 m. (Nussbaum and Gygax, 1952), 1,300 m. on the northern face of the Sierra Nevada (Paschinger, 1954), compared with 600-700 m. on the southern flanks and 1,400-1,500 m. on the northern face of the Pyrenees (see Solé Sabarís et al., 1957, pp. 15-17). In a more general way the regional climatic snowline depression can be estimated at about 1,000 m.

In Morocco the Rif ranges (2,000-2,450 m., Würm snowline at 2,400 m.) and Middle Atlas (crest elevations 3,500-4,100 m., Würm snowline at 3,200-3,500 m.) had localized glaciers (summarized by Mensching, 1955a; Raynal, 1956). The regional snowline depression is estimated at 1,000 m. in the maritime Rif, at 700-800 m. in the continental interior. The low Jurjura Mountains (2,308 m.), southeast of Algiers, were also glaciated, with a snowline estimated at 1,900 m. (Büdel, 1952).

The now unglaciated Apennine ranges of Italy (crest elevations 1,600-2,900 m.) have dispersed glacial forms in the highest regions, suggesting a Würm snowline at 1,200-1,500 m. in the Italian Riviera region, at 1,700-2,000 m. in central Italy, at 1,900 m. in the southern part of the ranges (summarized by Klebelsberg, 1948-49, Vol. II). As the highest mountains of the Gran Sasso reach 2,921 m., the snowline depression presumably exceeded 1,100 m. In Corsica (to 2,707 m.), the Würm snowline is estimated at about 1,800 m. (see Klaer, 1956). The other large Mediterranean islands (Mallorca, 1,445 m.; Sardinia, 1,843 m.; Sicily, 3,263 m.; Crete, 2,456 m.; and Cyprus, 1,953 m.) show no convincing evidence of glaciation.

Further east, the highlands of Albania and Greece (crest elevations 2,100-2,900 m.) were locally glaciated, indicating a Würm snowline rising from about 1,800 m. in the western coastal range to 2,300 m. in the interior (summarized by Klebelsberg, 1948-49, Vol. II). Anatolia was likewise affected with numerous local glaciations in the major ranges (summarized in Butzer, 1958a, pp. 43-46). The Pontic or Black

Sea ranges, rising from crests of 2,400-2,500 m. in the west to 3,700-3,900 m. in the east, had Würm snowline elevations of 2,300-2,600 m. In the western Taurus of southwestern Anatolia (2,300-3,000 m.) the snowline varied from 2,100-2,500 m.; for the central Taurus (crestlines 2,700-3,900 m.) this value is 2,500-2,900 m.; for the southeastern Taurus (crestlines 3,400-4,100 m.), 2,600-3,000 m.

In the Armenian Plateau conditions were similar, while the important Caucasus range (crest elevations 3,600-5,600 m.) was extensively glaciated (see Klebelsberg, 1948-49, Vol. II). The modern snowline here lies at 2,800-3,500 m., rising from west to east; the Würm snowline is estimated at 2,000-2,800 m. The climatic snowline depression for eastern Anatolia and the Causasus can be estimated at 700-800 m.

Beyond the immediate confines of the Mediterranean area, evidence of glaciation is recorded from the northern Zagros, Kurdistan, where Wright (1962b) obtains a phenomenal snowline depression of 1,200-1,800 m. for the 3,000-3,600 m. ranges. H. Bobek, however, finds it impossible to confirm these conclusions on the basis of air photo surveys (personal communication). Elsewhere in Iran (Butzer, 1958a, pp. 46-47, with references), the Würm snowline in Persian Azerbaijan (Seidan, 3,615 m.; Savalan, 4,812 m.; Sahend, 3,690 m.) was located at 3,200-3,500 m., in the Elburz range (crest elevations 4,000-5,600 m.) at 3,300-4,150 m., in the southern Zagros (Zardeh Kuh, 4,286 m.) at 3,350-3,400 m. The snowline depression amounts to at least 700-800 m. in northern Iran, 600-650 m. further south. Possible glaciations in Lebanon (3,076 m.) and on Mt. Sinai (2,641 m.) have been negated by Klaer (1959).

Snowline depressions applied to temperature estimates would theoretically suggest that the western Mediterranean was 5°-6° C. colder, the Near East only 4° C. colder. This serves to emphasize that the assumption of similar precipitation and radiation is not justified. The most likely factors able to cause such significant differences between the western and eastern basins are precipitation and cloudiness. It is commonly assumed that Würm-age precipitation in the western Mediterranean was greater than today. The writer however believes that since the main glacial was generally dry in the first place, it is more likely that the eastern Mediterranean was comparatively drier than the western basin. An intermediate value of 5° C. may be a fair approximation of the true temperature depression for the area as a whole. This value coincides with the (main glacial) O^{18}/O^{16} isotopic temperature obtained by Emiliani (1955b) from a deep-sea core from the eastern Mediterranean. Snowline depression temperature estimates are obviously not a desirable class of information, but at least they are helpful when other means of estimation are absent.

LATE PLEISTOCENE SOLIFLUCTION IN THE MEDITERRANEAN HIGHLANDS

Reliable evidence of Pleistocene permafrost is lacking in the Mediterranean region. However cold-climate phenomena are relatively frequent in the highlands and were of considerable areal extent during the late Pleistocene. Generally, the evidence consists of solifluction mantles, occasionally with cryoturbations or grading over into block streams. True involutions are very scarce. Such evidence of periglacial activity is a result of short-term soil frost, on a daily or seasonal basis. Its significance is mostly indirect: the lower limit of cold-climate solifluction gives a fair approximation of the altitudinal forest limit and so delimits the zone of alpine meadows. The Würm-age depression of the lower solifluction limit is also of some value in itself.

Features due to late Pleistocene solifluction are best known from the Iberian Peninsula, the French Midi, and from Morocco. Similar features have been little studied elsewhere. A major difficulty is stratigraphic dating. Raynal (1956) has indicated that in the Rif of Morocco, cold-climate solifluction sheets grade over imperceptibly into pluvial slope breccias of colluvial origin, which in turn extend down to and below modern sea level. It has been shown that such colluvial deposits are of early glacial age in eastern Spain (Butzer 1964a, 1964b) so that in good probability many of the solifluction deposits in question do not date from the period of greatest cold during the full glacial. They may instead reflect comparatively cool, pluvial conditions during the earlier Würm. In many areas there is evident confusion concerning the identification of cold-climate solifluction and pluvial slope breccias due to colluviation ("pluvial solifluction").

Starting with Spain, the lower limit of modern solifluction in the central, southern Pyrenees appears to lie at about 2,200 m. (Solé Sabarís et al., 1957, pp. 70-71), whereas Würm (?) solifluction mantles occur down to 800 m. in the same area (see Butzer and Fränzle, 1959). On the northern coast of Spain, colluvial deposits with evidence of cryoturbation appear to occur to below elevations of 100 m. (Llopís-Lládo, 1957, p. 32; H. Franz, cited by Fränzle, 1959a, p. 64). In northwestern Spain, in the province of Pontevedra, evidence of solifluction is lacking below 300 m. (or higher) (Butzer, unpublished). In Mallorca, late Pleistocene solifluction is wholly absent below 950 m.

(Butzer, 1964b) and does not occur down to 500 m. (as previously reported by Mensching, 1955b). An "ice-wedge" reported from an elevation of 200 m. near Zaragoza (Johnsson, 1960) cannot be accepted as valid evidence, but must be interpreted as colluvial filling of a crack due either to microtectonics or dehydration. In the central cordillera, where solifluction features occur above about 2,000 m. today (Fränzle, 1959a, p. 34 ff.), late Pleistocene block streams occur to below 1,100 m. elevation (Fränzle, 1959, p. 62), while colluvial slope breccias with limited evidence of solifluction (Würm?) occur to a lower limit of 1,000 m. (Butzer, 1964b). Finally, in the Sierra Nevada Pleistocene solifluction features occur to a lower limit of 1,000 m., about 1,100 m. lower than today (Paschinger, 1961). In summary, the upper limit of *closed* forest for the Iberian Peninsula can be estimated at about 1,000 m. in southern, eastern, and central Spain, at 800 m. in the southern Pyrenees, and possibly below 100 m. north of the Cantabrian Mountains. As shown below, this is substantiated by critical pollen studies in Catalonia and northwestern Spain as well as by faunal evidence. The depression of the lower limit of solifluction amounted to perhaps 1,400 m. in the far north, to 1,000-1,100 m. elsewhere in the country. This exceeds the value of the regional snowline depression. The exceptionally high value in the Pyrenean and Cantabrian regions may indicate the presence of strong horizontal temperature gradients in these areas, which separated the subarctic and temperate parts of Europe during the glacial periods.

In Morocco, the lower limit of Würm-age solifluction in the western Rif lies at 800-1,000 m. (Mensching, 1955a), in the eastern Rif at 800 m. (today 1,500-1,550 m.), in the central Rif at 900-1,000 m. (today 2,000 m.) (Raynal, 1956). In the Middle Atlas, Würm solifluction deposits of semifluvial character are typical to elevations as low as 1,600 m. and occur to 1,400 m. (1,900-2,000 m. today) (Raynal, 1956, 1960b). In the High Atlas such features occur above 2,700-3,100 m. today (Raynal, 1956), but extended down to 1,800-1,900 m. during the late Pleistocene (Raynal, 1960b). The lower limits of Pleistocene cold-climate solifluction in Morocco seem to lie at about 800-1,000 m. in the northwest, rising gradually to 1,800-1,900 m. in the southeastern ranges. The Würm-age depression varied regionally between 700 and 1,100 m., averaging about 850 m. This value is less than the one for Spain, a fact which may either reflect greater aridity or smaller Würm temperature depressions at lower latitudes.

In southern France, Würm solifluction with evidence of cryoturbation is found to elevations of 200-300 m. in the western French Alps

(Raynal, cited by Mensching, 1955a), and possibly to about sea level in Languedoc and in the French Riviera (Tricart, 1956a). In Corsica, similar features occur to elevations no lower than 500 m. (Büdel, 1953; Klaer, 1956; see also Tricart, 1956a). Information for Italy is almost limited to some cursory remarks by Nangeroni (1952) and Tricart and Cailleux (1956) about Würmian (?) cold-climate deposition of vague implications at 550 m. in the Umbrian Apennines. Büdel (1951b) reports fossil solifluction deposits from about 1,000-1,200 m. in southern Italy (today above 2,000 m.).

In the eastern Mediterranean basin the only known evidence appears to concern Crete, where the present lower limit of "periglacial" phenomena is at 1,800 m., the lower limit of Würm solifluction at 800 m. (Poser, 1957). Evidence in the Near East is scanty and summarized by Butzer (1958a, p. 50) and Klaer (1963). Fossil slope breccias, presumably related to solifluction, occur down to 1,500 m. in the central Taurus of Anatolia, to 2,300 m. in Iran. The Würm-age depression may amount to about 700 m. No general conclusions can be suggested for either the central or eastern Mediterranean areas.

PALEOBOTANICAL EVIDENCE FOR THE WÜRM PERIOD

Palynological and macrofossil study of late Pleistocene vegetation in the Mediterranean region is still in its infancy and practically confined to Spain and Italy. Its significance here is confined to corroboration of the upper forest limit estimated from geomorphic evidence, and to broad identification of the forest types in the northwestern Mediterranean borderlands.

A pollen profile from the Laguna de las Sanguijuelas at 1,000 m., near the Portuguese border in northwestern Spain (Prov. Zamora), has been studied by Menéndez-Amor and Florschütz (1961) and radiocarbon dated. The lowest part of the profile, prior to a C14 date (Gro. 705) of 13,700 B.P., is characterized by 65-85 per cent NAP, and 15-35 per cent pine, together with traces of birch (8 out of 8 samples), willow and oak (each in 6 samples), hazel and alder (each in 2 samples). Grasses, Artemisia (to 20 per cent) and other steppe indicators such as Ephedra, Helianthemum, Thalictrum, and Hippophae account for the NAP. Macrofossils of birch have been identified in the same profile. The interpretation of an open parkland with scattered groups of pine suggests an alpine forest-tundra with some few thermophile species growing at lower elevations. A temperate woodland was already found in the area during the later Alleröd, while oak and pine dominate the vegetation today.

Equally valuable is a pollen profile studied from the Cueva del Toll at 750 m. near Moyá, 50 km. north of Barcelona (Donner and Kurtén, 1958). In what is faunistically the late Pleistocene, pollen spectra recording forests dominated by *Pinus silvestris* (NAP 15-34 per cent) alternate with spectra suggesting open herbaceous vegetation (NAP 49-51 per cent) with a few deciduous trees. Donner and Kurtén (1958) interpret the former associations as "temperate-humid," the latter "warm-dry." In one case of the high NAP assemblages (51 per cent, layer *h*), however, the geologic deposits (Serra Ráfols *et al.*, 1957) consist of a breccia of uncorroded, non-cemented, very flat and angular éboulis, with a mammalian fauna containing such alpine species as *Microtus nivalis*, *Rupicapra rupicapra*, and *Capra ibex pyrenaica*, as well as *Tichorhinus antiquitatis*. Admittedly, a half of the fauna of this stratum is woodland in character, while among the 49 per cent arboreal pollen, oak accounts for 4 per cent, elm 1 per cent, hazel 1 per cent, with birch 2 per cent and pine 41 per cent. Despite these apparent contradictions layer *h* may represent the Würm maximum. The remainder of the profile leaves no doubt that cool-temperate, subboreal forests dominated the area during most of the late Pleistocene. The present vegetation consists of evergreen oak (*Quercus lusitanica*) and beech, and is submediterranean in character.

In northern Italy pollen has been obtained from some peaty clays present in deep bores near Ravenna. Two sections studied at —22 and —26 m. at Forli (Firbas and Zangheri, 1954; Dubois and Zangheri, 1957) showed an average of 85 per cent pine, 4 per cent spruce, 4 per cent birch, 4 per cent willow, 2 per cent larch, 1 per cent aspen. A single pollen of oak is the only thermophile representative, leaving no doubt that this was a time of boreal forest. Judging by the modern distribution of oak in Europe (Walter, 1954, Fig. 135) this vegetation assemblage belongs in the *Db* or *Dc* climates of Köppen, possibly suggesting a mean annual temperature under +6° C. (today +16° C.) and a July mean in the order of +16 to 18° C. (today +25° C.) for the lower Po Valley. This is analogous to the Würm temperature depression suggested for middle latitude Europe. A last glacial age is suggested for these spectra by the presence of an interglacial type assemblage, with 49 per cent pollen of deciduous species, found at —75 m. in the same area. A similar glacial spectrum was studied underlying a postglacial pollen sequence near Este in the Po-Adige lowland by Lona (1957, cited by Firbas and Frenzel, 1960). Also analogous is the succession of macrobotanical evidence studied northwest of Pisa in the Bassa Versilia (A. C. Blanc, 1936; Tongiorgi, 1938), and south-west of Rome in the Agro Pontino (A. C. Blanc, 1935, 1959, with references; Tongiorgi, 1938; Blanc, De Vries, and Follieri, 1957).

In the Agro Pontino a series of peat strata overlie a typical Tyrrhenian II beach with the mollusca *Strombus bubonius* and *Conus testudinarius* at +5.1 m. At the base of the terrestrial deposits, species such as wild grape (*Vitis vinifera*), *Quercus robur*, *Cornus mas*, and *Carpinus betulus* indicate submediterranean to warm-temperate con-ditions. At higher levels, further warm-temperate species such as hazel, yew, and beech, as well as a cool-temperate indicator, white fir (*Abies alba*), appear in a stratum dated at 59,000 B.P. by C[14] (com-ment by A. C. Blanc on Movius, 1960). *Abies alba* dominates the top of these peats. The fauna of the peats include typical sylvan forms such as *Elephas antiquus, Dicerorhinus mercki, Cervus elaphus, Capre-olus capreolus,* and at another contemporary site, hippopotamus. The sequence is followed up by regressional dunes containing bones of woolly mammoth and showing evidence of frost-weathering, but with no plant remains. The Bassa Versilia sequence shows that the *Abies alba* forests were eventually replaced by cool-temperate forests of sub-boreal type with *Pinus montana mugo* and *P. silvestris*. According to profiles compiled by Dubois and Zangheri (1957) from the Ravenna-Forli area, an *Abies* stage also seems to precede the full glacial boreal forests there.

The above evidence for the western Mediterranean Basin seems to indicate that true mediterranean-type woodlands were confined to low elevations and to the southerly half of the western Mediter-ranean basin.

This appears to be substantiated from several pollen analyses of early Würm strata from near the Chott el-Djérid in central Tunisia (Van Campo and Cocque, 1960). The spectra are variable, though always dominated by steppe species. But a component of cedar (*Cedrus*), cypress (*Cupressus*), aleppo pine, and wild olive suggests the presence of typical mediterranean woodlands at slightly higher and moister elevations. A scattering of warm-temperate species is also of interest: the lime, hazel, and hornbeam are unknown in North Africa today, while fir is absent in Tunisia. Climate must have been somewhat cooler and moister.

Evidence from the eastern Mediterranean region and its border-lands is rather sparse. In the Derna coastal area of Cyrenaica, in pluvial deposits postdating a 6 m. Upper Pleistocene beach, McBurney and Hey (1955, pp. 109-110) found the Canary laurel (*Laurus canariensis*) and aleppo pine, suggesting a mediterranean-type woodland. In the Lebanon Mountains, at 2,000 m., tufa impressions of apparent late Pleistocene age include warm-temperate species such as oak, beech, elm, and hazel, rather than submediterranean forms as present there today (see Butzer, 1958a, p. 81). In northeastern Iraq preliminary pollen studies are available from Shanidar Cave at 650 m. (Solecki and Leroi-Gourhan, 1961). A spectrum at —4 m. (unspecified C^{14} date 31,000 B.P.) had 90 per cent NAP, with a few grains of date palm (?). Another spectrum at —3 m. (unspecified C^{14} date 30,400 B.P.) had less NAP (unspecified), with alder and ash present. The earlier phase suggests open country, very possibly mountain tundra. Preliminary pollen cores from a lake at 1,300 m. elevation near Marivan in nearby Iran (Zeist and Wright, 1963) show that a cool, dry *Artemisia* steppe was replaced by an oak-pistachio savanna about 13,000 B.P.

FAUNAL EVIDENCE FROM THE LATE PLEISTOCENE

In lieu of further paleobotanical information a selection of faunal assemblages from different parts of the Mediterranean region will provide a better ecological picture.

Three particular faunal assemblages are of interest in Spain. They include first, an annotated bibliographic study of archeologically associated fossils from the north coast province of Asturias (Oviedo) by Fraga Torrejon (1958), specifically Aurignacian to Magdalenian in date (*ca.* 25,000-11,000 B.C.). This provides a fair picture of the fauna, as paleontologically verified, for the environment of the 0-500 m. elevation range of the northern Spanish coast. This picture coincides remarkably well with that of the contemporary cave art representations of the Cantabrian region (J. M. Leverenz, unpublished research paper, 1960). From northeastern Spain, the rich fauna of the Cueva del Toll (750 m.) (Serra Ráfols *et al.*, 1957) is equally interesting. In Table 15 dominantly woodland animals are indicated with (w), open-country forms (tundra, grassland, mountain) with (o), and more or less indifferent types with (i).

Of the 31 species identified for the Asturian and Cantabrian area, 10 are essentially woodland forms, 10 non-woodland types, while 11 are more indifferent in their ecological requirements. Of the 21 species identified in Catalonia, 9 are woodland types, 6 open country

TABLE 15
MAIN AND LATE WÜRM FAUNAS IN SPAIN
(Woodland (w), Open Country (o) and Indifferent Forms (i) Indicated)

Species	Asturias (Fraga Torrejon, 1958)	Cantabrian Cave Drawings	Cueva del Toll (Serra Ráfols et al., 1957)
Ursus spelaeus (cave bear) (i)	x	x	x
Ursus arctos (brown bear) (w)	x		
Canis lupus (wolf) (i)	x		
Vulpes vulpes (red fox) (w)	x		x
Crocuta crocuta spelaea (cave hyena) (i)	x	x	x
Felis silvestris (wildcat) (w)	x		x
Felis pardina spelaea (cave lynx) (i)	x	x	
Felis leo spelaea (cave lion) (i)	x		x
Meles meles (badger) (i)	x	x	x
Mustela erminea (ermine) (i)	x		
Putorius putorius (polecat) (i)	x		
Lutra lutra (otter) (i)	x		
Erinacaeus europaeus (hedgehog) (w)			x
Marmota marmota (marmot) (o)	x		
Oryctolagus cuniculus (rabbit) (i)			x
Lepus timidus (snowshoe "rabbit") (o)	x		
Castor fiber (beaver) (w)			x
Apodemus silvatica (field mouse) (i)			x
Arvicola amphibius (water vole) (i)	x		
Microtus nivalis (alpine vole) (o)			x
Talpa europaea (bat) (w)			x
Elephas antiquus (w)		x [*]	
Elephas primigenius (o)	x	x	
Dicerorhinus mercki (w)	x		
Tichorhinus antiquitatis (o)	x		
Equus caballus ssp. (wild horse) (o)	x	x	x
Equus asinus hydruntinus (ass) (o)	x	x	
Sus scrofa (boar) (w)	x	x	x
Cervus elaphus (red deer) (w)	x	x	x
Capreolus capreolus (roe deer) (w)	x	x	x
Dama dama (fallow deer) (w)	x	x	
Alces alces (elk) (w)	x	x	
Rangifer tarandus (reindeer) (o)	x		
Rupicapra rupicapra (chamois) (o)	x		x
Capra ibex pyrenaica (ibex) (o)	x	x	x
Bison priscus (o)	x	x	x
Bos primigenius (w)	x	x	x

[*] Confirmed as such from a characteristic Aurignacian drawing in the cave El Pindal located at 15 m. above sea-level, province of Santander, by the proboscidian authority H. F. Osborn (1934-42, Vol. II, pp. 1184, 1252).

forms, 6 indifferent. In each case specific tundra or alpine types are present. But the high percentage of sylvan forms implies that extensive woodlands must have persisted in the 0-500 m. elevation range of Catalonia throughout even the coldest phases of the Würm. The Asturian area was presumably a forest-tundra, while in Catalonia one might expect a subalpine parkland above the lower limit of solifluction (800-1,000 m. in northeastern Spain). Similar conditions must have persisted elsewhere in the Spanish uplands, as suggested by the mixed fauna of Castilian and Andalusian cave drawings in the 500-1,000 m. elevation range, or by contemporary fossils found at cave sites in Gibraltar (Garrod *et al.,* 1928).

The main Würm faunas of Italy are as important as those of Spain. The information provided by the Monte Circeo caves (A. C. Blanc, 1942), the Grotta Romanelli near Otranto (G. A. Blanc, 1921), the Grotto San Teodoro near Messina (Vaufrey, 1928), the Agro Pontino (A. C. Blanc, 1935), or the Ghar Dalam cave of Malta (Vaufrey, 1929) corroborates the sketch of geomorphic and paleobotanical features above, and is faunistically quite analogous to the Iberian Peninsula. Similar mixed faunal associations occur in the Riviera caves at Grimaldi (Boule *et al.,* 1906-19; Boule and De Villeneuve, 1927).

In northwestern Africa, an Ethiopian rather than Palearctic fauna remained dominant through most of the Pleistocene. However several new Palearctic forms appeared during the Würm regression (Arambourg, 1952a, 1962), presumably via Asia and the southern Mediterranean littoral. The Palearctic species include *Bos primigenius,* several deer (*Megaceroides algericus, Cervus elaphus*), the brown bear (*Ursus arctos*), a bear (*Ursus faidherbi*) intermediate between the brown and the cave bear, barbary sheep (*Ammotragus lervia*), boar (*Sus scrofa*), the extinct woodland rhinoceros *Dicerorhinus mercki,* and a dwarf elephant (*Elephas* [*Palaeoloxodon*] *iolensis*). These temperate woodland species, presumably indicative of cooler climate and a southward faunal migration, occur alongside of Ethiopian (or Saharan) species such as the hippopotamus, the white rhino (*Ceratotherium simum*), an elephant closely related to the modern African species, wart-hog, zebra, camel, and a number of antelopes and gazelles. Both the hippo and Merck's rhino had disappeared by the time of the main Würm.

The contemporary fauna of the Upper Paleolithic strata of the Hagfet ed Dabba cave Cyrenaica (Bate, 1955), seem to suggest that a number of Palearctic species passed through the area during the Pleistocene. Together with the bat and rodents such as shrew, gerbil, field mouse, and dormouse, the fox, an extinct Asiatic buffalo (*Homoio-*

ceras antiquus), aurochs (?), barbary sheep, and an unidentified rhinoceros occur in association with Ethiopian forms. The latter include lion, antelope, gazelle, and zebra. The fauna of the Egyptian Nile Valley were also dominated by Palearctic species, e.g., at Kom Ombo (see Gaillard, 1934).

No comparable faunal studies are available from southeastern Europe or Anatolia, but the Levant area provides much interesting information. Exceptionally rich faunas have been studied at the Mt. Carmel caves of Palestine (the Aurigacian beds *D-F* of Mugharet el-Wad, *ca.* 70 m. elevation, by Garrod and Bate, 1937) and at Ksar Akil on the Lebanese coast (*ca.* 25 m., by Hooijer, 1961). The fauna include rodents and other small mammals such as porcupine, squirrel, hare, and hedgehog; carnivores such as marten, badger, wildcat, spotted hyena, wolf, brown bear and its subspecies the ·Syrian bear (*Ursus arctos mediterraneus*), leopard (*Felis [Panthera] pardus*), red fox, and the mustiline (*Vormela peregusna*); herbivores such as boar, red deer, roe deer, fallow deer (*Dama mesopotamica*), wild cattle, gazelles, wild goat (*Capra aegagrus*), the onager (*Equus hemionus*), and wild horse. Of a total of no fewer than twenty-seven species present, nine are more or less indifferent forms, twelve are preferably associated with woodland environments, six with open landscapes. Numerically, the woodland form *Dama mesopotamica* dominates the fauna of both sites during what presumably represented the main Würm. Merck's rhinoceros disappeared from the area at the beginning of the Würm. The fauna of the Umm-Qatafa cave in Judaea, studied by Vaufrey (in Neuville, 1951), is quite analogous to that of Mt. Carmel. No strictly contemporary faunas are known from other parts of the Near East, although late Würm levels at Palegawra (*ca.* 1000 m.) and Shanidar (*ca.* 650 m.) also have a comparable fauna (see Braidwood, Howe, *et al.*, 1960, pp. 58-59, 168-70). The complete absence of truly cold forms in North Africa and the Near Eastern lowlands or foothills is suggestive, while the appearance of numerous temperate zone species points to a southward extension of submediterranean woodlands.

All in all, the faunal evidence of the Mediterranean Basin well substantiates the fragmentary pollen record of a southward shift of temperate woodlands into the now subtropical Mediterranean lowlands. Furthermore, the migration of woodland species of Asiatic derivation into northern Africa during the early Würm probably suggests the presence of non-tropical woodlands fringing the northern coasts of Egypt and Libya.

LATE PLEISTOCENE PLUVIAL PHENOMENA IN THE MEDITERRANEAN LOW-
LANDS

Throughout the mediterranean climate zone of the Mediterranean Basin the early Würm was heralded by intensive sheetflood erosion and deposition of a heterogeneous class of colluvial silts and alluvial gravels. The characteristically "mediterranean," fossil colluvial silts of this true pluvial phase are largely derived from reddish inter-glacial soils (terra rossas in limestone bedrock areas), hence the French technical term of *limons rouges*. One group of these sediments is located in caves, where Arambourg (1952b) first outlined their stratigraphic peculiarity in association with a Mousterian-type indus-try and an Upper Pleistocene fauna of warm-temperate affinities. Another group is largely fluvial, for example the great spreads of red silts associated with the last pluvial of Morocco, first interpreted by Choubert (1948a, 1948b). Probably by far the most characteristic are slope breccias of colluvial origin, such as described by Wiche (1961) for southeastern Spain. More recently local aeolian components have been recognized in Catalonia (Virgili and Zamarreño, 1957) and Tripolitania (Hey, 1962).

Colluvial silts occur through most of the mediterranean wood-land zone. For example they are of considerable importance in the Balearic Islands and to a lesser extent in Catalonia. Analogous although sporadic phenomena can be observed in the interior of Spain where they intergrade with solifluction deposits. The following generaliza-tions are based on field and laboratory studies by the writer in these areas (Butzer, 1963b).

The morphology of these deposits is mainly one of relatively thin areal sheets (to 1 m.), attaining greater thicknesses only at the foot of slopes or in original topographic hollows (to 5 m. or more). Surface slopes seldom exceed 15 per cent, and characteristic examples can be cited where the bedrock topography has slopes of 1-3 per cent. In drainage channels these beds grade laterally into alluvial fill with rounded gravel.

Sedimentology is highly variable. Stratification of individual beds rather than individual coarse components is usual, sorting is less common. At the base of steeper slopes beds may be detrital in character. The amount of coarse component over two millimeters diameter is usually confined to coarse, angular to subrounded gravel embedded in finer sediments. The fines show a grain-size spectrum distributed more or less uniformly among the clay, silt, and fine, medium, and coarse sand fractions. Often a moderate maximum may be found in the coarse silt and finer sand fraction. The writer knows of no spectra over 70 per cent by weight in the silt-fine sand range, so that typical loess deposits are unknown. However, semiaeolian beds are not uncommon in association with regressional dunes—specifically, aeolian materials bedded by rainwash. Most frequently the grain-size distribution is analogous to that of the source materials, i.e., soils and weathered aeolian beds.

Frequently the colluvial silts are interrupted by, interbedded with, or capped by calcareous crusts of the *croûtes zonaires* type (see chap. 11), which occasionally grade into true travertines.

The stratigraphy of the colluvial silts is well defined in the Mediterranean littoral regions (Butzer and Cuerda, 1962a, 1962b). The silts are often interbedded with marine beds of the Tyrrhenian III and were gradually superseded by regressional dunes during the major negative movements of sea level accompanying the advance of the Würm glaciers. Terrestrial silt beds can be found to well below modern sea level, and laterally conformable alluvial fill shows abnormally steep gradients at the coast.

It may also be mentioned that two or three positive interruptions of the Würm regression were followed by colluviation and subsequently by renewed aeolian deposition. This leaves no doubt that several major oscillations of the continental glaciers in higher latitudes had direct repercussions in the Mediterranean area, i.e., the readvances were associated with secondary maxima of the peculiar climatic regime responsible for silt colluviation.

Geomorphological interpretation of the *limons rouges* must account for extensive denudation accompanied by colluviation and valley alluviation. The primary fact of greater water transporting capacity by streams is quantitatively confirmed by morphometric gravel analysis. Comparative statistical analyses of recent and various Pleistocene gravels in identical stream valleys showed that although the early Würm was not the wettest pluvial, it was certainly moister than the Holocene. Colluvial spreads on nearly flat surfaces indicated a fair degree of rolling of the contained pebbles, often more so than in modern torrent beds. No assumption of perennial stream flow is warranted for torrents which now enjoy only episodic or seasonal waterflow. But the periodic flash floods must have been more frequent or capable of carrying a load over greater distances.

The paleoclimatic interpretation is then one of (*a*) greater rainfall intensity to permit effective erosion,[1] and (*b*) greater rainfall amount to permit widespread transport of materials. A pronounced dry season must have persisted to account for the nature of the vegetative mat.

The colluvial silts of eastern Spain, here singled out as the most characteristic Mediterranean pluvial phenomena, are widespread. Associated with several Pleistocene phases they are not limited to the littorals of the western Mediterranean Basin but also occur in western Morocco and have been described from Tripolitania, Palestine, and Lebanon. Their affinities to colluviation in the humid subtropics and the savannas are apparent.

In many coastal areas of the Mediterranean, colluvial silts are followed up by regressional aeolianites (see chap. 14), probably indicating that conditions were no moister than now during the main Würm. For the subsequent glacial retreat the paleoclimatic record is covered by the soils developed upon the colluvial silts and aeolianites of the earlier Würm. These soils are practically identical in type and depth of profile with the climax soils on Holocene dunes, namely dry rendzinas. The soil profiles consist of 40-65 cm. A-horizons of light brown color, with moder (or mulliform moder) humus and fine granular structure. A *Ca-C*-horizon of 10-40 cm. may underlie the A-horizon. In other words climatic conditions since the glacial maximum have generally been as dry as or drier than today's. A more detailed climatic chronology of broad Mediterranean validity is, however, not yet possible for the late Pleistocene. Local stratigraphies have been suggested for the Levant by Howell (1959a) and for Mallorca by Butzer and Cuerda (1962a).

RETROSPECT OF THE MEDITERRANEAN ECO-ZONE DURING THE LATE PLEISTOCENE

In comparison to the many studies of late Pleistocene geography of mid-latitude Europe or certain parts of Africa, no systematic attempt to discuss the major features of the Mediterranean late Pleistocene has been made to date. Therefore this discussion has necessarily been detailed, the presentation topical rather than regional in approach. Without a proper understanding of this area, the interplay of cold and pluvial phenomena in different latitudes cannot be properly deciphered.

---

[1] Quantitative work by Barat (1957) confirms that erosive capacity and sheet-flood level are proportional to rainfall intensity and raindrop size.

Some of the salient features are apparent:

a) Localized mountain glaciations were found in numerous high-lands, indicating a snowline rising from about 1,500 m. in the far northwest to over 3,000 m. in the south and east. Würm snowline depressions range from 1,000 m. in the maritime west to 700-800 m. in the continental interiors and in the Near East.

b) Cold-climate solifluction, in what was probably alpine meadow or subalpine parkland, affected most of the highlands of southern Europe above elevations of 1,000 m. or so, the highlands of North Africa and the Near East at considerably higher elevations (900-1,900 m. in Morocco, with scattered data in the Near East suggesting 1,500-2,300 m. [?]). The Würm depression of this "lower limit of solifluction," and implicitly of the altitudinal forest limit, amounts to 1,000-1,100 m. in Spain, 800-1,000 m. in Italy, 1,000 m. in Crete, 850 m. Morocco, 700 m. (?) in the Near East.

c) Biological information leaves no doubt that subtropical wood-lands were largely replaced by temperate species in southern Europe, and that submediterranean species were of major importance along the coasts of northern Africa and in the Levant. Similarly cold-temperate forests or mountain tundras were widespread in the hill country of southern Europe and were frequented by a good number of cold-tolerant mammals. Temperate woodland fauna were impor-tant in the Levant and spread westward along the littoral of northern Africa.

d) Geomorphic evidence, particularly of alluvial beds, colluvial silts, and slope breccias, strongly supports the hypothesis of greater although torrential, seasonal rainfall at the onset of the Würm. Wide-spread coastal aeolianites during the later stages of the early and main Würm, as well as semiarid soil development during the late glacial and postglacial, suggest that subsequent precipitation was generally no greater than today.

Quantitative estimates of temperature depression during the main Würm are limited to Emiliani's isotopic temperature determination of surface waters in the eastern Mediterranean (Emiliani, 1955b). A 5° C. lowering of the midsummer mean seems to correspond with the general depression of the snowline and lower solifluction limits, although this value was somewhat greater in the northerly borderlands.

20

The Sahara and Eastern Africa during the Late Pleistocene

INTRODUCTION

A continent the size of Africa includes several distinct environments, none of which need have responded in similar degree or kind to the great paleoclimatic changes of the Pleistocene. Two environments, the low-latitude deserts and the subhumid tropics, are still of "case" interest. How did such areas respond to the glacial ages that converted much of Europe into a tundra or loess steppe, and brought initial pluvial conditions, followed by greater cold, to the Mediterranean world? An understanding of the changes in lower latitudes is therefore desirable. Two regions—the Sahara and eastern Africa—are best suited for this purpose since they form an integrated picture with Europe and the Mediterranean. Furthermore, these areas are as well understood as any part of Africa.

Unfortunately, detailed and reliable evidence is only available on a very local scale, even in these subregions of Africa. Much good geomorphological work has been done but the "empty" spaces in between are vast, the problems of stratigraphic correlation difficult to overcome, the number of isotopic dates still very scarce. Mammalian faunas are not available in many cases, and even where present, lack specific environmental implications as in the case of Europe (Cooke, 1963). Palynological work has only been initiated, and apart from a few incomplete profiles, results have been confined to interesting but often inconclusive local data. It would be presumptuous to attempt a detailed discussion, such as in chapters 18-19, of even the best of these areas, East Africa.

Surveys and appraisals of the existing information on eastern and southern Africa have been made by H. B. S. Cooke (1958) and Flint (1959), of the Saharan region by Monod (1963). Excellent reviews of certain areas have also been made, namely of the Rhodesias by Bond (1963), of Uganda by Bishop and Posnansky (1960), and of the former French Sahara by Schanfield (1962). The results of several independent field studies, underway in southern Egypt and the northern Sudan since 1961, will lend an entirely new perspective on the late Pleistocene of the Nile Valley and its tributary wadis.

LATE PLEISTOCENE GEOMORPHIC SEQUENCES OF THE SAHARA

General.—The most conspicuous late Pleistocene event of the Sahara was a modest increase in rainfall corresponding to parts of what may be called the last pluvial. Probably most of the late Pleistocene was as uneventful as the present, geomorphically speaking. But certain brief periods of greater moisture are recorded by wadi alluviation of coarse gravels or sands in existing wadi channels. by the creation or expansion of existing lakes, and by pollen evidence of mediterranean tree species in desert uplands of the inner Sahara. There is also evidence of intervals with greater aeolian activity, when wind-borne sands were deposited (or redistributed) well south of the present southern limit of mobile dunes.

Even though the evidence of pluvial features and fossil dunes is rather scattered at times, a certain pattern seems to emerge—provided we can assume that the major events were broadly contemporary. Strict stratigraphic correlation from country to country is next to impossible at the moment. Stratigraphically meaningful mammalian or molluscan faunas are hardly ever available and human industries are incompletely understood—and certainly not of stratigraphic value except perhaps on a local scale. Most of the local stratigraphic sequences can therefore only be correlated to other areas by inference. Only in the Libyan coastal regions, the Nile Valley, the Red Sea coast and the Senegal Delta have glacio-eustatic correlations been made so far. Radiocarbon dating of Pleistocene beds has only just begun, namely in relation to the international campaign underway in Nubia.

A few local sequences will be discussed briefly here (Fig. 53), making major use of those that have glacio-eustatic sea level correlations.

Cyrenaica.—In the Mediterranean coastal area of Derna, McBurney and Hey (1955, p. 72 ff.) and Hey (1963) established a wadi sequence, postdating a six meter beach platform of Tyrrhenian II (or Eem interglacial) age:

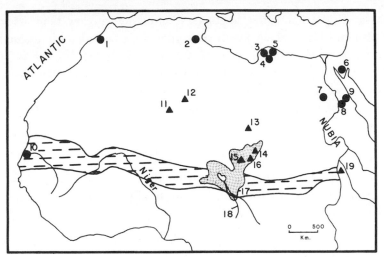

FIGURE 53.
Northern Africa. (1) Sidi Abderrahman, (2) Chott el-Djerid,
(3) Tocra, (4) Haua Fteah and Hagfet et-Dabba, (5) Derna,
(6) Mt. Sinai, (7) Kharga Oasis, (8) Kom Ombo, (9) Mersa
Alem, (10) Senegal Delta, (11) Hoggar Mtns., (12) Tassili-
Ajjer Range, (13) Tibesti Massif, (14) Borkou, (15) Bodélé,
(16) Djourab, (17) Shari, (18) Logone, (19) Gezira Plain.
Broken line pattern shows location of fossil dunes of the southern
Sahara, dotted area gives extent of Pleistocene Lake Chad (after
Grove, 1958, Grove & Pullan, 1963).

a) Greater activity of perennial springs is indicated by deposition
of massive tufas, calcareous marls, and occasional gravel beds. Plant
remains included aleppo pine (*Pinus halepensis*) and Canary laurel
(*Laurus canariensis*), suggesting a warm, subhumid or humid climate.
Animal remains include zebra and an extinct buffalo (*Homoioceras*).
The tufas were part of a general wadi alluviation, overlying the late
Tyrrhenian II beaches disconformably but containing Middle Paleolithic artifacts broadly similar to those found *in situ* in the beach
deposits (McBurney and Hey, 1955, pp. 141 ff., 160 f.).
b) Following a period of wadi erosion, there was renewed deposition of wadi fill and fans of coarse, rounded gravel with a matrix
of derived terra rossa sediments. Hey attributes these wadi gravels
to increased frost-weathering, leading to overloading of streams, without greater rainfall. Intercalated with regressional aeolianites at the
coast, these beds are also younger than the Tyrrhenian beaches and
in turn contemporary with the Würm regression.
c) Talus, due to frost-weathering, overlies the wadi gravels and

contains Upper Paleolithic artifacts. Contemporary cave deposits from the 60 km. distant Haua Fteah cave include a considerable accumulation of *éboulis secs* dated from 32,000 to 11,500 B.P. (Hey, 1962). This last phase is thought to have been both colder and drier than the wadi gravel stage.

At a later date the wadis re-excavated parts of their courses by downcutting.

The Derna sequence is an excellent example of a warm, very moist phase at the transition of the Eem to the Würm, followed by greater cold, with precipitation gradually declining to about the present level during the course of the Würm.

The Egyptian Nile Valley and tributaries.—Although the lower Nile sequence and its relationship to Mediterranean sea levels is difficult to establish for much of the Pleistocene (Butzer, 1959b, 1960a), the Upper Pleistocene is comparatively well understood, particularly in the light of more recent work in southern Egypt.[1]

A stratigraphic base in the Nile Valley is provided by a reddish, terra rossa-type soil developed on fine river beds of the lowermost Nile, alluviated during the early Tyrrhenian sea level of +10 to 13 m. The sediments in question show little or no evidence of lateral water influx derived from local water courses. Instead the river waters were more or less exclusively derived from south of the Sahara. The subsequent soil development involved rubefaction of the top 15 cm. of these lime and quartz sands, a (B)-horizon suggestive of a mediterranean-type climate with a fair amount of vegetation and moisture. The same rubefaction is evident on Middle Pleistocene wadi terraces in southern Egypt.

The "last pluvial" deposits of Egypt are younger than this soil, and can often be distinguished by their lack of rubefaction. These late Pleistocene deposits consist of (a) foreign Nile deposits, ranging from clays and marls to coarse sands, partly or largely derived from the Sudan or Ethiopia; (b) local wadi deposits, including gravel, sands and derived soil sediments.

In southern Egypt, where alluviation was not complicated by Mediterranean base-level changes, these Nilotic and wadi beds show

[1] Butzer and Hansen (1965), based on field work during 1962-63. The results of field investigations by R. Paepe and J. de Heinzelin in Sudanese Nubia are still unavailable. Radiocarbon dates of late Pleistocene sedimentary units were also unavailable at the time of writing. Dates published by Fairbridge (1962) have little stratigraphic value other than that the deposits here considered as late Pleistocene are indeed no younger than 8000 B.C.

complex intercalations. The Nilotic beds can be subdivided into three units, beginning with (1) basal sands and marls, containing Middle Paleolithic artifacts; (2) widespread floodplain silts and clays, also with Middle Paleolithic artifacts; and finally, (3) channel fill of sands and silts contemporary with Late and Upper Paleolithic cultures, including the Sebilian. Some of these beds occur to 34 m. above the present floodplain in Egyptian Nubia and can only be explained by greater Nile floods, i.e., pluvial climates in Ethiopia. The local Nilotic and Palearctic fauna described from Kom Ombo by Gaillard (1934) has not been significantly added to by recent excavations, and elephant, rhinoceros, and giraffe remain conspicuously absent. This probably suggests a cooler local climate, although pollen analyses underway should provide a more complete picture.

Local wadi activity was periodically accelerated during the long time span of threefold Nilotic deposition (a total of no less than 75 m. in Lower Nubia), interrupted by two stages of downcutting to about (or lower than) the level of the modern floodplain. The increased wadi activity was partially accompanied by widespread deposition of colluvial beds with the snail *Zootecus insularis,* while gravel transport and rounding also suggests a wetter climate. The details of wadi alluviation have not yet been worked out as laboratory studies are still pending. But several pluvial maxima can be identified, the last occurring very late in the terminal Pleistocene. Some of the intervening millennia were probably at least as dry as now, so that the "last pluvial" was certainly not a continuous period of more frequent and more regular winter rains. But a general correspondence with the time span of the Würm seems to be established. Accelerated aeolian activity succeeded the last wadi alluviation phase.

The Red Sea coast.—Studies of the direct relationship between the late Pleistocene wadi terraces and the shorelines of the Red Sea were made at Mersa Alam in southeastern Egypt (Butzer, unpublished). Here there is a series of fossil coral reefs indicating former high sea levels at 3 m., 5.5 m., 9.5 m., 14.5 m. and 18.5 m.—increasing in age with elevation and position inland. The molluscan faunas of these deposits are still represented in the Red Sea today, although the relative composition may have varied. There is no reason why these beaches, at least the lower three, should not correspond to the Eem interglacial levels: in terms of consolidation, erosion, and development they are quite comparable with Tyrrhenian II sandy beach deposits of the Mediterranean Sea.

The late Pleistocene wadi terraces postdate at least the upper three of these shorelines, and are later than an interval of downcutting through these coral reefs. Although estuarine gravels already suggest greater wadi activity during the 5.5 m. and 9.5 m. stages, the major wadi terrace was deposited subsequently at an abnormally steep gradient near the coast, sweeping over the edge of all of these coral reefs to below modern sea level. Later during the same regression, downcutting was resumed. The Holocene rise in sea level flooded many of the lower stream courses which have since been partly filled in with wadi and beach sands.

Contemporary wadi activity does not transport coarse gravels on the coastal plain. The terminal interglacial and particularly the early glacial wadi gravels consequently suggest phases of somewhat moister climate.

The Atlantic coast (Senegal Delta).—Each of the three areas discussed so far have been within the peripheries of the Mediterranean winter rainfall belt. Only the late Pleistocene Nilotic deposits implied a pluvial climate in the tropical, summer rainfall belt of the Sudan and Ethiopia. A summer rainfall regime dominates the Senegal Delta, where Tricart (1961) established a sequence of continental deposits intercalated with several shoreline stages.

During the Riss glacial regression, continental dunes with a general northeast-southwest orientation were deposited right across the present Senegal Delta, where they attain a local relief of 30 m., and extend to below modern sea level. At the time of their formation the Senegal may not have reached the coast, indicating a much drier climate.

The next stratigraphic feature is a deep, red weathering profile, exceeding 2 m. in depth. A relict (B)-horizon with evidence of incipient latozation is preserved and found buried under a +3 to 5 m. Eemian beach. This soil is attributed to a period of moist savanna climate, presumably during the earlier part of the Eem. Estuarine and alluvial deposits of the Senegal, contemporary with the +3 to 5 m. shoreline are also preserved. They suggest that the contemporary climate was comparatively moist.

During the subsequent Würm regression some localized aeolian activity is evident but the Senegal did not disappear. Instead it cut down its bed in response to a lower sea level, occupying thereafter a more restricted, better-defined course. The final part of the local sequence includes various Holocene estuarine beds, littoral dunes, etc.

Tricart (1961, p. 44 f.) interprets this chronology by simply equating "regression" with "very arid" and "transgression" with "warm and seasonally very humid." Pleistocene events are, however, much more complex, and wherever detailed stratigraphies are available, moisture and temperature fluctuations are invariably rather complex. Furthermore, the mouths of large rivers are not ideal for studying microstratigraphy, particularly when abundant deep, bore profiles are unavailable. As it stands the Senegal sequence only shows that one, extensive arid period corresponded to part of a glacial regression, and that part of the Eem was accompanied by red soil formation—as indeed it was in the Nile Valley and in the Mediterranean area. Alluvial deposits from the early Würm regression may well be preserved farther upstream or below the surface of the delta. Parts of the Würm regression were obviously drier.

The Lake Chad Basin.—A last area of major interest in the Saharan late Pleistocene is the great basin formerly occupied by an inland sea ancestral to modern Lake Chad (Grove and Pullan, 1963; Monod, 1963, with references).

The present lake surface stands at 280 m., with an area fluctuating between 10,000 and 25,000 sq. km., a mean depth varying between 3 and 7 m., and a maximum depth of 11 m. The lake is separated from two extensive depressions—the Bodélé and Djourab—by a low divide, breached by the dry valley of the Bahr el-Ghazal. The lowest strandline of Lake Chad, at +4 to 6 m., would already permit water to overflow into the 500 km. distant Bodélé depression. At its highest stand (332 m.), the Pleistocene lake ancestral to the Chad formed conspicuous shorelines at +40 to 50 m. and so occupied an area of about 400,000 sq. km. Intermediate, less universal shorelines are also indicated. The great evaporative losses of the present lake are largely balanced by the inflow of the Logone and Shari from the south. Grove and Pullan (1963) estimate that the evaporation of the Pleistocene lake may have been sixteen times greater, so that it must have received annually a volume of water equal to one-third the annual discharge of the Congo.

The ancient Chad Sea is then an excellent piece of evidence in favor of greater moisture in adjacent subhumid tropical latitudes. Unfortunately there has been no correlation of shorelines between different parts of the basin. The complexity and age of lacustrine sedimentation is illustrated by the 600 m. of Pleistocene beds known to underlie parts of the basin. In the case of Nigeria, Grove and

Pullan (1963) suggest that a +52 m. lake stage (during the Upper Pleistocene) was followed by a period of dry climate, with extensive dune formation on the former lake plain. Re-establishment of a stream network at a later date was followed by another wetter period with a rise of lake level by at least 12 m. The age of this last feature, by inference, seems to be Holocene.

It is to be hoped that detailed pollen studies will be attempted in the lacustrine sequence, and that isotopic dating may be possible.

PALYNOLOGICAL EVIDENCE FROM THE
SAHARAN AREA

During the last decade, pollen studies have become available from parts of the former French Sahara. Much of the work has been due to P. Quézel. Although reference to almost fifty pollen spectra of Saharan origin can be found in a comprehensive survey by Quézel and Martinez (1961, and earlier references), only a few of these samples can be assigned to the late Pleistocene. Two belong to humic horizons found within a "Moustero-Aterian" terrace at about 1,000 m. elevation at In Eker in the Hoggar Mountains. Two further samples consist of diatomites of the last major Chad lake found at Yogoum (Djourab) and Kaortchi (Borkou), both at 250 m. (Table 16). Other samples of suggested Pleistocene age are from undated wadi terraces of the Hoggar (Wadi Ahor and Tin Tessandjelt), and from beds underlying

TABLE 16
POLLEN FROM LATE PLEISTOCENE PLUVIAL BEDS OF
THE WESTERN AND CENTRAL SAHARA

Locality	No. of Pollen Identified	Per cent NAP	Source
In Eker (lower bed)	11	36	Pons & Quézel (1957)
In Eker (upper bed)	28	60	Pons & Quézel (1957)
Kel Tarhenanet	125	86	Van Campo (1964)
Djourab	129	84	Quézel & Martinez (1958)
Borkou	118	71	Quézel & Martinez (1958)
Wadi Ahor (terrace-3)	1	0	Pons & Quézel (1957)
Wadi Ahor (terrace-2)	3	33	Pons & Quézel (1957)
Wadi Ahor (terrace-1)	unspecified		Pons & Quézel (1957)
Tin Tessandjelt (t-2)	8	37	Pons & Quézel (1957)
Tin Tessandjelt (t-1)	4	75	Pons & Quézel (1957)

"late" basalt flows (Wadi Segueika). Pollen numbers under the basalt of Wadi Segueika are not specified by Quézel & Thébault (1960). Recently, Van Campo (1964) has also reported on last pluvial pollen from a dark silt at Kel Tarhenanet (2,300 m.) in the Hoggar.

It is obvious that the pollen numbers of the spectra are, with some obvious exceptions, inadequate for more than suggestive interpretation. The presence of a single pollen grain of *Tilia* at In Eker does not verify the existence of lime in the Upper Pleistocene Hoggar. Possibilities of secondary derivation or long-distance transport are not considered by Quézel, and although practically no macrobotanical remains are available, detailed species identifications are made rather optimistically. Consequently, theoretical reservations can be voiced concerning a vegetational interpretation such as that suggested by Quézel and Martinez (1961) for the western Sahara during the pluvial maxima:

Elevations above 1,500 m. Important forests of conifers, including cedar (*Cedrus atlantica*), Aleppo pine, evergreen oak (*Quercus* cf. *ilex*), with linden, maple (*Acer* cf. *monspeliensis*), walnut (*Juglans regia*), and alder along watercourses.

Elevations at 700-1,500 m. Conifers (Aleppo pine) dominant, but with more xerophytic species such as juniper (*Juniperus phoenicea, J. oxycedrus*), cedar, cypress (*Cupressus* cf. *dupreziana*), and wild olive (*Olea laperrinei*).

Elevations below 800 m. Probably grassland or semidesert with desert shrubs and grasses.

In view of the exceptionally poor dating of all but a few samples,[2] the elaborate chronological deductions of Quézel and Martinez (1961) are not fully warranted. The pollen evidence so far suggests no more than limited tree growth in the highlands during the pluvial phases. A number of the typical mediterranean species are still present in these highlands, and others were presumably only eradicated by man. Whether or not these, or a few odd pollen grains of temperate deciduous species, indicate a cooler climate is still debatable. However, the occurrence of fossil Palearctic mollusca in the Hoggar (Sparks and Grove, 1961) seems to support this hypothesis.

---

[2] Three C[14] dates for Holocene samples (Délibrias, Hugot, and Quézel, 1959), and a few samples with archeological associations; others with black paleosols— which may be partly Neolithic, but also partly Aterian (see Chavaillon, 1960)— are really not properly dated at the present stand of soil stratigraphy in the Sahara.

LATE PLEISTOCENE PLUVIAL CLIMATES OF THE SAHARAN AREA

In overview, information for the Saharan region is still rather incomplete, and the quasi-absence of well-founded biological evidence is disconcerting. A picture of relative rainfall increase during parts of the last pluvial can be envisaged, at which time deserts persisted in the hyperarid lowlands while lush grasslands or local mediterranean-type woodlands were found in the high country or along the now semidesert peripheries to the north and south. Whether or not all of what appear to be late Pleistocene pluvial phenomena in the northern and southern Sahara are indeed contemporary, is likely but not certain.

The moistest part of the last pluvial seems, at least in Cyrenaica and eastern Egypt, to have occurred at the transition of the Eem and Würm. Some parts of the 60,000 years contemporary to the Würm were also very dry, and there is reason to suppose that much of the fossil dune country extending 400 to 600 km. south of the present margins of the Sahara (see Grove, 1958) was activated on at least one occasion during the late Pleistocene. Until radiocarbon dates are available we shall not know how general such dry interruptions were, or to what higher-latitude phenomena they were equivalent. At any rate, the last pluvial was a rather discontinuous event in the Saharan area, and probably much of the late Pleistocene was at least as dry as the present.

A distinction should be made between the phases of accelerated wadi and spring activity (pluvial alluviation) and the periods of rubefaction (soil development). The latter are clearly of interglacial age and must have corresponded to rather different climatic conditions. Soil development of sufficient intensity to produce rubefaction requires a vegetative mat and a warm, seasonally humid climate. Pluvial alluviation, however, can be explained by periodic intensive rains of moderate frequency, promoting runoff, erosion, and deposition in areas with sparse vegetation. This suggests a semiarid environment.

It seems that the desert margins and the inner Saharan highlands were affected by two kinds of pluvial phases: "warm" pluvials, characterized by rubefaction, and "cold" pluvials, accompanied by alluviation. The "warm" pluvials represent interruptions of the normal trend of arid interglacial climate, the "cold" pluvials interruptions of the normal trend of arid glacial-age climate. The Sahara has always been a desert, but the environment of the peripheral areas has varied considerably. The exact character of these changes is still not fully understood.

LATE PLEISTOCENE CLIMATE IN ETHIOPIA

The three Nilotic series deposited in Nubia during the late Pleistocene imply summer floods of greater magnitude and duration. A proportion of the heavy minerals are derived from Ethiopian vulcanics, and the clays and silts are largely from south of the Sahara. Since the Nile floods of today are almost exclusively maintained by the Blue Nile and Atbara, it is indirectly shown that Ethiopia must have experienced three major pluvial subphases during the late Pleistocene.

Unfortunately the Pleistocene records of the Sudan and Ethiopia are imperfectly understood, and evidence is still rather fragmentary.

Preliminary studies of the Gezira alluvial clay plain between the Blue and White Niles (Tothill, 1946, 1948) suggest that an important link between Egypt and Ethiopia has been preserved there. These clays were deposited at a time when the summer floods lasted longer than they do today. The snail faunas indicate somewhat moister conditions such as are today found in areas at least 100 km. further south. The clay plain antedates the local Neolithic cultures and has apparently been observed overlying Fauresmith implements, and is therefore thought to be of late Pleistocene age. Remnants of a +20 to 25 m. silt and fine gravel terrace seem to occur near Sarsareib on the Atbara (Arkell, 1949a). They also deserve further study.

The Ethiopian highlands are not glaciated today, but the highest peaks of Semien (Ras Dashan, 4,580 m.; Sazza, 4,500 m.; Lagata, 4,490 m.; Buahit, 4,470 m.) harbored a number of Pleistocene glaciers. Early work by Nilsson (1940) demonstrated two former glaciations with climatic snowlines at 3,600-4,100 m. and 4,200 m. Werdecker (1955) confirmed Nilsson's results, setting the snowline for the period of major glaciation at 3,600-3,700 m. A glacial retreat stage, correlated with the terminal Pleistocene, corresponded to a snowline at 4,400 m. Since the modern snowline is estimated at 4,700-4,800 m.—a little above the highest peaks—the (late?) Pleistocene snowline depression is set at 1,100 m. Nilsson (1940) also describes a late Pleistocene glaciation of Mt. Kaka (4,133 m.), with a snowline elevation estimated at 3,700 m.[3]

---

[3] Hövermann (1954) claims two major glacial stages (the younger correlated with the Würm) in the plateau regions of northern Ethiopia. The Würm snowline is set at 2,750-2,940 m., the pre-Würm snowline at 2,600-2,700 m. The evidence presented is not convincing, and C. Troll (personal communication) believes the so-called glacial deposits are due to solifluction.

The present lower limit of marked solifluction and soil-frost activity is located at 4,200-4,300 m. (Büdel, 1954; Werdecker, 1955), while restricted solifluction under grassy vegetation occurs down to 3,600 m. Fossil solifluction deposits—possibly including colluvial screes—from the highlands on either side of the Ethiopian Rift Valley are mentioned by Büdel (1954). They suggest that the lower limit of solifluction was at 2,700 m. during the late Pleistocene.

Although there is little doubt that the Ethiopian area was considerably colder during what presumably was the Würm glacial, local evidence of greater moisture is still unsatisfactory.

Nilsson (1940) described high shorelines from Lake Tana, the source of the Blue Nile, and from several non-outlet lakes of the Ethiopian Rift Valley. Lake Tana (surface level 1,830 m.) has five major shorelines to +125 m., with a less distinct level at +148 m. Büdel (1954) suggests these high lake levels must predate the present topography and may be of pre-Middle Pleistocene age. According to Nilsson (1940) four lakes of the Rift Valley (Zwai, Abyata, Langana, and Shala) were linked up and temporarily overflowed northward into the Awash River. Büdel (1954) disclaims the existence of such levels and argues that the absence of crocodiles in these lakes precludes a connection with the Awash River, which has crocodiles.[4] Büdel (1954) describes a 15 m. terrace of the central Awash, part of a dissected piedmont alluvial plain. The possibility of tectonic factors cannot, however, be excluded.

Less controversial are the two late Pleistocene phases of wadi alluviation established by J. D. Clark (1954) for the Somaliland area. They provide the only unequivocal evidence of pluvial phases postdating the last interglacial, represented on the coast by high shorelines.

In overview, the Ethiopian record suggests a somewhat cooler and also a moister climate during much of the late Pleistocene. The evidence is, however, incomplete, qualitative and still controversial. There is no possibility of environmental reconstruction so far.

LATE PLEISTOCENE CLIMATE IN EAST AFRICA

The late Pleistocene phenomena of East Africa are again of two kinds: glacial features of the volcanic peaks, and pluvial phenomena largely related to higher-lying lake sediments or shorelines in several closed basins (Fig. 54).

---

[4] In view of Nilsson's detailed description of these features, one is inclined to question whether Büdel's rather brief visit to this area was adequate.

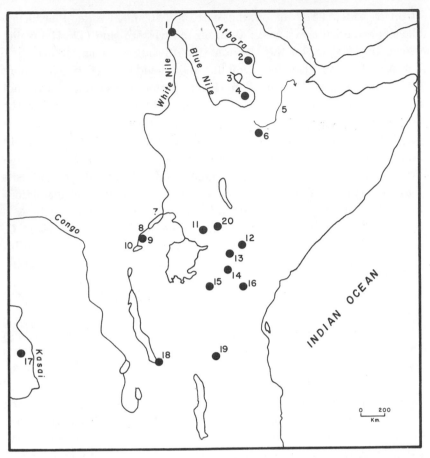

FIGURE 54.
Eastern Africa. (1) Khartum, (2) Semien, (3) Lake Tana,
(4) Mt. Kaka, (5) Awash River, (6) Lake Zwai, (7) Lake
Albert, (8) Semliki River, (9) Mt. Ruwenzori, (10) Lake
Edward, (11) Mt. Elgon, (12) Mt. Kenya, (13) Lake Naivasha,
(14) Olorgesailie, (15) Olduvai, (16) Kilimanjaro, (17) Mufo,
(18) Kalambo Falls, (19) Isimila, (20) Cherangani.

The present snowline of Mt. Kenya (5,158 m.) is at 5,100 m., the
maximal Pleistocene snowline depression is estimated at 900 m. (Flint,
1959, with references). Mt. Kilimanjaro (5,897 m.) apparently lies
just above the climatic snowline; the major Pleistocene depression
exceeded 1,300 m. (Flint, 1959, with references). Mt. Elgon (4,315 m.),
today well below the climatic snowline, was also glaciated. Mt. Ruwenzori (5,119 m.) has a modern snowline at 4,750 m. on the western

(Congo) side, 4,575 m. on the eastern (Uganda) side. Pleistocene glaciers extended down to 2,900 m. on the western side (De Heinzelin, 1963), to 2,000 m. on the Uganda side (Whittow *et al.*, 1963).

All of these glaciated summits show evidence of two or more Pleistocene stages of glaciation. Stratigraphic correlations have not been possible so far, with the exception of Mt. Ruwenzori where the late Pleistocene glaciofluvial deposits appear to integrade with last pluvial (Gamblian) terraces downstream (De Heinzelin, 1963). In addition to the other variables complicating interpretive use of snow-line depression data, continued recent uplift of the volcanic massifs must be assumed. But the significance of the local highland glaciations is great, despite the hazard involved in tentative guesses such as a 5°-7° C. temperature depression according to Flint (1959), 6-9° C. according to De Heinzelin (1963, and discussion). Firstly, a world-wide temperature depression was effective even here, while secondly, the suggested correlation of glacial and pluvial deposits on the western slope of Mt. Ruwenzori appears promising for stratigraphic purposes.

The pluvial evidence of eastern Africa is primarily based on high strandlines and fossil lake deposits of three, formerly contiguous lakes northwest of Nairobi (Naivasha, Elmenteita, and Nakuru). Naivasha, which attained a maximal depth of 200 m. (Nilsson, 1931, 1940) and probably overflowed across a nearby watershed, has one high beach level immediately predating a cultural layer of Upper Paleolithic type. Both Cooke (1958) and Flint (1959) accept this great lake in a small catchment area as good evidence of a wetter climate, particularly since, as the deepest of the modern lakes, it is a bare 10 m. deep.

Other evidence of higher lake levels in Kenya (Nilsson, 1931) is generally considered as suggestive but inconclusive. Possibilities of tectonic displacement of shorelines, modifications of lake overflow levels, and gentle tilting of lake basins must first be excluded in this extremely unstable area.

Another kind of evidence is provided by De Heinzelin (1963) from the Semliki River draining from Lake Edward into Lake Albert on the Congo-Uganda border. Here massive beds of cobbles, gravel, sands, and red soil sediments were alluviated together with colluvial deposits. De Heinzelin makes a good case that these deposits are pluvial in character. The youngest artifacts *in situ* are those of the Sangoan and Lupemban, considered to be contemporary with glacio-fluvial deposits of Mt. Ruwenzori.

Considerable paleo-environmental evidence has recently become available from a number of well-studied Paleolithic sites. One of the more important is the site of Kalambo Falls, southwestern Tanganyika (most recent data compiled in Howell and Clark, 1963, and discussion pp. 612-613). Pollen and macrobotanical remains show that the climate was cooler and wetter about 50,000-60,000 years ago than it is today according to a radiocarbon dated sequence. The open montane woodland zone was then located at elevations 450-600 m. lower than today's, judging by pollen of holly (*Ilex*), *Curtisia*, Ericaceae, and the conifer *Podocarpus*, as well as various fruit remains at the site. Moister conditions prevailed, with interruptions, to about 12,000 B.P. Corroborative evidence is available from Mufo in northeastern Angola, another site with pollen data and a fair number of radiocarbon dates (J. D. Clark, 1963). A good geomorphic sequence has also established the existence of a late Pleistocene pluvial at Isimila, in south-central Tanganyika (Howell *et al.*, 1962).

A final class of paleo-ecological evidence, of only indirect application, is provided by certain faunal distributions. Moreau (1933, 1963) examined the modern distribution of non-migratory song birds endemic in disjunct localities of montane rainforest found through different parts of tropical Africa. To account for the distribution of identical species in such disjunct areas Moreau believes that montane forests must once have extended throughout East Africa. This could best be explained by a greater and more regular rainfall (30-50 per cent more?) and lower temperatures (in the order of 5° C.). Since little subspeciation has taken place among the montane forest avifauna of different parts of East Africa, Moreau (1963) believes that these former "corridors" probably existed as recently as the late Pleistocene.

Clearly the East African evidence leaves much to be desired, but when the pollen work now underway by E. M. van Zinderen Bakker (1962a, 1962b) and Dan Livingstone has become more comprehensive, the late Pleistocene environment of East Africa should be understood at least as well as that of the Mediterranean. In retrospect it appears that both greater cold and moisture are suggested for the approximate time span of the last glacial. Snowline depressions, geomorphic deposits, pollen evidence, and possibly even certain avifaunal distributions support this. Although more evidence is necessary, it seems that the climatic changes involved were appreciable and of far greater persistence than in northern Africa. The broadly simultaneous nature of pluvial climates in East Africa, Ethiopia, and the southern Mediterranean region is noteworthy, and glacial-pluvial correlation has practically been established for the late Pleistocene. Broad estimates for the vertical and horizontal shifts of vegetation belts should be possible within a few years, and a radiocarbon chronology comparable to that of Europe will be established.

21

Some Paleoclimatic
Problems
of the Interglacials

INTRODUCTION

Considering that high latitude glaciers were not "normal" during the greater part of geological history, the contemporary glaciation of Greenland and Antarctica implies that the Holocene is a comparatively cool era of geological history. In fact the Holocene is presumably nothing else but an interglacial period. For obvious reasons the Pleistocene interglacials are thought to have had a climatic character similar to that of the Holocene. However, there are differences involved. For one, the time intervals are quite different. The deep-sea core data (see Table 2) suggest that the Eem lasted at least 35,000 years, compared with 10,000 years for the Holocene so far. Interglacial paleosols and many other lines of geological and biological evidence suggest an even longer time interval for the Holstein.

Within the broad pattern of physical conditions recalling those of the Holocene, the various interglacials may conceivably have experienced phases of climate warmer or moister, as well as cooler or drier than the average for the Holocene. Judging by the evidence, such deviations did occur and may have had considerable ecological significance. The following chapter is devoted to a brief discussion of phenomena suggesting the existence of "anomalous" interglacial climates. It is not intended to be comprehensive, since the evidence does not yet warrant it.

GEOMORPHIC EVIDENCE

Geomorphic processes were analogous to those of the present during the Pleistocene interglacials both of Europe and the Mediterranean area. Both erosion and deposition were quite limited, with soil development proceeding with little interruption.

In the Saharan area little definite information is available about the interglacial intervals. The great fossil dune fields of southern Algeria and Tunisia were probably activated during especially dry interglacial periods (see Tricart and Cailleux, 1960-61), although no exact dating is available. In fact the occurrence of fossil dunes in much of the completely arid Sahara is rather perplexing. Possibly the pluvial phases provided large expanses of wadi and lacustrine sands which were later available for deflation under quite arid conditions. They were finally fixed by soil development under moister conditions. Consequently dunes in true desert country do not necessarily indicate exceptionally arid conditions. Another problem of the Saharan area is the broad belt of fossil dunes extending through the· Sudanese grassland belt between the White Nile and the Atlantic Ocean (see Grove, 1958). These dunes can only be explained by greater aridity. But the age of the dunal complex, which has apparently been subjected to repeated deflation and deposition, is largely obscure. At least a part of the aeolian activity recorded is of glacial age (see Tricart, 1961).

Although evidence of abnormally dry interglacial climates is not proven in the case of East Africa (Flint, 1959), southern Africa promises to be more rewarding in terms of "abnormal" interglacial deposits (Cooke, 1946, 1958, 1962; Bond, 1957, 1963). Of particular interest here are wind-blown sands derived from the late Tertiary Kalahari beds. These sands are largely under vegetation today, but on account of their arid subsoil environment they respond rapidly to a rainfall decrease by active deflation. Such sands form a useful index of greater aridity when found in stratigraphic context in nearby areas (e.g., the Rhodesias, Transvaal). A part but not all of these "Kalahari sands" appears to be of interglacial age, but dating is still comparatively uncertain.

More informative than continental sedimentation are the marine deposits associated with high interglacial sea levels. Thermophile molluscan faunas, such as those formerly found in the North Sea or Mediterranean Sea, are useful as an index of greater warmth. On this evidence, parts of the Eem interglacial must have been warmer than at present. The tentative O^{18}/O^{16} isotope measurements of a deep-sea core in the eastern Mediterranean (Emiliani, 1955b) suggest that summer surface water temperatures were at least 1°-2° C., and possibly as much as 7° C. (?) warmer than today during parts of the last interglacial.

Contrary to a once widely-held opinion, high interglacial sea levels do not by themselves establish the existence of warmer climates by arguing for a greater melting of the residual ice caps and mountain glaciers. Short, comparatively important oscillations about the inter-glacial "mean," such as are evident on the island of Mallorca (Butzer and Cuerda, 1962a), must however be attributed to glacio-eustasy.

THE EVIDENCE OF PALEOSOLS

African, European, and North American paleosols dating from the Holstein and Eem suggest somewhat different conditions of soil development. Profiles are invariably deeper, implying a considerably greater duration of soil development. Also the degree of chemical alteration is much greater, also suggesting greater intensity of weathering than during the Holocene. The great profile depth of Holstein or Eem soils can be particularly well observed in the case of buried soils, which more or less exclude further soil development after burial. For example soils developed on Riss moraines or terraces are often buried under Würm moraines or loess, so providing comparable soil profiles of Eem and Holocene age.

To illustrate the differential of soil development a few cases can be cited: (*a*) In northern Italy the *in situ* (*B*)-horizon of buried Holstein soils which developed on morainic deposits varies between 4-6 m. in depth; for the Eem the depth is 120-150 cm.; for the Holocene, 50-90 cm. Fränzle, 1959b). The local climax soil of the interglacials is a braunlehn or rotlehm, of the Holocene a podsolic braunerde. (*b*) In Catalonia the *in situ* (*B*)-horizon of buried Holstein soils which developed in river terrace deposits varies between 1-5 m. in depth, with red colors (2.5 YR on the Munsell scale); in the case of Eem soils this value is 60-100 cm. with reddish yellow colors dominant (5 YR); in the case of Holocene soils a comparatively weak soil profile of only 30-50 cm. depth and brownish color (10 YR) is developed. The Holstein climax soil approaches a rotlehm, the Eem a braunlehm, the Holocene a meridional braunerde (Butzer, 1964a). Numerous examples can also be cited from temperate Europe where deep braunlehms were particularly characteristic for the interglacials, compared with the more modest Holocene climax soil development. None of these features can be entirely explained by a greater duration of soil development.

Of particular interest are the ecological conditions associated with the development of the terra rossa or rotlehm paleosols of the Mediterranean region. Approximately comparable soils today only appear to be developing in the savanna belts with high temperatures and noticeable periodicity of rainfall (see Kubiena, 1957). The intensity of chemical weathering suggested is much greater than that possible under modern climatic conditions in the area. The dry summer must have persisted but the transitional seasons must somehow have provided an optimal combination of warmth and moisture. Consequently warm, moist phases—stratigraphically of interglacial age (see references in chap. 6)—were at times characteristic for the Mediterranean region. These were not accompanied by alluviation, presumably on account of a very complete and luxuriant vegetative mat with a subtropical rainforest rather than an open subtropical woodland (Durand, 1959). The striking lack of geomorphic evidence makes the term "pluvial" seem rather inappropriate. It is important to realize that present climatic conditions do not represent the totality of interglacial climates in the Mediterranean region. Instead, there have also been very warm, seasonally humid, "tropical" interglacial climates. The contemporary climate suggests a subhumid, comparatively "temperate" interglacial. Just as there were both cool-moist (classical "pluvial") and cool-dry phases during the Mediterranean glacial-age record, there also were warm-moist and warm-dry phases during the interglacials.

In the Saharan area red paleosols of interglacial age were already mentioned in chapter 20. Kubiena (1955, 1957) also describes fossil and relict braunlehms from the Canary Islands and the Hoggar Mountains, where they presumably are of interglacial age as well. Unfortunately too little is known of paleosols in tropical Africa.

In the case of Europe one might presume that a moderately warmer climate during a part of certain interglacials would have sufficed to produce the intensity of weathering suggested by the *braunlehm* soils. However too little is known about soil development to permit estimates of the quantitative differences in climate which were involved; the qualitative conclusions are already of sufficient importance.

Despite a lack of geomorphic evidence, the European, Mediterranean, and Saharan paleosols leave no doubt that ecological conditions were different during some parts of the Holstein and Eem interglacials. Soil development records chemical weathering and is therefore capable of recording changes not reflected in the sedimentary or erosional record. Most difficult to identify are periods of climate like that of the present, since such periods would leave a minimum record of soils and geomorphic features. Such "uneventful" interglacial phases may well have dominated the greater part of both the Holstein and Eem, but within these two intervals, conditions must occasionally have been somewhat different from those of today. This recognition of anomalous interglacial climates by paleosols raises an important problem of interglacial paleoclimates.

PALEOBOTANICAL EVIDENCE FROM MID-LATITUDE EUROPE

Floral information is particularly abundant in the interglacial record of temperate Europe, although comparatively unknown in lower latitudes. Ecological interpretation of the interglacial vegetation known from middle and higher latitude Europe may be attempted on the basis of two different classes of evidence: the Tertiary relicts particularly important among the older Pleistocene flora, and the occasional northward or eastward spread of "modern" warm-temperate species beyond their present ecological boundaries.

At the close of the Pliocene the forest composition of Europe was quite unlike that of the present. Many of the species present are now limited to the tropical rainforest; others are found in the subtropics or in the temperate woodlands of other continents. Others yet are extinct. During each cold climate phase, beginning in the Villafranchian, climatic conditions in middle latitudes were evidently unfavorable, so requiring a southward migration of thermophile species or otherwise, local extinction. Particularly in the case of the Netherlands the gradual diminution of exotic species as *Liquidambar, Taxodium, Liriodendron, Pseudolarix, Parrotia,* and *Zelkowa* is well understood as a result of painstaking study (see Florschütz and Van Someren, 1950; Van der Vlerk and Florschütz, 1953). The terminal Pliocene Reuver flora contains species 79 per cent of which are now extinct in the Netherlands. The Tiglian flora only has 41 per cent exotic species. At an even later date the Holstein has only 17 per cent, the Eem 9 per cent. The persistence of many species such as cedar (*Cedrus*), certain pines (*Pinus pithyusa, P. aldarica*), and the lotus in southern Europe shows that there was a progressive southward displacement of the European vegetation belts during the successive Pleistocene interglacials. In large part this can be attributed to the gradual net cooling of higher middle latitudes during the Basal Pleistocene.

Of particular paleo-environmental interest are the Middle and Upper Pleistocene interglacials. The different distribution of thermophile species can be informative for a study of climatic zonation. So

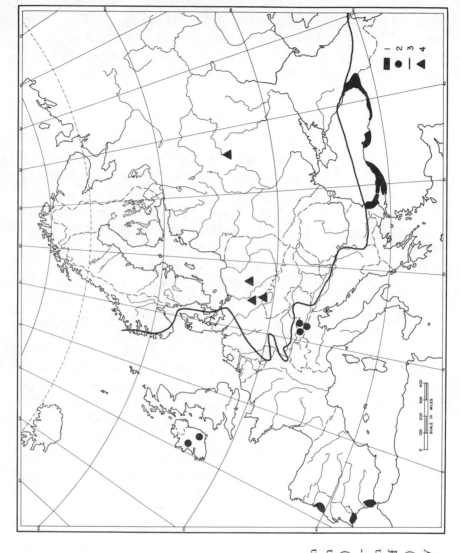

FIGURE 55.
Interglacial shifts of European floras. (1) modern distribution of *Rhododendron ponticum*, (2) interglacial beds with *Rhododendron ponticum*, (3) modern northern and eastern limits of holly (*Ilex aquifolium*), (4) interglacial beds with holly (after Walter, 1954.)

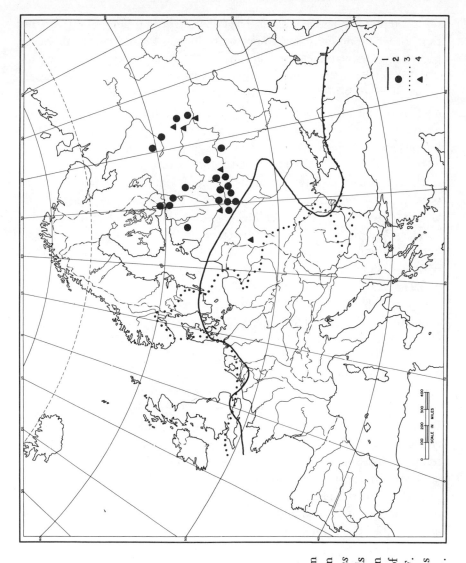

FIGURE 56.
Interglacials shifts of European floras. (1) modern northern limit of hornbeam (*Carpinus betulus*), (2) interglacial beds with hornbeam, (3) modern northern and eastern limits of beech (*Fagus silvatica*, *F. orientalis*), (4) interglacial beds with beech (after Walter, 1954).

323

for example seven species of the Polish Holstein and eight of the Eem either do not occur or do not reproduce in Poland today, although they thrive in warmer parts of Europe. The map diagrams (Figs. 55 and 56) of the modern and interglacial (Holstein or Eem) distribution of beech (*Fagus silvatica, F. orientalis*), hornbeam (*Carpinus betulus*), and holly (*Ilex aquifolium*), and the Pontic alpine rose (*Rhododendron ponticum*) (see Walter, 1954, Figs. 55, 22, and 6) are particularly instructive. The beech seems to be roughly delimited by the January isotherm of —2° C. (Walter, 1954, p. 30), although six Russian localities have provided interglacial evidence for its occurrence in areas with January means as low as —13° C. Hornbeam has been found at some twenty Russian localities beyond the present limits of the species. The holly, whose northeasterly limits approximately coincide with a January mean of 0° C.—or better—with 345 days per year with maximum temperatures over the freezing point (Walter, 1954, p. 29)—has been found in fossil form at several localities in eastern Germany (January —2° C.) as well as at a site south of Moscow (January —11° C.). The yew, which does not occur northeastward of the —4° C. January isotherm today (Walter, 1954, Fig. 5), has also been found at Moscow (January —11° C.). *Rhododendron ponticum*, today confined to the Iberian Peninsula, Turkey, and Caucasia occurs in association with the wild grape (*Vitus silvestris*) at three Alpine localities—Hötting near Innsbruck, Calprino near Lugano, and Re near Locarno (see Woldstedt, 1958, pp. 189-91). The Hötting site is generally considered to be of Holstein age, and implies a mean temperature 3° C. warmer than today's. The Lugano and Locarno sites are apparently of Eem age.

All in all the paleobotanical evidence of the last two interglacials, unfortunately not all dated, suggests January temperatures as much as 2° to 11° C. warmer and mean annual temperatures at least 3° C. warmer than at present. Biological evidence cannot be rigorously employed in this way, but the information provided is highly suggestive. A minimum mean temperature increase of 2°-3° C. for both the Holstein and Eem would, at a guess, seem a reasonable assumption to explain some of the fossil interglacial soils of Europe. Probably winter temperatures—only incompletely recorded by surface planktonic foraminifers of the cooler world oceans—were somewhat higher, particularly in higher latitudes.

No radical ecological change is indicated by the vegetation composite of Eem-age pollen profiles in mid-latitude Europe. The over-all succession of vegetation is quite analogous to that of the Holocene (see West, 1961; Woldstedt, 1954, p. 225 ff.). But the Holstein pollen diagrams of England (West, 1956), eastern Germany, and Poland (see Woldstedt, 1954, p. 228 ff.; 1958, pp. 105 f., 125 ff.) are quite different. The warm-temperate mixed oak-forest never attains the prominent position it held in Eem and Holocene time, instead coniferous pollens, particularly those of pine, play a more important role. This different forest spectrum is probably due to the presence of numerous Tertiary coniferous relicts (A. Srodoń, 1957, cited by Woldstedt, 1958, p. 128). Without careful ecological interpretation based upon macrobotanical and palynological evidence, accurate evaluation of the Holstein pollen spectra is impossible. A rather different vegetational and possibly also ecological picture must however be assumed for much of Europe.

PALEONTOLOGICAL EVIDENCE FROM MID-LATITUDE EUROPE

Unlike the local evidence of marine molluscan faunas, the continental mammalian faunas of the interglacials do not provide much information concerning temperature conditions other than in a very general way. Possibly the specialized interglacial woodland elephant (*Elephas antiquus*) or Merck's rhino would not thrive in the more continental climates of modern Europe. But since these genera are extinct, such speculation is fruitless. One of the few animals of possible interest is the hippopotamus, a warm to warm-temperate species requiring perennial waters, and unlikely to be found in seasonally frozen rivers. Interglacial hippos have been recorded from southern Europe, France, England, Germany, and Hungary. Lack of evidence from Scandinavia or eastern Europe may indicate that no radical changes in winter temperatures need be assumed. The extinct water buffalo (*Buffelus murrensis*) found in Germany and the monkey *Macaca sylvana* ssp. found in different parts of temperate Europe during the Holstein may however be more suggestive of warmer conditions (Thenius, 1962).

RETROSPECT ON INTERGLACIAL CLIMATES

In a general way the paleoclimates of the Pleistocene interglacials were approximately analogous to those of the present. This is particularly substantiated by the geomorphic record, which is everywhere quite similar to that of the Holocene. But temporary anomalies of both temperature and moisture seem to have occurred during parts of the Holstein and Eem. Unequivocal evidence is lacking for the older warm phases.

Several comments can be ventured on temperature conditions during the thermal maximum of the Eem, the best understood of the interglacial phases.

a) According to O^{18}/O^{16} isotope measurements by Emiliani (1955a, 1955b) the surface waters of the tropical north Atlantic were about 1° C., the Mediterranean at least 1°-2° C. warmer in summer;

b) Thermophile molluscan faunas indicate that the North Sea and Mediterranean Sea were comparatively warmer;

c) The relict or fossil terra rossa and rotlehm soils of the Mediterranean area imply much more intensive chemical weathering, conceivable only with a warmer rainy season (September through May);

d) The occurrence of thermophile plants well beyond their present northern or eastern limits during the Eem or Holstein (or both) suggests warmer winters (January means at least 2° C., possibly 11° C. higher) and higher annual temperatures (by 3° C.) in mid-latitude Europe.

The dangers involved in unqualified use of biological evidence, and the limited nature of data, almost entirely confined to Europe, require great caution in evaluating the quantitative implications of temperature change. But there can be little doubt that temperatures were somewhat warmer than today's during the thermal maxima of the Eem and Holstein. Mean annual temperatures in Europe were probably at least 3° C. warmer than at present, with inferences that the difference was more a matter of winter than of summer temperatures. Possibly the tropics were only a little warmer, implying that higher temperatures were pre-eminently characteristic of higher latitudes. This in turn supports a hypothesis of reduced winter cold, a reduction of equator-to-pole temperature gradients, and possibly, an open Arctic Ocean (see Brooks, 1949).

Evidence of anomalous rainfall conditions in higher latitudes is unavailable. Nevertheless parts of the interglacial periods were comparatively moist in both the Mediterranean and Saharan areas. This is strikingly shown by the red interglacial paleosols. Other parts of the same interglacial periods appear to have been normally or even abnormally dry (so-called "interpluvials"). Consequently the interglacials witnessed both warm-dry and warm-moist climatic anomalies, although the correlation of interglacial precipitation anomalies in different latitudes has yet to be established.

The interglacials offer a fascinating field for further research. So far most of the literature has only considered interglacials as important stratigraphic markers within the record of repeated Pleistocene glaciation. More emphasis directed toward a fuller paleo-environmental understanding of the interglacials will surely be rewarding. Only in this way can the conventional stereotype of uncomplicated, warm-dry interglacial periods be replaced by a more realistic concept.

22

The Climatic Changes of the Pleistocene

Discussion of the climatic changes of the Pleistocene inevitably leads to the question of ultimate causes. Theories accounting for aberrant Pleistocene climates are formulated anew every few years. They range from changes in solar radiation, solar particle emission, and sunspot activity, to terrestrial volcanic activity, ocean circulation, and mountain-building as well as to astronomical features of the earth's axis and orbit. It is basically absurd, even though frequently stimulating, to speculate on ultimate causes when the empirical paleoclimatic evidence is as scanty as it is, and when the theoretical meteorological patterns are as little understood as a UNESCO-World Meteorological Organization symposium on changes of climate (Rome, Oct. 1-7, 1961) has recently demonstrated (see Wallén, 1963). There are then two quite distinct aspects of Pleistocene climate: the *causes* of the climatic changes, and the *patterns* of such change.

Fundamental to our whole understanding of the Pleistocene is the accumulation of well-dated, local paleoclimatic information. The foregoing chapters have attempted to outline current information of this type, a picture which is obviously far from satisfactory. Considering that our knowledge for Asia, Australia, and South America is limited or practically nil, the gathering of sound empirical paleoclimatic data remains a basic prerequisite.

The second step towards an understanding of Pleistocene climatic changes involves synthetic analysis of paleoclimatic data: strictly contemporary data, quantitative or qualitative, must be collated and compared. Thus regional atmospheric patterns may be deduced, as they are for example in Poser's (1950) study and interpretation of late Würm wind directions and large-scale circulation features on the basis of European dunes. Theoretical reconstructions of atmospheric patterns on a continental or world-wide scale may then be possible by comparing regional paleoclimatic information with meteorological theory. Such meteorological deductions should, however, be based upon two principles:

a) Any reconstruction of atmospheric patterns must be founded upon sound empirical paleoclimatic evidence and must be fully compatible with it.

b) All meteorological deductions so allowed must have present-day counterparts in short or long-term weather patterns. In other words, it is undesirable to assume the existence, in the Pleistocene, of weather patterns unknown today.

Only when an understanding of the patterns of observed climatic change has been attained for the northern hemisphere can scientific attention be directed towards the problem of ultimate causes. So far, short-term variations of the general circulation have not been conclusively associated with extra-terrestrial phenomena, as Berg (1957) has convincingly shown with particular reference to the alleged weather significance of sunspot cycles.

METEOROLOGICAL THEORY ON PLEISTOCENE ATMOSPHERIC CIRCULATION

Although the causes of climatic change are beyond the scope of this book, the interested reader will probably demand an elucidation of the climatic patterns of Pleistocene glacials and interglacials. It should be remembered, however, that any such discussion is theoretical and incompletely founded on empirical data, and consequently to be rated as a summary of probable or possible hypotheses.

Work directed toward an understanding of the Pleistocene general atmospheric circulation has a long tradition, extending back to a first discussion by A. Penck (1914). Penck postulated that primary atmospheric cooling induced continental glaciation, with certain corollary changes. In particular, despite a general persistence of existing atmospheric circulation patterns, the continental ice sheets will have deflected traveling cyclonic disturbances equatorward. This would increase rainfall in the subtropical desert belts (pluvials) and might lead to a simultaneous equatorward shift of the lower latitude deserts at the expense of the humid tropics. Subsequent work, until 1948, did not add substantially to Penck's ideas.

The introduction of then novel meteorological tenets into Pleistocene research by H. C. Willett (1949) and by H. Flohn (1952, 1953) was of epoch-making importance. Willett, in particular, argued that the short-term patterns of the general circulation occurring over a period of several days or weeks today are essentially similar in character to those which occurred on a larger scale in historical and geological times.

According to Willett and Flohn these short-term fluctuations can be broadly grouped into two major patterns, known as *high index* and *low index* circulation types.[1] During the former, the world wind belts tend to be well developed and aligned latitudinally, with lower and middle latitudes comparatively warm, and high latitudes comparatively cold. Middle latitudes enjoy a uniform weather succession, with lower middle latitudes remaining undisturbed by traveling lows and attendant rainy periods from higher latitudes. Willett and Flohn consider this as the prototype of an interglacial circulation. The low index circulation type, on the other hand, is characterized by massive latitudinal airmass exchange in middle latitudes, leading to frequent cold-air outbreaks into lower latitudes, and warm-air thrusts into high latitudes. Middle latitude weather is then subjected to rapid and often violent changes, while the frequent cyclonic depressions provide abundant moisture in lower middle latitudes. This was considered as the typical glacial-type circulation. Both circulation types are necessary for the mechanism of the atmospheric circulation and must have existed at all times. But the comparative frequency or intensity of the one or other pattern may have varied in longer-term periods just as it does today in short-term periods.

Subsequent work (see Wallén, 1953, and Butzer, 1957, 1961a) has shown that the above patterns are very much oversimplified, and that changes of circulation patterns cannot be conveniently grouped into glacial and interglacial units. Instead the dominant circulations accompanying glacial advances, glacial standstills, and glacial retreats must each be considered as distinct. On a larger scale this would apply to the major last glacial subdivision of the early, main, and late Würm (see Büdel, 1950b; Viete, 1951). Similarly allowance must be made for both moist and dry interglacial periods in lower middle latitudes.

---

[1] On a local scale a high index pattern is equivalent to *zonal* circulation, with little airmass transfer across the parallels of latitude, and low index is equivalent to *meridional* circulation, with considerable latitudinal transfer of airmasses.

CLIMATIC PHASES OF THE EUROPEAN UPPER PLEISTOCENE

In order to outline the broader climatic implications of the Eem and Würm in Europe and the Mediterranean area, a synthesis of the paleoclimatic data bearing on each of the climatic stages may be tentatively attempted. Turning first to the Würm glaciation, the major lines of paleoclimatic evidence can be summarized as follows (see chaps. 18 and 19):

I. Europe (north of the Pyrenees, Alps, and Balkans)
    a) Periods of ice accumulation and advance and the early Würm in general were characterized by
        1) the major part of cold-climate stream alluviation (Schaefer, 1950)
        2) major large-scale solifluction (Büdel, 1950b; Woldstedt, 1958; Frenzel, 1959-60)
        3) gradual lowering of temperatures
    b) Periods of glacial standstill or retreat, and the main and late Würm in general were characterized by
        1) fluvial equilibrium, eventually going over to stream down-cutting (Schaefer, 1950)
        2) a general reduction of solifluction (Büdel, 1950b; Woldstedt, 1958; Frenzel, 1959-60)
        3) major aeolian activity with loess and parabolic dune deposition (Büdel, 1950b; Poser, 1950)
        4) full glacial temperature depressions of at least 10°-12° C. on the yearly mean, of about 7°-9° C. in July
        5) an apparent temperature inversion at 1,000-2,500 m. elevation
II. Mediterranean Region (including southern Europe and northern Africa)
    a) Periods of incipient marine regression (and advance of the continental glaciers) and probably the early Würm in general were characterized by
        1) "pluvial" phenomena such as stream alluviation and slope colluviation (Butzer, 1958a, 1963a)
        2) gradual lowering of temperatures
    b) Periods of protracted low sea level (glacial standstills) and the late Würm rise of sea level were characterized by
        1) cessation of alluviation with semiarid soil development (as today)
        2) full glacial temperature depressions in the order of 5° C.

From the available evidence it seems that the ice advance of the early Würm was characterized by cool, maritime climate in higher latitudes coupled with considerably increased rainfall in subtropical latitudes. In other words, the pluvials of the subtropics were roughly contemporary with the growth of the continental glacier. High latitudes need not have been moister than today, but it is improbable that they were drier. A local meteorological explanation can be provided to account for glacier growth in Scandinavia and increased precipitation in the Mediterranean area. It involves shifting proportions of the common large-scale weather patterns affecting the European area: many of the meridional weather types introducing cold, maritime air and winter snowfall to Scandinavia bring cool, stormy weather to the Mediterranean Basin; other meridional types associated with cold, winter high pressures and surface inversions over higher latitude Europe also favor cool, stormy weather further south.[2]

High pressures and surface inversions were assumed to be common in middle and higher latitude Europe during the glacial maximum or main Würm. These would fall into a class of meridional weather types with southerly storm tracks producing particularly heavy rainfall in the Mediterranean region. Since, however, the latter area did not experience pluvial conditions during the full glacial, another meteorological explanation must be sought. A plausible solution is provided by the reduction of evaporation induced by a 5° C. lowering of ocean surface temperatures, which according to Flohn (1953) would reduce evaporation by at very least 20 per cent. This would decelerate the evaporation-precipitation cycle. However, the glacial retreat must have been associated with frequent warm airmass transfer into higher latitude Europe,[3] while Poser's (1950) reconstruction of moderate or strong wind directions in summer suggests a predominance of zonal and mixed classes for that season at least. Simultaneously those

[2] Of the twenty-eight European large-scale weather patterns identified by Hess and Brezowsky (1952), Wallén (1953) has shown that six "north meridional" types and most of the nine zonal or mixed types are responsible for heavy winter snowfalls in the Scandinavian highlands, while seven "south meridional" types lead to warm air advection from southerly, southwesterly, or southeasterly quadrants, and five "warm meridional" types produce clear, cold winter weather in Fennoscandia. In summer the zonal situations favor cool, cloudy weather, the warm meridional situations steady, warm weather. In the Mediterranean region the north meridional types are associated with a 13 per cent increase in cyclonic activity during the winter half-year (October through March); the warm meridional, a 37 per cent increase; the zonal and mixed types, a 37 per cent decrease (Butzer, 1960c). Consequently in winter time, only the north and warm meridional types would simultaneously favor glaciation in Scandinavia and greater rainfall in the subtropics. These classes occur with frequencies of 12.2 per cent and 11.4 per cent in the winter half-year today, and presumably experienced increased winter frequency during the early Würm. Summer circulation patterns are less significant for the Mediterranean area.

[3] These south meridional circulation patterns are partly favorable, partly unfavorable for cyclonic activity in the Mediterranean area. The over-all average is only 10 per cent above normal (Butzer, 1960c).

weather situations favoring both glacier growth and Mediterranean storminess must have decreased. Late Würm circulation patterns were then probably quite different from those of the early Würm. This over-all decrease of meridional types in favor of zonal circulation was probably unfavorable for cyclonic activity in the subtropics, a suggestion which may explain late Würm arid phases in northern Africa. A climatological outline of the glacial retreat in Europe and North America is given by Manley (1951, 1955).

The problem of moist and dry interglacials in the Mediterranean region and northern Africa appears to be complex. A very simple solution can be offered to explain the aberrant, moist interglacial type however. Four meridional circulation patterns responsible for much of the warm air advection to higher latitude Europe today are combined with great cyclonic activity in the Old World subtropics.[4] An abnormally high frequency of these situations could explain the local evidence well.

In summary, Table 17 includes some tentative suggestions concerning climatic phases of the Upper Pleistocene.

TABLE 17
UPPER PLEISTOCENE CLIMATIC PHASES IN EUROPE
AND THE MEDITERRANEAN REGION

Phase	Middle Latitudes	Subtropical Latitudes	Increased Frequency of Circulation Class
Dry Interglacial	As today	\s today	As today
Moist Interglacial	Warmer	Moister, warmer	Moist South-Meridional
Early Glacial	Cooler, moist	Moister, cooler	North and Warm-Meridional
Full Glacial	Colder, drier	Drier, colder	Warm-Meridional, Zonal (?)
Late Glacial	Cooler, drier	Drier, cooler	Zonal, South-Meridional

[4] This "moist south meridional" class has an index of cyclonic activity 27 per cent above average, and occurs with a frequency of 11.3 per cent during the winter half-year today (Butzer, 1960c). It is a major rain-bringer in the Mediterranean region.

CURRENT PROBLEMS IN PALEOMETEOROLOGICAL RESEARCH

Those few meteorologists with an interest in the Pleistocene are unfortunately hampered by difficulties of two kinds: (a) the empirical paleoclimatic data are painfully inadequate so far, and (b) meteorological theory concerning the modern general circulation is not considered to be satisfactory as it is. In fact, as Sutcliffe (1963) has emphasized, it has not yet been convincingly shown that the climate of the earth should be distributed as it is.

The meteorologist obviously cannot be expected to collect and evaluate the specialized paleoclimatic data he is to anlayze. This must be provided by the Pleistocene specialist who should attempt to interpret his data with great caution, so that better catalogued materials with qualified evaluations such as "reliable," "probable," or "possible" may be accessible to the meteorologist. A great deal of more satisfactory paleoclimatic information must be available before this major barrier to paleometeorological study is removed. But there can be little doubt that the information will indeed be forthcoming.

Another obstacle of a purely meteorological kind must also be overcome. Further work such as that on the secondary effects of particularly snowy winters on radiation, temperature, pressure distributions, etc. seems highly promising, especially since the valuable study of Namias (1963). Indeed, it remains to be determined whether a relative change of circulation patterns might by itself induce higher latitude glaciation, with planetary temperature depression as an indirect result rather than a primary cause. Sutcliffe (1963) has suggested that the difference between the winter and summer general atmospheric circulation today is greater than that between a glacial and an interglacial. Consequently, Sutcliffe raises the question whether the climatic changes of the Pleistocene might still be within the normal, built-in range of variability of the general circulation. Obviously these are considerations of prime significance for a fuller understanding of the Pleistocene.

It is to be hoped that more meteorologists will devote attention to related problems. Only then can the present impasse in paleometeorological interpretation be overcome. When and if this is accomplished, an answer to the burning question of ultimate causes for the phenomenal Pleistocene era will probably not be far away.

PART VI

Man-Land Relationships in Prehistory

23

Early Subsistence
and
Settlement Patterns

THE SCOPE OF ENVIRONMENTAL ANALYSIS

A study of man-land relationships in prehistory requires a good understanding of the many aspects of the geographic environment. Such environmental analysis would include contributions by the earth and biological sciences as well as by ethnology. Study should be directed toward three major goals:

1. Understanding the *regional environment,* including the climate, vegetation, soils, and geomorphic agencies. This has been the topic of the preceding chapters and needs no further detailed discussion here. This class of information can often be readily obtained as a result of geomorphological and palynological work.

2. Understanding of the regional food resource base or *"economic area."* In the case of hunter-gatherer populations this requires:

a) analysis of fossil faunas from several archeological sites or natural sediments;

b) estimation of the biomass existing in the region, based on paleontological data and an understanding of vegetation and animal ecology;

c) identification of preserved vegetable foods or at least pollen of species with edible fruits, bark, roots, etc.;

d) understanding of the nutritional patterns of modern "primitive" groups with comparable technology and living in comparable environments; and

e) over-all assessment of the human resource base in terms of potential population level.

This class of material is usually difficult, if not impossible, to obtain. Studies of animal ecology in relation to vegetation and abiotic environmental features are still rudimentary in most areas. Comparative ethnological studies available are often inadequate. And, the common absence of vegetable remains in archeological assemblages may distort our image of Pleistocene hunter-gatherer economies.

In the case of agricultural populations, understanding of the "economic area" would entail:

a) assessment of how much of the human diet was based upon (1) agricultural plants, (2) domesticated animals, and (3) native food resources, including game and wild vegetable foods;

b) assessment of area of local arable land as bounded by topographic features (coasts, rivers, swamps, mountains) and conditioned by vegetation cover (grassland, parkland, open or dense forest), soil depth, and terrain slope;

c) assessment of native vegetation as an obstacle to clearing and tilling;

d) assessment of soils as to friability and fertility;

e) assessment of available grazing for herd animals; and

f) assessment of game and fishing resources.

3. Understanding of the *local setting* of a site, i.e., location with respect to the terrain, hydrography, groundwater and other local features. This would include:

a) factors other than food supply influencing selection of a settlement site on a seasonal or perennial basis (water availability, natural shelter, exposure, dry ground);

b) factors impeding or facilitating human movements (coasts, rivers, swamps, steep slopes, vegetation patterns);

c) factors affecting game movements, such as availability and localization of drinking water, topographic barriers impeding or channeling movements into select areas, etc.; and

d) factors providing an added marine or aquatic food element, such as location near the seashore, lakes, rivers, or streams.

This general class of information is usually available, at least for later Pleistocene and Holocene sites.

Obviously, total environmental analysis is seldom possible. But the complexity of the geographic environment must be understood, and a complete understanding should always be attempted. It is important to know

> precisely what geographic conditions obtained at each state of human settlement; the extent to which the economic activities of any particular community were limited by the external environment; and above all how far the economic activities of the people (studied) are reflected in and can be reconstructed from changes in the geographic surroundings (J. G. D. Clark, 1957, p. 20).

MATERIAL MANIFESTATION OF HUMAN CULTURE

Turning from the environment *per se* to the activities of man *per se*, we find that the full complexity of human culture—in the widest sense of the word—is far more difficult to outline than the geographical environment. But for a discussion of man-land relationships among pre-literate peoples, the material aspects of culture are paramount. There is, in fact, little choice other than to place major emphasis on an empirical economic approach such as suggested by J. G. D. Clark (1953).

A few of the more significant material aspects of culture are as follows:

1. *Economy.* The basic economic patterns in prehistoric times include (1) unspecialized food-collecting, (2) specialized hunting-gathering, (3) primitive agriculture, based in some part upon crop planting and limited keeping of domesticated animals. Nomadic herding and more advanced agricultural or mixed urban-agricultural economies had also evolved by the beginning of the historical era in the Near East. Apart from functional tool interpretation, archeological evidence on economies is largely confined to analysis of biological remains and refuse. In the case of non-agricultural groups such analysis includes:

a) Composition of the faunal remains as to orders and species, giving evidence as to the range of ecologic niches exploited;

b) Indications of possible selectivity of species, suggesting deliberate choice, particular hunting methods, seasonal availability of certain species, etc.;

c) Age and sex composition of the fauna, giving further information on hunting techniques and seasonal activities;

d) Disposition of faunal remains in a site, providing evidence of human behavioral patterns, methods of butchery, etc.;

e) Determination and over-all interpretation of any vegetable remains.

In the case of agricultural populations study of biological remains is directed towards the determination of:

a) Proportions of wild to domestic animal species and individuals, possibly suggesting relative importance of hunting;

b) Presence of the "normal" domesticated animals (dog, goat, sheep, pig, cattle, horse) and in which proportions; absence or poor representation of some species may have cultural significance;

c) Age and sex composition of domesticated animals, giving indications of relative and seasonal aspects of animal food use;

d) Kinds and species of cultivated plants present, and in what proportions;

e) Evidence of wild vegetable foods.

2. *Technology.* Technology includes a wide variety of features: tools (in the broad sense of the word), fire, clothing, shelter, transport, hunting techniques, etc. Unfortunately, stone tools, by virtue of their preservation are by far the most common evidence of human technology in the Paleolithic culture range. It is therefore reasonable but nonetheless unfortunate that stone tool typology has long been equated with both culture and economy. Style and function are, however, not identical and stone typology only exemplifies a limited part of human technological skills. In the case of non-agricultural groups the kinds and proportions of stone tools, and the site associations of tools, bones, and other vestiges of human activity are all vital to functional interpretation. Careful study of worked bone and wood is equally important. In more advanced cultures, the kinds, functions, and sources of pottery and metal objects can be equally informative. The materials employed in tool-making frequently provide information about group movements or trade connections.

3. *Settlement.* Settlement includes architecture, settlement morphology, location and permanence, population distribution and density, etc. A more detailed discussion of settlement patterns is given below, so that brief reference to the question of settlement duration will be sufficient. Müller-Wille (1954) recognizes the following settlement types based on duration of site occupation:

a) *Ephemeral* settlements of a few days duration;

b) *Temporary* settlements of several weeks duration;

c) *Seasonal* settlements of some months duration;

d) *Semipermanent* settlements of some years duration;

e) *Permanent* settlements lasting for several generations.

Although these settlement classes cannot be freely equated with economic traits or cultural level—either in modern primitive groups or prehistoric cultures—consideration of these criteria in archeological evaluation can be rather useful.

4. *"Land use,"* i.e., human impact on the environment. Direct modification of the biological environment was possible since the earliest times through hunting, the use of fire for hunting or plot clearance, and ultimately field cultivation and herd grazing. Such environmental modifications are another material manifestation of man's activity.

CLASSIFICATIONS OF PREHISTORIC CULTURES

The standard Old World nomenclature employed for prehistoric cultures is primarily based on stone tool typology. They are divided into an old (Paleolithic), a middle (Mesolithic), and a new stone age (Neolithic). The Paleolithic is further subdivided into lower, middle, and upper units, each composed of a constellation of implement assemblages. Chronological criteria have also slipped into this classification: the break between Lower and Middle Paleolithic is frequently defined by the Riss-Eem boundary, while the Mesolithic is usually separated from the Paleolithic by the Würm-Holocene boundary. Clearly, the existing terminology can only be justified as a matter of convenience.

Braidwood (1960a; Braidwood and Howe, 1962) has proposed a more economic classification of prehistoric cultures, based primarily on levels of subsistence:

1. *Unspecialized Food-Collecting.*

a) Naturally determined mammalian subsistence and free-wandering,[1] with tools fashioned but not yet standardized. This is thought to include the australopithecine groups and the very crude and typologically variable early pebble tools.

b) Food-gathering, with free-wandering, hunting, and earliest standardized tool-making traditions. Subsistence patterns are significantly determined culturally. Tools of the early standardized traditions of core bifaces, flakes, and choppers appear, with broad distribution for a given tool type.

---

[1] Presumably this should not indicate areally unlimited wandering but rather shifting, ephemeral settlements of a few days duration within limited territories.

c) Food-gathering, with elemental restricted wandering, hunting, and some variety in standardized tool forms within regions. This includes a great number of mixed industrial assemblages.

2. *Specialized Hunter-Gatherers.*

d) Food-collecting, with selective hunting and seasonal collecting patterns for restricted-wandering groups. Considerable typological variety and "tools to make tools," with rather marked regional restriction of any given industry, although a generalized tool-preparation tradition such as blade tools may be widespread.

e) Food-collecting, with intensified hunting and collecting with seasonally different activities by restricted-wandering or center-based-wandering groups. Beginning of plant manipulation and greater concentration on the taking of fish, fowl, molluscs, and fleeter mammals.

3. *Primary Food-Producers.*

f) Incipient plant cultivation and animal domestication, within the natural habitat of potential plant and animal domesticates. This elusive stage involves experimental manipulation within a subsistence milieu of the food-collecting type, among restricted-wandering to semipermanent groups.

g) Food-producing with the appearance and diffusion of the primary village-farming community—in which a marked proportion of the dietary intake is of produced food. Settlement is semipermanent or permanent.

h) Food-producing, with expanded village-farming and, possibly, incipient urbanization. Permanent settlement is possible on a subsistence pattern of predominantly produced food. Plow and draught animals in wider use, craft specialization and metallurgy common.

Many anthropologists will disagree with this scheme, partly because of the apparent equation of culture and technology, partly because of its emphasis on cultural rather than technological evolution. Furthermore, both Pleistocene cultures and technology are far too elusive to fit any preconceived system. But Braidwood's classification provides a more meaningful synopsis for non-archeologists than do the conventional tool typologies.

MODERN SETTLEMENT PATTERNS OF PRIMITIVE
FOOD-GATHERERS

No modern "primitive" group provides an accurate picture of prehistoric populations. In particular, the technological traits vary strongly between dispersed groups of a similar economic level so emphasizing acculturation to nearby higher cultures. But certain aspects of the economic and social structure may provide a fair analogy to prehistoric communities. Geographically, these economic and social attributes are possibly expressed most usefully in the settlement patterns. Accordingly, such settlement features as observed among contemporary "primitive" peoples are outlined below as a valuable aid toward understanding prehistoric settlement, and indirectly man-land relationships in prehistory. The discussion is freely based upon a recent study of settlement geography by Gabriele Schwarz (1961, Part 2).

Modern or subcontemporary ethnological groups of primitive food-gatherers are found in tropical rainforests (the Negritos of the Philippines, the Kubus of Sumatra, the Toala of Celebes, the Tapiros of New Guinea, the Semang of Malaya, the Congo Pygmies, and small bands of the Amazon Basin), in dry grasslands or semideserts (the Australian aborigines and the Kalahari Bushmen), and in cool temperate forests (the Alacaluf of southern Chile). Probably each of these environments was too marginal and unattractive for the Pleistocene populations to be discussed, but the information provided transcends these limitations.

Such groups as fall under the category of primitive food-gatherers consist of groups of families or bands, without any social differentiation. A head or chief, if present at all, owes his advisory functions to strength or experience, and has no vested authority, and certainly none that may be inherited from father to son. In the economic sphere the group's needs are modest, and the necessary food, clothing, and shelter can all be provided by the community itself, without recourse to any special craftsmanship or organized exchange of goods. In other words, each band is a self-supporting entity except where recent trade relationships have been established with neighboring agricultural populations. Since technological skills are poorly developed, the environment has comparatively little to offer for exploitation at this low cultural level. Consequently the subsistence area is large and 20-400 square kilometers per person seems a fair estimate of population densities. This requires considerable shifting of camp sites.

The topographic location of such food-gatherers' (ephemeral or temporary) campsites is not chosen with much deliberation. Natural glades along or close to a stream, and hence water supply, are preferred in forest country. In case of danger such groups retreat into the dense forest. In dry country, watering places are selected, although such water-holes may be evacuated to attract scarce mammalian faunas on which the livelihood depends. Obviously then the suitability of a location is not a strong motive of choice, since if the site is unsatisfactory one can move on with little trouble.

Both natural and artificial shelters are employed. Hollow trees were widely used by the Australians and Tasmanians, and in part, fire was used to enlarge existing cavities. Caves were also widely used after being lined with leaves, grass, and bark. Rock crevices and over-hangs, amplified by branches, grass, and moss, were used by the Bushmen. Where natural shelter is unavailable various artificial con-structions are used. Most elementary is the *wind shelter* or *lean-to*. The principle is that of two upright stems with forked tops, a cross-pole, and various sticks supported against this at 45-degree angles. Used as a rain protection in tropical areas, the roof framework is then covered with large palm or banana leaves. Part of the structure may be derived from growing saplings. In Australia the lean-to was often closed in on both faces. In other areas, a crude type of *basket hut* is employed as shelter. Branches are stuck into the ground in a crude semicircle and the tops bound together. This framework is then covered with palm leaves in rainforest areas; grass, reeds, or bark in other areas; hides or furs in cold regions. In the latter case, earth may be thrown up around the base.

The size of the settlements is characteristically one of small group settlements with anywhere from 4 to 24 families and 20-100 people. Each individual family occupies one shelter. As community effort is vital, dispersed settlement is unusual. As social organization is not rigid, individual families may leave one band and join another, so that the size of the shifting settlements is rather variable. Larger settlements in southeastern Australia attained 800 people but in such cases the settlement was subdivided into individual bands. Lack of social differentiation implies that no special structures exist. The size of the group(s) is essentially determined by availability of nourishment in an area.

Morphology of settlements is variable. In the forests, irregular, circular, or semicircular arrangements are common, with the wind shelters facing inward. This is partly attributed to the natural con-figuration of the forest glades, partly to protection against wild animals.

It is questionable whether the wind shelters or basket huts described here were known in the Lower or Middle Pleistocene. But many attributes of the subsistence-settlement pattern are pertinent to an understanding of early Paleolithic cultures.

MODERN SETTLEMENT PATTERNS OF ADVANCED FOOD-GATHERERS

Contemporary groups frequently considered as "advanced" food-gatherers include the Eskimo, the northern woodland Indians of Canada, and some Paleoasiatic groups of Siberia.

Each of these arctic or subarctic groups shows distinct preferences in settlement location. The coastal Eskimo choose coastal headlands or islands in the center of good hunting areas. The Indians of the tundra or forest prefer locations along streams and lakes. Reasons for the latter choice are manifold: rivers and lakes provide an extra source of food supply in the form of fish; hunting can be done by boat; many mammals may be conveniently attacked while crossing rivers; and finally, rivers provide the principal transportation lines (by boat).

Construction among the Eskimo is widely characterized by different summer and winter abodes, occupied on a temporary basis of several weeks and occasionally months. Primitive huts may in some cases be dug into the ground during winter, and sunken dwellings are frequent. Where little wood is available, stones are built up with decreasing circumference in a roundish, domed structure. Where wood is available, a rectangular plan with pyramidal shape is employed, wooden beams or animal bones supporting the roof. In summer the same people usually exchange such sunken dwellings for tents of basket or conic structure. The forest Indians frequently live in tents the year around and do not share the architectural tastes of the Eskimo.

Settlement size is usually not greater than that of the more primitive food-gatherers, although seasonal concentrations of several groups may occur for the purpose of common organized battue hunts, e.g., buffalo hunting. Among such temporary or seasonal settlements it is not uncommon to find a community or council hut for ritual purposes, around which the other huts are grouped. Other analogies to the primitive food-gatherers' settlements are applicable.

Archeological evidence suggests that such subsistence-settlement patterns were common although not necessarily characteristic in late Pleistocene Europe.

MODERN SETTLEMENT PATTERNS OF SPECIALIZED HUNTERS AND FISHERS

Recent or contemporary populations of specialized hunters or fishers with possible analogy to terminal Paleolithic and Mesolithic groups, are certain hunting and fishing communities of the tundra and subarctic forests, as well as the Yuki and Maidu Indians of north-central California.

Some of the few changes from previous patterns, for example, include more carefully chosen topographic location with security as a dominant motive. Summer settlements are temporary, with primitive huts or tents used for shelter. Winter dwellings are occupied on a seasonal basis so that care is taken to provide maximum protection against the cold. *Sunken dwellings* are most characteristic, although rectangular, gabled houses of crude planks were used in some areas. In California basket or conic huts were most commonly used in the winter seasonal settlement.

As an example of settlement size and morphology the Yuki and Maidu of California (population density: 1 person per 2.2 sq. km., see Baumhoff, 1963) settled in groups of about 100 individuals. The groups maintained a major settlement of some permanence, with auxiliary sites of sporadic occupation. Huts were loosely arranged according to topographic considerations so that many settlements tended to display linear morphology. As the chieftain had little authority or permanence his hut was generally not singled out in terms of noticeably careful construction.

Compared with a settlement density of one person per every 20-400 square kilometers in the case of the food-gathering populations, these specialized food-collectors lived in comparatively dense concentrations. Furthermore, the seasonal character of settlement reflects more effective food acquisition. Some of the late Pleistocene and early Holocene food-collecting cultures of Europe and the Near East appear to have approached similar efficiency at the close of the Pleistocene.

MODERN SETTLEMENT PATTERNS OF PRIMITIVE AGRICULTURISTS

Primitive agriculture as practiced by farmers employing the hoe, or digging or planting stick is largely synonymous with the practice of shifting agriculture in the tropics of the Old and New World. Used in this sense, primitive agricultural settlements show adaptations to their peculiar economic pattern. The gradual reduction of fertility of the surface soil requires continuous shifting of plots. Similarly, the temporary invasion of cultivated lands by tough weed grasses may also make the soil too difficult to work. When all land in an area has thus been "used" within a decade, for example, a fallow period of thirty years or more would mean that another decade or two would have to elapse before any of the local fields could be cultivated again. In the meantime it may be preferable to abandon the settlement. Plow agriculture, permitting easy working and regular mixing of a deep soil layer can better guarantee a permanent basis for settlement—at least in extra-tropical areas.

With primitive agriculture the "economic area" is much more limited in size than in the case of a food-collecting economy. At first the settlement is immediately surrounded by land in cultivation, but as these fields are left in fallow the belt of cropped plots lies farther and farther afield with unproductive land in between. Field huts are often set up to provide shelter while sowing or harvesting takes place in very distant fields which may eventually lie as much as 10-20 kilometers from the settlement. When this inconvenience becomes too great or when concentric expansion is limited by geographic or social barriers, the settlement may be abandoned. Consequently, a rather loose association between site and "economic area" is characteristic for the settlements of primitive agriculturists. Needless to say there are important modern exceptions where primitive agricultural settlements are permanent.

The topographic location of sites of primitive tropical agriculturists today is primarily dictated by terrain. River levees or terraces are highly favored in the rainforest because of the better alluvial soils, the possibility of river transport, and the added food resource of fish. Steeper slopes are avoided because of the danger of slumping. In the savannas small elevations are favored because of greater air movement and safety from sheetflooding. Invariably, alluvial flats, swampy terrain, or flood-periled savanna plains are avoided. Elevated locations or mountain spurs are also more secure, and riverine sites between complex meander systems may be occupied as a defensive measure. The security factor of many primitive agricultural settlements reflects both a need for safety in a semipermanent settlement as well as a tribal social structure without central authority.

The typical shelter form employed is that of one-roomed houses. Huts and houses with conic roofs are constructed by a circular row of posts joined by wickerware of plant fibre, usually coated with mud, mixed mud and dung, or mud with chaff or straw ("daub-and-wattle"). The roof is supported by vertical as well as oblique beams, and closed off with grass, straw, or reeds. These house-types are characteristic in open tropical landscapes.

A gabled house-type is more common in the rainforest, designed to permit better ventilation. Vertical posts in rectangular array support the walls and a saddle roof. The latter is covered by palm leaves, palm leaves and ribs, or sugar cane. Wickerware of leaves, sliced bamboo, or bark is used for the walls, or possibly crude planks. The posts are obtained from palm stems, breadfruit trees, bamboo, etc. Raised pile dwellings are common.

Household or small herd animals are kept in the house (or in the case of pile dwellings under the house) at night, while enclosures of some form are used for larger herd animals. Storage facilities are not required in rainforest areas where agricultural products are available continuously, but they are necessary where seasonal drought impedes cultivation for part of the year. Storage houses or huts, often on posts, are common in the seasonal tropics, large pottery storage urns or mud silos in the drier subtropics. Community buildings serving complex social or religious functions are usual, and stand out by their greater size, better craftsmanship, and ornamentation. The same applies to the house of the local chieftain.

The size of such settlements is generally that of the clan group— hamlets or small villages of fifty to a few hundred inhabitants. Large villages with several thousand inhabitants may develop when (*a*) protection requires greater concentrations of population, (*b*) advanced political and social organization has been developed, (*c*) strong leaders require settlement amalgamation for military purposes, and when (*d*) natural resources are particularly good. Population density estimates in the order of 5-10 persons per square kilometer (Braidwood and Reed, 1957) seem well founded as an average, although there is considerable variability.

The morphology of these primitive agricultural settlements is oriented along topographic lines in the rainforest: a linear orientation along streams or along pre-existing forest trails. In open landscapes the morphology is related to social or economic features, and in both cases circular forms dominate. In the latter instance, larger herd animals may be enclosed within a circle of huts. Where social rather than economic factors prevail, the living huts are located around a core area which includes the chieftain's house, community buildings (for school, social, council, religious, or craft purposes), and storage facilities. Protection is commonly obtained through construction of palisades, thorn fences, and the like.

Settlement patterns in Egypt appear to have been of analogous type as late as the Old Kingdom (mid-third millennium B.C.), but the archeological evidence from southwestern Asia suggests that many settlements of an early agricultural type already had considerable permanence. Construction in the mediterranean climate zone of the Near East was also more elaborate, long before the advent of plow cultivation. Architecture was commonly rectangular in plan, making use of adobe mud or even sun-dried bricks. But the general analogy is still useful for a better understanding of late prehistoric, agricultural settlement.

24

Human Origins
in Sub-Saharan Africa

Men, by the definition of "Man the Toolmaker," are first known from the Villafranchian of Africa. Less than a decade ago a variety of pebble and core-choppers, rough retouched end-struck flakes, and a chopper hammerstone were first found together with teeth and jaw fragments of *Australopithecus* at the Sterkfontein Extension site, near Krugersdorp in the Transvaal (Mason, 1961, with earlier references). Faunistically the Sterkfontein Extension breccia is dated in the late Villafranchian (Brain, 1958; Cooke, 1963). A few years later, several cultural floors, associated with australopithecine fossils, were discovered in Bed I of Olduvai Gorge, Tanganyika (Leakey, 1963, with earlier references). Faunistically these beds belong to the Upper Villafranchian (Cooke, 1963), while potassium-argon dates (Evernden and Curtis, 1964) give an average of 1.75 million years for the younger cultural floors. Pebble tools [1] in less convincing situations have also been found in Basal Pleistocene (pre-Sicilian regression?) beds of Morocco, known as the Moulouyian (Biberson, 1961a, 1961b).

The apparent dispersal of tool-makers in Africa during the late Villafranchian suggests that tool-making was invented rather early in the Pleistocene. The question that remains unanswered is: who were the tool-makers? They may have belonged to the Villafranchian ape-men or to evolving hominines directly related to modern man.[2]

[1] Made from pebbles by removing two or three flakes from two faces in order to obtain a jagged cutting edge on one side.

[2] According to a widely favored taxonomic classification the higher primates are subdivided into the hominoids and cercopithecoids (Old World monkeys). The hominoids in turn are subdivided into the hominids and pongids (anthropoid apes). The pongids include two living subfamilies, the pongines (including gorilla, chimpanzee, and orangutan) and the hylobatines (gibbons). The hominids include two subfamilies, the australopithecines (extinct) and the hominines (including *Homo erectus, H. sapiens neanderthalensis,* and *H. sapiens sapiens*).

APE-MEN OF THE BASAL PLEISTOCENE

The fossil ape-men of the Villafranchian, grouped under the heading "australopithecine," are divided into two genera by Robinson (1963, with earlier references): (a) *Paranthropus*, a large creature without a forehead, bearing an apelike sagittal crest on the top of the skull, with large molars but small incisor and canine teeth (Fig. 57),

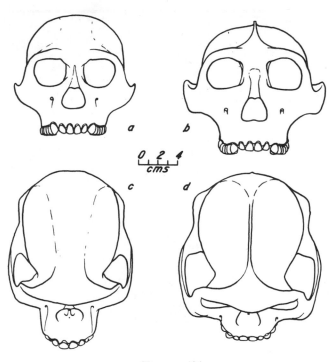

FIGURE 57.

Facial and top views of skulls of *Australopithecus* (a,c) and *Paranthropus* (b,d). Both skulls are of females. (From J. T. Robinson, 1963, with kind permission of the author and of the Wenner-Gren Foundation for Anthropological Research.)

and (b) *Australopithecus*, a somewhat smaller creature with a distinct forehead, without a sagittal crest, with moderately large canines and large incisors. Both genera, also variously considered as subgenera had a cranial capacity of 450-550 cubic centimeters. *Australopithecus* was about four feet tall and weighed about 40-50 pounds. *Paranthropus* or species, were erectly bipedal, i.e., could walk upright, and both may have weighed about 100-140 pounds. According to Robinson (1963), the *Zinjanthropus* of Olduvai and the Javan *Meganthropus* both belong to the *Paranthropus* group. He considers the "pre-Zinj" child of Olduvai Bed I similar to *Australopithecus* in some respects, rather different in others. Leakey *et al.* (1964) believe that "pre-Zinj" is a hominine. Australopithecine remains have also been found

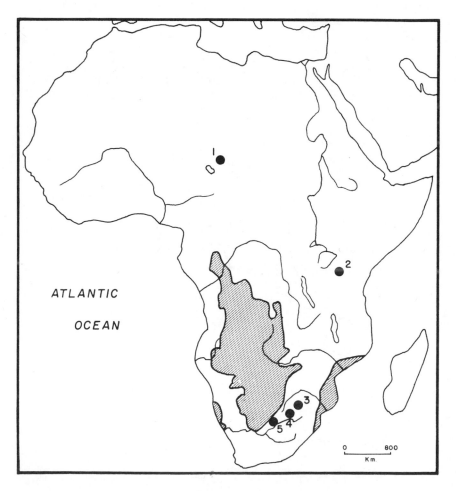

FIGURE 58.
Australopithecine sites in Africa. (1) Koro Toro, (2) Olduvai, (3) Makapansgat, (4) Sterkfontein, Swartkrans and Kromdraai, (5) Taungs. Distribution of Kalahari and related sands (simplified after Cooke, 1958) indicated by shading.

together with a Villafranchian fauna at Koro Toro on the northeastern side of the Lake Chad basin (see Monod, 1963, with references) (Fig. 58).

On the basis of the dentition, *Paranthropus* was probably herbivorous in his dietary habits, and evidence for grit in that diet suggests that the plant food included roots and bulbs (Robinson, 1963). *Australopithecus*, on the other hand, has dental adaptations suggesting an omnivore, obtaining a large part of his dietary subsistence in the form of meat. The bone and dental morphology of both of the australopithecines is hominid rather than pongid, i.e., manlike rather than apelike. Robinson believes it quite probable that both australopithecines were tool-*users*, but that neither were tool-*makers*. Although both taxa were contemporary during the later Villafranchian, they probably lived in disjunct areas as they have not yet been shown to occur simultaneously at any one site. *Paranthropus*, in its youngest range, has been shown to be more or less contemporary with early forms of the genus *Homo* in South Africa ("Telanthropus" in the Cromer(?)-age Swartkrans beds, Cooke, 1963) and Java ("Pithecanthropus" in the Elster(?)-age Kabuh conglomerates at Sangiran— Koenigswald, 1957; Movius, 1955). Robinson (1963) considers that *Paranthropus* represents the original australopithecine stock, which probably originated in the Pliocene or even in the Miocene. *Australopithecus* represents an adaptively different line of the same basic stock.

The difficulty of demonstrating the humanity (i.e., tool-making capacities) of either or both *Australopithecus* and *Paranthropus* lies in the controversy of *who* made the tools found together with the *Australopithecus* at Sterkfontein Extension, with *Paranthropus* ("Zinjanthropus"), or with the "pre-Zinj" child in Olduvai Bed I. They may have been made by the same australopithecine stock, or however, the australopithecine may have been killed and eaten by a more advanced hominine not represented in the fossil record. The possibility that "pre-Zinj" belongs to a very early hominine stock is particularly interesting in this regard (see Leakey and Leakey, 1964; Leakey *et al.*, 1964).

Whatever the eventual outcome of the problem, in the light of future excavations, two facts remain: (*a*) deliberately manufactured stone implements are known from the Upper Villafranchian of Africa; (*b*) indisputable cultural floors occur in the Villafranchian Bed I at Olduvai and suggest ephemeral camps by people whose subsistence was at least partly based on scavenging and/or killing a limited part of the vertebrate faunal spectrum.

ENVIRONMENTAL CHANGES AND AUSTRALOPITHECINE EVOLUTION

There is abundant evidence for late Tertiary and early Pleistocene climatic change in southern Africa (see Cooke, 1958, 1962; Brain, 1958; Robinson, 1963). Fluvial erosion under savanna-type climate sculptured the surface of much of southern Africa during mid-Tertiary times, but during the time span of the Upper Miocene-Lower Pliocene arid conditions accompanied the deposition of the Kalahari System, found between the Vaal River and the lower Congo Basin. Interpretation of these geological features is confirmed by botanical and entomological studies which have demonstrated forest expansion in the Miocene with marked recession in the Pliocene, leaving residual forests in a ring around the central Congo Basin and in East Africa, and with a certain amount of expansion again in the Pleistocene (Cahen, 1954; Cooke, 1958; Robinson, 1963). The sands of the Kalahari System (Fig. 58) predate extensive river cutting during the early Pleistocene. Even during the early Pleistocene considerable climatic change occurred in the Transvaal, and the careful sedimentological studies of Brain (1958) suggest that rainfall varied from 70 per cent to 150 per cent of that of the present value. There were then marked oscillations between "pluvial" and "interpluvial" conditions, which presumably resulted in repeated, wholesale movements of vegetation belts.

The original, herbivorous *Paranthropus* line of the australopithecines was almost certainly adapted to a comparatively moist, forest or open woodland environment, as are all monkeys and apes (see DeVore and Washburn, 1963; Schaller and Emlen, 1963). Gradual desiccation of most of southern Africa during the Mio-Pliocene may have reduced the area of suitable habitats severely so that competition for such environments would have been great. Simultaneously grassland and desert environments expanded, providing increased opportunity for animals adapted, or capable of adapting, to such conditions (Robinson, 1963). Robinson (1963, pp. 409-11) suggests that:

> Australopithecines living in areas which subsequently became semi-arid will have found that the dry season gradually became longer and drier. The critical time of the year, the latter part of the dry season, will gradually have become more difficult to cope with. It is reasonable to suppose that in these times of hardship insects, reptiles, small mammals, the eggs and nestlings of birds, etc., will have been eaten to supplement their diet. It is known that purely vegetarian primates will readily eat meat in captivity and that baboons, for example, will occasionally do so in the wild. Taking to a certain amount of meat-

eating under environmental pressure could therefore occur fairly easily. As desiccation proceeded, such a deme will have found that it had to rely on the seasonal supplement to its normal vegetarian diet more frequently and to a greater degree. Under these circumstances it could be expected that population density will have dropped, probably to the vanishing point in the most heavily affected areas. But it is probable that in at least some areas the creatures will have adapted satisfactorily to the altering circumstances and adopted a certain amount of carnivorousness as a normal part of their way of life. That is to say, the originally vegetarian diet will have become altered by the addition of a certain amount of meat-eating to an omnivorous diet.

It is quite clear, however, that such modifications to the environment will have altered the nature of selection acting on the group. Even an elementary level of tool-using will have had obvious advantages in the changing food situation. For the vegetarian part of their food, implements for digging will have made possible greater exploitation of the larger number of bulbs found in drier areas. Implements for bashing, hitting, or throwing as well as digging, will have made capture and consumption of small animals much easier. Improved tool-using will thus have been favored by selection and any improvements in this respect will have improved adaptation, especially in respect of the carnivorous aspect of their diet. It is also obvious that improved intelligence will have been of great benefit in improving tool-using ability and dealing generally with the stresses of a somewhat hostile environment. Improved intelligence will consequently also have been favored by selection. . . .

The changed environmental circumstances resulting from the known desiccation of a substantial part of Africa during the late Tertiary could therefore very easily have led to . . . the establishment of a second phyletic line in the australopithecines. In this the introduction of a carnivorous element in the diet and an enhanced level of cultural activity were important features. *Australopithecus* is evidently precisely such a line. It is of interest that this form is present in the Sterkfontein valley in the more arid periods, while *Paranthropus* is present only in the wetter periods. . . .

The development of the hominine grade of organization would appear to have been a natural consequence. The next threshold of evolution was crossed when simple cultural activity and increasing intelligence reached a stage where tool-using gave way to tool-making and the typical cultural activity and approach to environmental challenges of man appeared (Robinson, 1963).

Apart from the adaptation and natural selection emphasized by Robinson, other genetic forces were possibly also responsible for an acceleration of evolution among the australopithecines, and conceivably among some later populations as well. Hiernaux (1963) emphasizes that gene flow or cross-breeding may be accelerated by environmental changes. Seasonal migrations resulting from alternating wet and dry seasons, or migrations favored by long-term climatic changes, may result in gene exchange between different groups. Similarly, the greater number of bands of primitive scavengers or hunters supported by a given area during periods of favorable climate will favor gene flow and acculturation. Other ecological conditions may, according to Hiernaux (1963), favor the reverse process of random genetic drift. Wide dispersal of small bands in dry country, or increased isolation during the course of desiccation will favor inbreeding and genetic drift. Through premature death of certain individuals of a breeding isolate, certain blood groups or genes may be lost to a small population, whereas other biological traits may be accentuated. The same result may be obtained by dispersal of offspring of a group into daughter communities. In other words, certain environmental changes may enforce or favor group isolation and hence genetic drift, other modifications may facilitate gene exchange and fusion of population aggregates. It is possible that alternating cross-breeding and genetic drift, motivated by alternating pluvials and interpluvials at the dawn of African prehistory, may have influenced and accelerated human evolution.

Bourlière (1963, comments p. 642) has distinguished the possible influence of environmental changes on early hominids at several levels:

a) Individual level: effects on stature, body build and fecundity;
b) Population level: effects on size of breeding populations, on over-all population density, isolation, and possibly also on population cycles (see also Bartholomew and Birdsell, 1953);
c) Continental level: At the carnivorous hominid and early hominine level dense populations would be found in open woodlands, savannas, and grasslands, with little or no occupation of dense rainforests or desert country. In mountainous terrain a number of distinct ecological niches are provided by moist, wooded uplands, drier open lowlands, galeria forests along streams and lakes, etc. Isolated groups could grow up and evolve within such niches.

These mechanisms help to illustrate how environmental changes can produce significant changes in the density and general distribution of primitive populations. As tool-users, early Pleistocene hominids certainly had no mastery over their environment. Without knowledge of clothing (which one must assume) or fire (something empirically apparent, Oakley, 1961), they probably could not operate comfortably outside of warm climates due to the tropical adaptations of most monkeys, pongids, and hominids.[3] Within the tropics carnivorous hominids were again restricted to areas with available water and animal foods. The latter is scarce both in the desert and in dense forest. In association with the archeological and paleontological evidence it seems that the decisive biological, cultural, and intellectual evolution of the hominid line took place in the tropical woodlands and savannas of Africa during the Basal Pleistocene. This leaves open the exact relationship of the hominines to the australopithecines. Whatever that relationship, it seems rather probable that the environmental changes of the Tertiary and early Pleistocene had a great biological impact on hominid evolution.

SIGNIFICANCE OF VILLAFRANCHIAN HOMINIDS FOR THE ENVIRONMENT

The Villafranchian hominids were unable to modify or noticeably effect the environment. Hunting activities were probably confined to scavenging of larger animals and limited hunting of smaller prey (Howell, 1959b; J. D. Clark, 1960; Leakey, 1963). So for example the apparent australopithecine booty of the Taungs cave, on a Vaal River tributary, consisted of eggs, crabs, tortoise, birds, rodents, and juvenile antelopes and baboons. Much of the booty of the cultural floors in Olduvai Bed I consists of small animals such as rodents, insectivores, bats, chameleons, tortoise, lizards, fish, birds, and juvenile ungulates. Larger animals were apparently driven into swamps or water and, at any rate, despatched through clubbing or stoning after they became bemired. A good example is known from Olduvai, where the disjunct lower limb bones of a primitive elephant (*Dinotherium*) were found standing upright in a former boggy sediment, while the scattered bones of the upper body had clearly been dismembered and devoured nearby by hominid carnivores. Scavenging the kills of larger carnivores, a well-known practice among some primitive groups today, may also have been common. At any rate the hunting efficiency of the Villafranchian hominids was rather limited. The impact of such hominids upon wildlife must have been minimal.

Modifications of the vegetation were not possible since fire was probably not at their control, while the vegetable-gathering habits of such small, dispersed bands were of no importance. Man-land relationships during the early Pleistocene were then entirely one-sided. If anywhere in human history, environmental determinism would have been significant at this stage of biological and cultural evolution.

[3] Schaller and Emlen (1963) showed that the mountain gorilla ranges up to elevations of 4,000 m. in the eastern Congo. The temperature tolerance of the primates is consequently greater than commonly assumed.

25

Man-Land Relationships at the Early Paleolithic Culture Level

THE ADVENT OF THE LOWER PALEOLITHIC

Whoever their maker, simple pebble tools of late Villafranchian (in the broad sense of the word) age are found in many parts of Africa. So far pebble tools are not verified from such early stratigraphic horizons elsewhere, suggesting that the human stock had not dispersed through the Old World tropics before the beginning of the first continental glaciation, the Elster. But the typologically standardized tools of early Paleolithic type are widespread in the tropical and temperate climate zones of the Old World, implying comparatively rapid colonization of new environments and several continents in the Lower Pleistocene.

The Lower Paleolithic is marked by the appearance of bifacial tools, of which the major formal types were so-called hand-axes and cleavers (Fig. 59). Their main function appears to have been that of mattocks and flensers for removing hide, cutting ligaments, parceling meat, and removing flesh from bone or hide of large game (J. D. Clark, 1960). The tools consisted of large flakes or nodules trimmed down by flaking off so as to obtain two, regular opposite faces. In the case of the hand-axe a cutting edge is trimmed with a point at one end. Numerous unspecialized flakes, chipped off in the preparation of hand-axes or cleavers, were perhaps retouched a little, and together with polyhedral stones (possible missiles) and other chopping or pounding equipment, were variously put to use in carcass salvage. Whether stone tools were also used to secure vegetable food is difficult to decide. The dominant industrial element is consequently the hand-axe, hence the crude Lower Paleolithic synonym of "hand-axe cultures."

The first appearance of typologically-standardized Lower Paleo-lithic industrial assemblages may have been contemporary with the Cromerian, and certainly no later than the early Elster. Industries of early Acheulian type (including those variously called "Chellean" or "Abbevillian") appear in Africa and Europe during the Elster Com-plex, and analogous but distinctive industries show up in parts of southwestern and eastern Asia. Before the close of the Elster II glacial a pattern of human settlement had been established that seems to have lasted throughout the middle Pleistocene—in western and southern Europe, most of Africa (excluding the rainforests), southwestern, southern, and eastern Asia. Most of eastern Europe and Central Asia appear to have been devoid of man, not to mention northern Eurasia (Fig. 60). This raises the question of man's first passage into Europe (Chard, 1963b): Lower Paleolithic cultures are absent in Russia and southeastern Europe with exception of Hungary, thus possibly exclud-ing immigration via the Dardanelles-Bosporus or across the Caucasus. Instead there are unmistakable cultural affinities between northwestern Africa and southwestern Europe. The absence of a land bridge at Gibraltar (since the early Pliocene, on geological grounds) or via Sicily (since at least the Basal Pleistocene, on archeological and faunal grounds, Vaufrey, 1929) implies that man must have somehow crossed the Straits of Gibraltar during the Cromerian or Elster I.

FOSSIL REMAINS OF EARLY MEN

A number of localities have produced Lower Pleistocene strata with human fossils, some of them associated with early Paleolithic tools. These fossils are probably best referred to the genus *Homo,* and they represent the general stock ancestral to modern man. Cranial capacities exceed 800 cubic centimeters, browridges are massive. Although some authorities (see Le Gros Clark, 1955) prefer to group the early hominines as a separate genus, *Pithecanthropus,* the fossil evidence does not really warrant the mass of generic names applied to each fossil, nor does it support a generic distinction from later human types (see Howell, 1960, 1964). The designation of *Homo erectus* is probably applicable to all the fossil men in this time range.

Some of the more important localities with early human remains (listed by their superfluous generic names) include the following (Fig. 60):

a) Swartkrans, South Africa ("Telanthropus"), dated as Cromer (?) (see Cooke, 1963);

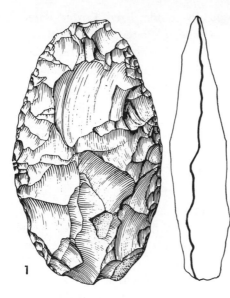

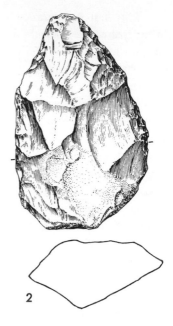

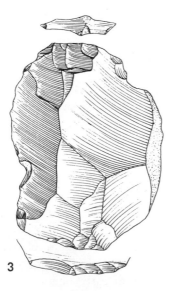

FIGURE 59.
Some Middle Acheulian stone implements from the Somme
Valley (Cagny) (from F. Bordes, 1961a, with kind permission

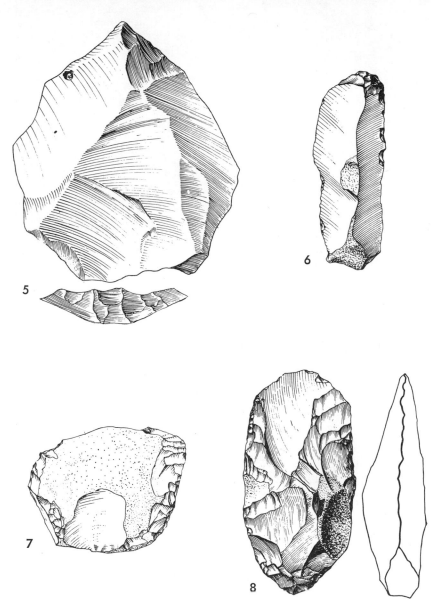

of the author). (1, 2) different bifaces or "hand-axes," (3)
flake, (4) notched flake, (5) core, (6) end scraper, (7) side
scraper, (8) cleaver. Reduced to one-half natural size.

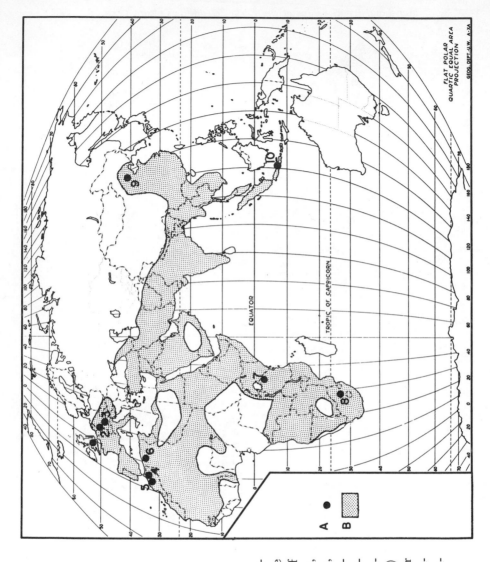

FIGURE 60.
The distribution of early Pleistocene man. (A) Lower and Middle Pleistocene sites with fossils of *Homo erectus:* (1) Swanscombe, (2) Heidelberg, (3) Steinheim, (4) Rabat, (5) Sidi Abderrhaman, (6) Ternifine, (7) Olduvai, (8) Swartkrans, (9) Choukoutien, (10) Sangiran. (B) Approximate distribution of Lower Paleolithic industries (interpretation of Russian Paleolithic chronology after Chard, 1963b).

b) Heidelberg, Germany ("Palaeanthropus"), dated as Cortonian (see Howell, 1960);

c) Ternifine, Algeria ("Atlanthropus"), dated as Elster II (see Howell, 1960);

d) Choukoutien, near Peking, China ("Sinanthropus"), dated as Elster II (see Kurtén and Vasari, 1960);

e) Olduvai Bed II, Tanganyika (so-called Chellean Man), dated as Elster (?) (see Cooke, 1963; Evernden and Curtis, 1964);

f) Sangiran, Javan ("Pithecanthropus robustus"), presumably Cromer or very early Elster complex (see Movius, 1955; Koenigswald, 1940, 1957);

g) Swanscombe, England, dated as late Holstein (see Howell, 1960);

h) Steinheim, Germany, dated as late Holstein (see Howell, 1960);

i) Sangiran, Java ("Pithecanthropus erectus"), dated as Middle Pleistocene (Koenigswald, 1940);

j) Rabat, Morocco, dated as transitional late Holstein to early Riss (see Howell, 1960);

k) Sidi Abderrahman, Morocco, *ibid.* (see Howell, 1960).

All of these fossils pertain to the Lower or Middle Pleistocene.

Stratigraphically questionable late Middle Pleistocene fossils have been omitted. For a comprehensive survey see Coon (1962).

EVIDENCE OF LOWER PALEOLITHIC SETTLEMENT

No direct information is available on the size of early Paleolithic communities, although the analogy of modern unspecialized food-collectors may be useful. The aboriginal Australians, ranging over a whole continent in contact times, are probably most suitable for this purpose. They lived in bands of about 40 people, which formed the primary land-owning unit. These local groups in their turn belonged to tribes numbering between 200 and 800 people, forming a fairly well defined genetic isolate (Birdsell, 1953, see also chap. 23).[1]

The distribution of cultural evidence suggests major settlement in tropical Africa was focused in open or lightly wooded country, in close proximity to rivers, lakes, or the seashore (J. D. Clark, 1960).

[1] Inferences drawn from other primate populations are open to question since behavorial patterns vary greatly, and it would be presumptuous to assume that early hominids necessarily offered parallels to living primates (Schaller and Emlen, 1963).

Such localities would presumably supply an abundance of water and both animal and plant foods. Raw material for tool-making is present in most areas, and the tools used for animal dissection were apparently made-to-order on the spot.

Apparent living sites of the Lower Paleolithic take the form of areal tool and bone concentrations recording both the tool-making and meat-eating activities of man. Some parts of such "cultural floors" were primarily used for tool-flaking, others for the dismemberment and efficient use of animal game for food. Various foci of archeological concentration may suggest that a band reoccupied a site on several occasions, or also that several groups may have temporarily occupied it together. In either case the lack of appreciable thickness to such cultural floors seems to indicate that sites were only ephemeral camps, possibly in a seasonal movement within a hunting territory.

> Some of these sites can have been no more than stopping places for consuming a single large food animal. Others, however, provide signs of deliberate and more prolonged occupation and are believed to represent butchery sites where a number of animals, on more than one occasion, were killed, cut up, and eaten, or where a seasonal crop of vegetable foods determined a stay of several days (J. D. Clark, 1960, p. 314).

Such sites appear to qualify as ephemeral settlements.

Occasionally there is evidence of what may have been primitive shelters. For example, one or two irregular shallow depressions on a living floor at Olorgesailie, Kenya, possibly represent sleeping places such as are known from among the Bushmen and Hottentots. Similarly, at the late Pleistocene site of Kalambo Falls, Tanganyika, a rough arc of intentionally placed stones may have formed the base of a wind shelter (J. D. Clark, 1960). On the same floor, three separate accumulations of carbonized matted grass stems, fibrous roots, and twigs occupy shallow depressions up to a meter wide, recalling grass-lined bedding places. Even in Bed I at Olduvai (site DK) concentrations of artificially accumulated and sometimes heaped-up, natural stones (Howell, personal communication) offer further ideas for speculation on dwelling structures. The Choukoutien Locality 1 site probably represents an actual cave dwelling (see Teilhard de Chardin, 1941).

EVIDENCE OF LOWER PALEOLITHIC ECONOMY

The hunting technology of the early Paleolithic shows an improvement upon that of the pebble-tool-makers of the Villafranchian. Small mammals play a minor role among the faunal remains of living sites.

Record of offensive weapons is rather meager, probably as a result of widespread use of wooden implements such as spears, clubs, or throwing sticks. The apparent remains of such wooden weapons are known from several European sites (Torralba, Clacton, Lehringen). Many of the unworked or crudely-shaped stones found in association with animal remains were also possibly used for throwing. With such a limited inventory preserved, it is not surprising that fossils are frequently associated with lacustrine beds, suggesting attack on bogged-down animals driven into swamps or lakes (J. D. Clark, 1960). Whatever the technique, group-hunting, particularly of big game, seems to have been of prime importance. There can be only little doubt that early Paleolithic men were less dependent on fortuitous chance and scavenging activities than were the hominids of the Villafranchian.

Although no empirical evidence is available yet, it may be assumed that wild vegetables—roots, bulbs, stems, etc.—also formed an appreciable part of the human diet.

Use of fire is first evidenced during the Elster II glaciation at Choukoutien (Oakley, 1961) and at Torralba and Ambrona, Spain (Howell, 1962). The use of controlled fire apparently spread slowly into warmer latitudes, but seemingly remained unknown in Africa prior to the Upper Pleistocene (J. D. Clark, 1960). Whether or not the early Paleolithic culture-bearers knew how to use fire as a hunting device remains unknown.

MAN-LAND RELATIONSHIPS

Early Paleolithic men ranged through a wide variety of environments, from the African savannas and open woodlands (Olduvai, Olorgesailie) to the temperate woodlands (Swanscombe, Mauer, Choukoutien) and the forest-tundra (Torralba). Acheulian hand-axes are even relatively common in parts of the Sahara. Man still had to take what the environment had to offer, but he could obviously now make more efficient use of available animal resources. Cold climates presented a problem at first, but the conquest of fire during the Elster marks a first step toward emancipation from the environment. Despite the cold environment of Elster-age Torralba (see below), man still showed noticeable reluctance to occupy the tundra, the boreal woodlands, and the cool steppes of Eurasia (Fig. 60). The total absence of contemporary culture groups from the tropical rainforests is also remarkable.

Despite his versatility, early Paleolithic man was still limited in both distribution and numbers by the availability of water and food supply. He was technologically not sufficiently advanced to impress his stamp upon the environment in any way. Lack of specialization in hunting techniques precludes any significant modification of the fauna. However, the use of fire as a possible device for hunting or regeneration of food plants requires attention. West and McBurney (1954) found evidence of a sudden appearance of pioneer weed plants in the Acheulian cultural layer of the Holstein-age pollen profile of Hoxne, Suffolk. This suggests forest burning with subsequent recolonization by lower, light-loving plants and ultimately tree species. Deliberate burning by man or an accidental forest fire may have been responsible. Certainly the ethnological, historical, and archeological work of C. O. Sauer (1944, 1947) and Stewart (1956) make it impossible to ignore the potential effects of burning of the vegetative cover by man. It is improbable however that any appreciable, large-scale influence was exerted on the natural vegetation during the course of the early and middle Pleistocene.

In overview, man-land relationships at the early Paleolithic level were still entirely one-sided. Whether or not the climatic changes evident in the geological record exerted an influence on cultural advancement is difficult to establish, although quite possible. So, for example, J. D. Clark (1960) suggested that cultural speed-ups took place during the African "interpluvials." Apart from the fact that we know next to nothing geologically and archeologically about the Cromerian (?) and Holstein (?) periods in Africa, the relative duration of interpluvials versus pluvials remains to be established (see Howell's comments to J. D. Clark, 1960). It is theoretically plausible, however, that pluvial periods in the semiarid and subhumid tropics would encourage population movement, contact, gene flow, and cultural experiment, while dry phases would encourage isolation, restricting gene flow and encouraging cultural specialization (J. D. Clark, 1960). When the environment changes, the economic structure of society is upset as well, so that readjustment may have to take place (J. D. Clark, 1958, p. 2).

AN EXAMPLE OF AN EARLY PALEOLITHIC LIVING SITE: TORRALBA, SPAIN

The early Middle Acheulian site of Torralba is located 156 km. northeast of Madrid at an elevation of 1,115 m. Originally studied by the Marqués de Cerralbo from 1909-11, the site was nearly completely excavated by F. C. Howell from 1961-63 (Howell, et al., 1963).

Stratigraphically, it can be dated in a period of cool climate preceding the Tyrrhenian I, i.e., probably Elster II. The following discussion is based on as yet unpublished materials, with Howell and L. G. Freeman responsible for the archeology, E. Aguirre for paleontology, Butzer for geology and paleogeography, J. Menéndez-Amor for palynology.

The geographical setting consists of a broad, steep-sided valley incised into a limestone plateau. The lower part of the valley cuts into impermeable strata of gypsum and siltstone, so that springs are frequently found at the base of the porous and permeable limestone bedrock above. A spring of this kind almost certainly existed at the site during the time of occupation. Running water is now available in a local stream at 500 m. distance, and was certainly once accessible in nearby torrents at 300 m. during most of the year. The topography itself is such that the steep slopes accompanying the valley margins would have impeded free passage of some animal species from the valley to the uplands. Furthermore, this valley represents one of the few low level passes joining Old Castille to the north of the central sierras, and New Castille to the south (Fig. 61). Torralba is therefore located along what may have been a seasonal migratory route for larger game moving northward in the late spring, southward in the late summer. Also of significance is the absence of surface water on the limestone plateau as a result of very rapid percolation. This means that man and animals have at all times been required to water in the valleys.

The geologic setting of the Torralba site, and its twin at nearby Ambrona, is within a river terrace at 40 m. above the local stream, part of the headwaters of the Jalón, a major tributary of the Ebro. The stratigraphic column of the 40 m. terrace deposits is given in Fig. 62. The over-all climate was both cooler and moister than today's, although subject to repeated oscillations. Human occupation is first recorded here during a cold, moist interval. Subsequently conditions were temperate but then once more reverted to a cool, moist climate. Occupation is no longer recorded during a later warm oscillation. Geomorphic phenomena include evidence of considerable frost-weathering, solifluction (partly as a result of soil frost, partly due to lubrication of clayey beds), and valley alluviation. Most of the occupation levels are found in a series of intercalated slope deposits and stream alluvium. The richest level (Bed IIb) is found within and on top of a stratum of coarse, subrounded, frost-weathered gravel which mantles the upland surfaces and hillsides of the area. Stone rings and garlands were found at the Torralba site indicating significant soil-frost phenomena. All in all, the geomorphic record suggests a marginal periglacial

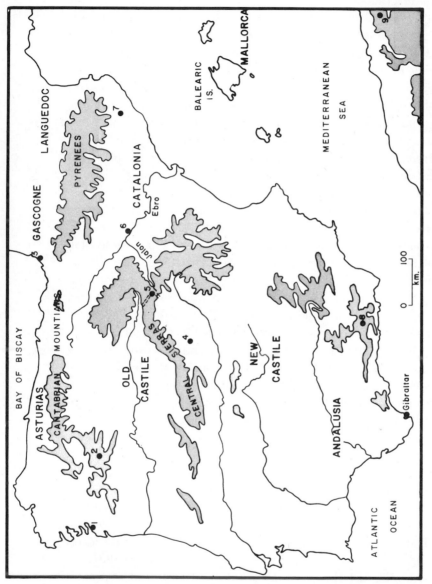

FIGURE 61. The Iberian Peninsula. Areas over 1000 m. elevation shaded. (1) Vigo, (2) Laguna de las Sangujuelas, (3) Biarritz, (4) Madrid, (5) location of Torralba and Ambrona with route of low-level pass, (6) Zaragoza, (7) Moya, (8) Sierra Nevada, (9) Jurjura Mtns. Topography modified after *Prentice-Hall World Atlas* (2d ed.), with permission of Geographischer Verlag Ed. Hölzel, Vienna.

UNIT	SEDIMENT	THICKNESS(cm) TORRALBA	THICKNESS(cm) AMBRONA	ASSOCIATED PROCESSES	CLIMATIC INFERENCES	MAMMAL FAUNA	HUMAN OCCUPATION TORRALBA	HUMAN OCCUPATION AMBRONA	TENTATIVE CORRELATION
UPPER COMPLEX	IV. Reddish colluvium	120	200	Soil colluviation with local fan alluviation at valley margins ~EROSION~	(Human interference)				Historical
	III. Fine dark alluvium	80		Valley alluviation	Moist, temperate		Upper Paleolithic (surface traces)		Middle Holocene
	II. Coarse brown alluvium	70		Alluviation at valley margins by lateral tributaries; tufa deposits locally. Some solifluction initially. ~EROSION~	Cool, moist				Würm Glacial
	I. Reddish colluvium	125							
MIDDLE COMPLEX	II. Yellowish sands	10		Colluviation and valley alluviation, following intensive frost-weathering. Slumping of subsurface, lubricated Keuper silts producing faulting at both sites. Some solifluction.	Cold, moist				Riss Glacial Complex
	I. d. Reddish colluvium	55							
	c. Reddish alluvium	60							
	b. Reddish colluvium	30							
	a. Cryoclastic detritus	20		~EROSION~					
PEDO-GENESIS	Terra fusca soil developed on Lower Complex IV and V exclusively. B 160 / Bc 10 / Ca 10-20	160 10 10-20	150 35 10-60	~EROSION~	Warm seasonally very moist				Great (Holsteinian) Interglacial (=Tyrrhenian I stage)
LOWER COMPLEX	V. d. Coarse reddish alluvium	95		Shallow alluviation at valley margins by lateral tributaries.	Very cold				
	c. Fine reddish alluvium	165	85						
	b. C-gravels		60						
	a. Gritty marl		90	~EROSION~					
	IV. b. Gray marl	200		Valley back swamps filled with homogeneous fine silts from sluggish flood waters; pseudo-gley conditions indicated by limonitic Fe-horizons.	Moist, temperate			EARLY MIDDLE ACHEULIAN OCCUPATION / Hiatus	Moist, cool
	a. Marl with channel beds	150	220	Valley flood-plaining dominated by very fine alluviation, but with coarse, moderate cryoclastic channel beds locally. ~EROSION~	Moist, cool				
	III. b. B-gravel	—	15	Coarse valley alluviation with reduced soil frost.	Moist, cool			STERILE	
	a. Upper gray colluvium	80	80	Fine valley alluviation with some solifluction. ~EROSION & CONGELIFLUCTION~	Cold, moist			EARLY MIDDLE ACHEULIAN OCCUPATION	
	II. d. Sandy marl	90	150	Fine valley filling.	Moist, temperate				
	c. Lower gray colluvium	100	?	Well-stratified gritty sands with intercalated gravels. Valley alluviation.	Cold, moist				
	b. A-gravel	30	60	Coarse cryoclastic gravels on slopes, partly calcrete, partly interbedded with grey silts. Some congelifluction.	Cold, moist				
	a. Light sand	70+	300	Fine valley filling of homogeneous sands, partly silty at top. ~EROSION~	Cool, moist				
	I. Red colluvium	400+	?40	Medium, highly cryoclastic detritus at base of slopes.	Very cold				
	O. Redeposited Keuper (several phases)	100+	200+	Congelifluction and earth flows of lubricated clays, silts and marls.	Moist, cold				

Tentative correlation (right column): LATE ELSTER — Stadial ↔ Interstadial ↔ Stadial ↔ Interstadial ↔ Stadial ↔ Interstadial? / Stadial

FIGURE 62. Stratigraphic columns of Torralba and Ambrona.

environment with certain pluvial phenomena. The latter include well-rounded, coarse gravel in the stream bed deposits, considerable spring activity, widespread fine valley alluviation on the floodplain peripheries and typical colluvial deposits.

Three major terraces were observed in the upper Jalón valley, the oldest and highest of which is equivalent to the mixed alluvial-slope deposit sequence at Torralba and Ambrona. Evidence of significant frost-weathering and some frost-heaving is limited to the "high terrace." Similarly, evidence of subsequent, intensive reddish soil development is confined to the "high" terrace, whereas the "middle terrace" was less intensively weathered. Instead it may contain derived red sediments of the older soil at its base. This fossil red soil, stratigraphically fixed in the time interval separating the high and middle terraces, is distinctive, particularly as developed *in situ* on the sediments at Torralba and Ambrona. External correlation with the equally striking rotlehm found developed on the "high terrace" of several Catalonian coastal streams is permissible. The Catalonian rotlehm soil is contemporary with the Tyrrhenian I or Holstein (Butzer, 1964a). There can be no question that the sites predate the Middle Pleistocene.

Palynological work corroborates the geomorphic evidence. Corresponding to the cool, moist phases are pollen spectra with 50-70 per cent pine pollen, and a large proportion of grasses and some sedges. During the moist, temperate oscillations pine pollen attains over 90 per cent, with sedges accounting for most of the remainder of the spectrum. Traces of hardwoods may be due to long distance transport. In conjunction with the geomorphology this suggests that the cold, moist phases were characterized by seasonally inundated grasslands or swamps in the valley, with an open pine scrub or scattered pine brush on the slopes and plateau. Much bare soil was probably exposed here with an incomplete mat of lower vegetation, including some *Artemisia*. During the more temperate phases pine woodlands dominated the uplands while open country in the valley was reduced to a few sedge swamps. A fringe of deciduous trees accompanied the stream throughout this period.

Macrobotanical remains confirm that Scot's pine (*Pinus silvestris*) was the dominant tree type at Elster-age Torralba. The cold moist intervals represented a transitional forest-alpine meadow or forest-steppe environment such as found above the tree line at about 2,000 m. in the central sierras today (see Welten, 1954). This suggests a depression of the altitudinal vegetation belts by about 900 m. Modern January averages lie at about +2° to 3° C., July averages 18° C.

The January means must have been at the very least 5°-6° C. lower in Elster times in order to account for the significance of frost-action.

The abundant mammalian fauna is limited in terms of species. The inventory to the end of the 1961 season shows elephants dominant, with at least 40-50 individuals represented, almost exclusively of the woodland form *Elephas antiquus,* with a single molar of *Elephas trogontherii,* a steppe form. Next in importance is a primitive horse (*Equus caballus* spp.), with at least two dozen individuals. The red deer (*Cervus elaphus*) and aurochs (*Bos primigenius*) are represented by a dozen each, and at least three specimens of the steppe rhinoceros (*Dicerorhinus hemitoechus*) are present. Carnivores, smaller mammals, and birds were also present at Torralba and Ambrona, but have not all been identified. The faunal composition is decidedly one of woodland forms with about 70 per cent of the ungulates preferring woodland habitats, the remainder probably preferring open environments. Three of the six species are woodland forms. This suggests abundant woodland in an otherwise mixed or transitional environment, in keeping with the geomorphic and pollen evidence.

The regional environment was that of a sub-boreal woodland with open, swampy lowlands during the warmer oscillations, a forest-alpine meadow during the colder intervals. The climate was not excessively harsh at either time. The local setting of the site was at the fringe of a sedge swamp—below a wooded slope—during the warmer phases, while during the colder intervals open pine scrub occupied the slope, grasslands dominating the valley.

Turning to the cultural inventory, a great variety of stone implements, waste chips, as well as deliberately worked wood, bone, and tusk tips are interspersed with butchered faunal remains. A few distinct occupation levels with articulated or semiarticulated elephant bones were found, almost completely undisturbed by subsequent sedimentation. In other horizons disarticulated remains of several species occur in association, and suggest a certain amount of derivation by slope wash or solifluction. Nevertheless, the distribution of disjunct associations or true "floors" through a vertical column exceeding 3.5 m. at Torralba and 6.5 m. at Ambrona indicates repeated use of both sites for kill or butchering purposes during a protracted period of many millennia. Most of the fauna shows distinct evidence of butchery practices and there is an unusually high frequency of juvenile individuals. There can be little doubt that, with a few possible exceptions, all of the fauna was killed by man. The animals were eaten more or less where killed, bones were dismembered and in part scattered considerably. Bones with marrow were frequently cracked and split open. No traces of shelters or the like have been found, and it is fairly certain that both the Torralba and Ambrona localities repeatedly served as ephemeral camp-settlements of a few days duration.

The stone implements include numerous flake tools of several kinds (especially scrapers of different sorts) and bifacial tools, including cleavers and hand-axes. These are specifically adapted for butchering purposes. Raw material was provided by quartzite, flint, and limestone, which was either available locally in the stream gravel or within a few kilometers distance. Bone fragments and elephant tusk tips with traces of cutting and purposeful trimming, as well as worked wood have been found. Some of the wood may belong to wooden weapons, others may have been used as pointed tools. Several pieces of charcoal, charred wood, much carbon, as well as charred bone have been found, suggesting human control of fire even though there is no direct evidence of hearths. In default of preserved vegetable foods it would seem that hunting was the mainstay of the economy, with elephants representing over four-fifths of the total meat obtained. This was probably a matter of deliberate selection, partly dictated by the facility of hunting proboscidians in the often swampy terrain of a narrow, steep-sided valley.

In retrospect, the small or moderate sized, primitive hunting group or groups which occasionally preyed on migrating herds of herbivores on the swampy river floodplain at Torralba are probably characteristic of the early Paleolithic. Seasonal abundance of animals was assured each spring and autumn as the herds moved between their winter grazing grounds in the coniferous woodlands of southern Spain, to their summer habitats in the cooler forest-alpine grasslands of the northern plains and plateaus. Man was only one of the many elements of the biological environment, and for all practical purposes was unable to disturb the biological equilibrium.

26

The Middle Paleolithic
Neanderthalers
and Their Environment

In the course of the later Pleistocene several major cultural innovations preceded and accompanied a major expansion of hominid population into the Eurasian subarctic and into the Americas and Australia. But equally intriguing is the more subtle, geographically significant appearance of new population centers in Eurasia, which continent had eclipsed the African heartland by the late Pleistocene. If tool-workmanship be an index of cultural progressiveness, and site tool density an index of population size, then Africa would probably qualify as the major center of population and cultural innovation of early and middle Pleistocene times. But during the last interglacial tool-craftsmanship found a new focus in Europe, at least judging by the artful hand-axes of the Micoque culture, or the fine flaking techniques of the Mousterian. And population density, in so far as can be inferred from the evidence, achieved a new high during the European late Pleistocene. By this time Africa had deteriorated to a cultural backwater (see J. D. Clark, 1960).

The transfer of man's cultural and biological focus from the tropics to middle latitudes was possibly in large part a result of improved environmental control. Knowledge of fire had apparently first opened middle latitudes to man during the Elster. Other advances in technology not recorded in the inventory of stone implements may have included hides or furs used as clothing. Whatever the case, by the onset of the Würm, man insured for himself a suitable micro-climate through clothing and shelter so as to be comfortable even in subarctic climates. The rapid, subsequent cultural development of these "new" lands was possibly facilitated by a sound ecologic subsistence.

Ironically, the European focus of accelerated cultural innovation during the last glacial was found in the then prevailing forest-tundra and cold loess steppes, rather than in the warmer, temperate woodlands of the Mediterranean region. Assuming that the Franco-Cantabrian cave art marked the heart of the European culture area, one could suggest that the forest-tundra of Europe had displaced the African savannas as a center of innovation. This poses new ecologic problems. The clue seems to lie in the economic basis of food-collecting societies, namely hunting resources. Animal meat need not necessarily have provided the bulk of Paleolithic man's diet, but in most cases it probably provided the greatest part of the calorie intake. Dahlberg and Carbonell (1961) studied the dentition of a late Paleolithic skeleton of a young woman from Cap Blanc (Dordogne), emphasizing the lack of wear. This implies a grit-free, i.e., mainly carnivorous, diet. Relevant to the argument of hunting resources is the high biomass and carrying capacity of the tundra and probably also the forest-tundra (see chap. 9). In addition, the low-latitude Pleistocene tundra must have enjoyed rather favorable radiation conditions [1] while the better-drained loess environments must also have had a greater carrying capacity than the modern, high-latitude tundras. The masses of animal fossils retrieved at such late Paleolithic sites as Solutré, France (many thousands of wild horses, Woldstedt, 1954, p. 279) or Předmost, Czechoslovakia (600 woolly mammoths) supports this suggestion. The low-latitude Pleistocene tundras possibly provided an environment as favorable as that of the temperate grasslands today. Glacial-age Europe was consequently not a marginal resource base for sufficiently advanced hunting populations.

CULTURAL PATTERNS OF THE MIDDLE PALEOLITHIC

Neanderthal Man (*Homo sapiens neanderthalensis*) is pre-eminently associated with the Middle Paleolithic, although he does not span the entire time sequence nor the geographical distribution

[1] The length of day varies from 24 hours on June 21 to 0 hours on Dec. 21 at the arctic circle in Lapland. In southern France this range is only 16 and 8 hours. Such differences in the length of the photoperiod may have been significant for animal grazing activity. Similarly the midsummer angle of incidence of solar radiation is much higher in France than in Lapland, implying that given identical conditions of air temperature, moisture, and cloudiness, plant photosynthesis would be more effective in glacial-age France than in modern Lapland. The food resources of herbivores would be correspondingly greater in a low-latitude tundra.

of mankind at the time. The Middle Paleolithic is conventionally assigned to the later Eem interglacial and the early Würm, although a stratigraphic definition of culture is necessarily an unhappy one. The significant cultural and ecological innovations of the Middle Paleolithic are more or less contemporary with the Neanderthal period, from the middle Eem to about 35,000 B.P.

The anatomical traits of the "classical" Neanderthalers of early Würm-age Europe were characterized by large, massive skulls, with a record endocranial capacity averaging 1,600 cu. cm. Body-build was short but heavy, and mean stature is estimated at 157 cm. Since the early Neanderthalers of the Eem as well as the later neanderthaloid populations of Asia and Africa do not show equally extreme cranial specializations, it is believed that the "classical" Neanderthalers developed as a result of close intermarriage in the European forest-tundras (see Howell, 1958). However the characteristics of Neanderthal-like skeletal materials (Fig. 63) found outside of Europe such as in Uzbekistan (Teshik-Tash), Iraq (Shanidar), Palestine (Mt. Carmel), Cyrenaica (Haua Fteah), Morocco (Jebel Irhoud), Northern Rhodesia (Broken Hill), South Africa (Florisbad and Saldanha), China (Mapa), and Java (Ngandong) leave no doubt about the broad continuity of related human stock.

The Middle Paleolithic still was a culture with multi-functional tools, although both regional and ecological specialization had begun. For the first time the technological affinities of the Old World, excepting the Far East, are interrupted. The industrial assemblages of contemporary sites in different areas show appreciable differentiation, even within the framework of broad cultural affinity. The several Mousterian cultures of the European Neanderthalers (Fig. 64) consist of variable assemblages of flake tools, in part finely retouched, in possible combination with older tool-types such as small hand-axes (see Bordes, 1953, 1961a, 1961b). Regional specialization or differentiation is also noticeable on other continents, as for example in Africa (J. D. Clark, 1960).

The greater part of this incipient regional specialization is probably a matter of ecological adaptation to new environments: (a) the European tundras of the Würm, the first known case of human occupation of a subarctic or arctic environment, (b) the African rainforest, now first colonized by man, and (c) local cave environments, which had previously only been occupied sporadically, but were now in vogue.

An example of colonization of new environments can be cited

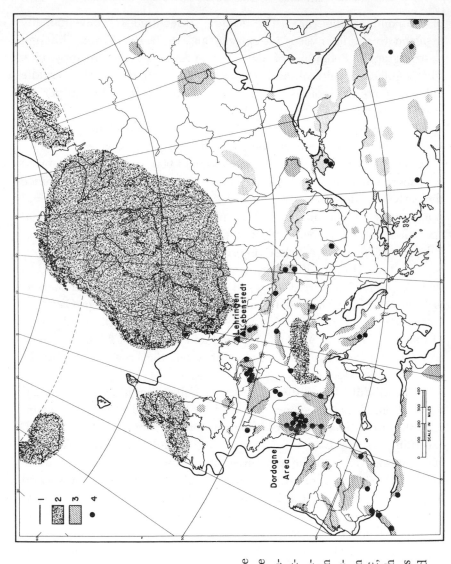

Figure 63.
European Settlement during the early Würm. (1) approximate position of coastlines; (2) glaciers, borders tentatively approximated by analogy to the Pomeranian stage; (3) distribution of Mousterian and related industries during the early Würm (after Narr, 1963, Elisséeff, 1960, and others); (4) sites with Neanderthal skeletal remains dating from the late Eem and early Würm.

376

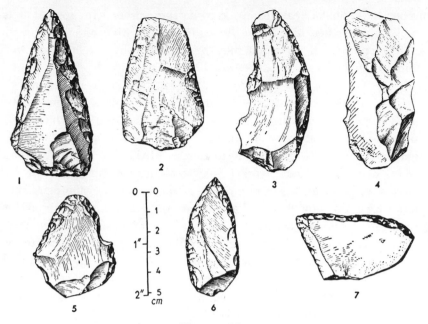

FIGURE 64.

Some stone implements of the "typical" Mousterian from the Dordogne (from F. Bordes, 1961a, with kind permission of the author). (1, 6) points, (2, 3) side scrapers, (4) flake, (5) end scraper on a flake, (7) transverse scraper.

from the case of the African rainforest. The Middle Paleolithic Sangoan and Lupemban emphasized wood-working tools and equipment, suggesting a greater dependence on, or greater use of, vegetable foods (J. D. Clark, 1960). Among the changes involved are replacement of the hand-axe by a picklike tool, and the appearance of chisels, gouges, planes, lanceolate points, etc.

ENVIRONMENTAL ADAPTATION OF THE EUROPEAN NEANDERTHALERS

Little is known about the specific adaptations of the Neanderthalers to an arctic environment. Their tools represent specialization in the direction of meat and possibly skin preparation. It may be justified to conclude from this that they effectively prepared skins, hides, and furs as clothing. For a convincing argument, however, bodkins or belt-fasteners should be present, but are not. Although their offensive weapons are better known, e.g., the alleged "bola" stones of various sites, the wooden spear of Lehringen, or the antler "clubs" of

Lebenstedt, similar features are known from earlier sites so that it is unlikely that much innovation distinguished the Mousterian inventory in that sphere. An exception may be provided by the barbed bone points of Lebenstedt (Tode *et al.*, 1953).

The archeological evidence of open-air sites such as Lebenstedt supports the opinion that some Neanderthalers followed the gregarious herds northward into the open tundra in summer, during which time they possibly employed wind shelters of some form at ephemeral or temporary camp sites. According to Bordes (1953) the fine Mousterian flakes may have been worked as tools for longer-term use by seasonal or permanent cave occupants, while rougher Levalloisian flakes without lateral retouch may have been frequently manufactured for brief use by groups wandering on the tundra during the summer. In parts of southwestern Asia the Middle Paleolithic of cave sites is also more carefully worked than that of open-air sites (Braidwood and Howe, 1962). Some of the Neanderthalers may then have adapted to a seasonal movement, following the herds of reindeer, mammoth, horse, and bison into the forest-tundra during the winter, and returning with them onto the broad expanse of herbaceous tundra in summer. Vallois (1961) suggests that the extreme morphological resemblance between certain Neanderthal groups of France and Italy implies widespread group relationships, possibly a result of seasonal migrations.

In apparent contradiction to seasonal migration is the evidence from the Mousterian and late Paleolithic cave sites of southwestern France. On the basis of reindeer antlers and dentition,[2] Bouchud (1954) showed that most of these sites must have been occupied all year around. Similarly, the regional complexity of the Mousterian cultures, at least of the southern half of France, precludes anything but well-established territoriality and semipermanent settlement (see Bordes, 1953, 1961b). Bordes (1953) also suggests that our current physical anthropological concepts of the European Neanderthalers may be oversimplified.

In overview it would seem that seasonal migration was probably not a general phenomenon. Possibly it was confined to marginal populations at the edge of the tundra, while the Neanderthalers of

[2] Adult male reindeer shed their antlers in November or December, females and juveniles during the late winter or early spring. The relative frequencies of shed and broken antlers and the sex composition within a group can be used to determine the season of hunting. Fawns are usually born in the spring so that age, as determined from the dentition, is also useful in this regard (for discussion see Bouchud, 1954, and Zeuner, 1963, p. 123 ff.).

the less severe forest-tundra environments were able to settle on a basis of more permanent animal resources. The fuller archeological picture of the European Upper Paleolithic sheds more light on the complexities of settlement patterns (see chap. 27). At any rate the existence of seasonal movements may be considered as a possible—localized—adaptation to the more rigorous environments of Würm-age Europe. It is extremely important that more work be done to establish the true patterns of settlement.

So far no evidence of tents or wind shelters has been uncovered at open-air sites. Cave interiors were rendered comfortable by fires, and possibly also by branches and hides suspended across the cave entrance. In fact, a posthole at the entrance of Combe Grenal (Dordogne) suggests a row of shafts used to support skins or woven branches (Bordes, 1961b).

The animal booty of Neanderthal Man suggests that he was a courageous as well as an efficient hunter. Woolly mammoths and rhinos were successfully hunted, and the presence of various fish and fowl at the Lebenstedt site underscores his proficiency. Neanderthal Man was not the patient, slow-witted and muscular hillbilly he is often made out to be. Although there is uncertainty as to the exact nature of the adaptations involved, the Middle Paleolithic Neanderthalers certainly did open up a new environment for human colonization since the arctic tundra seems to have been the "last frontier." For a while at least the Neanderthalers were successful in their new environment. Their ultimate failure may have been due to biological factors, although the causes remain obscure. Between about 40,000 and 30,000 B.P. the Neanderthalers were gradually displaced by anatomically modern men of *Homo sapiens sapiens* type, carriers of a more advanced culture. Skeletal remains dating from the later Würm have so far shown no evidence of cross-breeding between these two populations, although logically the remnants of the Neanderthalers would have been absorbed by the biologically more progressive and more numerous *Homo sapiens* peoples. Possibly the Neanderthalers were pushed out into the more marginal environments by the encroaching newcomers, and ultimately succumbed to the inhospitable environment during the maximum cold of the full glacial period (for discussion see Narr, 1963, p. 74).

AN EXAMPLE OF MIDDLE PALEOLITHIC HABITAT AND ECONOMY:
SALZGITTER-LEBENSTEDT

The Mousterian-type site of Salzgitter-Lebenstedt in northern
Germany was excavated in 1952 by Tode, Preul, Richter, Kleinschmidt
et al. (1953; also Tode, 1954), and is particularly important on account
of the thorough excavation techniques employed. This open-air,
summer camp-site has been dated at 55,000 B.P. ± 1,000 (Gro. 2,083)
and belongs to a slightly warmer interval in the early Würm. The
location is on a small tributary stream of the Aller-Weser drainage
system, some 15 km. south of the city of Braunschweig, at an elevation
of 82 m. above sea level.

The geological setting is provided by a cold-climate stream terrace
immediately overlain by the ground moraine of the Riss-Saale glaciation. The stream has since dissected the Riss deposits, and the
Würm-age sediments, which contain the site, are embanked against
the foot of the Riss terrace (Fig. 65). These Würm beds consist of
alternating stream and slope deposits with the following stratigraphy,
beginning at the base:

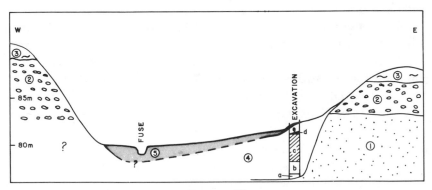

FIGURE 65.

Geographical and geological setting of the Salzgitter-Lebenstedt
site. (1) Lower Pleistocene (?) sands and gravel, (2) Riss-Saale
periglacial stream terrace, (3) Riss-Saale groundmoraine, (4)
Würm stream terrace intercalated with solifluction beds from
slope: the letters in the excavation column refer to text description; (5) Holocene alluvium and peat. Data obtained from
1:25,000 topographic map and geological sections by F. Preul
(Tode *et al.*, 1953). Vertical exaggeration approx. 30x.

a) 50 cm. fluvial sand with evidence of patterned ground or frost cracks, overlying an older, eluviated layer of stones.

b) 150 cm. stream gravel grading laterally into solifluction mantles at base and top, generally showing evidence of cryoturbation and patterned ground or frost cracks. The cultural layer is associated with peaty beds in the stream gravels.

c) 350 cm. alternating silts and sands showing considerable evidence of cryoturbation, in part stream bedded, in part bedded downslope by solifluction. Another peaty layer is located at the base.

d) 0-100 cm. solifluction mantle derived from the Riss terrace, eluviated at its outer edge.

e) 100-200 cm. silts with evidence of cryoturbation, disconformably underlying fluvial peat with Holocene pollen.

The interpretations given were obtained after careful study of pebble orientation, gravel morphometry, particle-size spectra and microstratigraphy.

Paleobotanical studies were carried out in the peaty layers of (*b*) and at the base of (*c*). The pollen spectrum of the peat in (*b*) was dominated by NAP, particularly sedges. The arboreal pollen was mainly that of pine, with some birch, willow, spruce, and a trace of alder. The macrobotanical remains included various mosses and lichens (mainly determined by the stems), alpine or arctic herbaceous plants (determined by seeds, fruits or stones), as well as leaves of *Salix polaris* and *S. herbacea*. The interpretation is one of low willow brush in moist depressions, with sporadic stands of pine at a distance. The locality was probably very close to the northern margins of the forest-tundra, i.e., near the arctic tree-limit. Considering that the modern July temperature is 17° C., July temperatures were 5°-7° C. cooler at the time. The apparent presence of permafrost further suggests that the annual mean (+8.5° C. today) was at least 10.5° C. lower, i.e., the major temperature depression occurred during the winter season.

The highly organic bed at the base of horizon (*c*) contains only a little pollen of willow, birch and pine, being almost exclusively a spectrum of NAP. The macrobotanical remains are confined to mosses and sedges, indicating that the local environment was that of a moist poorly-drained tundra lowland.

The faunal remains from Lebenstedt were studied in minutest detail, and contained the following species:

reindeer	*ca.* 80 individuals (19% juveniles), 72% of animals present
woolly mammoth	*ca.* 16 individuals, 14%
bison	6-7 individuals, 5.4%
horse	4-6 individuals, 4.6%
woolly rhino	*ca.* 2 individuals, 2%

Further single specimens included wolf, muskrat (*Desmana moschata*), crane or swan, duck, an extinct vulture, perch, pike, other unidentified fish, crabs, aquatic mollusca, and insects. The horses are of the heavy-headed, woodland type, so that three species (reindeer, mammoth, rhino), totalling 88 per cent of the mammalian fauna, are by preference tundra forms. Two characteristic tundra forms, the musk-ox and lemming, are conspicuously absent. It is thought that the wolf and vulture were killed (by stoning?) while scavenging at the fringes of the camp; the muskrat was probably killed while insect-hunting in the refuse heaps.

Careful recording of the location, orientation and level of every bone fragment, subsequently enabled a reconstruction of summer conditions at the site: the cultural floor was seasonally flooded by rapidly moving waters, presumably the spring meltwaters. Otherwise tiny rivulets, ponding as stagnant pools with peat development, flowed around the small alluvial bench occupied by the hunters in the valley bottom.

The cultural inventory itself is classified as Mousterian of Acheulian tradition, and about 10 per cent of the 2,000 stone tools are well-worked hand-axes of Late Acheulian or Micoquian typology. The remainder are flake tools, mainly scrapers and points, with careful Mousterian retouching on both surfaces. The stone tools are functionally related to butchering practices. Of further interest are worked reindeer antlers (clubs?), bone points of mammoth ribs (digging sticks?), and barbed bone points (spearheads?). These items may represent a part of the weapon inventory. On the basis of the animal remains it is believed that a moderately large band, not exceeding 40-50 individuals, occupied the site for a few weeks during several summer seasons.

Essentially the temporary camp of these Mousterian hunters—located in a small, sheltered valley bottom following the late spring thaw—was not unlike that of Torralba. But the cultural floor is better defined and of greater concentration and depth, suggesting longer occupation. The actual site may also have been better chosen. Although evidence of fishing is known from the early Paleolithic of Africa (J. D. Clark, 1960), the birds of Lebenstedt are of interest from the perspective of hunting proficiency. From all available evidence these hunters of the early Würm must have managed comparatively well in the European tundras. Man-land relationships had become more complex.

27

Late Paleolithic
Man-Land Relationships
in Eurasia

THE APPEARANCE OF ADVANCED HUNTERS IN EUROPE

No single culture group of the Pleistocene stands out as distinctly as the late Paleolithic hunters of Europe. The picture of man-land relationships at the Middle Paleolithic culture level probably also does justice—at the present state of information—to Africa and tropical Asia during the late Pleistocene. But during the main and late Würm rather specialized hunter-gatherers occupied the Eurasian stage, requiring a new assessment of man-land relationships. For the first time an acceleration of cultural and technological innovation is noticeable. Compared with a half million years of early Paleolithic occupation in the Old World, the European Middle Paleolithic comprised a time span of 40,000-50,000 years, the Upper Paleolithic about 25 millennia.

There is a common tendency to equate several distinct phenomena: the appearance of *Homo sapiens,* the advent of the Upper Paleolithic blade-tool industries, and the colonization of Australia and the Americas during a "secondary dispersal" of man. The apparent association of these late Pleistocene events is misleading and probably fortuitous. Only in Europe does the equivalence of *Homo sapiens sapiens* and the Upper Paleolithic appear to be real, because both traits were introduced from without. In Asia and Africa, on the other hand, the temporal and anatomical distinctions of *Homo sapiens neanderthalensis* and *H. sapiens sapiens* are rather fluid. And above all, there is no necessary association of the new racial types with the Upper Paleolithic blade industries. The biological evolution and cultural innovation first evident during the last part of the late Pleistocene is at best incompletely understood. It is therefore necessary to limit discussion to empirical manifestations of the advanced hunter-gatherer economies.

The appearance of the late Paleolithic hunters in western Europe can be dated to before 35,000 B.P. (Movius, 1960), although the replacement of the European Neanderthal populations may have taken as long as ten millennia or more. In this long time span (*ca.* 40,000-30,000 B.P.) the exact temporal relationships of various culture groups are vague as a result of inadequate radiocarbon chronology and technological stratigraphy. The confusion accompanying the geologic stratigraphy of the Würm interstadials has so far ruled out reliable correlation of cultures with climatic or geologic events at such an exact scale. There seems to be a sharp biological and technological break in parts of Europe at about this time (see Narr, 1963, p. 50 ff.). Yet both in France and the Levant the earliest known Upper Paleolithic assemblages, the Chatelperronian and Emiran respectively, show evidence of technological evolution from the local Middle Paleolithic (Delporte, 1955; Bordes, 1961b; Howell, 1959a). It is just this, the complexity of the early Upper Paleolithic assemblages, that suggests that the advent of *Homo sapiens* in Europe was not a vast, sweeping movement. According to Bates (1953), migration at the food-gatherer's level would be an infiltration process, an accumulation of small territorial readjustments and perhaps, under environmental stress, the complete displacement of small tribal groups. Narr (1963, p. 74) argues that the distribution of the Neanderthalers and the new, infiltrating groups formed a complex mosaic of semicontiguous but generally distinct territories.

UPPER PALEOLITHIC TECHNOLOGY

The Upper Paleolithic of mid-latitude Eurasia was essentially a blade-tool assemblage, characterized by an abundance and variety of long, parallel-sided flakes known as "blades." Comparable blade-tools are almost or wholly absent from contemporary late Paleolithic industries in most of Africa, southern, and eastern Asia. Although existing tool-making techniques were still maintained in some instances, the Eurasian Upper Paleolithic was novel and specialized. The blade-tool inventory, usefully summarized by Braidwood (1961, p. 75 ff.), was in part especially devised for bone and wood-working (Fig. 66). *Burins* are chisel-shaped blades for engraving or working in wood, bone, or antler, in turn often used as handles or shafts for other implements. *Borers* are blades worked to a narrow, sharp point and used for drilling holes into wood, bone, shell, skin, etc. *Notched* or strangulated blades were probably employed for preparing arrow or

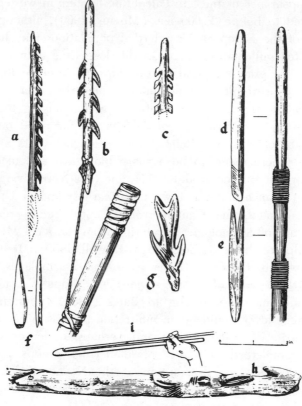

FIGURE 66.

Bone and antler weapons from the European Upper Paleolithic
(from K. P. Oakley, 1958, with permission of the Trustees of
the British Museum, Natural History). (a) Barbed point of
antler, (b), (c) harpoons of antler, (d), (e) spear-point and
link-shaft of antler, (f) split-base bone point, (g) bone fish-
gorge (?), (h) antler spear-thrower, (i) wooden spear-thrower
of modern Australian aborigine (not to scale).

spear shafts by scraping or shaving wood. *End-scrapers* were prepared
with a blunted end and probably used to hollow out wood or bone,
scrape hides, or remove bark from wood. Round or *nosed* scrapers
have a well-worked, sharp-edged semicircular end or nose, presumably used to plane and scrape wood and bone. Other tools were
more generally employed for cutting or scraping purposes. These
include the *backed blade*, with one purposely blunted edge, presumably to facilitate holding. Other stone implements were used for

offensive purposes. *Tanged* or shouldered *points* were designed as projectile points, to be fixed to a wooden shaft. *Laurel-leaf* blades were carefully worked to thin, sharp-edged knives or arrowheads, possibly used as daggers.

Eiseley (1955) has emphasized the economy of late Upper Paleolithic stone workmanship in general. In the pebble tool cultures a pound of flint provided about 5 cm. of cutting edge; in the hand-axe technique 20 cm.; in the middle Paleolithic, 100 cm.; and in the late Paleolithic, 300 to 1,200 cm. This exponential rate of flint-working economy probably provides an index of the technological advance of the period.

Upper Paleolithic bone and antler tools include new items such as polished pins or awls, and split-based and other types of points, to be fixed on to spear shafts. The later, Magdalenian inventory of western Europe (dated *ca.* 17,000-12,500 B.P., see Movius, 1960) further includes hooked rods employed as spear-throwers, barbed points and harpoons for fishing purposes, fish-hooks, needles with eyes, bone and ivory bodkins, belt-fasteners, as well as other tools of less clearly understood use. Such implements were in many cases artistically engraved, depicting various animals of the hunt.

The use of bow and arrow is first verified from the late Palaeolithic. Stone arrowheads are claimed from the late Pleistocene Aterian industry of North Africa. More convincing are the archeological remains unearthed from a former lake at Stellmoor near Hamburg, dating from the Ahrensburg culture *ca.* 10,500 B.P. (Rust, 1943, 1962). Some 100 wooden arrows were found. They were made from pine splints varying between 20 and 80 cm. in length. About a quarter of these arrows were designed for use without flint arrowheads. One such untipped arrow was in fact found in a wolf vertebra. Rust (1943) believes that flint arrowheads may have been used for large game only, while the untipped type of arrow was used for smaller animals. Obviously the antiquity of the untipped arrow may be much greater. Two bows of pine wood were also found at the Stellmoor site. Gaping holes in reindeer shoulderblades bear mute testimony to the effectiveness of flint arrowheads.

UPPER PALEOLITHIC ECONOMY

In the sphere of daily life, Upper Paleolithic hunting techniques were still comparable to those of earlier times. Spears, javelins, harpoons, clubs, stone missiles, bow and arrow, boomerangs or throwing-sticks all counted among the offensive weapons. Bolas, consisting of stone balls joined by thongs and thrown among the legs of running animals, may also have been known. Snares and pitfalls were almost certainly used for hunting some large game, while gregarious herbivores were stampeded into enclosures or defiles or over precipices in organized battue hunts. The bones of countless horses in the Upper Perigordian occupation horizon, at the foot of the cliffs at Solutré in the Rhone Valley, attest to the hunting efficiency of contemporary man. Modern analogies of the Scandinavian Lapps bear out the practice of organized hunts designed to drive reindeer herds over precipices or into pitfalls (see Broegger, 1926). Kühn (1929, p. 314) believes that cave drawings at Montespan, Marsoulas, Niaux, Font-de-Gaume, Bernifal, and Les Combarelles in southwestern France and at La Pileta, La Pasiega, Castillo, and Buxu in Spain, represent various forms of snares, traps, pitfalls, enclosures, etc. Soergel (1922) pointed out that juveniles formed a large percentage (25-35 per cent) of the animals caught at many stations, suggesting destruction of entire herds, particularly in autumn, probably in order to provide a winter meat store. But individual attack on animals in the open is also confirmed—e.g., by a drawing of the formidable woolly rhinoceros at La Colombière, showing a number of arrows penetrating the body.

The taking of fish was already practiced in the late Villafranchian of Africa (J. D. Clark, 1960). It was apparently easy to catch fish in the shallow lakes or ponded rivers during the low-water season. Weirs may also have been built to strand fish in shallow waters. Possibly the same simple method was employed by the Mousterian people at Lebenstedt. During the late Paleolithic however, fishing was revolutionized by the invention of harpoons and fish-gorges. Aquatic foods already had considerable dietary significance in some terminal Paleolithic economies.

Little direct information is available concerning late Paleolithic clothing habits in Europe. However the frequency of bone sewing needles, bodkins, and belt-fasteners suggests that elaborate wearing apparel, presumably of tanned skins and furs, was in common use. The material civilization has been compared with that of the Eskimo, undoubtedly the result of ecological convergence rather than direct ethnic or cultural association.

Some authors have argued that the reindeer was semidomesticated and that some form of reindeer nomadism had been invented during the terminal Paleolithic. There is, however, a complete lack of supporting empirical evidence to this effect. Smolla (1960, pp. 84-87), who has presented both sides of the case in detail, believes that neither the ethnological nor archeological evidence supports this hypothesis.

UPPER PALEOLITHIC SETTLEMENT PATTERNS IN EURASIA

Blade-tool industries of main and late Würm age are widespread, occurring through most of the unglaciated parts of Europe, the Near East, southern Siberia as far east as Lake Baikal, and parts of northern China. Despite their over-all similarity, these industries are diversified and suggest strong regional differentiation of cultural traditions and, presumably, breeding populations. Some of the culture areas were large—the eastern Gravettian ranging from Germany through southern Russia into Siberia being an example.

Settlement patterns were variable, as can be seen from open-air habitation sites excavated at Fourneau-du-Diable (Dordogne), in the Usselo area of the Netherlands, Poggenwisch and Borneck near Hamburg, Moravany and Unter-Wisternitz in Czechoslovakia, Langmannersdorf in eastern Austria, Pushkari, Gagarino, and Kostjenki in Russia (Fig. 67), and Buret and Mal'ta in central Siberia. To these must be added a large number of better-excavated cave habitation sites ranging from Spain to the Altai Mountains. Wherever the state of archeological investigation is good, it seems that both cave and open-air habitation sites were occupied in one area, although the relative importance of the one or the other varies regionally. Some areas suggest seasonal, winter cave occupation with temporary summer habitations in the open. Others suggest semipermanent open-air settlements. Settlement patterns were complex and the regional diversification contrasts strongly with the simpler patterns apparent from the earlier Paleolithic.

Group economies were specialized on certain animals. So, for example, the reindeer was by far the most important meat source in what is now France and Germany, while the woolly mammoth was the common staple of life in regions farther east. Horses were also important locally. In Spain, where gregarious ungulates were few or absent, game resources were more diversified. Specialization, wherever suitable animals were available, was not unique to the late Paleolithic. It had been practiced at Torralba and Ambrona (elephants) during the early Paleolithic. But it was specialization that dictated the settlement type.

If the staple game species was a seasonal migrant in a particular environment, specialized hunters would probably have resorted to

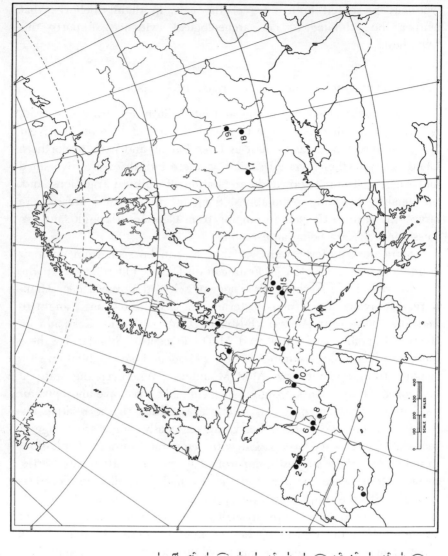

FIGURE 67.

Some European Upper Paleolithic sites. (1) Dordogne area
(La Mouthe, Font-de-Gaume,
Les Combarelles, Bernifal, Fourneau-du-Diable, Cap Blanc), (2)
Buxu, (3) La Pasiega, (4) Castillo, (5) La Pileta, (6) Montespan, (7) Marsoulas, (8) Niaux,
(9) Solutré, (10) La Colum-
biére, (11) Usselo, (12) Kesslerloch and Schweizersbild, (13)
Hamburg area (Ahrensburg,
Meiendorf, Borneck, Stellmoor,
Poggenwisch), (14) Langmannersdorf, (15) Unter-Wisternitz,
Pollau, Moravany, (16) Předmost, (17) Pushkari, (18)
Kostjenki, (19) Gagarino.

390

seasonal changes of settlement. On the other hand, if the gregarious herds were locally present all year around, semipermanent settlement would have been possible. The Gravettian mammoth hunters of the forest steppe and loess steppe of eastern Europe obviously belonged to the latter category. The Magdalenian, Hamburgian, and Ahrensburgian reindeer hunters of the central European tundras belonged to the former, judging by antler studies carried out on several thousand animals found in Swiss caves at Kesslerloch and Schweizersbild (for autumn and winter occupation, see Soergel, 1922) and at open-air sites in the Hamburg area (for summer or winter occupation, see Rust, 1962). On the other hand, in the forest-tundra of southwestern France both the antlers and dentition of late Pleistocene reindeer remains suggest that these animals were locally available as well as hunted throughout the year (Bouchud, 1954).

Whether cave shelters or open-air tents and huts were occupied probably depended on (*a*) whether suitable caves were available locally and (*b*) whether such caves were suitably located with respect to animal trails or grazing areas. Although little is preserved to prove the point, habitation sites at cave entrances or under overhangs were probably improved by use of branches, hides, or other insulating materials.

Of greatest interest are the open-air shelters, first recognized on cave drawings from Font-de-Gaume, Les Combarelles, and La Mouthe. Conscious search for such features in archeological situations uncovered ample evidence of elaborate tents and huts in recent years. The amount of information available is so great that only two examples can be outlined here, the semipermanent settlement of Pollau (Pavlov) at Unter-Wisternitz (Dolní Věstonice) (Klíma, 1954, 1962), and the seasonal tent camps of the Hamburgians at Borneck and Poggenwisch (Rust, 1958, 1962).

At Pollau several hut plans were found along the banks of a small stream and surrounded by heaps of animal bones representing about one hundred mammoths, mostly juveniles. One hut had a 9 by 15 m. ground plan, containing five hearths in regular distribution. It is thought to have been a tentlike, roofless summer enclosure. More impressive was a second winter or permanent hut with a circular plan 6 m. in diameter. The floor was dug into the slope on one side, where it was retained by means of a carefully laid wall of limestone slabs. Vertical post holes suggest that a roof of bones or branches with animal skins spanned the dwelling pit. In the general area mammoth tusks were rammed into the ground to form the framework of simple defensive walls, presumably filled out with brush. Fires, both within the huts and in the general camp area, were probably fed by the drippings of fat-laden animal bones. A radiocarbon date of 24,800± 150 B.P. (Gro. 1325) places the small settlement in the period of maximum cold during the main Würm. On the basis of ethnographic parallels and the amount of faunal remains Klíma (1962) suggests that each hut housed 20-25 persons and that the community may have numbered about 100-120 members. This assumes that all or most of the huts were occupied at one time. The Pollau patterns are repeated at Langmannerdorf in nearby Austria and in the more elaborate Gravettian settlements of southern Russia. All in all, the impression of semipermanent habitation, at least of a part of the population, is convincing.

Some of the more important habitation sites at Ahrensburg, near Hamburg, include summer tents at Borneck and Poggenwisch, and a winter tent-complex at Borneck. The summer tents belong to the Hamburgian cultures, dated about 15,500 B.P. (W-93, 15,200 ± 800), the winter tent to a later culture dating from about 11,500 B.P. on pollen-stratigraphical grounds. The summer tent at Borneck (I) consisted of an interior oval tent with a ground plan measuring 2.5 by 3.5 m., and a horseshoe-shaped exterior tent measuring 5.5 m. across (Fig. 68). The furs or hides presumably used were weighted down

FIGURE 68.
Reconstruction of a Hamburgain (Borneck I) summer tent
(from A. Rust, 1962, with kind permission of
K. Wachholtz Verlag, Neumünster).

by heavy rocks, while earth was thrown up around the base of the outer tent. The fire was built at the entrance. Most of the flint-working was done outside, implying summer occupation. The later, winter tent at Borneck (II) consisted of two circular tents, joined by a narrow, covered corridor (Fig. 69). The larger of the two circular

FIGURE 69.
Reconstruction of a Magdalenian (Borneck II) winter tent complex
(from Rust, 1962, with kind permission of
K. Wachholtz Verlag, Neumünster).

tents was 4 m. in diameter, set on a base of laid rocks, with a deep hearth in the middle and insulated by earthworks around the base. The smaller tent probably served for storage. Built during the warmer Alleröd interval, this tent-complex suggests winter occupation. Neither of the Borneck habitation sites is completely understood in a community context, but they give an impression of seasonal shelters as constructed during the terminal Pleistocene.

In general the more complete archeological record of the European late Paleolithic suggests that the population size of individual bands was not much larger than in Middle Paleolithic times (Vallois, 1961; Narr, 1963, p. 51 f.), but the density of sites and the immense faunal accumulations at the individual localities suggest a much greater over-all population. Possibly, although there is no way to substantiate it, the European population had increased by as much as a factor of ten between the early and late Würm. Regional cultural autonomy suggests that a considerable degree of territoriality was practiced.

FIRST COLONIZATION OF THE AMERICAS

The problem of first colonization of the Americas has by no means been resolved. Various appraisals of Asian and North American cultural traits during the terminal Pleistocene do however permit some reasonable speculation on the subject. C. S. Chard (1963a) suggests that this colonization took place in two basic movements across the exposed continental shelf linking eastern Siberia and Alaska during the last glacial (Fig. 70). The initial movement is postulated from

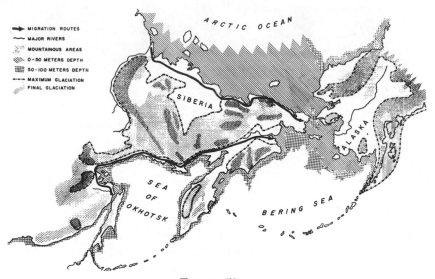

FIGURE 70.
The Bering Strait area showing possible routes from Asia
to North America (from C. S. Chard, 1960, with
kind permission of *American Antiquity*).

eastern Asia, along the Pacific shores, bringing an industrial tradition of choppers, bifaces, and amorphous flakes—perhaps during the early Würm glacial, say 40,000 years ago. A second movement from central Siberia subsequently brought a Middle Paleolithic tradition of flint-working and possibly the germ of bifacial flaking. This movement may have followed the Arctic coastal plain route. Chard (1963a) believes there is no technological evidence for subsequent population or cultural movements until the appearance of the Paleo-Eskimos, perhaps 8500 B.P. (see Black and Laughlin, 1964).

Whatever the exact nature of the colonization, man was present in both the western United States and northern South America by at very latest 15,000 B.P. (see R. J. Mason, 1962, with various discussion comments). This places the probable time of immigation in the late Pleistocene, when the Bering Strait emerged during the last glacial regression. The shelf sediments exposed are comparatively flat and a regression of 100-150 m. would expose a broad expanse of land (see Hopkins, 1959; Haag, 1962). The circumpolar nature of several elements of the Würm cold-climate fauna (reindeer, musk-ox, woolly mammoth, arctic hare, arctic fox, etc.) supports this fact, as does a great wealth of botanical and zoölogical evidence. The Asiatic routes of possible migration would be confined to the circuitous, comparatively narrow Pacific coastal strip and the broad Arctic coastal plain. The intermediate mountainous country had local glaciations. According to the vegetational reconstruction of Frenzel (1960), the Pacific route would have been the more favorable at the maximum of the Würm: forest-tundras were widespread from the mouth of the Amur to the Kamchatkan west coast, with tundra beyond. The Arctic coastal route ran through the tundra belt from the middle course of the Lena onwards. Obviously, environmental conditions would have been far more favorable during warm, interstadial intervals—the impact of which would not seriously narrow down the Beringian corridor. Further eastward, an ice-free passage was probably available along the Yukon Valley and the eastern foothills of the Rocky Mountains during a good part of the late Pleistocene.

Assuming that the Beringian land bridge was available throughout the Würm regression, the most suitable times for Middle Paleothic food-collectors to move eastward through Siberia and on to Alaska would have been during the Brörup-Amersfoort and the Paudorf interstadials. Possibly Chard's postulated first migration even took place at the very beginning of the Würm, as soon as the straits were passable, but before the climate had become too harsh. It seems improbable that food-collectors at the Neanderthaler level would venture through thousands of kilometers of harsh environment at the height of any of the Würm stadials. As both the archeological and environmental evidence become more substantial, this should become a fascinating problem in Pleistocene geography.

COLONIZATION OF AUSTRALIA

The late Pleistocene colonization of Australia poses an equally interesting problem. Unfortunately the state of archeological exploration is painfully incomplete, so that the cultural associations of Australia, Tasmania, and New Guinea on the one hand, with the Indonesian area on the other, are understood in a most rudimentary way only.

Borneo, Java, and Sumatra are attached to Malaya by the broad, shallow Sunda Shelf (Fig. 71). This area was at least partly emergent during the Würm glacial regression. The most substantial archeological evidence from this sector comes from (a) Ngandong, Java, where parts of eleven neanderthaloid crania were found in late Pleistocene deposits (see Movius, 1955), (b) Wadjak, Java, where parts of two *sapiens*-type crania were found in what appears to have been a late Pleistocene breccia (see Coon, 1962, p. 399 ff.), (c) Niah, Sarawak, where a *Homo sapiens* skull has been found in cave strata dated at 41,500 B.P. by radiocarbon (see Brothwell, 1961), and (d) Aitape, New Guinea, where another, poorly preserved cranial fragment appears to come from late Pleistocene beds (see Coon, 1962, p. 399).

New Guinea and Australia were similarly attached by the Sahul Shelf during the Würm regression, while Bass Strait between Australia and Tasmania was dry. The only late Pleistocene evidence of man in Australia appears to come from Keilor, near Melbourne, where hearths and possibly a human cranium were found in stream deposits. Charcoal samples gave a radiocarbon age of 18,000 years (see Mulvaney, 1961, with references). Whether or not the Keilor skull and further fossil skeletal material of unknown age from Australia are indeed of Pleistocene age, Coon (1962, p. 410 f.) emphasizes their broad anatomic relationships both with the modern Australian aborigines and with the Ngandong, Wadjak, Aitape, and Niah fossils.

Assuming first colonization of Australia during the late Pleistocene, there seems little possibility that man crossed dry-shod from the Sunda to the Sahul land masses—unless considerable tectonic movements have taken place since. But two major island routes via (a) Java and Timor, or (b) Borneo, Celebes, and the Moluccas could have been readily managed with rafts or small boats. The mass of small islands along either route would, during a glacial regression, reduce the maximum water distance to 180 km. in the case of the Timor route,

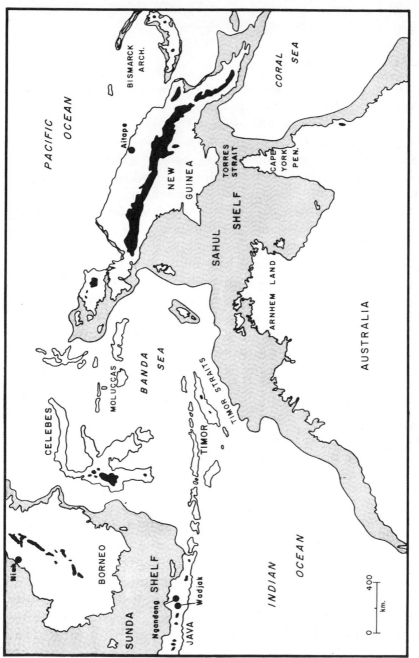

FIGURE 71. The East Indies, New Guinea and northern Australia, with major late Pleistocene fossil sites and location of the Sunda and Sahul shelves. Continental shelf (0 to 150 m. depth) stippled, elevations over 1500 m. black. Base map modified after Goode's World Atlas (11th ed.), copyright 1960 by Rand McNally & Co., Chicago.

95 km. in the case of the Celebes-Moluccan route. Paleo-environmental evidence is scarce even from Java, and totally absent in the case of lowland New Guinea or northern Australia.

MAN-LAND RELATIONSHIPS

The previous discussion of Upper Paleolithic technology and settlement suggests that man had, by this time, learned to live successfully in all environments except the high arctic barrens and the true deserts. In fact the subsistence patterns of tundra, forest-tundra, and loess-steppe residence had possibly developed into the highest standard of living known at any time and at any place prior to the Holocene. Ecologic adaptations are increasingly evident in many phases of human culture, ranging all the way from clothing to hunting practices. Even the European mastery of bone-working may reflect on the scarcity of wood in tundra environments.

An ample food supply may have encouraged Upper Paleolithic man to develop the astounding degree of artistic perfection particularly evident in southern France and in Spain. Not only were bone and antler skillfully engraved, but large semirelief sculptures were done in clay, and outstanding line or polychrome drawings affixed to the walls and ceilings of interior cave galleries.[1] The indication of the animal's heart, or the association of arrows or spears with an animal drawing, suggest sympathetic magic as a primary motive.

Yet despite man's comparative technological efficiency in hunting, fishing, clothing, and providing shelter, mortality rates were frightfully high. Less than 50 per cent of the 76 Upper Paleolithic skeletons known from Eurasia are those of people who had attained the age of 21, while only 12 per cent had passed the age of 40. Practically no women had reached the age of 30 (Vallois, 1961). This represents no improvement on the mortality rate of the Neanderthal populations.

The comparative skill and diversity of late Paleolithic man seriously poses, for the first time, the possibility of human impact on the environment. Any such modifications would almost certainly have been confined to modifications of the biological world.

The question of fire, used as a hunting tool or as a device to facilitate removal or regeneration of vegetation, is equally enigmatic as in earlier paleolithic times. However, one important exception can

---

[1] Possibly one of the most thoughtful of the many evaluations of Paleolithic art has been given by Bandi and Maringer (1952).

be cited. The humic paleosol horizons of the Alleröd are commonly developed on aeolian sand or loess of late Würm age, and buried by further aeolian beds of the Younger Dryas. In Belgium, the Netherlands, and adjacent parts of northwestern Germany fire horizons, particularly rich in pinewood charcoal, are commonly found in the horizons of the Alleröd rankers and micropodsols (Hijszeler, 1957; Van der Hammen, 1957a, 1957b, and earlier references). There is no question that these charcoal strata were the result of forest fires during the Alleröd. In one case the crowberry (*Empetrum nigra*) was strongly favored by such burning; in other cases high pollen values of the pioneer fire weed *Epilobium angustifolium* also substantiate a conflagration. The radiocarbon date of the charcoal horizons is 11,000 B.P. and such horizons frequently coincide with archeological strata belonging to the Tongrian culture (Late Magdalenian or Federmesser), a hunting population inhabiting northern Germany, the Low Countries, and adjacent parts of England.

Van der Hammen (1957a) suggests that many of these forest fires had human rather than natural causes. Narr (1961, p. 105; 1963, p. 100), with reason, raises the question that these fire strata may represent deliberate burning by man rather than accidental forest fires in dead pine woodland during the climatic deterioration heralding in the Younger Dryas. Narr cites several possible incentives for deliberate burning, in part following Stewart (1956): (*a*) to permit easy sighting of game, (*b*) to favor the growth of plants and grasses required by the desirable game species, (*c*) to increase the size of game pasture at the expense of the forest, or to localize grazing areas and so facilitate hunting, or (*d*) to favor the growth of wild vegetable foods and berries for human consumption. It is possible and probable that the Tongrians did indeed practice burning on a large scale. These widespread charcoal horizons in conjunction with the isolated evidence of a forest fire from the cultural horizon at Hoxne (West & McBurney, 1954) emphasize the need for systematic restudy of Pleistocene pollen profiles for possible evidence of human disturbance of vegetation.

In Africa, according to J. D. Clark (1960), the redistribution of the Kalahari sands at the close of the Pleistocene may have been a consequence of deliberate bush burning in game drives or to generate new growth. Cooke (1958) on the other hand considers the vegetation balance on the arid subsoil of the Kalahari System particularly precarious for climatic changes. The evidence here could then be explained by natural forces alone.

The question of human modifications of the native fauna, particularly through indiscriminate hunting of large, slow-breeding species, is inconclusive. By the end of the Alleröd oscillation the mammoth, woolly rhino, musk-ox, steppe bison, giant "elk," cave bear, cave lion, and spotted hyena had become extinct in Europe if not throughout Eurasia (see Thenius, 1961a). Similarly, a large number of carnivores and ungulates became extinct in North America at the end of the Wisconsin glacial (see Mason, 1962). Opinions differ strongly as to the possible involvement of man in this faunal change. Various species became extinct at different occasions during the glacial-interglacial and interglacial-glacial transitions of the Pleistocene. But at the beginning of the Holocene, several genera or families were eradicated for the first time since the Villafranchian. So, for example, elephants and rhinos are now absent from temperate Eurasia for the first time since the Tertiary. Yet great caution must be exercised in attributing these faunal extinctions to man. As Thenius (1961a) emphasizes, most of the European species in question were ecologically specialized, and their disappearance coincided with significant environmental changes (see chap. 28). Specifically, the gradual diminution and final disappearance of the tundra fauna from Europe is in keeping with the northward migration of the forests during the late Würm.

There are other weighty reasons for doubting the agency of man in promoting wholesale extinction of species. Why should a good proportion of the extinct genera represent carnivores such as the sabre-tooth tiger and jaguar (*Felis atrox*) in America or the cave lion in Europe? Certainly no Paleolithic hunter would have had reason to hunt such formidable felids. There is for that matter little evidence that the cave bear or spotted hyena were frequently hunted by man (see Schmid, 1958); instead they were usually left to themselves. Turning to modern analogies, it is equally significant that practically no African ungulate has become extinct during the last ten millennia—despite the intensive hunting activity of far more numerous and technologically superior populations. Even in Europe the wild horse, aurochs, and woodland bison managed to survive into modern times, while the wolf and brown bear were only displaced from central Europe less than two centuries ago. Lastly, ethnological data show that "primitive" hunters are seldom wasteful and often fully aware of the need to conserve game resources (see Heizer, 1955). It seems that more intensive examination of the chronological, geographical, and environmental aspects of local or total extinction should be made before recourse is taken to the intangible force—man.

At the present stage of investigation there is no proof that any one species became locally or totally extinct at the hands of Pleistocene man. On the other hand however, the massive slaughtering of game evident at some sites must have had serious repercussions on both the biomass and equilibrium of animal populations in Europe and North America. All in all, it would therefore seem justified to say that the terminal Pleistocene marks the beginning of significant environmental modification by man.

28

Environmental Change and Cultural Adaptation in Early Postglacial Europe

INTRODUCTION

The onset of the Holocene in Europe brought climatic and ecologic conditions analogous to those of the present. During the subsequent 10,000 years there· evidently were numerous short-term fluctuations as well as longer-term trends to cooler or warmer, moister or drier climate. But none of the changes involved approached the importance or possible ecologic significance of environmental changes during and at the close of the Pleistocene proper.

In the cultural realm, the Holocene and the last millennia of the Pleistocene mark a period of rapid cultural evolution culminating in the literate civilizations of the Near East, Europe, and Asia. Some archeologists have found reason to see environmental adaptation or responses as the root of several cultural changes. In particular, the termination of the Pleistocene is thought to have had a profound impact on certain populations in both Europe and the Old World subtropics. In the case of Europe, continued specialization led to persistence of food-collecting subsistence in a somewhat different environmental setting. In the Near East however, more spectacular results followed upon the invention of agriculture and animal domestication during the last millennia of the late Pleistocene.

ENVIRONMENTAL CHANGES OF THE TERMINAL PLEISTOCENE

Throughout most of the late glacial, accompanying the gradual retreat of the Scandinavian, British, and Alpine glaciers, climatic conditions remained cold and rigorous in mid-latitude Europe. This is shown by widespread aeolian activity as well as by tundra vegetation in northwestern, central, and northeastern Europe.

First heralded by a brief warm oscillation, known as the Bölling, the warm *Alleröd* interval or interstadial began some 12,000 years ago. The Alleröd resulted in forest recolonization of most of the Würmian tundras (Lemée, 1954; Lang, 1963; Firbas, 1949-52; Gams, 1950; Iversen, 1954; Godwin and Willis, 1959). According to numerous pollen spectra, pine woodlands are known to have dominated the southern half of France, southern Germany, and northern Poland, with spruce and pine dominant farther to the southeast (Fig. 72). A birch woodland with some pine occupied northern France and northern Germany, a birch parkland most of England and Denmark. Tundra was confined to small areas marginal to the ice sheets in southern Sweden and Finland.

Most of Fennoscandia was still glaciated during the Alleröd, the ice margin being located a little inland of the Norwegian coast and extending through south-central Sweden into southern Finland. The British glacier had been reduced to a highland glaciation of northern Scotland. In the Alps, glaciers were confined to the inner mountain valleys. Deglaciation had proceeded so far that world sea level was only about 30-35 m. lower than today's (see data in McFarlan, 1961; Fairbridge, 1961) still, however, leaving the Straits of Dover and the southern North Sea dry. The basin of the Baltic Sea was partly occupied by a large freshwater lake.

Various estimates of average July temperatures have been made. Basing himself on remains of various thermophile plants, Iversen (1954) suggests a July temperature of 13°-14° C. for Denmark (15°-16° C. today); on the basis of the altitudinal limit of pine in the Black Forest, Firbas (1949-52, Vol. I, p. 287) suggests a July temperature depression of 2.5° C. for southern Germany. The upper tree-line of the Alps was 500 m. lower than today's according to Lüdi (1955), possibly suggesting an analogous temperature depression. This would imply that the July temperatures were 5°-6° C. warmer during the Alleröd than during the main Würm. Climate was rather continental and possibly on the dry side (Iversen, 1954; Schweitzer, 1958).

The climatic deterioration of the Younger Dryas (*ca.* 8850-8300 B.C., see Godwin *et al.*, 1957; Movius, 1960) was as spectacular as the forest advance of the Alleröd. Glaciers readvanced in Europe and North America, and world sea level dropped by another 5-10 m. (see Fairbridge, 1961). NAP pollen dominates the pollen spectra of northwestern Europe and forest-tundra probably dominated in the former Würm tundras of Europe (Fig. 73). North of the Alps, birch and

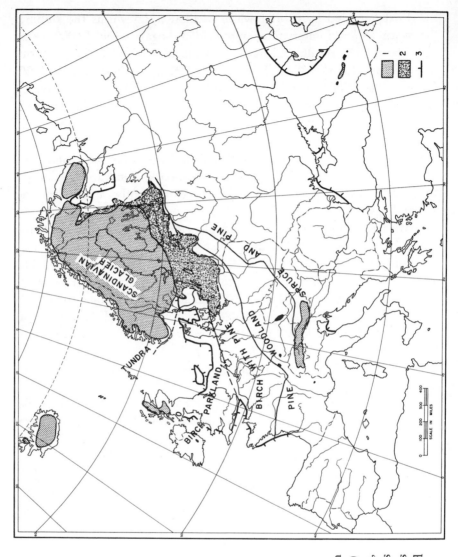

FIGURE 72.
Environment of Northwestern Europe during the Alleröd. (1) Glaciers, (2) Baltic ice lake, (3) Coastlines. Vegetation zones after Firbas (1949), Gams (1950), Iversen (1954) and Godwin (1956).

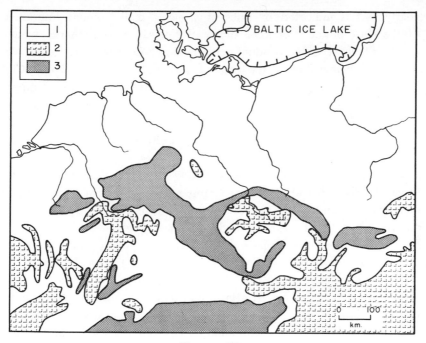

FIGURE 73.

Vegetation zones in central Europe during the Younger Dryas
(modified after Firbas, 1949). (1) Forest-tundra,
(2) birch and pine woodland, (3) alpine meadows.

pine woodland were first encountered in the warmer lowlands of central France and southern Central Europe, with the arctic tree-limit located somewhere in Denmark and Britain. The altitudinal tree-limit in the Alps was 800 m. lower than today's (Lüdi, 1955). From various lines of botanical evidence Firbas (1949-52, Vol. 1, p. 288) and Iversen (1954) suggest sudden and drastic July temperature depressions of 5.5°-7° C. for Germany and 5°-6° C. for Denmark. Similar values probably apply to other parts of mid-latitude Europe as well.

During the Preboreal (*ca.* 8300-7500 B.C.), the first phase of the Holocene, environmental conditions were once more reversed. Rapid forest recolonization of the ground lost during the Younger Dryas reduced the forest-tundra to small areas in Britain and southern Scandinavia. The remnants of the British glacier in the Scottish Highlands disappeared, while the Alpine glaciers were reduced to approximately their present dimensions. The Scandinavian glacier began its final retreat and dissipation. This retreat was comparatively rapid, averaging a little over 300 m. per year in Sweden and Finland. Each yearly halt is indicated by lines of stones—small "annual" moraines. At the close of the Preboreal, much of Norway and northern Sweden were still covered by residual ice masses, and world sea level was still 15 m. below that of the present (see data in Fairbridge, 1961). Yet the presence of various thermophile water plants in Denmark (Iversen, 1954) and England (see J. G. D. Clark, 1954), and a tree-line elevation coinciding with that of today in the Alps (Lüdi, 1955) all suggest that July temperatures were quite similar to those of the present.

The environmental changes marking the transition of the Older Dryas to the Alleröd and the Younger Dryas-Preboreal are similar in magnitude and kind. They were probably not very sudden due to the retarding effect of the slowly dissipating glaciers. But in each case a few centuries apparently sufficed to enable the forests to migrate several hundred kilometers northward. The warming trends were probably gradual, so that the local appearance of certain species provides rather arbitrary stratigraphic dates within the transitional period. Equally arbitrary is the original Pleistocene-Holocene boundary, defined by the draining of the Baltic ice-lake and establishment of intercommunication with the North Sea.

Climatically then, there was no sudden changeover from glacial to postglacial conditions at 8300 B.C., rather an irregular, violent, oscillation of warmer and colder conditions, producing an over-all warm-up, gradual ablation of the continental glaciers, and a climate ultimately warmer than that of the present. About 12,000 years elapsed between the maximum extent of the ice during the Brandenburg stage and the final dissipation of the ice when world sea level once more reached its present *niveau* in about 4000 B.C. (see data in Fairbridge, 1961). The composite picture of environmental change can therefore not be arbitrarily broken down into oversimplified units delimited by the date 8300 B.C. A survey of the floral and faunal changes can provide further information toward a more realistic understanding of this problem.

EARLY POSTGLACIAL VEGETATION CHANGE IN EUROPE

The standard pollen zones of Europe were established by L. von Post in 1916, and with some modifications are still accepted today (Table 18; Fig. 74). Apart from the addition of new detail to the late glacial sequence, considerable reinterpretation has been necessary of the ecological implications of the vegetational changes. It was originally thought that the Preboreal, with its birch-pine vegetation, provided

TABLE 18
LATE GLACIAL AND HOLOCENE POLLEN ZONES OF
NORTHWESTERN EUROPE

Zone	Date (B.C.)	Name	Dominant Vegetation	Inferred Climate
VIII	After 800	Subatlantic	Beech	Maritime
VII	3000-800	Sub-boreal	Oak-beech	More continental
VI	5600-3000	Atlantic	Oak-elm	Warmer and maritime
V	(7500)-5600	Boreal	Hazel-pine-oak	Warmer and continental
IV	8300-(7500)	Preboreal	Birch-pine	Warm-continental
III	8850-8300	Younger Dryas	Forest-tundra	Arctic
II	10,000-8850	Alleröd	Birch-pine	Temperate-continental
Ic	10,500-10,000	Older Dryas	Tundra	Arctic
Ib	11,500-10,500	Bölling	Birch parkland	Subarctic
Ia	before 11,500	Oldest Dryas	Tundra	Arctic

an analogy to present-day vegetation in Lapland. As a result the Preboreal was thought to be a period of subarctic climate in northwestern Europe. Similarly, the hazel maximum of the pollen profiles was thought to be evidence of increasing temperatures. In 1954 Iversen indicated that botanical evidence in Denmark implied a warm climate during the Preboreal, an opinion seconded by Godwin (1956) for the case of Britain. In 1960 Iversen was able to show convincingly that most of the climatic interpretation of the Holocene pollen zones requires considerable modification.

According to Iversen (1960), much of the vegetation change recorded by early Postglacial pollen profiles represents no more than a succession from "pioneer" to "climax" species. Pioneer species have a high rate of reproduction, effective seed production, and dispersal, attaining maturity at an early age. Consequently, such species, which

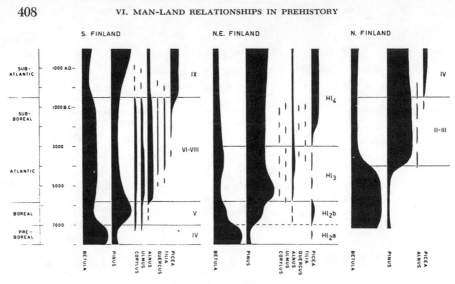

FIGURE 74.

Composite post-glacial pollen diagrams for southern,
northeastern and northern Finland (from J. J. Donner,
1963, with kind permission of the author).

include willow, aspen, and birch, are particularly adapted to rapid
colonization of new ground left by retreat of the ice, by the filling-in
of lakes, the abandonment of cultivated land, or the destruction of
primary woodland through forest fires. The weakness of pioneer species
is their high light requirement and short life span. Consequently, they
succumb easily in competition with so-called climax species. The
latter reproduce slowly, but are notably tenacious, and they tolerate as
well as provide ample shade. Species such as elm, lime, oak, and beech
gradually follow the pioneer species and ultimately displace them.

Iversen and Godwin showed that the Preboreal and Boreal intervals record exactly such a forest succession. So, for example, in the
case of Denmark the Preboreal began with a juniper (*Juniperus*)
maximum, soon followed up by a brief aspen (*Populus*) maximum,
then by an extended birch (*Betula*) maximum, during which time pine
(*Pinus*) gradually increased. Juniper and aspen were locally present,
and hence marked the first maxima. Juniper, a small tree, was easily
overshadowed and soon displaced by aspen. Birch and pine then
rapidly invaded the area and displaced the shade-intolerant and
short-lived aspen. Other climax species were located at greater distances and travel slowly, so that their immigration required several
millennia. In the meantime the birch forest of northwestern Europe

did not imply a cool, dry climate as formerly postulated, but simply represented a stage in colonization. Vegetational changes are not as rapid as the primary climatic changes, and colonization of many different soil environments on till, outwash, loess, or marshy ground had to be completed first. Persistence of tundra patches as a result of edaphic factors is substantiated by the importance of *Artemisia, Hippophae*, and *Ephedra*.

The Boreal is now usually defined by the first appearance of hazel, a shade-tolerant shrub which first had to migrate from southern France before it would take its place in the northern forests. Hazel thrives well under birch and pine, but prevents their regeneration, particularly that of birch. As the first shade-tolerant shrub, *Corylus* remained unchallenged until the arrival of elm and lime, which then crowded out hazel. As a result, neither the extended maximum of *Corylus* nor the disappearance of *Betula* have climatic significance (Iversen, 1960). Similarly the Preboreal-Boreal border is not climatic, and cannot be synchronous, as it simply marks the local arrival of hazel. Consequently, the very broad approximation of a date such as 7500 B.C. (see Godwin and Willis, 1959), indicated in parentheses by Table 18, should be regarded with caution.

The same laws governing the stages of the Preboreal are also involved in the sequence of maxima found in the Boreal and the early Atlantic. Sequence of immigration—depending on rate of travel and distance from the nearest refuge location—and species competition were entirely responsible for the vegetational change. Already during the Preboreal the presence of a thermophile water plant such as *Cladium* indicated a warm climate in Denmark. During the Boreal, mistletoe (*Viscum*) and ivy (*Hedera*) indicate warmer summers and warmer winters than is the case today.

From the perspective of vegetation, the environmental changes of the early Holocene proceeded gradually. Forest did not abruptly replace tundra at the close of the Pleistocene. Rather, forest-tundras and parklands, succeeded by open and irregular woodlands—dotted by numerous undrained tundra lowlands, and reflecting a multitude of edaphic factors—only gradually superseded the herbaceous tundra.

FAUNAL CHANGE AT THE CLOSE OF THE PLEISTOCENE

The ecologic impact of the final climatic oscillations of the terminal Pleistocene on animal life was indirect, through the intermediary of available food. The previous discussion has shown that the picture of climatic and vegetational change was complex and that there was no sudden disappearance of the tundra environment at the close of the Pleistocene. The woodlands of the forest-tundras had probably been preferred by reindeer and bison in winter. Consequently, the former range of the gregarious tundra animals would not appear to have been suddenly eliminated at 8300 B.C. or 10,000 B.C. Instead, conditions must have spasmodically deteriorated during a 4,000 year interval, from the beginning of the Bölling to the close of the Pre-boreal. Only by the mid-eighth millennium had the tundra of temperate Europe been fully eliminated.

Faunal evidence documenting the local disappearance of individual species in western Europe is fairly good. Both the late Magdalenian cave art and corresponding paleontological evidence in cave strata show that reindeer, bison, horse, and woolly mammoth were still present in southwestern France in considerable numbers as late as 13,000 B.P. during the Bölling. The absence of musk-ox from these later drawings may be significant, but such representations were always rather scarce. The woolly rhino may still have been present judging by a single late drawing from La Mouthe (see Breuil, 1950). The contemporary Hamburgian sites of Meiendorf, dated ca. 13,500 B.P., yielded a rich faunal inventory with 127 reindeer, 3-4 hares, 3 ground squirrels, and single specimens of lemming, horse, badger, fox, polecat, and wolverine (Rust, 1937, 1962). There is no ready explanation why bison and woolly mammoth should be completely absent in the Hamburg area other than by reason of deliberate specialization on reindeer by prehistoric man.

Woolly mammoth and rhino as well as musk-ox, giant "elk," bison, and the cave predators are conspicuously absent from west European faunal assemblages of the Younger Dryas, while reindeer remained the staple food. It seems that the local extinction of most of the tundra fauna took place between 13,000 and 11,000 B.P., i.e., at latest during the Alleröd. Possibly the warmer climate and reduction of suitable grazing, and in some instances, possibly even man were responsible (see chap. 27). Only the more versatile reindeer survived. Of the 668 mammalian individuals represented in the Younger Dryas cultural stratum of Stellmoor (Rust, 1943), 650 are reindeer. This suggests that reindeer was still very plentiful in the northern and eastern parts of Europe during the terminal Pleistocene. Yet among the faunal remains of early Postglacial cultures such as Star Carr, ca. 7600 B.C., and the Maglemosian of the Baltic and North Sea areas (during the Boreal), reindeer and horse are both absent. The reindeer must have withdrawn from most of temperate Europe during the first half of the Preboreal, although there is reason to believe that woodland reindeer persisted in Scotland and eastern Europe into the Subatlantic. Wild horse and forest bison (*Bison bonassus*) lived in the European woodlands until recently, but not the steppe horses of the tarpan and Przewalski type, nor the extinct Pleistocene steppe bison (*Bison priscus*).

Summing up, the Pleistocene tundra fauna of western Europe became locally extinct in stages. Certain larger species, including the mammoth, woolly rhino, giant "elk," and musk-ox appear to have disappeared or become extremely scarce during the Bölling or Alleröd. This was most probably the result of environmental change. Throughout the terminal Pleistocene reindeer formed the overwhelming bulk of man's food supply, this dietary pattern persisting into the Younger Dryas. The reindeer appears to have withdrawn to northeastern parts of Europe during the Preboreal, while a new animal spectrum was established in the birch and pine woodlands. Only the very end of some four millennia of ecological transition from tundra to forest (*ca.* 11,500-7,500 B.C.) seems to have driven the remaining tundra fauna from temperate Europe.

CULTURAL ADAPTATION TO NEW ENVIRONMENTS AT
THE CLOSE OF THE PLEISTOCENE

The original terminology employed for the Old World stone age cultures did not include a Mesolithic but rather employed terms such as "Final Paleolithic" to describe terminal food-collecting groups in the early Holocene. The recognition of a Mesolithic phase was primarily due to V. G. Childe (1925). Childe believed that the environmental changes accompanying the onset of the Holocene in Europe had a sudden and serious impact on man. Childe realized the great herds of herbivores had been replaced by more solitary game such as deer, wild cattle, boar, and the like,

> the pursuit of which required more arduous tactics and a new equipment. That spelt the end of the cultures that had brought prosperity to Upper Palaeolithic hunters. Adaptations to the novel and really sterner conditions are represented by so-called mesolithic cultures (Childe, 1958, p. 25).

One of the alleged consequences of this apparent deterioration of hunting resources was the breakdown of the organized community-hunting activities thought to be characteristic of many Upper Paleolithic groups. This change of social order is believed to have been more or less responsible for the disappearance of the Franco-Cantabrian cave art. The Mesolithic was then considered a consequence of environmental changes, a fact clearly emphasized by the arbitrary delimitation of 8000 B.C. for the beginning of this last food-collecting stage.

The cultural innovations of Europe during the early Holocene have since been almost generally described as a matter of readjustment to new environments. The question may be raised whether this environmental interpretation of the terminal Paleolithic cultures in Europe is fully warranted. Several different problems are involved of which the deterioration of natural resources falls within the range of discussion.

The biomass potential of the European tundras was considerably greater than that of a deciduous or boreal woodland. There can be little doubt that the emigration of the great reindeer herds at some date after 8300 B.C. removed the cornerstone of the European meat supply. The Preboreal must therefore have introduced a major game crisis for the specialized hunters of mid-latitude Eurasia. There can also be no question that hunting of deer, wild cattle, or boar was difficult if large meat reserves were to be established. But the individual hunt did not require greater skills than a reindeer battue. Since the winters were now mild it was possible to hunt locally-abundant forest game throughout the year, and a winter larder was unnecessary. New hunting techniques did not have to be learned, for deer and wild cattle had been successfully hunted throughout late Paleolithic times.

The crisis was much simpler—the specialized hunting of a single animal, the reindeer, had enabled late Paleolithic man in western and central Europe to achieve a comparatively high population density. Regardless of technological skill the disappearance of reindeer meant a catastrophic decline in game resources. Possibilities of following the retreating herds were limited, due both to the general reduction of suitable reindeer habitats and the territoriality of other hunting peoples. No degree of hunting versatility—little short of agriculture—could preserve the Mesolithic peoples of western Europe from a drastic reduction of population density. This leveling off of the population to a reduced animal resource potential must have begun during the Bölling in southwestern France, when the reindeer began to come south in fewer and fewer numbers during the winter. Farther east, in southern Russia, the mammoth hunters must also have faced a similar crisis during the Bölling or at latest the Alleröd. In northern Germany, Denmark, and Britain the crisis came two millennia later.

It would appear then that the European hunters underwent a severe resource crisis, with almost certain decimation of their numbers, during the millennia between 11,500 and 7500 B.C. The exact period of disappearance of reindeer or mammoth, whatever the staple food, varied from place to place. The archeological record of the Alleröd and Upper Dryas in southwestern France, of the Preboreal and Boreal in most of northern France, the Low Countries, and central and eastern Europe seems to support the argument of sparse and culturally unimpressive populations. The nature of any cultural innovation here is certainly obscure and possibly more a matter of readjustment and readaptation.

Only along the shores of the North and Baltic Seas do we find some evidence of a new form of specialization and diversification in the Maglemosian cultures (Fig. 75). But even here, technological innovation was slow and by no means revolutionary. Braidwood (1961, pp. 97-98), in fact, questions the validity of the case for cultural readjustment, and Braidwood and Reed (1957) have challenged the existence of a "Mesolithic" unit defined geologically. Despite the validity of the terminal Pleistocene resource crisis in Europe, and the need for adaptation to a different environment and reduced resources, one cannot help but feel a certain overemphasis of environmentalism in the thinking of some archeologists who define a Mesolithic culture stage on the basis of cultural innovation in the wake of ecological readjustment. It would be ecologically more significant to classify all of the specialized food-collecting economies at a single level. The following discussion of a proto-Maglemosian site in Preboreal England may illustrate the point.

AN EXAMPLE OF MESOLITHIC HABITAT AND ECONOMY:
STAR CARR, YORKSHIRE

The early Mesolithic site of Star Carr, located 8 km. south-southeast of Scarborough, near the English North Sea coast, was excavated by J. G. D. Clark in 1949-51. Through painstaking evaluation of the paleo-ecological evidence, particularly by H. Godwin and D. Walker, the subsistence patterns of the group are quite well understood. The locality is at 23 m. above sea level on the margins of a poorly drained peat lowland once occupied by a lake in early Postglacial times.

The cultural strata are found over solifluction deposits of Younger

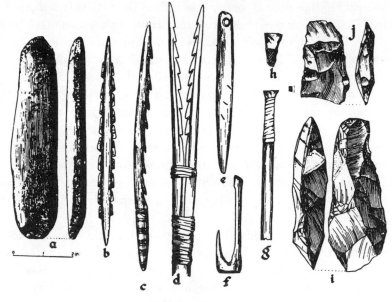

FIGURE 75.

Mesolithic fishing and hunting equipment (from K. P. Oakley, 1958, with permission of the Trustees of the British Museum, Natural History). (a) a hammer for clam and mussel bashing, (b) bone fish-spear with microlith barbs, (c) barbed point in deer antler, (d) leister prongs of modern Eskimo fisherman, (e) net-making needle (?), (f) bone fish-hook, (g), (h) microlith (transverse arrowhead) hafted in wood with sinew binding, (i), (j) axes.

Dryas age, and under a meter or so of peat. Pollen analysis and macro-botanical evidence showed that the horizon is within the upper part of pollen zone IV, i.e., the late Preboreal. Two C[14] dates of 7535 ± 350 B.C. (C-353) and 7600 B.C. ± 210 (Q-14) confirm this strati-graphic position.

The dominant tree species of the land areas was birch (*Betula pubescens*), and a closed birch forest with some pine (*Pinus silvestris*) probably covered the hillsides and the drier parts of the valley bottom. Willow and a little alder fringed the reed swamps indicating · the presence of the lake edge. Although a number of aquatic birds record the presence of water nearby, the mammalian fauna is entirely one of woodland forms: at least 80 individuals of red deer (*Cervus ela-phus*), 33 of roe deer (*Capreolus*), 11 of elk (*Alces*), 9 of aurochs (*Bos primigenius*), 5 of boar (*Sus scrofa*), together with a varying number of beaver, marten, red fox, wolf, badger, hare, and hedgehog. Fish or invertebrates are absent. Both the aquatic plants and mammalian fauna suggest a warm-temperate forest environment, not unlike that found in Britain today.

The areal extent of the settlement area is about 200 square meters, the vertical depth of cultural deposits about 15-40 cm. There are no remains of huts or of any kind of structure, although these are known from contemporary cultures in Denmark, northern Germany, and the Netherlands. The occupation area suggests that the group did not exceed a total of 16 to 25 individuals of whom 5 were adult men able to hunt large game. The state of the deer antlers suggests that the site was occupied during winter and spring, and abandoned during the summer.

The artifactual materials include some 2,500 finished or utilized flints, dominated by scrapers, burins, and microliths—minute, carefully retouched bladelets employed as arrowheads or projectile barbs. A number of axes or adzes were also found. Considerable use of bone and antler was made, particularly for barbed antler points, mattock heads, batons (for working flint?), bodkins, fastening pins, and in one case, as a harpoon head. Apart from various bone ornaments a 26 cm. long wooden paddle was found, possibly suggesting the presence of boats. On the basis of the meat represented by the faunal collection, 20 people might have been supported for 6.2 years. In view of seasonal occupation from October through April, and the use of some vegetable foods, even in winter, the site may have been repeatedly occupied for at least 12-15 years, possibly with some interruptions.

The general subsistence pattern of the Star Carr people is thought to have been one of seasonal winter settlement, with almost total emphasis on game hunting during that season. During the summer, the group possibly spent its time fishing in nearby lakes or rivers or food-collecting at the coast. Considerably more vegetable food could be obtained then, so that camps were possibly occupied on a temporary basis only. The general proficiency or cultural level of this population is not obviously advanced beyond that of the Upper Paleolithic, although the settlement patterns are adapted to a different environment. The later Maglemosian culture has a few better-worked tools, and indicates an appreciable calorie source from sea fish and invertebrates. But man's modification of or mastery over the environment was no more conspicuous than during the late Pleistocene.

29

Agricultural Origins
in the Near East
as a Geographical Problem

INTRODUCTION

The previous chapters attempted to appraise man-land relationships during the slow process of cultural innovation characterizing the Paleolithic and "Mesolithic." These hunter-gatherer populations had all been very sparsely settled and technologically simple, with a limited or even negligible impact on the natural environment. However, the same transition of Pleistocene and Holocene that left Europe at the cultural level of advanced food-collecting, witnessed the dramatic beginnings of agriculture in the Near East.

The culture groups of the Near Eastern late Pleistocene were specialized hunter-gatherers, particularly fond of cave habitation. But, at least as far as their tool inventory is concerned, these Upper Paleolithic people were comparatively uninteresting and not remarkably progressive or specialized. Then about 11,000 years ago two cultures appear in the Levant and northeastern Iraq: the Natufian and Karim Shahirian. Both assemblages were characterized by so-called agricultural implements such as sickle-blades, grinding stones, and polished stone axes known as celts and presumed to have been used as hoes in many cases. None of these tools as such necessarily indicate agricultural activity, but the combination suggests partial subsistence on either wild grains or cultivated cereals. And at Zawi Chemi Shanidar, one site of the Karim Shahirian assemblage, there is fairly good proof of the presence of domesticated sheep (Perkins, 1964), *ca.* 8900 B.C.[1] By 7000 B.C. subsistence-farming had become a common economic trait in parts of the Near East.

[1] C[14] dates 8910 ± 300 B.C. and 8640 ± 300 B.C., W-681, W-667 (Solecki and Rubin, 1958).

A focus of agricultural origins in this particular area and at this particular time is of environmental and geographical interest. Firstly, localization of early domestication is to some extent circumscribed by environmental factors. Suitable biological resources must be present if local domestication is to be possible. A second problem concerns possible environmental influences on the cultural processes implied by agricultural origins. And thirdly, the invention of agriculture is of great physical import, marking a drastic change in man-land relationships. The following chapter attempts to outline some of these environmental problems in relation to the hearth of domestication in the Near East. Beyond doubt the environmental problems related to first domestication in other culture areas, for example in the New World, are quite distinct. But their consideration lies beyond the scope of a selective survey of man-land relationships at different cultural and technological levels.

THE NEAR EAST AS A HEARTH OF DOMESTICATION

There have been several hearth areas in which domestication of specific associations of plants and animals was apparently first carried out. Basically such areas are habitats with a number of wild plants and animals suitable for domestication, and presumably where such species could first be domesticated in the habitat of their wild ancestors (Braidwood, 1958). There were at least two independent hearths of domestication (in the Old and New World) and possibly three, specifically (*a*) Mesoamerica and the Andean Highlands, (*b*) the Near East, particularly the hill country of southwestern Asia, and (*c*) southeastern Asia, probably along the margins of the Bay of Bengal or the Malayan Peninsula (see Sauer, 1952). At least the first two hearths had no obvious cultural intercommunications; in the case of areas (*b*) and (*c*), one in a subhumid winter rainfall belt, the other in the humid tropics, techniques and cultural backgrounds are so different that any *initial* contact would be rather difficult to establish. Lastly there *may* be minor hearths of domestication in which single species were first domesticated before an agricultural economy had been introduced from without. North China (Chang, 1962), Ethiopia, and West Africa provide possibilities of this kind.

The Near Eastern hearth region provided the biological materials, intellectual achievements, and cultural associations that underlie the civilizations of western Asia, northern Africa, and Europe. The basic biological inventory includes seed plants (cereals) and herd (as opposed to household) animals. More specifically, the food-producing cultures of these areas have from the very beginning depended primarily on the cultivation of wheat and barley for subsistence (Helbaek, 1959).

THE NATURAL HABITAT OF THE CEREALS

According to Helbaek (1959) the locus of domestication of a wild plant would presumably be within its area of original distribution in the wild state. Consequently, a prehistoric group dependent upon wild wheat as its main food should have developed its subsistence pattern within the original area of natural distribution of that species. The same should apply to a culture primarily dependent upon barley.

The wild ancestor of domesticated barley (*Hordeum spontaneum*) is now distributed across the Near East and in several parts of southern Europe and northern Africa (Fig. 76).[2] On the other hand the two wild wheats, from which all domestic wheats have been derived directly or by complex hybridization, are more restricted in range. The large-grained *Triticum dicoccoides*, direct ancestor of emmer wheat (*T. dicoccum*), has its natural distribution in the Zagros Mountains of Iraq and Iran, the Taurus of southeastern Turkey, and much of the Levant. The wild small-grained *T. aegilopoides*, straight-line ancestor of einkorn (*T. monococcum*), occurs throughout Turkey, the Zagros, and the highlands of the Levant. If one can assume that the distribution of wild wheat and barley was 12,000 years ago as it is today,[3] it would seem that the cradle of the "western" plant husbandry cultures lies in the winter rainfall zone of the Near East (Helbaek, 1959).

Helbaek (1959) considers that cereal domestication proceeded in several stages. The first essential change from reaping of wild cereals to planting may have included concentration of the desired plant by sowing, improvement of growth by tilling, exclusion or removal of unwanted plants from the tilled plot, and protection of the crop against animals and birds.

Another major step was to select particular types of grain and thus begin the process of selection, specialization, and ultimately

---

[2] J. R. Harlan (*personal communication*) feels that the six-rowed barley reported from the Himalayas is weed rather than wild barley, as is the case for much of the so-called wild barley distribution known today.

[3] Different climatic conditions during the terminal Würm may have modified the natural distribution, while man may since have eradicated the wild species in some areas.

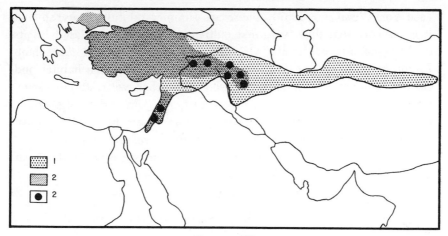

FIGURE 76.

Natural distribution of the wild wheats and wild barley (modified after Helbaek, 1959). Native habitats of (1) *Hordeum spontaneum*, (2) *Triticum aegilopoides* and (3) *Triticum dicoccoides*.

adaptation to peculiar environments outside of the limited natural range of distribution. In the case of wheat it meant moving down the domesticant to (*a*) the plains or, later on, into the artificial ecology of the irrigated floodplains, and (*b*) into more northerly zones or higher altitudes.

The last major step was the hybridization of the wheats into more advanced, specialized types such as club wheat, bread wheat, spelt, and naked wheat and the apparent evolution of barley into another, six-rowed type.

Besides conscious "primary" domestication, Helbaek distinguishes a "secondary" domestication, namely the segregation, for intentional cultivation, of a weed growing in cultivated soil which already unintentionally was subjected to selection through being reaped along with the intended crop. Either wheat or barley was probably so introduced, and rye and oats are typical examples. Both of the latter were introduced as weeds in wheat fields, rye from west-central Asia and oats from the Near East or eastern Europe. Both "appear" very late in the archeological record and were probably never primarily planted anywhere but in cooler latitudes where they proved to be particularly hardy plants. They play no role whatever in the Near East.

Regarding other plants, the various millets have an obscure history (see Von Wissmann, 1957). These are summer rainfall plants, so that it is unlikely that they were first cultivated in the Near East with its mediterranean-type climate. Of further note is the wild flax plant, *Linum bienne,* used for fibre and oil, which has the same habitat and cultural context as wheat and barley. Together with starchy vegetables of Near Eastern origin, the wine grape, olive, date, fig, apple, pear, cherry etc. also seem to originate somewhere in the Near East. In overview, winter-rainfall *cereal cultivation, orchard husbandry, and viticulture* are characteristic of early plant domestication in the Near Eastern hearth (Helbaek, 1959, 1960a).

THE NATURAL HABITAT OF THE HERD ANIMALS OF THE NEAR
EAST

Present knowledge on the locus of first domestication of the herd animals is far less satisfactory than that of the "western" cereals. The former range of the wild ancestors is usually extensive; the wild progenitor(s) is frequently a matter of strong controversy, often due to rather muddled taxonomic situations; and the archeologic-osteologic material is far less complete. The most up-to-date survey of the problem has been made by Zeuner (1963, with references; also Reed, 1960; Smolla, 1960), whose materials are freely employed here.

The dog (*Canis familiaris*) is generally considered to be descended from the wolf, although later interbreeding with jackals may have taken place in the semiarid subtropics. The natural habitat of the wolf includes the greater part of the forest zone of Eurasia and North America. As the domestication of the dog took place rather early among European Mesolithic groups during the Preboreal or Boreal, the dog has no necessary association with agriculturists. In fact, there is no certain evidence of domesticated dogs in the Near East until after 5000 B.C. (see Clutton-Brock, 1963).

The goat (*Capra hircus*) is most generally thought to be descended from the bezoar goat (*Capra aegagrus*), ranging from Palestine to the Caucasus, from Greece to the Indus. Fossil bezoar goats are also known from the late Pleistocene of the Levant. The actual habitat of the wild goat is somewhat more limited as a result of the ecological niche to which the goat is adapted, i.e., rough ground with rocky slopes which enable this agile climber to escape possible predators.

The sheep (*Ovis aries*) is probably mainly descended from the urial (*Ovis orientalis*), although other species of wild sheep may have contributed to certain breeds of domesticated sheep. The urial occurs in northern Iran, Afghanistan, northwestern India, and adjacent parts of Central Asia. Another possible wild ancestor, the eastern moufflon (*Ovis musimon* ssp.) inhabited Anatolia, Caucasia and western Iran. Yet another, the argali (*Ovis ammon*), is found in Central Asia. Sheep are adapted to open, rolling country, avoiding open plains or dense forest.

Cattle (*Bos taurus*) are in all probability descended from the large, long-horned, wild *Bos primigenius* or aurochs once distributed throughout the forested regions of Europe, southwestern Asia, and northern Africa. A shorthorned species called *B. longifrons* or *B. brachyceros* has been postulated, but these animals were probably females of *B. primigenius*. Wild cattle favored woodland or forest as a habitat.

Originally there were several subspecies of wild pig (*Sus scrofa*) native to the woodlands of Eurasia and North Africa. The European domesticated pigs are essentially descendants of the wild boar (*Sus scrofa scrofa*), and the Chinese ones of the banded pig (*Sus vittatus*) native to southeastern Asia.

Domestication of horse, reindeer, and camel came relatively late and played no role in the original transition to food production, so that these genera are of peripheral interest in this discussion.

The natural habitats of the western Asiatic herd animals in a broad way overlap with the native distribution of the wild wheats and barley in the Near Eastern highlands. The range of the wild ancestors of the herd animals is very much greater than that of the wild wheats and barley however. Although the boar, aurochs, and possibly also barley were native to the alluvial floodplains of Mesopotamia and Egypt, sheep, goat, and wild wheats were absent. The Syrian, Iranian, and Central Asian deserts fall outside of this natural habitat zone.

THE NATURAL HABITAT ZONE

If there was sound reason to believe that cereal domestication preceded animal domestication, the Near Eastern hearth of agricultural origins could be more or less localized into a zone of preference—the Near Eastern highlands, and possibly a more peripheral zone, the alluvial floodplains of the Nile and Tigris-Euphrates. So far archeological evidence of animal domestication predates the earliest proven domesticated grains by as much as two millennia. It is only as a matter of convenience that the zone of overlap of the wild cereals

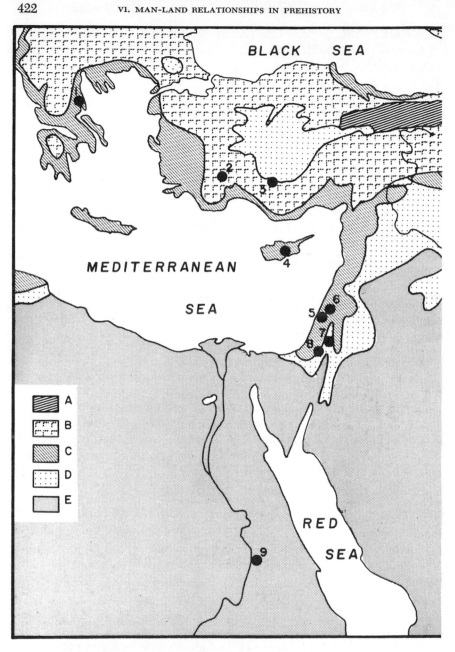

FIGURE 77.

Natural post-glacial vegetation of the Near East and location of early agricultural and proto-agricultural sites (*ca.* 9000-5750 B.C.). (A) Coniferous forests, (B) Deciduous and mixed forests, (C) Subtropical woodlands, (D) Grassland, (E) Desert-grass-land, semidesert and desert. The galeria woodlands of the major

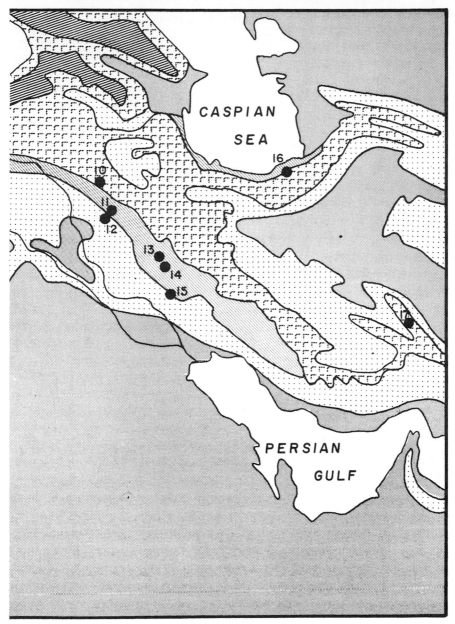

rivers are not shown. Sites: (1) Sesklo, (2) Haçilar, (3) Catal Hüyük, (4) Khirokitia, (5) Mt. Carmel caves, (6) Ain Mallaha, (7) Jericho, (8) Judean Desert caves, (9) Gebel Silsila and Sebil, (10) Shanidar and Zawi Chemi, (11) Karim Shahir, (12) Jarmo, (13) Asiab, (14) Sarab, (15) Ali Kosh, (16) Hotu Cave, (17) Kerman.

and wild herd animals is emphasized here, even though the available archeological evidence suggests that the evidence may not be fortuitous.

A brief examination of the physical geography of the modern natural habitat of the wild wheats can be rather informative. The areas involved are characterized by irregular and diversified terrain and a minimum annual precipitation of 300-500 mm., and they coincide with the subtropical mediterranean-type woodlands of the Fertile Crescent and the temperate forests of Anatolia (Fig. 77). Significant is the exclusion of this particular habitat from the steppe or semi-desert areas. Equally interesting is the location of known agricultural communities predating *ca.* 5000 B.C. These were all found within or at the peripheries of the woodland belt.

The alluvial valleys enjoy somewhat different environmental conditions. Apart from the peculiar terrain features of floodplains, neither the lower Nile Valley nor the Tigris-Euphrates lowlands have sufficient rainfall for non-irrigated agriculture. But crops could be planted as the annual floods receded (October in Egypt, June in Mesopotamia), and the moisture retained in the soil would normally be sufficient to bring one crop to maturity. The ecologic patterns of these alluvial floodplains were generally quite distinct from those of the highlands, even though a winter growing season would be common both to Egypt and the wooded hill country.

The geographical traits and subsistence economy of the earliest known Near Eastern farming communities speak for agricultural origins in the winter rainfall belt. This region corresponds closely to that ideal physical environment envisaged for first agriculture by C. O. Sauer (1952). From a different premise, Sauer argued that agriculture began in wooded lands rather than in grasslands with deep and continuous sod. This argument is based on the difficulty of cultivating heavy sod with primeval agricultural tools. Rather, a varied, open woodland could be more easily cleared by deadening the trees, so providing open spaces with looser topsoil for easy sowing. Dense forests were also inimical to primitive hoe agriculture. Sauer emphasizes that diversity of terrain is optimal in providing numerous ecologic niches—"a land of hills and valleys, of streams and springs, with alluvial reaches and rock shelters in cliffs" (1952, pp. 5-6). For it is here that the greatest diversity of plants and animals and suitable genetic reservoirs are to be found.

POSSIBLE ENVIRONMENTAL CHANGES IN THE NEAR
EASTERN AREA AT THE CLOSE OF THE PLEISTOCENE

Climatic conditions in western Asia during the main Würm were discussed briefly in chapter 19. Any specific changes that may have occurred at the close of the Pleistocene are largely obscure, reflecting a lack of detailed geological work, particularly in the cave sites of Iraq and Iran.

The fauna of the Mesolithic-type Zarzian culture of Iraq, dated 12,400 ± 400 B.P. (W-179), is not considered indicative of a different climate than today's according to Braidwood, Howe *et al.* (1960, pp. 167-70). The fauna at Palegawra (965 m. elevation) includes gazelle, wild goat and sheep, wild cattle, red and roe deer, boar, onager (?), red fox, wolf, lynx (?) and a hedgehog (Braidwood, Howe *et al.*, 1960, pp. 58-59) while the fauna of the corresponding Shanidar level B-2 (730 m. elevation) is dominated by wild goat (60 per cent and red deer (20 per cent) together with bear, wild sheep, and boar (Perkins, 1964). Tentative pollen analyses of the same level at Shanidar suggest the presence of cypress, pine, and chestnut (Solecki and Leroi-Gourhan, 1961). Two of these species are mediterranean in character. Scrub oak is the only local tree vegetation there today. At Marivan (1,300 m.) in western Iran, an oak-pistachio savanna dominant since about 13,000 B.P. also infers a mediterranean-type climate (see Zeist and Wright, 1963). The late Upper Paleolithic fauna of Ksar Akil, Lebanon (Hooijer, 1961), is equally indicative of more or less contemporary conditions. From this, one must conclude that local ecological conditions during the late Würm were similar to those of the present.

However, the cold relapse of the Younger Dryas probably did not pass quite unnoticed in this part of the world. *Éboulis secs* horizons are found in contemporary horizons of Ksar Akil, Lebanon (see Butzer, 1958a, pp. 104-5 with references), and Higgs (1961) argues that the fauna from cave strata at Haua Fteah, Cyrenaica, suggest a cooler and moister climate at the close of the Pleistocene. Similarly there is evidence for recessional stages of the Würm glaciers of the Caucasus, eastern Anatolia, and northwestern Iran, some of which have been compared with the final Würm oscillations of the Alpine glaciers (see references in Butzer, 1958a, pp. 105-6). It is quite probable, although beyond the possibility of accurate dating at the moment, that a small glacial readvance occurred in the highlands at this time. Seen in this perspective it would, therefore, be unjustified to say that ecologic conditions were truly "modern" prior to *ca.* 8000 B.C.

Although the rather modest temperature changes suggested for the Younger Dryas cannot have been significant for human habitation, a possible depression of 1°-3° C. would have had an effect on the distribution of the wild cereals. So, for example, wild wheats are now found to an upper elevation limit of about 1,400 m. in northwestern Turkey and Iraq, to 2,000 m. in northwestern Iran (J. R. Harlan, personal communication; Helbaek, 1959). Colder late glacial climates may therefore have excluded these species from parts of the Near Eastern highlands during the late Würm.

Locally, in Palestine and Egypt, conditions may have been somewhat moister during a part or all of the Natufian period (*ca.* 9000-7000 B.C.). The gazelle, a characteristic open-country biotype, is comparatively infrequent at this level in the Mt. Carmel caves of Palestine, and a half dozen species of this genus disappeared at the time (Bate, 1940). Complementing the faunal record is archeological evidence of fishing in the dry wadis of the arid south Judean Highlands. This suggests permanent pools of water available throughout the year. The presence of hunting populations in the Negeb and Sinai deserts, as indicated by plentiful distribution of Natufian flints, also seems to support this opinion. Undated corroboration may possibly be recorded in several comparatively recent, high strandlines as much as 50 m. above the Dead Sea. And in Egypt there is good evidence of local wadi alluviation during the teminal late Pleistocene (Butzer and Hansen, 1965). These seem to be the available indications of greater moisture during the last millennium or so of the Pleistocene. The evidence appears to be limited to the lowland areas peripheral to the subtropical deserts. Such a "moist spell" probably did not have ecological significance in the hill country.

ARCHEOLOGICAL EVIDENCE OF EARLY AGRICULTURE AND LIVESTOCK-RAISING

In reviewing the archeological record it is often difficult to determine whether a particular community practiced food-production or whether agriculture and livestock-herding were entirely unknown. Smolla (1960) has devoted considerable attention to this problem of archeological evidence for early agriculture and animal domestication.

The stone artifacts commonly associated with agricultural operations are not unequivocal.

Sickle-blades, consisting of rectangular flint blades, were designed to be mounted into a wooden or bone haft. Such bone hafts have been found on numerous occasions. However the sickles need not have been used to reap cereal crops, but may just as well have been employed on certain wild grasses or on reeds used for matting and hut construction. The sheen or lustre frequently developed on such blades may be a silicon deposit derived from straw or grasses (Smolla, 1960, p. 109 ff., with references). Since wild cereals "shatter" upon touch, it is questionable whether sickle-reaping would be possible at all. In fact the ethnological record shows that the simplest primitive reaping of wild cereals is performed by plucking the ears or by beating the plants and catching the grain or seeds in a basket (Smolla, 1960, p. 110). Sickle-harvesting in the unripe state would not produce sickle-sheen, while the seeds may not be reproductive.

Mortars, consisting of hollowed stone vessels, and querns or pestles used as handstones, are pre-eminently effective as grinding stones for grain or seed crushing to make flour. However *some* Natufian mortars were used to grind pigment (Garrod, 1958), while mortars and pestles are sometimes used for meat-grinding today (L. Binford and R. J. Braidwood, personal communication), and could also be employed for grinding acorns, wild grains, or bone grease.

Stone celts, resembling polished axes or hoes, may have been used as axes or hoes. There are, however, no good ethnological parallels for stone hoes (Smolla, 1960, p. 53).

All in all, the so-called agricultural tools are difficult to interpret, although when found in association and in large numbers they strongly suggest the intensive use and preparation of vegetable foods and probably of domesticated crops. Unfortunately there is no archeological record of more meaningful items such as digging sticks.

Botanical evidence of plant domestication can be recognized, but many of the morphological changes resulting from domestication take place very slowly. Theoretically, a single mutation will produce a "non-shattering" grain, so that selection of "non-shattering" mutants could rapidly produce a new domesticated stock with new morphological characteristics (J. D. Sauer, personal communication).

Osteological evidence for earliest domestication would be difficult or impossible to demonstrate by bone anatomy alone. An interesting example of circumventing this problem has been made by Perkins (1964) at Zawi Chemi Shanidar, the site of the earliest evidence of animal domestication to date. Here the faunal compositions of the Middle and Upper Paleolithic strata were quite uniform with wild goat outnumbering wild sheep by 3:1, and constituting about 60 per cent of the fauna. About 25 per cent of the animals were juveniles under a year of age. Suddenly, in the Zawi Chemi horizon, sheep bones jumped to 75 per cent, of which 60 per cent were immature. Goat dropped down to 10 per cent, still with 25 per cent juveniles. It is concluded that the sheep must have been domesticated at this stage, and that the larger part of each year's young were killed for food and skins before the end of the year. The hunting of wild goats had consequently become relatively unimportant.

As a result of these difficulties in accurate assessment of the archeological record, the absence of evidently domesticated cereals or animals from many sites need not prove that agriculture was unknown. Equally so, the presence of so-called agricultural implements does not necessarily prove knowledge of crop-planting.

THE NEAR EASTERN ARCHEOLOGICAL RECORD PERTAINING TO EARLY AGRICULTURE

The Near Eastern tool inventory of various Upper Paleolithic cultures, culminating with the Kebaran assemblage in Palestine, the Nebekian in Syria, and the Zarzian in northeastern Iraq (see Howell, 1959a, with references), is broadly comparable with the European counterparts, although showing early microlithic traits. Settlement was largely concentrated in caves, although some Zarzian open-air sites have been tentatively identified (Braidwood, Howe, et al., 1960, pp. 155-57). The only contemporary cultural group which falls out of this framework is the Middle Sebilian of the Egyptian Nile Valley. The Middle Sebilians are of particular interest since they were semisedentary, occupying campsites on the banks of the Nile, where they intensively used the aquatic and riverine food-resources of their localized environment. Modest kitchen middens in the Kom Ombo area of Upper Egypt testify to considerable use of fresh-water molluscs, fish, and, more rarely turtle and crocodile; in addition, a wide range of woodland and steppe mammals were hunted. Grinding stones are already present, often in great numbers. Geologically, the Middle Sebilian is broadly contemporary with the late Würm (Butzer and Hansen, 1965), i.e., no later in time than the Kebaran or Zarzian.[4]

Rather abruptly, archeological indications of agriculture appear in the Levant and Iraq ca. 9000 B.C., suggesting a very early diffusion of agriculture in the Near Eastern highlands. Sickle-blades and pound-

---

[4] An ecological interpretation of the Middle and Upper Sebilian will undoubtedly contribute to understanding agricultural origins in the Near East. This should be possible after evaluation of the 1962-63 excavations of M. A. Baumhoff and H. Walter at Gebel Silsila.

ing and milling stones appear more or less simultaneously in both the Natufian assemblage of Palestine, Lebanon, and Syria (Garrod, 1958), and the Karim Shahirian of Iraqi Kurdistan (Braidwood, Howe *et al.*, 1960). The contemporary Asiab assemblage of northwestern Iran (Braidwood *et al.*, 1961) does not yet appear to have sickles, grinding stones, or celts. An analogous culture with microliths, sickle-blades, and grinding stones has also been discovered at Kerman, in south-eastern Iran (Hückriede, 1962). No evidence of cereals is available yet from either the Natufian or Karim Shahirian, but it is very probable that plant domestication was at least well underway. Domesticated sheep are present in the Karim Shahirian. These two cultures, which possibly extend through most of the ninth and eighth millenia precede a bona fide agricultural economy, certainly established in parts of western Asia by 7000 B.C. Both assemblages are essentially found within the natural habitats of wild wheat, barley, sheep, and goat. This may be the elusive stage of "incipient agriculture and animal domestication"—which Braidwood (1960a) describes as experimental manipulation of potential domesticates within a dominant food-collecting economy, at first still within the ecological niche to which the wild ancestor of the domesticate was adapted. It may be significant that some of the Natufian and Karim Shahirian sites are located in the open. This may be an indication of new ways of life, of improved technology, or also of warmer climate after *ca.* 8300 B.C.

By 7000 B.C. agriculture had become the primary subsistence of village farmers found in the Levant, the Zagros area, and southwestern Anatolia. These people grew einkorn, emmer, and barley, and kept domesticated goats and sheep. The domesticated pig also appears in archeological context somewhere in the seventh millennium in the pottery levels of Jarmo, northeastern Iraq. For the sixth millennium village-farming communities are verified in Thessaly (Milojčić, 1959), Khirokitia (Cyprus) (Dikaios, 1953), Catal Hüyük and Haçilar (S. W. Anatolia) (Mellaart, 1961), a good range of sites in the Levant, northern Iraq, and adjacent parts of Iran as well as in the Belt Cave on the Caspian shores of Iran (Ralph, 1955).

The regional appearance of the various achievements of cultural innovation and evolution in the Near East are summarized in Table 19. The major expansion of food-producing populations of the Neolithic level into the cooler environments of temperate Europe and into the different environment of the Tigris-Euphrates and Nile floodplains, appears to postdate 5000 B.C. These later aspects will be considered in chapters 30 and 31.

TABLE 19

STRATIGRAPHY OF EARLY AGRICULTURE IN THE NEAR EAST

(Based on Braidwood, 1958; Braidwood, Howe et al., 1960; Helbaek, 1959, 1960b; Reed, 1959, 1961; and others. Assemblages with "Agricultural Implements" are italicized)

	Egypt	Levant	Anatolia	N.E. Iraq	N.W. Iran
	Merimde (emmer, barley, goat, sheep, cattle, pig)			*Halaf* (emmer, einkorn, barley, flax, sheep, cattle)	
5,000 B.C.					
		Amouq (goat, cattle, pig)		*Hassuna* (emmer, barley, goat)	*Sialk* (goat)
6,000 B.C.					
		Jericho (goat)	*Haçilar* (emmer, einkorn, barley, goat, sheep)	*Jarmo* (emmer, einkorn, barley, goat, sheep, pig)	*Sarab* (goat, sheep)
7,000 B.C.					
		Upper Natufian			
8,000 B.C.					
	Upper Sebilian	*Lower Natufian*		*Karim Shahir* (sheep)	Asiab
9,000 B.C.					
10,000 B.C.		Nebekian Kebaran		Zarzian	
	Middle Sebilian				

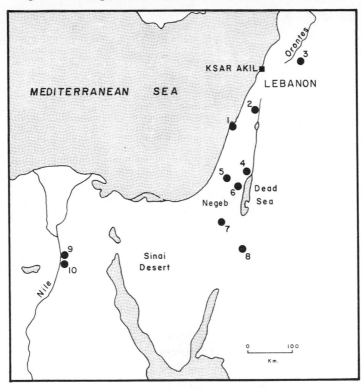

FIGURE 78.
Distribution of the Natufian industries (*ca.* 9000-7000 B.C.).
(1) Mt. Carmel (Wadi Fallah, el-Wad, Kebara), (2) Ain
Mallaha, (3) Jabrud, (4) Jericho, (5) Shuqba, (6) Tor Abu
Sif, Erq el-Ahmar and el-Khiam, (7) Nahal Rimon, (8) Beida,
(9) el-Omari, (10) Helwan.

THE ECOLOGY OF THE NATUFIAN IN PALESTINE

Remains of the Natufian cultural assemblage, dating from approximately 9000-7000 B.C., are widely distributed in the southern
Levant (Fig. 78).[5]

[5] Sites have been found in the Jabrud cave of Syria (Rust, 1950), at Beirut,
in three caves of the Mt. Carmel area of Palestine (Garrod and Bate, 1937; Garrod,
1958), at the base of Jericho (Kenyon, 1959), at Ain Mallaha near Lake Huleh
(Perrot, 1957, 1960, 1962), as well as in a number of caves in the wadis of the
Judean hills both northwest and southeast of Jerusalem (Neuville, 1951). Surface
finds have been made east of the Jordan river, in the Negeb and Sinai deserts, and
at el-Omari and Helwan, near Cairo.

One of the best published and culturally important sites of the Natufian is found in the Mugharet el-Wad cave of Mt. Carmel, at an elevation of 45 m. on the southern face of a small wadi.[6] The base of the cave is 12.5 m. above the wadi floor, and extends for some 85 m. with an average height of 10 m. The Natufian strata underlie 0.3-1.2 m. of a consolidated brown earth and limestone rubble with early Bronze Age and later remains. About 0.2-3.0 m. thick, these beds consist of unconsolidated, stony red earth with limestone talus in the sections located in front of the cave entrance. The underlying deposits of the interior cave contain Upper and Middle Paleolithic industries. Interpretive geomorphological work has not yet been carried out, so that the implications of the beds are obscure.

In the further absence of known botanical remains, the rich faunal collection of the Mugharet el-Wad is ecologically important. It includes rodents and insectivores with two species of hedgehog, mole rat (*Spalax*), a vole, squirrel, hare, the gerbil, and coney (*Procavia*). Spotted hyena, red fox, wolf (not dog, Clutton-Brock, 1963), badger, marten, musteline, the Syrian bear (?), wild cat, and leopard number among the carnivores, while the bulk of the animals represented is composed of various ungulates: fallow deer (*Dama mesopotamica*), gazelle, wild goat, wild cattle, onager, and boar. Ecologically these species are partly woodland, party open country, and partly even desert or cliff forms (the gerbil and coney). They corroborate the local situation of wooded upland to the northeast and perennial streams or ponds with fringing forests and widespread open country on the Pleistocene dunes of the coastal plain to the south. They also show that diversified hunting played an important role in the Natufian economy.

The cave floor included a mass of flint implements, waste materials, broken and occasionally charred animals bones, burials, and some crude stonework, possibly associated with the interments. Although architecture is lacking at this site, house foundations have been uncovered at Ain Mallaha (Perrot, 1960). Some thirty-nine burials have been found, the dentition of which shows excessive wear and a very high frequency of abscesses of the premolars. Dahlberg (1960 and personal communication) believes this indicates a gritty diet, probably with a dominance of cereals or other coarse vegetable foods.

[6] The present day climate has a January mean temperature of 13°C., a July mean of 27°C., and an annual precipitation of 625 mm. falling almost exclusively during the three winter months. The natural vegetation of the area is mediterranean woodland.

The technological inventory contains, in part, a number of implements common to the Upper Paleolithic: backed blades, burins, massive scrapers, rough picks, together with naturalistic carving in bone and stone. Great numbers of microliths, and at certain other sites, also bone spear points, harpoons, fish-hooks, pins, needles, and awls recall certain Mesolithic innovations. Novel for the Natufian in general, however, are lustrous sickle-blades (sawtoothed varieties appearing in the Upper Natufian), some blades with bone hafts, as well as celts, mortars, and pestles. Flint arrowheads figure among the few innovations of the Upper Natufian. However the total assemblage shows a distinct shift of relative proportions between a dominance of Paleolithic artifacts in the Lower, of more characteristically Neolithic artifacts in the Upper Natufian.

The Natufian culture represents one of the most interesting transitional assemblages of the Near East. Partly dated at 8840 B.C. (GL-70, Zeuner, 1963, p. 31; see also younger dates in Kenyon, 1959) from the Middle Natufian underlying Jericho, the populations in question were at least semisedentary judging by cave occupancy or house habitation in the open. Intensive exploitation of the different ecologic niches of the natural environment is a well-established characteristic, recalling both the earlier, Middle Sebilian and the later European Mesolithic. Simultaneously, cereal agriculture was very probably known, judging by the abundant presence of all so-called agricultural implements, and the dietary value of gritty foods as suggested by the dentition. Unfortunately no plant foods have been found so far, and he suggested domestication of pig, goat, and cattle at one of the Judean cave sites is unverified (Reed, 1959). But the beginnings of plant and animal domestication must be conceived of at a stage and.in a setting such as that of the Natufian or the broadly contemporary Karim Shahirian of Iraq.

ECOLOGY OF A VILLAGE-FARMING COMMUNITY: JARMO, NORTHEASTERN IRAQ

The townsite of prehistoric Jarmo is located on a bluff at some 770 m. above sea level in the rolling hill country of the Kurdish foothills of northeastern Iraq.[7] The village appears to have been occupied more or less continuously for about a quarter of a millennium shortly after 7000 B.C., judging by a wide scatter of radiocarbon dates

[7] By extrapolation from other climatic stations in the area the January mean temperature is about 6.5°C., the July mean 29°C., the annual precipitation about 630 mm., falling predominantly in winter. The natural vegetation is that of a mediterranean woodland.

(Braidwood, Howe *et al.*, 1960; see also the ecological synthesis of Braidwood and Reed, 1957).

Jarmo

The irregular terrain is a consequence of dissection of late Pleistocene silts by steep-sided stream valleys and gullies. An intermittent stream, probably perennial before the destruction of the natural vegetation, has partially destroyed the western end of the site by undercutting. During the period of settlement (Wright, 1952), the site was located at about 36 m. above this stream bed, which probably formed the major water supply of the village.

Botanical remains at Jarmo include both domesticated and wild emmer and einkorn wheat, domesticated two-row barley as well as acorns, pistachio nuts, lentils, the field pea, and blue vetchling.

Faunal materials include the remains of domesticated goat and pig (the latter in the upper strata of the site only, Reed, 1961), as well as a fair number of wild animals representing the hunting booty of the community. Species listed are red fox, wolf, gazelle, wild cattle, red and roe deer, wild sheep, boar, and onager (?).[8] Great masses of terrestrial snails (*Helix salomonica*) are present together with some fresh-water crabs and fish. The faunal selection suggests a woodland environment with some areas of open plain or rough country.

The village covered a total area of about 12,500 sq. m., and the cultural materials attain about 7 m. in depth. A good third of this area was never occupied by houses, and a total of 25 houses is estimated as the maximum size of Jarmo. This includes a guess on how much of the site has been destroyed by gullying. Each house presumably represented a family unit. Assuming a family-household size of 5 to 7 people, 25 houses would indicate a population of 125 to 175 people. The lower figure is probably closer to the truth. This is, incidentally, the average size of villages in the area today.

The architecture itself, although well-defined, was not pretentious. Sun-dried mud was employed, being laid in successive 10 to 15 cm. tiers often set on foundations of unmortared stone. The resulting mud-walled house had several rectangular rooms and was not unlike the local houses of today. The village had no regular plan, and consisted of simple houses, animal shelters, and storage buildings, without evidence of community buildings or social structure.

The technological inventory of Jarmo contains various flint implements, among which great quantities of sickle-blades and microliths made of a glassy volcanic rock, obsidian, are of most interest. The

---

[8] Statistical analyses were apparently not carried out.

obsidian was quarried some 500 km. to the north in the Lake Van area, indicating commercial contacts. Together with the celts are various grinding stones and bowls. Pottery only appears in the upper third of the settlement strata. Other items include bone needles, awls and the like, as well as evidence of reed matting. The technology is then a complex of domestic, of hunting, and of agricultural equipment. The dentitions of seven skeletons show signs of only moderate wear (Dahlberg, 1960), implying a less coarse diet than was common for the Natufian population. This probably points toward better preparation of vegetable foods, and possibly also to a fair proportion of meat in the dietary economy.

All in all, the farmers of the village of Jarmo appear to have established a well-balanced economy which, even at the stage of primitive subsistence agriculture, insured adequate local food resources for permanent habitation over two centuries. The absence of the plow, or for that matter plow animals, means that some form of hoe agriculture was practiced. Although cereals dominated in the sown fields, a number of vegetable crops may also have been grown. Domesticated animals, apparently present in good numbers after the local introduction of the pig, supplied a dependable and possibly appreciable meat fraction to the diet. Hunting was still an important economic trait, while gathering of wild plant and animal foods is substantiated by finds of acorns, pistachio nuts, and snails. Jarmo is indeed the prototype of agricultural villages which already dotted the moister hill country of the Near East by the close of the seventh millenium. The origins of the cultural landscape and the expression of man-land relationships at the food-producing level will be considered in the subsequent chapters.

THE DESICCATION THEORY OF AGRICULTURAL ORIGINS

Although the cultural and intellectual processes basic to the economic transition from food-collecting to food-producing are of no direct concern to the natural scientist, the abundant environmentalist theories on that topic certainly are. These theories are based on the belief that late glacial or early Holocene desiccation affected wide areas of the subtropics that had enjoyed pluvial conditions earlier during the Pleistocene. As a result, the former hunting populations of the deserts of northern Africa, Arabia, Iran, India, and Central Asia were allegedly expelled or forced to concentrate along sources of permanent water at springs or along permanent streams.

The oldest of these hypotheses can be associated with R. Pumpelly (1908, pp. 65-66), who excavated at the Neolithic site of Anau, southern Turkmenistan:

> With the gradual shrinking in dimensions of habitable areas and the disappearance of herds of wild animals, man, concentrating on the oases and forced to conquer new means of support, began to utilize the native plants; and from among these he learned to use seeds of different grasses growing on the dry land and in marshes at the mouths of larger streams on the desert. With the increase of population and its necessities, he learned to plant the seeds, thus making, by conscious or unconscious selection, the first step in the evolution of the whole series of cereals.

In the same sense Peake and Fleure (1927, p. 14) write:

> . . . men naturally turned their attention back to the old habit of collecting food as their hunting became less successful. In certain regions however, men were led towards a new idea; it occurred to them to produce food by the cultivation of edible plants.

Or as Childe (1929, p. 42) describes the same process in more detail:

> Enforced concentration in oases or by the banks of ever more precarious springs and streams would require an intensified search for means of nourishment. Animals and man would be herded together round pools and wadis that were growing increasingly isolated by desert tracts and such enforced juxtaposition might almost of itself promote that sort of symbiosis between man and beast signified in the word domestication.

For Childe, the resulting "emancipation from dependence on the whims of the environment" (1929, p. 46) was *the* impetus for the economic revolution ("Neolithic revolution") heralded by the invention of food-production. Toynbee (1935, Vol. I, pp. 304-5) adopted the same economic revolution and the same impetus as the "physical challenge" at the root of ancient Egyptian and Mesopotamian civilization, as well as for the origin of nomadic pastoralism (1935, Vol. III, pp. 10-12). Similar ideas persist in more recent revisions of both Childe and Toynbee.

There is no doubt today that the simple patterns envisaged by the theories of Pumpelly, Peake and Fleure, Childe, and Toynbee are archeologically not tenable, since the food-producing revolution does not seem to have taken place in the deserts. In the hill country of western Asia, where the decisive steps of local agricultural invention were probably undertaken, the desiccation theory loses all meaning. These are well-watered regions where pluvial-interpluvial oscillations would not seriously reduce wild game resources. The native vegetation of the Near Eastern highlands is a subtropical or warm-temperate woodland under modern climatic conditions. Streams from the higher country provide abundant, perennial waters or at least did so before the catastrophic impact of deforestation and soil erosion in historical times. Even if rainfall changes had occurred, they would only have carried limited ecological implications in an area of varied topography and with numerous local ecological niches. Instead, temperature changes may have had greater importance, particularly, in late glacial times when the cold highlands once more became habitable. Such changes would therefore have enlarged the area of suitable lands at about the time of agricultural origins.

In conclusion, the previous review of paleoclimatic information does not suggest any incisive changes in the late glacial and early Holocene record of western Asia, and the climatic changes that did take place certainly did not follow a simple pattern of progressive desiccation. It seems unlikely that the cultural innovation of the Near Eastern hearth of domestication was associated with any dramatic ecological changes at the close of the Pleistocene. Instead, a bountiful natural environment with a fortuitous assembly of suitable domesticates presumably favored the geographic location of the Near Eastern hearth.

30

The Significance
of Agricultural Dispersal
into Europe
and Northern Africa

ECONOMIC MOTIVES FOR AGRICULTURAL DISPERSAL

Following the establishment of village farming communities in the Near Eastern woodlands during the seventh millennium, a rapid dispersal of agricultural techniques in the Old World began about 5000 B.C. Food-production had been introduced into much of Europe, the Mediterranean region, and northern Africa within a millennium after the Hassunan farmers of Iraq (*ca.* 5900-5200 B.C.) had begun to colonize the grasslands fringing the Near Eastern woodlands. By that time also agricultural communities are archeologically verified for southern and eastern Asia, although their origins are not yet understood. Much of this dispersal of technological features may have been associated with some form of ethnic movement, at least on a local scale. Yet the archeological evidence does not substantiate direct relationships between the earliest European or North African farmers and their contemporaries in the Near East. Needless to say, the routes and rates of dispersal are imperfectly understood. But the evidence available does permit a tentative discussion of possible motives for cultural diffusion and of the new ecologic problems arising from introduction of agriculture into new environments.

The subsistence economy of primitive agriculture may be fundamental in explaining this obscure migration of races, peoples, economies, or ideas. Primitive agriculture today is largely confined to the tropical woodlands, and it would be unwarranted to equate prehistoric Near Eastern farmers with modern Bantu populations in

Africa or Quechua peoples in South America. But in a very general way some of the traits of shifting agriculture (see chaps. 9 and 23, and Watters, 1960, with references) may have been common to the prehistoric Near East as well. The very extensive use of land, left to fallow for periods of up to 30 years and more, may have led to periodic overpopulation in some areas occupied to the limit of their possibilities with existing technology. Colonization of fresh lands must have been an appealing economic solution for groups living near the margins of the *oikoumene*.

Another factor possibly associated with early agricultural dispersals was chronic overpopulation. The invention and adoption of new tools and a new economic subsistence would inevitably promote a great increase of population, made possible by the increased and more reliable food supply. Food production per unit area was much greater, and even during a bad crop year a certain amount of food would be available. There would not be complete dependence on the seemingly erratic movements and biological cycles of wild game. Life and death were no longer so precariously balanced; birth rates increased and infant mortality declined. However, when a settlement reached its new carrying-capacity at agricultural subsistence, the rate of increase had to level off, either by emigration or by higher mortality rates. As long as fresh lands remained such as could be cleared and planted by fire or wooden or stone tools, the agriculturists probably sent out daughter colonies that supplanted or absorbed the sparsely settled food-gathering populations.

It would seem that the practice of primitive agriculture as well as chronic overpopulation could account for agricultural dispersals. Non-economic motives are not necessarily excluded, but it is also unnecessary to resort to an environmental factor such as climatic change.

One major environmental theory does in fact attempt to explain agricultural dispersals through the agency of "Postglacial desiccation" in the Old World subtropics. In particular, Childe (1925, 1929) thought that progressive postglacial desiccation in the Near East continued after the first general and successful steps to plant and animal domestication. The food-producing peoples expanded rapidly in numbers but were faced with a deteriorating environment. Desiccation eventually caused or, as others have put it more cautiously, played a part in the rapid expansion of Neolithic peoples and cultures into the moister lands of Europe. So, for example, Coon (1939, pp. 60-65) suggested that the dispersal of the Mediterranean race from the Near East (partly associated with early agriculture) was a consequence of desiccation incident upon the close of the Pleistocene. Childe (1958, p. 54) still suggests that Postglacial desiccation of the Sahara promoted ethnic and cultural movements from North Africa into Spain in the fifth millennium. In practice these arguments have no foundation in fact. As discussed below, the period after *ca.* 5,000 B.C. was on the moist side in many of the areas in question. Furthermore, agricultural expansion was not confined to Europe but also extended to the semiarid landscapes of western Asia and many arid regions of northern Africa.

SAUER'S THEORY OF AGRICULTURAL DIFFUSION FROM SOUTHEAST ASIA

C. O. Sauer (1952) has suggested that the primary hearth of first domestication was found in Southeast Asia, while several minor or "derivative centers of additional domestications" are postulated for India, the Near East, Ethiopia, and West Africa. Following E. Hahn, Sauer believes that vegetative planting of tropical tuber plants may have been the easiest and earliest step to domestication, and that this abstract concept subsequently spread throughout the Old World. Characteristic of this southeast Asian hearth in Burma and adjacent areas were household animals such as dog, pig, fowl, duck, and goose; non-seed, vegetative root plants such as banana, aroids, yams, sago, pandans, bamboo, sugar cane, and breadfruits. Postulated for the derived Indian-Himalayan center are plants such as the millets, pulses, gourd, jute, and other fibre plants, as well as some herd animals: goat, sheep, zebu, buffalo and yak. The only herd animals allotted to the Near East are cattle, together with seed plants such as the wheats, grape, olive, fig, and flax. For Ethiopia, these additional domesticants are thought to include teff, sorghum, cotton, and sesame; for West Africa, the guinea hen, yam and bush pig.

Although Sauer's ideas are only presented as a suggestive sketch, the sequence of archeological events presently available from the Near East and India (see Sankalia, 1962) suggest that agricultural origins were an essentially independent innovation in the former area. Unfortunately, archeological evidence is not yet available to substantiate or dispute the existence of advanced fishing and planting populations along the coasts and river valleys of southeastern Asia during the last millennia of the Pleistocene.

An elaboration of Sauer's dispersal concepts is due to H. von Wissmann (1957), who outlined several successive nuclei of cultural diffusion in their geographical characteristics: (*a*) the tropical forests along the rivers and coasts of the Bay of Bengal: fishers and planters; (*b*) the forest-steppe and savanna of India: seed-planters with millets and oil plants; (*c*) the subtropical highlands of Afghanistan: sheep and goat farmers; (*d*) the small oases of the highlands and deserts of western Iran and Armenia: wheat and barley farmers. From here the alleged wave of dissemination entered Mesopotamia, which is not considered a center of agricultural origins but rather of technological invention.

Several elements stressed by Wissmann are: (*a*) Each nucleus sent out waves of dissemination which may have caught up with each other or may have lost some cultural elements upon entering a different climatic region. Such waves were taken over, transformed, or rejected depending on physical or human factors. (*b*) Major movement of cultures is postulated in the wooded steppes where the soil is rich and supposedly easy to work. (*c*) The movements are compared with Postglacial climatic fluctuations: (1) the Holocene thermal maximum (*ca.* 5500-3000 B.C.) may have permitted the spread of food production over the cold Central Asian mountain zone; (2) a moist spell in the third millennium may have established agricultural contacts, across the Central Asian deserts, possibly leading to the origins of horse nomadism. (*d*) The Postglacial rise in world sea level was responsible for "burying" the archeological remains of the presumed late Pleistocene fishers and shell gatherers of southeastern Asia through marine submergence or intensive alluviation in lower stream courses. Reduced floodplain alluviation after 4000 B.C., when modern sea level was attained, may have been related to the beginnings of settlement and rapid technological advance in the lower valleys of the Tigris-Euphrates and Nile.

Although Wissmann's views are interesting and deserving of attention, they go far beyond the available archeological evidence and can therefore only be rated as a hypothesis.

EUROPEAN CLIMATE DURING THE ATLANTIC PHASE

The original dispersal of agricultural traits in Europe coincides with the warm, moist Atlantic phase (*ca.* 5500-3000 B.C.). The Scandinavian Glacier had completely disappeared, and many mountain glaciers of the Alps were smaller than they are today while others disappeared. The botanical evidence suggests a considerably warmer summer climate than today's (see Firbas, 1949-52, Vol. I, p. 60 ff., 289 ff.; Lüdi, 1955; Iversen, 1960). So for example the altitudinal tree-

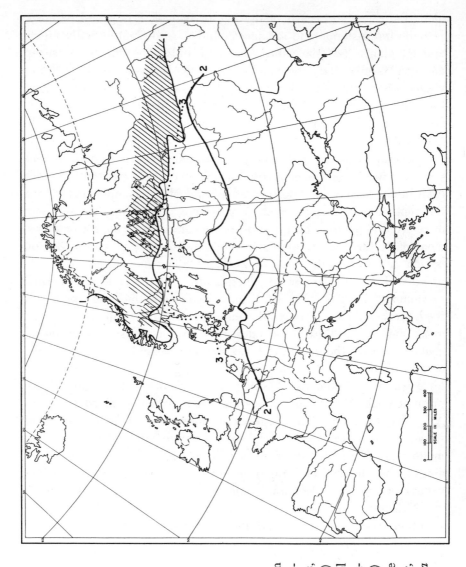

FIGURE 79.
Temporary northward migration of European plant species during the Atlantic (after Fries, 1963, and Walter, 1954). (1) Present northern limits of hazel (*Corylus avellana*), with extended Atlantic range, (2) present northern limits of the water chestnut *Trapa natans*, (3) Atlantic limits of *Trapa natans*.

limit was 200-300 m. higher than today's in the Scandinavian high-lands and in the Sudeten ranges, 300 m. higher in the northern and southern Alps. Various water plants and trees requiring considerable summer warmth occurred at higher elevations or at higher latitudes than is the case today. Tree pollen occurs in certain strata of bogs in the north European tundra, while plant fruits of now sterile peren-nials have been found on the Arctic islands. In fact a third of the 125 species of Spitsbergen do not reproduce under present climatic conditions. Massive oaks grew beyond the present limit of oak in northeastern Russia, while the hazel was found considerably north of its present distribution in Scandinavia (Fig. 79), and even the submediterranean wild grape (*Vitis silvestris*) thrived in southern Sweden. Particularly illuminating is a comparison of growing season temperatures at the northern limits of hazel (*Corylus avellana*) dis-tribution in Scandinavia (see accompanying tabulation):

Mean Temperature °C.	Apr.	May	June	July	Aug.	Sept.	Oct.
Former limit	0.3	5.5	11.7	13.7	11.8	7.8	1.7
Present limit	2.5	8.2	14.0	15.8	14.1	10.1	4.5
Difference	2.2	2.7	2.3	2.1	2.3	2.3	2.7

From this it may be concluded that summer temperatures in mid-latitude Europe were at least 2° C. warmer than they are today during the Postglacial thermal maximum. Evidence for warmer winter temperatures is contradictory and unconvincing so far. Maximum summer temperatures may only have been reached during the Sub-boreal (*ca.* 3000-800 B.C.), when the Alpine tree-line was at its highest, about 300-400 m. higher than the modern tree-limit (Lüdi, 1955). A greater melting of the world's glaciers may have occurred during the fourth millennium and the first half of the second millennium B.C., judging by glacio-eustatic sea-level fluctuations (see Fairbridge, 1961). At this time ocean surface waters may have been about 1° C. warmer than today's (see Emiliani, 1955a). Conditions were analogous to those of an interglacial maximum, although the time interval was com-paratively brief.

The forest composition of temperate Europe during the Atlantic was largely that of a mixed oak forest, with oak, elm, lime, ivy, and alder dominant in the western half of the continent, while pine played an important role farther east. Colonization of the drier lowland basins of central Europe by alder, spruce, and fir suggests that the Atlantic was considerably moister than today in much of mid-latitude Europe (Firbas, 1949-52, Vol. I, p. 290 f.). An extension of the forest into the present tundras and steppes is shown by Frenzel's (1960) palynological reconstruction of the Atlantic vegetation of European Russia.

ENVIRONMENTAL FACTORS INFLUENCING THE LOCATION OF EARLY
AGRICULTURAL SETTLEMENT IN EUROPE

A key environmental problem for early agricultural settlement in mid-latitude Europe concerns the physical attributes of the settled land: Did early colonization coincide with open grasslands, woodlands, or forest? Which soils and terrain were favored? Knowledge of the particular ecologic niches selected by agricultural colonists is useful both for assessing cultural adaptation and for explaining the observed patterns of dispersal.

Among the areas first settled by farming populations, the contemporary physical environment of central Europe is probably best understood. The culture in question is known as the early Danubian (Buttler, 1938; Narr, 1956), and dates from the fifth and fourth millennia. The Danubians were village farmers with a subsistence economy based on shifting agriculture. Three species of wheat, as well as barley, lentils, flax, beans, and peas were cultivated and presumably formed the staple diet, judging by the quantity of milling and pounding stones. Stone adzes were probably used for felling trees, hoes for tilling the fields. The cow was the common domesticated animal kept, with pig in second place. Sheep, goat, and dog were of minor importance. The refuse pits show evidence of hunting activity, with red and roe deer, boar, aurochs, and woodland bison as favored game. The Danubians occupied long rectangular, gabled houses of wood and wickerware, measuring 6 to 7 m. wide, and 15 to 40 m. long. Vertical posts supported the walls and roof. These structures suggest small clan dwellings, also serving the purpose of animal stalls. Various storage buildings were present. Individual villages, frequently abandoned and subsequently reoccupied, may have had 200 to 600 inhabitants. Animals were generally kept within a fenced enclosure surrounding the village.

The sites of the Danubian culture are very strictly limited to loess areas in the Low Countries, Germany, Poland, Austria, Czechoslovakia and Hungary (Fig. 80). No sites occur north of the margins

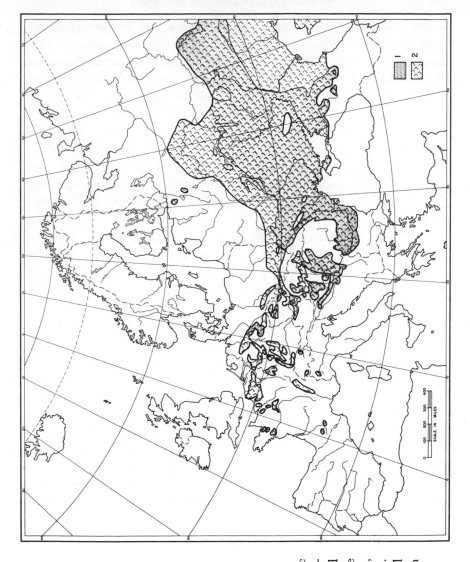

FIGURE 80.
Extent of loess and chernozemic soils in Europe. (1) Chernozems, degraded chernozems and kastanozems, (2) Loess; where not shaded, with braunerde, podsolic or semi-desert soils. Loess simplified after Frenzel (1959), soils after Ganssen (1957) and others.

445

of the Würm till. For the most part the warm, dry lowland plains or river terraces were selected, and within these, the loess areas (Gradmann, 1906, 1936). The natural vegetation of the central European loess lowlands has long been the subject of controversy. Gradmann (1933) argued that grasslands, parklands, or open woodlands were still widespread in late prehistoric times, and that such lands were optimal in terms of better soils, easier cultivation, good pasture, and more bountiful game. Others, including Nietsch (1939) and C. Schott (1939) have argued that more or less closed forests dominated even the drier basins, requiring clearance by felling or burning. Godwin (1944) was able to verify this second point of view in the case of England.

Palynological evidence (Firbas, 1949-52, Vol. I, p. 356 ff.) does not support widespread grassland or parkland during the Atlantic, even though the mixed oak woodlands on comparatively dry loess soils may have been lightly stocked. On account of the gradual decrease of *Artemisia* in the pollen record, Firbas believes that exposed bedrock, talus siopes, and stoney gravel or sand surfaces were colonized by tree vegetation late in the Holocene. Such natural gaps in the forest cover would obviously not have attracted settlers. Firbas concludes that the moister loess lowlands (wherever annual precipitation exceeds 500 mm. today) were occupied by closed mixed oak forests during the Atlantic, although the drier basins probably had a parkland or open woodland vegetation. Areas qualifying as comparatively dry are the interior basin of Bohemia-Moravia, the Elbe-Saale plain, the Upper Rhine basin, and the Hungarian plain.

Soil studies appear to substantiate Firbas' conclusions. Loess sediments are highly permeable and evaporate more soil moisture than any other sediment, so that loess soils are comparatively dry in the edaphic sense and do not favor tree growth. The climatically drier loess lowlands commonly have soils of the "degraded" chernozem type. Such chernozems originally developed under grassy vegetation with dry, warm summers—presumably during the continental climate of the Preboreal and Boreal. Subsequent woodland invasion during the moist, maritime Atlantic led to carbonate solution, increased acidity, and chemical weathering, with oxidation and some leaching (Scheffer and Schachtshabel, 1960, p. 275 f.; Wilhelmy, 1950). These soils prove the former existence of grasslands in certain dry basins, at least until the beginning of the Atlantic. Consequently, with local agricultural settlement well under way a millennium later (*ca.* 4500 B.C.), a fair amount of parkland or open woodland was available to the Danubian colonists in the south and east.

In overview, the earliest agricultural colonists entered the central European area during a period of optimal warmth and comparatively moist climate, increased rainfall more than compensating for increased evaporation. The settlements of the Danubian farmers are sharply restricted to loess sediments (Fig. 81), which obviously provided

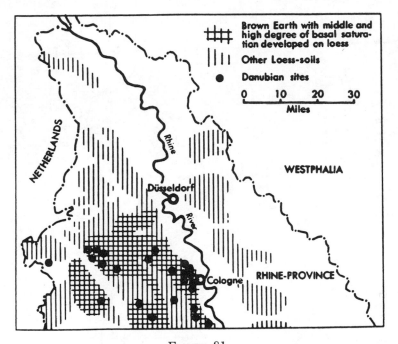

FIGURE 81.
Danubian sites and soil types in the northern Rhineland
(from K. J. Narr, 1956, copyright 1956 by the
University of Chicago Press, with permission).

greater soil fertility. At the same time, these often were areas with parkland vegetation and calcareous, chernozemic soils, or otherwise they had base-saturated forest soils under closely stocked mixed oak woodland. It is no mere coincidence that primeval settlement, loess, calcareous or basic soils, dry lowland basins, and comparatively open, oak parklands or woodlands should provide a common denominator for the earliest agricultural lands of mid-latitude Europe. Only at a later date, when less demanding crops such as rye, oats, or spelt had been developed, was colonization extended to the more acidic and partly leached forest soils. Swampy terrain and heavy waterlogged soils were only occupied at a somewhat later date.

The new agricultural lands of mid-latitude Europe (Fig. 82)

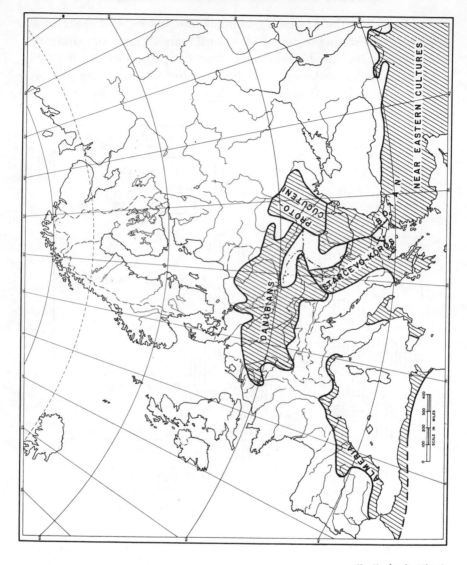

FIGURE 82.
Early village farming cultures in Europe and adjacent areas *ca.* 4000 B.C. Modified after Milojčić (1958), chronology based on Milojčić (1959) and more recent radiocarbon dates.

were not radically different from the subtropical or temperate wood-lands of Asia Minor and Greece, particularly during the warm Atlantic and Sub-boreal phases. Despite an increase in winter cold and summer moisture, the landscape of the new environments was different in degree rather than in kind. It was probably not accidental that the pioneer farmers of Europe should select the environment most like that of their cultural antecedents: not the humid lands of the west, nor the cool, poorly drained till plains of the north, nor yet the snowy plains or open steppes of the east. Rather, the more inter-mediate environment of the Balkan peninsula and central Europe provided the most compatible solution in terms both of climate and edaphic factors. Just as open woodlands had probably witnessed the birth of agriculture in the Near East, they also provided the setting to the first agricultural venture into higher latitudes.

However, the change in crop ecology was important. Winters were cool rather than mild, whereas summers were decidedly moist. The winter cold may have eliminated some winter crops from the array of domesticated plants, although "winter" wheat and barley are still frequently planted in autumn in much of central Europe today. Somewhere, however, the idea of spring sowing of mediter-ranean crops must have been experimented with and found to be expedient. Some of the evolution of new mutants and rapid hybridi-zation of wheat species in temperate Europe may have resulted from deliberate changes in plant ecology at the hands of man—just like those accompanying the deliberate cultivation of oats and rye on marginal soils and in cooler climates a few millennia later.

THE SAHARAN SUBPLUVIAL (CA. 5000-2350 B.C.)

Agricultural colonization of the Mediterranean Basin, in particular of the coasts of southern Europe and northwestern Africa, did not encounter appreciable environmental differences anywhere in the summer-dry subtropical woodland belt. The settlement of truly arid lands, such as the Sahara, did however require considerable ecological adaptation. Fortunately for the early agricultural colonists, the Saharan area enjoyed an abnormally moist climate during a time interval roughly synchronous with the Atlantic phase in Europe. The evidence in favor of a moister interval or subpluvial *ca.* 5000-2350 B.C. may be subdivided into three categories: faunal evidence, chiefly on the basis of rock-drawings; botanical evidence, both macrobotanical and paly-nological; and geological evidence, generally of a rather specific and detailed type.

The two oldest groups of rock pictures of the Sahara belong to a group of Mesolithic hunters and a nomadic livestock-raising culture of East Hamitic affinities (Rhotert, 1952; Lhote, 1959). Both of these peoples left a lucid record of themselves, their way of life, and the diverse natural fauna of now deserted Saharan highlands. The animals depicted include not only gazelles, antelopes, and ostrich, but a great number of representations show species now limited to the savannas of tropical Africa: elephant, both the single and two-horned rhinoceros, hippopotamus, and giraffe. The African elephant is a woodland or parkland biotype, requiring some 300-350 lbs. of green fodder daily (Bourlière, 1963). It may also be able to survive by digging for water. Requirements of the rhinoceros and hippopotamus are in the order of 200 lbs. Contrary to prevailing opinion, however, the hippo does not absolutely require open waters, but can live in grassland areas. The giraffe is seldom seen in the treeless steppes but prefers a parkland environment. Further faunal elements of the prehistoric Sahara include the crocodile, now surviving in miniature form in a few small perennial pools in some of the Saharan highlands, and the extinct Asiatic buffalo *Bubalus* (*Homoioceras*) *antiquus,* also known paleontologically from older deposits in the Maghreb and Cyrenaica.

Mauny (1956) has provided a valuable analysis of the former and present distribution of the four leading species (elephant, rhinoceros, hippopotamus, and giraffe) for the western Sahara. The writer (1958b) extended the study to the eastern Sahara, together with a survey of existing rainfall, water, and pasture conditions in those regions today. The subcontemporary distribution of both rhino and hippo was restricted to vegetation belts now receiving at the very least 150 mm. precipitation annually. This desert limit is 100 mm. in the case of the elephant and 50 mm. for the giraffe. None of these animals was commonly found in areas with less than several hundred millimeters precipitation, and obviously the local micro-ecology is of primary significance. But these theoretical values at least provide a general idea. On the basis of the rock drawings of various species, substantiated by ancient elephant remains in the Fayum or in the Erdi, a tentative attempt to reconstruct the approximate rainfall distribution for the period 5000-3000 B.C. is made in Figure 83. These hypothetical isohyets suggest increased precipitation in both the winter and summer rainfall provinces, rather than a northward shift of the Sahara. The marginal belts of semiarid vegetation shifted some 100-250 km. toward the core of the desert, while the highlands stood

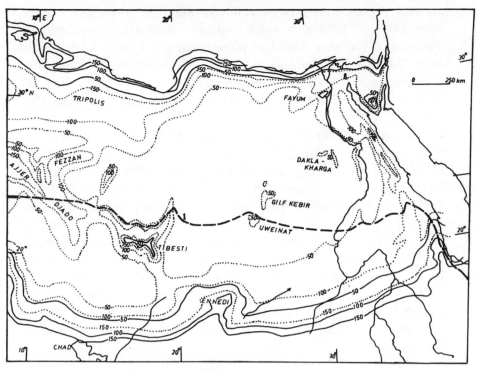

FIGURE 83.

Modern and mid-Holocene (*ca.* 5000-2000 B.C.) distribution of
annual precipitation in the central and eastern Sahara. Full lines
show modern isohyets (in mm.), dotted lines show same as deduced for the mid-Holocene. Heavy dashed line (1) shows
modern boundary between winter and summer rainfall regimes
(modified from Butzer, 1958b).

out as rather favorable reservoirs of life and water, rising above the
desert plains. They probably enjoyed an overlap of summer and
winter rains.

    Botanical evidence of such a subpluvial climate is available from
both the eastern and western Sahara. In the deserts west and east of
the Egyptian Nile there are numerous tree stumps of acacia, tamarisk,
and sycamore (*Ficus sycomorus*) which have been archeologically
dated as Badarian to Predynastic. They indicate a savanna-like vegetation, with small trees or copse at edaphically suited localities, e.g.,
wadi beds where water collects and ground water exists. Such stumps
up to 32 cm. in diameter and with roots up to 4.5 m. long have been
found to exist south of Luxor. In addition to literary sources there is

historical documentation on several Old Kingdom tomb and temple reliefs (Butzer, 1959b). A more abundant vegetation, resembling a dry savanna, probably flourished in northern and eastern Egypt from about 5000-2350 B.C. The core of the Libyan Desert would have been as lifeless as today. On the southern margins of the Sahara there is similar evidence of dead acacias (Murray, 1951), and although the dating is uncertain, they are quite possibly contemporary with those of Egypt. It is significant that such acacia stumps are as much as 30 of 40 cm. in diameter and sparsely set at about 3 to 5 per acre, indicating an open savanna some 200 km. farther north of the present limits of this same vegetation type.

In the western Sahara, pollen evidence is available from a number of early Neolithic sites. The rock shelter at Meniet in the Hoggar contains strata from which 87 pollen grains were identified by Quézel and Martinez (1958). Of these pollen, 56 per cent belong to arboreal species. In order of numerical importance they include: cupressaceae (largely Duprez's cypress), Aleppo pine (*Pinus halepensis*), evergreen oak, wild olive (*Olea laperrinei?*), hackberry (*Celtis australis*), the thorn bush *Zizyphus,* juniper, and tamarisk. Macroremains of *Zizyphus,* lotus, and hackberry help substantiate the pollen record, which further includes cereal, grass, sedge, and *Artemisia.* The uppermost stratum at Meniet has a C^{14} date of 3450 $\pm$ 300 B.C. (Délibrias *et al.,* 1959) and contains bones of *Bubalus antiquus.* Similar results were obtained from a sample of hyrax dung from Taessa in the Hoggar, at some 2200 m. elevation. Pollen (3,000 grains) included similar species together with pistachio and walnut. A C^{14} date of 2730 $\pm$ 300 B.C. was obtained for the dung. Scattered pollen grains were studied from sediments with cattle bones found below rock drawings in the Tassili (Quézel and Martinez, 1961). These grains included Aleppo pine, evergreen oak, and cypress. The evidence speaks for an open subtropical woodland or parkland at edaphically favored localities in the Saharan highlands.

Finally, the testimony of the rock drawings and biological evidence is substantiated by the local occurrence of geological sediments and organic alluvial strata suggestive of tirsified soils. Contemporary alluvial deposits frequently contain rich molluscan faunas. The evidence has been summarized by Monod (1963).

Another phenomenon suggesting more favorable ecological and hydrological conditions in the Sahara is the former level of the groundwater table. Artesian springs once functioned in several oases of the Libyan Desert in Neolithic times. Already in classical times, water had to be obtained from artificial wells. So, for example, at Kharga there are immense deposits of calcareous spring tufas in which Neolithic tools have been found in great numbers. They imply former agricultural subsistence around springs that disappeared millennia ago. Similar tufas or clay hummocks are known from other wells in southwestern Egypt (Murray, 1951). There is also evidence that the static groundwater table was much higher during the Neolithic, enabling nomadic cattle-herders to live there until perhaps the time of the Sixth Dynasty (2350 B.C.). A major factor responsible for decreased groundwater resources in the Sahara almost certainly has been the gradual depletion of "fossil" water derived from the Pleistocene pluvials (Knetsch *et al.*, 1963).

PREHISTORIC CATTLE-NOMADS OF THE SAHARA

Following the first agricultural colonization of the North African coasts in the fifth millennium B.C., settlement of the Sahara proved a challenge that could only be mastered by ecological adaptation. The response appears to have been the first verified example of nomadic pastoralism. The origins of the cattle-nomad culture are quite obscure. First recorded in southeastern Egypt and the central Saharan highlands, a point of origin in the Sudan would seem plausible (Rhotert, 1952). Yet the Sudanese Neolithic site of Shaheinab near Khartum, dated (average) 3253 ± 415 B.C. by radiocarbon, has evidence of domesticated goat or sheep only (Arkell, 1953). It has no apparent relationship to the cattle-nomad cultures.

Whatever their origin, the cattle cultures were dispersed through most of the Saharan highlands by the late fourth millennium: in the Red Sea Hills during the Nagada I of Egypt (C¹⁴ dates for the Nagada I are 3793 B.C., 3626 B.C., 3668 B.C.; see Libby, 1955), in the Fezzan of Libya (by 3445 B.C.; Mori and Ascenzi, 1959), and in the Tassili and Hoggar (C¹⁴ dates, 3450 B.C., 2730 B.C., 3070 B.C.; Délibrias *et al.*, 1959). Radiocarbon determinations are not yet available for the intervening areas. It seems that these cattle cultures had disappeared from most of the highlands by about 2000 B.C. (Fig. 84), giving a time range of *ca.* 4000-2000 B.C.

The apparent economic traits of these pastoralists have been discussed by Rhotert (1952) and Lhote (1959). Subsistence was based on cattle herds derived from local domestication of *Bos primigenius* (=*africanus*)—presumably somewhere in the middle Nile Valley. Lack of emphasis of the animals' udder in pictorial art suggests that

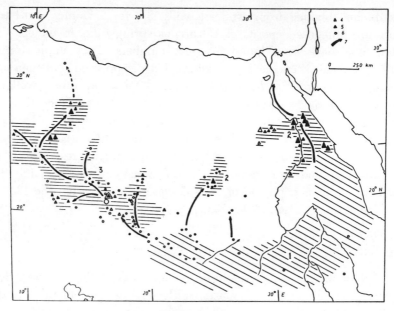

FIGURE 84.

Hunters and cattle nomads in the Sahara *ca.* 5000-2000 B.C. (1) possible extent of cattle herding cultures *ca.* 4000 B.C., (2, 3) domain of Mesolithic-type hunters *ca.* 4000 B.C., (4) rock drawings of the hunters, (5) rock drawings of both hunters and cattle nomads, (6) rock drawings of cattle nomads, (7) expansion routes of cattle nomads in 4th millennium. (from Butzer, 1958b).

meat rather than milk was the major form of exploitation. Domesticated sheep replace cattle in the Saharan Atlas and an overlap of sheep and cattle-raising is indicated in the Tassili region. Much game was hunted, probably reflecting local fusion with autochthonous food-collecting groups. Possibly, although not necessarily, these cattle-nomads were the users of the occasional grinding stones reported from different parts of the Sahara. This may indicate that cereals were known locally, a point suggested also by the pollen from Meniet. The strong concentration of archeological sites in wadi valleys and at existing or former groundwater localities suggests that settlement was largely confined to areas with available water—both for human and animal use. Caves were also occupied in some areas of the Tassili, Hoggar, and the Saharan Atlas.

No direct proof of nomadism is available for the Saharan cattle-herders. However, significant cultural associations have been shown with nomadic Kushitic or Eastern Hamitic groups of the Red Sea coasts of Egypt, the Sudan, and Ethiopia (Rhotert, 1952). The typical composite drawings of large cattle herds strongly suggests organized pastoralism. Also, the rapid dispersal of this culture through the Sahara may reflect a nomadic subsistence. With the erratic nature of the rainfall (even during the Atlantic subpluvial) and the sporadic distribution of water and pasture, it is unlikely that permanent or semipermanent habitation *could* have been practiced in any one area. It seems necessary to assume that adequate water and fodder could only be guaranteed by periodic movements, possibly into the better watered highlands or to permanent waterholes during the dry season, to ephemeral pastures among the foothills and on nearby alluvial plains during the episodic rains.

One may suspect that this very obvious case of adaptation of food production to an adverse environment had its origins in an agricultural community which gradually expanded or was displaced into marginal arid country where livestock-raising was more economical than cereal agriculture. Or, these same people selectively acquired cultural traits from agricultural populations in nearby, better watered areas. At any rate, planting played a very small role in an economy based primarily on meat animals. This contrasts with the contemporary village farmers of the Near East and Europe, among whom subsistence was primarily based on cereals.

In retrospect, the diffusion of food-producing traits into the arid zone, and in particular into the Sahara, was a case of cultural or technological adaptation to a new environment. Yet this dispersal was only made possible by the temporary improvement of the environment and resource base of the Saharan highlands during the Atlantic subpluvial. Not only did desiccation play no role whatever in agricultural dispersals after 5000 B.C., but instead the prevailing moister climate must have facilitated and perhaps motivated man's expansion over the world's greatest desert. In fact the spread of food-producing populations through the arid zone of the Old World followed close upon the migration of the Ethiopian faunas through the Sahara.

THE IMPACT OF FOOD PRODUCTION ON MAN-LAND RELATIONSHIPS

The impact of the new food-producing economies on the environment marks a rather significant change in man-land relationships. The million years of Pleistocene time had witnessed a very gradual development of technology and economic patterns permitting existence of the human species under most environmental conditions. Man had also begun to modify the biological world, even if only on a local scale. Now, with the spread of ecologically potent farming communities across the Old World, transformation of the natural environment began to leave great scars in the landscape—the areal importance of which almost everywhere increased with time and the continuity of which was assured by the persistence of human populations at ever higher technological levels. The major aspects of geographical interest include (a) an explosion of population, made possible by an improved subsistence economy, (b) physical transformation of the environment, particularly through decimation of the native flora and fauna and their partial replacement by non-indigenous domesticated species, and (c) the creation of a cultural landscape.

Population is essentially controlled by available food. Rapid demographic expansion has ensued upon several major, technological improvements of the food supply: (1) after the first invention of tool-manufacture, (2) after the invention of agriculture, (3) with the intensification of agricultural production accompanying urbanization, and in more recent times, (4) with the industrial revolution. C. O. Sauer (1947) described the history of man as a succession of higher and higher levels, each one brought about by discovery of more food, either through occupation of new territory or through increase in food-producing skill. When the maximum possible population is reached, population must level off, either by gradual convergence of birth and death rates, or by draining off the surplus into daughter colonies.

The introduction of a subsistence based on farming and herding would provide a greater and more stable food supply. A much smaller economic area could provide sufficient food for much larger communities. Domestic animals could be used for meat at most times of the year, while the highly productive cereal crops could be stored for the whole year following the harvest. There was no longer any need to move when the local supply of wild plant foods or of game was exhausted. Starvation no longer ensued when biological cycles reduced the local game population. Above all, the food supply was far more reliable, both in the course of the seasons, as well as during the passing of the years, so maintaining a much higher population level. Of course, exceptionally cold winters, drought years, crop and animal plagues, etc. would still exert a noticeable influence on the population curve. But man was becoming conspicuously less dependent on the vagaries of the environment.

Braidwood and Reed (1957) have discussed subsistence levels and modern ethnographic parallels, and suggested typical population densities of approximately 1 person per 100 sq. km. at the unspecialized Pleistocene food-gathering level, 5 per 100 sq. km. at the specialized late Pleistocene-early Holocene food-gathering level, 1,000 per 100 sq. km. at the early agricultural level, and 2,000 per 100 sq. km. at the early urban level. Obviously these are only meant to be orders of approximation, but the values help illustrate the degree of change involved.

The physical transformation of the natural environment was primarily the result of man's agricultural activities. Changes were originally confined to the biological sphere. The natural woodland or grassland vegetation was partly replaced by fields of wheat, barley, and vegetables. Such crops, originally native to a restricted area of western Asia, were to spread through most of the world, into lands where their very existence was often possible only through the caring hand of man. Species, which in natural competition shared minute ecological niches with countless other plants, now dominated acre upon acre of monocultures. Unconsciously agricultural or grazing activities favored certain local herbaceous plants by creating open spaces in woodlands, so increasing the importance of fire-tolerant plants in the course of slash-and-burn clearance. Similarly, new ecological niches were provided for a rash of new weed plants, whose original habitats and specific niches had been as insignificant as those of the cereals or vegetables.

The same can be said for the animal world. The wild fauna, with some exceptions, was decimated through a reduction of the natural habitat by cultivation, disturbance of breeding haunts, as well as improved hunting techniques by ever larger populations. Instead, the new farming populations tended select domesticated animals, thus enabling dispersal of certain species on a continental scale and causing drastic changes in the composition of the fauna. Certainly these qualitative and quantitative changes of flora and fauna required millennia, and the face of the earth was at first only altered locally. The cumulative effect over several millennia has, however, been significant and sometimes catastrophic.

The cultural landscape reflects intensive settlement with effective transformation of the biological environment through agricultural land use. With the introduction of village farming into an area, cultivated fields and biologically altered grazing areas began to dot the landscape. Architectural skills had improved and shelter requirements were met by construction of houses, stables, and storage huts. Individual farmsteads coagulated to form villages dispersed over the countryside. With incipient urbanization these man-made structures increased in size, number, and importance as towns and cities, market places, roads, bridges, fences, and the like were added. Irrigation and drainage schemes were implemented in marginal environments. Forests were removed for land clearance and timber, and grasslands plowed up. These innovations were often followed by such unpleasant corollaries as soil deterioration and soil erosion.

Although the record of man's early transformation of the physical into a cultural landscape is poorly preserved in the Old World subtropics, the case of mid-latitude Europe is better understood. The significance of forest clearance and crop cultivation by village-farming communities was first recognized in Denmark from the pollen records of the Sub-boreal by Iversen (1949). The earliest appearance of cereal pollen was accompanied by a rapid increase or the appearance of weed colonists such as *Artemisia, Rumex, Plantago,* and chenopodiaceae, with a corresponding decrease in mixed oak forest (Fig. 46). Such discontinuities were followed by temporary birch pollen maxima—common after forest fires—with subsequent increase of alder, hazel, and finally, oak. Evidence of burning is occasionally visible in the peat stratigraphy. Iversen explained these features through forest clearance by burning and felling, with subsequent livestock-grazing or cropplanting in the "opened" woodland. The fields were soon abandoned in the course of shifting cultivation, and so allowed to revert back to forest. Interestingly, open woodlands such as oak-birch forests on sandy soils showed little or no pollen discontinuity other than the presence of cereal and *Plantago* pollen. These show the existence of cultivation on plots available without recourse to intensive clearing.

This original picture of common, but not exclusive, slash-and-burn agriculture seems to be substantiated by the over-all archeological and palynological evidence in mid-latitude Europe (J. G. D. Clark, 1945; Firbas, 1949-52, Vol. I, p. 363 ff.). Fire was apparently not necessary in the more open landscapes. Tree-felling with stone axes was quite feasible, as recent experiments by Steensburg (1957) showed. Bark-peeling or girdling of trees was probably also an effective clearance method, particularly after brush and lighter growth had been removed through burning. An interesting form of semi-agriculture preceded true agricultural colonization in Denmark (Iversen, 1960, Troels-Smith, 1960). This Erteboelle culture may represent a contact culture, based largely upon stalled or tethered cattle. The animals were almost entirely fed with the foliage of elm, mistletoe, ivy, and ash. As a result there was a sharp reduction in elm pollen, formerly interpreted as a climatic change at the transition of the Atlantic to the Sub-boreal. A little wheat and barley was apparently grown, but there was no forest clearance worth speaking of. This example illustrates that the methods and significance of forest clearance by early agriculturists can hardly be generalized.

Prior to the first introduction of the ox-drawn plow from Mesopotamia into temperate Europe during the second half of the third millennium, soil preparation was made by hoe or digging stick. With such tools it is unlikely that most of the woodland soils yielded well for more than a year or two, requiring twenty or more years of fallow thereafter. Fertility must have been more enduring on the chernozemic soils, since recent plow agriculture without fertilization on the Ukrainian chernozems only required one fallow year in three. The exact nature of rapid soil depletion or yield reduction is complex, reflecting actual mineral depletion, rate of weed colonization, erosion resulting from soil structure changes, or humus destruction. The common symptom of sharply reduced yields probably results from a number of interacting factors.

Soil erosion was probably unimportant since cultivation was limited to the more productive lowland soils. Clearance and cultivation of hillsides was a late innovation in mid-latitude Europe. Deforestation or moderate grazing would not leave bare soil exposed for very long. Even in the Mediterranean region, in such an ancient land as the Lebanon, the commercial importance of lumber in historical times suggests that widespread deforestation was rather uncommon in prehistoric times. In fact Heichelheim (1956) and Darby (1956) emphasize that general deforestation and land deterioration even in the Mediterranean region fall largely within the two millennia of our own cra. It would therefore seem that early agricultural land use did not yet provoke its more unpleasant side-effects such as accelerated runoff, seasonally accentuated stream discharge, soil erosion, gullying, and gradual loss of soil moisture attendant upon the destruction or removal of humus. At any rate, both archeological and geological evidence to this effect is absent.

The preceding discussion of man-land relationships assumed that human populations automatically expand to the limit of resources available within a given technological framework. Such an assumption is of course questionable. Unfortunately the archeological data is inadequate for such evaluation of the underlying cultural patterns. Although less significant at the food-collecting level, efficiency of exploitation among technologically equivalent groups assumes considerable importance at the food-producing level. Was there a fundamental stability in the relationships of man to the exploitable resources of his habitat? Or, did local over-exploitation of resources already lead to temporary or semipermanent environmental crises? At the early agricultural level it would seem that a basic stability persisted, and with so much new land to occupy, it is possible that local over-exploitation was still uncommon. But the problem remains to be investigated more thoroughly.

31

Agricultural Settlement and Urban Origins in the Near Eastern Floodplains

THE NEAR EASTERN FLOODPLAINS DURING THE EARLY AGRICULTURAL SETTLEMENT

A new environmental situation for agricultural colonization was present in the alluvial valleys of the Tigris-Euphrates, the Nile, and at a later date, the Indus. In each of these areas rainfall is insufficient for crop-planting, but a regime of periodic annual floods provides ample moisture. In each case a hostile desert intervenes between the early village-farming communities of the wooded hill country. The seasons of available moisture vary as well: instead of mediterranean-type winter rainfall the flood season of the Tigris-Euphrates comes in late spring-early summer, that of the Nile and the Indus in late summer and early autumn. Consequently crop-planting must take place at different seasons, during the recession of the floods.

The original agricultural settlement of the Near Eastern flood-plains was no easy step for prehistoric man. Although the agricultural villages of the seventh and sixth millennia had sometimes tapped stream waters in the lower courses of highland streams or at oases, total readaptation was required for settlement on the floodplains. Planting had to be done at a different season, and the farmers had to learn to cope with seasonally declining water resources. Hoe or digging-stick cultivation was probably more difficult on muddy, heavy alluvial soils than it was with light, friable woodland soils. Possibly, the first colonists learned to broadcast seeds on wet alluvium, without prior working of the soil.

461

Not all of the staple crops developed under a winter rainfall regime did well with a floodwater regime on the alluvial plains. In fact einkorn wheat has not yet been found in ancient floodplain sites, while a new, six-rowed mutation of barley proved to be a successful adaptation to the same ecological change (Helbaek, 1960b). The new barley did very well on the rich alluvial soils and was not affected by the gradual salinization of the Mesopotamian lowlands following the introduction of irrigation. Emmer wheat and flax were salt intolerant, declined in importance, and were insignificant in lowland Iraq by the beginning of the historical era (Helbaek, 1960b). Similarly, many of the standard Near Eastern orchard crops did not thrive with the artificial ecology of the floodplains. Intead the date palm was cultivated, providing a (novel?) source of fruit and wood. In general, considerable cultural readaptation was achieved.

Another problem concerns the environment encountered by the first farmers in the Tigris-Euphrates and Nile floodplains shortly after 5000 B.C. Were the alluvial plains covered with jungle-like thickets and extensive swamps that required major clearance or drainage? Or could the floodplains be settled without technological improvement?

A combination of natural levees and seasonally inundated alluvial flats mark the lower courses of the Tigris and Euphrates and their many branches. Annual high water occurs in May and June when the snow meltwaters of Armenia combine with the spring rainfall maximum in Turkey. Depending on the synchronization of precipitation and temperature conditions in the high country, there may be appreciable floods. But the floods are generally irregular and highly variable from year to year, and consequently not dependable. Unlike the Nile, the Mesopotamian waters contain salt in solution which is concentrated in the soil through evaporation on irrigated land. In Egypt the hazard of salinization is largely confined to the coastal marshlands of the Delta.

With perennial water available along the river banks and in backswamp areas, the Mesopotamian floodplains would support a woodland vegetation without human interference. In the natural state tamarisk and poplar were probably characteristic trees of the levee embankments, in association with oleander, acacias, and thorny *Zizyphus* species. The seasonally inundated flats would be parched by late summer, permitting a vegetation of brush and grasses only. Beyond the flooodplain, on the desert uplands or on the ancient river terraces, plant growth was limited to desert or semidesert shrub.

Like the Tigris-Euphrates lowlands, the Nile north of the Egyptian-Sudanese border moves across an alluvial floodplain. The summer monsoon begins in Ethiopia during May, and the lower Nile reaches its flood peak in September. When the floodwaters recede, the levees are immediately left dry, although the lower-lying basins may remain inundated well into November. Backswamps were always localized in their occurrence, except in the northern Delta where swamps merge into brackish coastal lagoons, cut off from the open sea by sand bars. These characteristics of the Nile Valley have little in common with the jungle-thickets and endless papyrus swamps commonly postulated in the archeological literature (Passarge, 1940; Butzer, 1959b). The extent of perennial swamps and lakes in the Nile Valley was limited in prehistoric times, and as today, the greatest part of the plain consisted of seasonally flooded basins. Groves of acacia, tamarisk, sycamore, and Egyptian willow crowned the levees which were always available for permanent settlement. Papyrus swamps and quiet expanses of standing water with lotus, sedge, and reeds, and teeming with hippopotamus, crocodile, and a host of aquatic birds, were available. But these only constituted a small segment of prehistoric Egypt.

From the very beginning, man could take up his abode on the levees or on the desert margins of the Near Eastern floodplains. When the floodwaters receded he could throw his crop seeds on the wet mud of the alluvial flats or graze cattle and other herd animals on the lush grasses and brush vegetation. By the time the waters rose again, the harvest had long been gathered and livestock could be pastured on the levees or on the outer peripheries of the alluvium. Physical conditions in the Nile Delta were equally good (Butzer, 1959b), and the myth of a delta rapidly expanding seaward in historical times is as unfounded in the case of the Nile as in the case of the Tigris-Euphrates (Lees and Falcon, 1952).

Granting that drainage was not an acute problem for the prehistoric colonists of the Near Eastern floodplains, irrigation certainly was. The technological aspects of simple basin irrigation appear to have been mastered in the fourth millennium, and similar methods have remained in use until the construction of dams and barrages within the last century. The technique is as follows. The alluvial flats are naturally divided into a maze of irregular basins of variable size, resulting from abandoned levee ridges, small distributary branches, and abandoned stream channels. Depending on their elevation, these natural basins drain off successively as the flood begins to recede, unless the waters are temporarily retained through human efforts.

Dry season reservoirs can be artificially created by breaching the levees, allowing uncontrolled local flooding, and then subsequently damming-in the waters. These can be released later on and allowed to flow into the fields as required. Inscriptions, dating from the earliest historical times, confirm the significance of irrigation by the third millennium.

Settlement in the Near Eastern floodplains began before 4500 B.C. In the case of Egypt, the archeological evidence is confined to cemeteries, villages, and towns located on the desert edge. However settlement sites are far too few when compared with the many cemeteries. This shows that as early as 4000 B.C. most of the Egyptian population already lived on sites located within the floodplain. In Mesopotamia, sites are known both from the desert edge and the floodplains.

EARLY URBANIZATION IN THE NEAR EASTERN FLOODPLAINS

Agricultural colonization of the alluvial valleys of the Tigris-Euphrates and Nile was followed by a rapidly increasing population and the development of an intensive cultural landscape. Sporadic evidence suggests the presence of occasional overgrown villages with at least 10,000 inhabitants, e.g., Merimde on the western edge of the Nile Delta, during the later fifth millennium (see Butzer, 1960b, with references). The first copper tools are verified from Mesopotamia during the Ubaid culture (*ca.* 4300-3500 B.C.), from Egypt during the Badarian (*ca.* 4000 B.C.). Wooden, ox-drawn plows had been introduced in both areas during the late fourth millennium, and are referred to by some of the earliest written documents. Urban communities—with differentiation of labor and function—appeared in both of these areas and in the Indus Valley by 3000 B.C. All in all, the centuries preceding the dawn of history witnessed the establishment of metallurgy, irrigation, plow agriculture, and the first towns. This was the technological prelude to the literate floodplain civilizations of the Near East.

The innovations of the fourth millennium are probably epitomized in urban origins, so much so that Childe (1929, 1958) interjected some unfortunate socio-historical ideas into the archeological interpretation, introducing the concept of an "urban revolution." Childe correlates urbanization with the establishment of metallurgical industries, on grounds that the manufacture of copper or bronze tools would require a specialized craftsman. In this way the self-sufficiency of small farming communities would break down, while new economic pursuits would concentrate on mining, manufacturing, and distributing finished products. The new class of part-time or full-time artisans would require support by other members of the community, so that the local agricultural surplus had to be made available to the families of the non-food-producing metal-workers. Childe envisages this evolution as the crucial step from a classless "barbarian" social order based on kinship, to a class society, based on division of labor or function.

Objectively reviewed, the "urban revolution" was not a revolution but a stage of economic transition. It was not necessarily associated with metal-working, and urbanization itself was but one symptom of a complex cultural change. The beautifully decorated and well-fired pottery of the Halafian culture of northern Iraq (*ca.* 5200-4300 B.C.) leaves no doubt of craft specialization. One can then envisage part-time specialization and incipient division of labor at a much earlier date. The subsequent 1,500 years witnessed a number of technological innovations in the floodplains of the Near East, which possibly accompanied a considerable cultural and intellectual ferment. Some of the economic aspects of this change may have been as follows:

a) Production of food surplus, made possible by (1) more intensive, irrigation agriculture, (2) more fertile, perennially productive alluvial soils, and (3) improved sowing and harvesting techniques, culminating with the innovation of the animal-drawn plow.

b) Development of commercial contacts to obtain raw materials (flint, stone, metal in lower Mesopotamia, metal in the Nile Valley) from more distant areas, so requiring an exchange of commodities. Possibly food products and pottery craftsmanship formed the major export items.

c) Development of functional centers in some villages, designed for food storage and exchange, and possibly for manufacture or redistribution of finished products.

If these assumptions are correct, craftsmen, tradesmen, and clerks would be a necessary corollary. The craftsmen would include potters, metal and wood-workers, builders, and artists. The tradesmen on the other hand would perform the vital function of transferring raw materials or finished products from mines or quarries, town or village, on foot or on donkey, by land, river, or sea. The clerks would presumably handle the bureaucratic aspects of granary administration, regulation of raw material import, marketing, and outside commercial relationships. Given such prerequisites some villages—by accident, location, or ambition—outstripped their neighbors and assumed the

role of functional centers. These increasingly important foci of bureaucratic organization were necessary in an economy with large-scale,
planned surplus farming, commerce, and industry. Urbanization would
therefore be the culmination of the technological and economic
changes outlined. The terms "town," "city," or "urban" would be
applicable to such a center of organized and complex activity whenever an appreciable segment of the population was employed in crafts
or industries. The role of the bureaucracy would increase gradually,
and ultimately included community organization of drainage and
irrigation, of planting and harvesting, of town, harbor, and road-
building, of property demarcation and judicial settlements. From
this evolved a complex social elite of scribes, politically or militarily
endowed secular officials, and artistic and ritually oriented priests.
Childe's original emphasis of the significance of urban civilization is
justified in this more restricted sense. It should be remembered, however, that this brand of urbanism is strictly molded to the economic-
geographic character of the Near Eastern floodplains (Wittfogel, 1956).

THE SIGNIFICANCE OF URBANIZATION FOR MAN-LAND
RELATIONSHIPS

Urban origins on the Near Eastern floodplains had a greater affect
on man's relations with his fellow beings than on his relations with
his environment (Adams, 1960a, 1960b). The earlier steps of agricultural invention were accompanied by an increasing breadth or intensity
of environmental exploitation, associated with an improved technological inventory and a new means of subsistence. Urbanization, although
based on changes in exploitation of the environment, was accompanied
by the development of new institutions and a complex social structure,
freeing man even further from dependence on his immediate environment (Adams, 1960a, 1960b).

One of the leading results of urbanization was the development of
more balanced economies, based upon food surplus and food exchange,
and probably fostering diversification as well as specialization of
subsistence. In this way, organizational activity could offset aperiodic
calamities such as killing frosts, low or destructive floods, or locust
plagues. Hence the vagaries of the environment were of ever less
influence on the human population level.

A second major effect of urbanization was the development of
trade as an important enterprise. Some forms of commerce must have
existed even during the Paleolithic, but organized economic exploita-

tion of raw materials in distant lands became significant now. Surface ore deposits were mined extensively, and raw materials were frequently transported a 1,000 kilometers or more to distant centers of manufacturing. Complex marketing arrangements arose between town and village, farmer and herder, leading to a high degree of economic interdependence, and in some areas, political "unification."

A third ecological impact stemmed from the accelerated technological and cultural progress resulting from a division of labor and function. Manufactured products became widely accessible, while better tools permitted greater agricultural production. Community efforts such as irrigation and drainage, distribution of water, and engineering projects of various kinds all became possible. In some areas, such as the Nile Valley, complete political and economic centralization ensued. But the maze of city-states in lowland Mesopotamia provides an excellent counter-example to the concept that irrigation civilizations require centralized control.

Each of these immediate consequences of urbanization contributed to man's capacity to alter the face of the earth. The cultural landscape of the floodplain kingdoms had almost attained the status of a man-made environment by the beginning of the historical era. Wide adjacent tracts were exploited for mineral resources such as gold, silver, copper, tin, and amber, or forest products such as lumber, firewood, and charcoal. With the advent of political megalomaniacs, wars of conquest, slave-hunting and revolutions led to recurrent devastations of both the cultural and physical landscape. This then sets the patterns which have remained characteristic to the present day: man's interactions with the environment have been largely obscured by the social and cultural products of man.

RETROSPECT ON THE SIGNIFICANCE OF THE ENVIRONMENT FOR PREHISTORIC MAN

The preceding chapters have attempted to study man-land relationships during several stages of Old World prehistory. In a final overview we can turn first to the potential spheres of environmental influence on man:

a) *Human distribution.* (1) Warmth and clothing: Early hominids may have been limited to the tropics through physiological adaptations of the species to such environments. Low temperatures, which could only be counteracted by some sort of clothing and the use of fire may have excluded early hominids from higher latitudes. Late Pleistocene colonization of subarctic environments may have followed technological improvements guaranteeing better heat control. It seems possible to observe a step-by-step settlement of higher latitudes in the course of the Pleistocene. (2) Water and food resources: Prehistoric man was never found very far from sources of permanent surface water and animal or vegetable food. This partially excluded him from desert environments. (3) Environmental change: Major changes of the environment, such as the expansion of deserts or ice sheets, certainly promoted changes in the distribution of population. Less significant ecological changes in the range forest-woodland-grass-land-semidesert may have had similar, although less well-defined effects.

b) Population level. The size of Pleistocene communities was probably limited by the food supply available within their hunting territory. Climatic fluctuations or other biological factors controlling local animal population or plant productivity should have strong repercussions on the human population level. Although proof is obviously next to impossible, it remains likely that environmental control (in terms of average carrying capacity) and environmental vicissitudes (in terms of non-seasonal fluctuations of the food supply) were rather significant in determining the regional population level. Similarly, human population levels must have varied strongly from one environment to another.

c) Biological and cultural evolution. Much has been said but little convincingly proven of environmental influences on biological and cultural evolution. Environmental changes may have accelerated biological evolution during the early Pleistocene. But it has not been possible to demonstrate *general* validity for the analogous concept of environmental change and cultural innovation. None of the climatic changes attending the close of the last glacial can be genetically related with cultural innovation, either in the case of the European Mesolithic or in the case of Near Eastern agricultural origins. Possibly a more careful distinction should be made between cultural innovation and economic adaptation, at least for the better understood phases of prehistory.

d) Economic traits. The significance of the environmental setting of a community for its technological inventory, way of life, and subsistence economy must have been enormous in prehistoric times. It would be fascinating to know just how dietary economy, clothing, habitation, raw materials, etc. were adapted to particular environments at different cultural levels. Yet, during at least the Pleistocene, the archeological record does not provide a sufficiently coherent picture of man's economic life. Only with greatly improved cultural interpretation of archeological sites will it be possible to say more than trivia about man-land interactions at the Paleolithic level. Although modern ethnology has contributed significantly in this direction, much more needs to be done. The preceding discussions of prehistoric subsistence patterns and of adaptations to new environments show how incomplete and tentative much of our present information is. But the tentative picture that emerges is nevertheless interesting and often provocative. It is here that much remains to be done and gained.

RETROSPECT ON THE IMPACT OF MAN ON THE ENVIRONMENT

At the food-collecting level man was present in small numbers only, with limited technological skills. Combining the results of the paleo-ecological survey of the last chapters with Heizer's (1955) review of relevant ethnological data, the following possible patterns of environmental modification can be outlined:

a) *Vegetation change through human use of fire*. Fire may have been used as an aid in hunting or to promote vegetative growth, both of species palatable for man and species favored by game. In areas of vigorous forest growth such burnings may have favored the dominance of certain species, or at least temporarily disturbed the climax forest patterns. In areas of marginal tree growth frequent burning may have replaced woodland by grassland vegetation, or at least favored grassy vegetation out of all proportion to the available climatic and soil resources. Such regional or local vegetation changes may have effected the humus content and type of soils, and they could certainly alter the water balance of the soil. But they could hardly have had any effect on regional climates—even today man-made modifications of rural climate are quite negligible on air temperatures and precipitation except on a microclimatic level (see Thornthwaite, 1956).

b) *Vegetation change through accidental spread of plant species*. Unintentional and accidental spread of uncultivated plants in the wake of man's wanderings may have led to minor and localized changes in vegetation composition. Certain heliophytic local or foreign species, particularly certain weed colonists would find new ecological niches as a result of vegetation clearance near a settlement or in any area affected by deliberate burning. Similarly, plant seeds or nuts carried as food could become scattered and grow spontaneously near settlement sites.

c) Faunal changes through hunting activity. Selective hunting or conscious sparing of certain animals for dietary or cultural reasons could lead to changes of faunal composition and equilibrium. Hunting pressure may also have led to local movements or even to migration of animal groups, and man will certainly have altered the animal biomass significantly on occasion. Whether or not local or total extinction of species was indeed the result of prehistoric hunting practices remains questionable.

At the food-producing level man's impact on the environment became more significant and tangible. Activities were no longer confined to modification of the biological world but also began to affect the abiotic surroundings. These spheres of influence can be enumerated as follows:

a) Forest clearance. With the establishment of agricultural economies, primary forest clearance, plot-burning, and livestock-pasturing assumed a functional role in settlement. Conscious large-scale destruction of the native vegetation was now no longer incidental or local in occurrence, but characteristic. Deliberate eradication of non-useful plant species by farmers and herders probably began to assume importance as cultural biases toward the environment were formed.

b) Deliberate introduction of domesticates. Little needs to be added here to the discussion of how cultivated plants and domesticated animals were introduced to new lands or favored in their natural habitats. Selective favoring of economically useful plants may also have been locally extended to species not traditionally included among the domesticates: oak, ash, elm, etc. used for animal feeding.

c) Soil alteration and soil erosion through land use. Agricultural use of the soil inevitably led to changes in soil humus, structure, and over-all chemistry—changes partly matched by addition of fertilizer. Soil erosion was presumably less important in late prehistoric times than today, although it remained a potential danger wherever deforestation, cultivation, or overgrazing were practiced or hillsides and uplands.

The cultural transformation of the environment that followed in the wake of agricultural dispersal was concomitant with the beginnings of the cultural landscape. The new patterns of land use were gradually intensified as a result of increasing population density and technological advancement. And with the establishment of urban civilizations on the Near Eastern floodplains we cross the threshold of the historical era.

The relations of man to the land in prehistory are, as yet, poorly understood. But, with the growth of interdisciplinary interest for the many kinds of problems involved, a fuller understanding is bound to emerge—an understanding of man, his evolution, his cultural traits, and his environment.

Bibliography

AARIO, L, and H. JANUS
  1958. *Biologische Geographie*. Braunschweig: G. Westermann.
ADAM, K. D.
  1951. "Der Waldelefant von Lehringen," *Quartär*, 5: 79-92.
  1953. "Die Bedeutung der altpleistozänen Säugetierfaunen Südwestdeutschlands für die Gliederung des Eiszeitalters," *Geol. Bavarica*, 19: 357-63.
  1954. "Die Zeitliche Stellung der Urmenschen-Fundschicht von Steinheim an der Murr innerhalb des Pleistozäns," *Eiszeitalter und Gegenw.*, 4-5: 18-21.
  1961. "Die Bedeutung der pleistozänen Säugetier-Faunen Mitteleuropas für die Geschichte des Eiszeitalters," *Stuttgarter Beitr. zur Naturkunde*, 78: 1-34.
ADAMS, R. M.
  1960a. "Factors Influencing the Rise of Civilization in the Alluvium." In C. H. Kraeling and R. M. Adams (eds.), *City Invincible*, Chicago: University of Chicago Press, pp. 24-34.
  1960b. "Early Civilizations, Subsistence, and Environment," In *ibid.*, pp. 269-95.
AGER, D. V.
  1963. *Principles of Paleoecology*. New York: McGraw-Hill.
AHLMANN, H. W.
  1924. "Le niveau de glaciation comme fonction de l'accumulation d'humidité sous forme solide," *Geografiska Ann.*, 6: 223-72.
AITKEN, M. J.
  1961. *Physics and Archaeology*. London and New York: Interscience.
ALIMEN, H.
  1957. "Secteur Francais." In "Livret Guide de l'Excursion N_1 (Pyrenees)," *5th Int. Congr. INQUA* (Madrid-Barcelona), pp. 78-89.
ANDERSEN, S. T.
  1961. "Vegetation and its Environment in Denmark in the Early Weichselian Glacial," *Danmarks Geol. Undersoegelse*, series II, no. 75.
ANDERSEN, S. T., H. DE VRIES, and W. H. ZAGWIJN
  1960. "Climatic Change and Radiocarbon Dating in the Weichselian Glacial of Denmark and The Netherlands," *Geol. en Mijnbouw*, 39: 38-42.
ANDREW, G.
  1948. "Geology of the Sudan." In J. D. Tothill (ed.), *Agriculture in the Sudan*, London: Oxford University Press, pp. 84-128.

472

ANTEVS, E.
  1925. "Retreat of the Last Ice Sheet in Eastern Canada," *Geol. Survey Canada,* Mem. 146.
  1952. "Valley Filling and Cutting," *Jour. Geol.,* 60: 375-85.
ARAMBOURG, C.
  1952a. "La Paléontologie des vertébrés en Afrique du Nord française," *19th Int. Geol. Congr. (Algiers), Monographie région.*
  1952b. "The Red Beds of the Mediterranean Basin," *Proc. Pan-Afr. Congr. Prehist.* (Nairobi, 1947): 39-45.
  1955. "Le gisement de Ternifine et l'Atlanthropus," *Bull. Soc. Préhist. Franç.,* 52: 90-95.
  1962. "Les faunes mammalogiques du Pleistocene circumméditerranéen," *Quaternaria,* 6: 97-109.
ARAMBOURG, C., J. ARÈNES, and G. DEPAPE
  1952. "Sur deux flores fossiles quaternaires d'Afrique du Nord," *C. R. Acad. Sci.,* 234: 128-30.
ARAMBOURG, C., and M. ARNOULD
  1949. "Note sur les fouilles paléontologiques exécutées en 1947-8 et 1949 dans le gisement villafranchien de la Garet Ichkeul," *Bull. Soc. Sci. Nat. de Tunisie,* 2: 149-57.
ARAMBOURG, C., and L. BALOUT
  1952. "Du nouveau à l'Ain Hanech," *Bull Soc. Hist. Nat. Afrique Nord,* 43: 152-59.
ARKELL, A. J.
  1949a. "The Old Stone Age in the Anglo-Egyptian Sudan," *Occ. Papers Sudan Antiq. Serv.,* No. 1.
  1949b. *Early Khartoum.* London: Oxford University Press.
  1953. *Shaheinab.* London: Oxford University Press.
ARNEMAN, H. F., and H. E. WRIGHT
  1959. "Petrography of some Minnesota tills," *Jour. Sedimentary Petrol.,* 29: 540-54.
ARRHENIUS, G.
  1952. "Sediment Cores from the East Pacific." In H. Pettersson (ed.), *Reports of the Swedish Deep Sea Expedition 1947-1948,* Goeteborg: Elanders, Vol. 5, fasc. 1.
ASTRE, G.
  1937. "Faune des steppes froide à spermophile et climats du Pleistocene superieur aux Pyrénées," *Bull Soc. Géol. Franç.,* 7: 59-68.
AXELROD, D. I.
  1960. "The Evolution of Flowering Plants." In S. Tax (ed.), *Evolution after Darwin,* Chicago: University of Chicago Press. Vol. 1, pp. 227-305.
BAAS, J.
  1932. "Eine frühdiluviale Flora in Mainzer Becken," *Zeitschr. Botanik,* 25: 289-371.
BAGNOLD, R. A.
  1954. *The Physics of Blown Sand and Desert Dunes* (2d ed.). London: Methuen.
BAKER, F. S.
  1944. "Mountain Climates of the Western United States," *Ecol. Mon.,* 14: 229-43.
BAKKER, J. P.
  1957. "Quelques aspects du problème des sédiments corrélatifs en climat tropical humide," *Zeitschr. Geomorph.,* 1: 3-43.

BALOUT, L.
   1955. *Préhistoire de l'Afrique du Nord.* Paris: Arts et Métiers Graphiques.
BANDI, H. G.
   1944. "Nochmals die Frage: Überwinterte das Rentier?" *Ann. Soc. suisse Préhist.,* 35: 113-18.
BANDI, H. G., and J. MARINGER
   1952. *Kunst der Eiszeit.* Basel: Holbein.
BANNISTER, B.
   1963. "Dendrochronology." In BROTHWELL and HIGGS, 1963, pp. 162-76.
BARAT, C.
   1957. "Pluviologie et aquiolimétrie dans la zone intertropicale," Dakar: *Mém. Inst. Franç. d'Afrique Noire,* 49.
BARKER, H.
   1958. "Radiocarbondating: Its Scope and Limitations," *Antiquity,* 32: 253-63.
BARTHOLOMEW, G. A., and J. B. BIRDSELL
   1953. "Ecology and the Protohominids, *Amer. Anthropologist,* 55: 481-88.
BATE, D. M. A.
   1940. "The fossil Antelopes of Palestine in Natufian (Mesolithic) Times," *Geol. Mag.,* 77: 418-33.
   1955. "Faunas of Quaternary deposits in Cyrenaica." In McBURNEY and HEY, 1955, pp. 274-91.
BATES, M.
   1953. "Human Ecology," In A. L. Kroeber, (ed.), *Anthropology Today, an Encyclopedic Inventory,* Chicago: University of Chicago Press, pp. 700-13.
BAUD, C. A.
   1960. "Dating Prehistoric Bones by Radiological and Optical Methods," *Viking Fund Publ. Anthropol.,* 28: 246-64.
BAUER, A.
   1955. "Über die in der heutigen Vergletscherung der Erde als Eis gebundene Wassermasse," *Eiszeitalter und Gegenw.,* 6: 60-70.
BAULIG, H.
   1935. *The Changing Sea-Level.* London: G. Philips.
BAUMHOFF, M. A.
   1963. "Ecological Determinants of Aboriginal California Populations," *Univ. Calif. Publ. Amer. Arch. Ethnol.,* 49: 155-236.
BERG, H.
   1949. "Beziehungen zwischen Temperatur- und Niederschlagsanomalien (Bemerkungen zur Eiszeittheorie)," *Rev. Geofisica pura e applicata,* 14: 1-16.
   1957. *Solar-terrestrische Beziehungen in Meteorologie und Biologie.* Leipzig: Geest and Portig.
BIBERSON, P.
   1961a. "Le cadre paléogéographique de la préhistoire du Maroc atlantique," Rabat: *Publ. Service des Antiquités du Maroc,* Mém. 16.
   1961b. "Le Paléolithique inférieur du Maroc atlantique," *ibid.,* Mem. 17.
BIRDSELL, J. B.
   1953. "Some Environmental and Cultural Factors Influencing the Structuring of the Australian Aboriginal Populations," *Amer. Naturalist,* 87: 171-207.
BIROT, P.
   1954. "Problèmes de morphologie karstique," *Ann. de Géog.,* 63: 161-92.
   1960. "Le cycle d'érosion sous les differents climats," *Curso de altos estudos geográficos,* Universidade de Brazil, Vol. 1.
BISHOP, W. W.
   1963. "The Later Tertiary and Pleistocene in Eastern Equatorial Africa,

with Implications for Primate and Human Distributions," *Viking Fund Publ. Anthropol.*, 36: 246-75.

BISHOP, W. W., and M. POSNANSKY
1960. "Pleistocene Environments and Early Man in Uganda," *Uganda Jour.* 24: 44-61.

BLACK, R. F.
1950. "Permafrost." In P. D. Trask (ed.), *Applied Sedimentation*, New York: J. Wiley, pp. 247-75.
1954. "Permafrost—a Review," *Bull. Geol. Soc. Amer.*, 65: 839-56.
1959. "Geology of Raddatz Rockshelter, Sk 5, Wisconsin," *Wisconsin Archeologist* (Milwaukee), 40: 69-82.

BLACK, R. F., and W. S. LAUGHLIN
1964. "Anangula: a geologic interpretation of the oldest archeologic site in the Aleutians," *Science*, 143: 1321-22.

BLANC, A.C.
1935. "Sulla fauna quaternaria dell'Agro Pontino," *Atti Soc. Tosc. Sci. Nat.* (Pisa), *Proc. Verb.*, 44: 108-10.
1936. "La stratigraphie de la plaine côtière de la Basse-Versilia (Italie) et la transgression flandrienne en Méditérranée," *Rev. Géogr. phys. Géol. dyn.*, 9: 129-62.
1942. "Variazoni climatiche ed oscillazioni della linea de riva nel Mediterraneo centrale durante l'era glaciale," *Geol. der Meere u. Binnengewässer*, 5: 137-219.
1957. "On the Pleistocene Sequence of Rome. Paleocologic and Archaeologic Correlations," *Quaternaria*, 4: 95-109.

BLANC, A. C., H. DE VRIES, and M. FOLLIERI
1957. "A First C14 Date for the Würm Chronology on the Italian Coast," *Quaternaria*, 6: 83-93.

BLANC, G. A.
1921. "Grotta Romanelli, Stratigrafia dei depositi e natura e origine di essi," *Arch. Antropol. Etnolog. di Firenze*, 50: 65-103.

BLENK, M.
1960. "Ein Beitrag zur morphometrischen Schotteranalyse," *Zeit. f. Geomorph.* (N.S.), 4: 202-42.

BOISSE DE BLACK, Y.
1951. *Les glaciations de l'Auvergne.* Aurillac: Imprimerie Moderne.

BOND, G.
1946. "The Pleistocene Succession near Bulawayo," *Occ. Paper Nat. Mus. Southern Rhodesia*, 12: 104-15.
1957. "The Geology of the Khami Stone Age Sites," *Occ. Paper Nat. Mus. Southern Rhodesia* (Vol. 3), 21a: 44-55.
1963. "The Pleistocene in Southern Africa with Implications for Primate and Human Distribution," *Viking Fund Publ. Anthropol.*, 36: 308-34.

BOND, G., and J. D. CLARK
1954. "The Quaternary Sequence in the Middle Zambezi Valley," *South Africa Arch. Bull.*, 9: 115-30.

BONIFAY, E.
1956. "Les sédiments détritiques grossiers dans les remplissages des grottes: méthode d'étude morphologique et statistique," *Anthropologie*, 60: 447-61.
1957. "Age et signification des sols rouges méditérranéens en Provence," *C. R. Acad. Sci.*, 247: 3075-77.

BONIFAY, E., and P. MARS
1959. "Le Tyrrhénien dans le cadre de la chronologie quaternaire méditérranéenne," *Bull. Soc. Géol. Franç.* (ser. 7), 1: 62-78.

BORDES, F.

    1953. "Essai de classification des industries 'Moustériennes,'" *Bull. Soc. Prehist. Franç.*, 50: 457-66.

    1961a. "Typologie du paléolithique ancien et moyen," *Publ. Inst. Préhist., Univ. de Bordeaux, Mém.* 1, 2 Vol.

    1961b. "Mousterian cultures in France," Science, 134: 803-10.

BOUCHUD, J.

    1954. "Le renne et le problème des migrations," *Anthropologie*, 58: 79-85.

BOULE, M., E. CARTAILHAC, R. VERNEAU, and L. DE VILLENEUVE

    1906-19. *Les Grottes de Grimaldi (Baoussé-Roussé).* Monaco and Berlin: Friedlaender. 2 vol.

BOULE, M., and L. DE VILLENEUVE

    1927. "La Grotte de l'Observatoire a Monaco," *Arch. Inst. Paléont. Humaine* (Paris), mém. 1.

BOURLIÈRE, F.

    1963. "Observations on the Ecology of some Large African Mammals," *Viking Fund Publ. Anthropol.*, 36: 43-54.

BOSWELL, P. G. H.

    1952. "The Pliocene-Pleistocene Boundary in the East of England," *Proc. Geol. Assoc.*, 63: 301-15.

BRAIDWOOD, R. J.

    1957a. "Means towards an Understanding of Human Behavior before the Present." In *The Identification of Non-artifactual Archeological Materials*, Washington, D.C.: Nat. Acad. Sci.—Nat. Res. Council Publ. 565, pp. 14-16.

    1957b. "The Old World: Post-Palaeolithic." In *ibid.*, pp. 26-27.

    1958. "Near Eastern prehistory," *Science*, 127: 1419-30.

    1960a. "Levels in prehistory: a model for the consideration of the evidence." In S. Tax (ed.), *Evolution after Darwin*, Chicago: University of Chicago Press, Vol. 2, pp. 143-51.

    1960b. "Preliminary Investigations Concerning the Origins of Food-Production in Iranian Kurdistan," *Advancement of Science*, pp. 214-18.

    1961. *Prehistoric Men* (5th ed.). Chicago: Chicago Nat. Hist. Mus.

BRAIDWOOD, R. J., and B. HOWE

    1962. "Southwestern Asia beyond the lands of the Mediterranean Littoral," *Viking Fund Publ. Anthropol.*, 32: 132-46.

BRAIDWOOD, R. J., B. HOWE, et al.,

    1960. "Prehistoric Investigations in Iraqi Kurdistan," *Studies in Ancient Oriental Civilizations* (Chicago), Vol. 31.

BRAIDWOOD, R. J., B. HOWE, and C. A. REED

    1961. "The Iranian Prehistoric Project," *Science*, 133: 2008-10.

BRAIDWOOD, R. J., and C. A. REED

    1957. "The Achievement and Early Consequences of Food-Production: a Consideration of the Archeological and Natural-Historical Evidence," *Cold Springs Harbour Symposia on Quant. Biology*, 22: 19-31.

BRAIN, C. K.

    1958. "The Transvaal Ape Man Bearing Cave Deposits," *Transvaal Mus. Mem.*, 11: 32-48.

BRANDTNER, F.

    1956. "Lösstratigraphie und paläolitische Kulturabfolge in Niederösterreich und den angrenzenden Gebieten," *Eiszeitalter und Gegenw.* 7: 127-75.

BRELIE, G. VAN DER

    1955. "Die Pollenstratigraphie im jüngeren Pleistozän," *Eiszeitalter und Gegenw.*, 6: 25-38.

BREUIL, H.
1950. *Four Hundred Centuries of Cave Art.* Montignac: Centre d'Études et de Doc. Préhist.

BREUIL, H., and L. KOSLOWSKI
1931-32. "Étude de stratigraphie paléolithique dans le nord de France. La Vallée de la Somme," *Anthropologie,* 41: 449-88; 42: 27-47, 299-314.

BRINKMANN, R.
1956. "Tertiär und alt-Quartär in den nordwestlichen Keltiberischen Ketten," *Stille Festschrift, Deutsche Geol. Ges., Geol. Verein., und Paläontol. Ges.,* pp. 77-84.

BRINKMANN, R., K. O. MÜNNICH, and J. C. VOGEL
1960. "Anwendung der C-14 Methode auf Bodenbildung und Grundwasserkreislauf," *Geol. Rundschau,* 49: 244-53.

BROECKER, W. S., and J. L. KULP
1956. "The Radiocarbon Method of Age Determination," *Amer. Antiquity,* 22: 1-11.

BROECKER, W. S., and E. A. OLSON
1960. "Radiocarbon from Nuclear Tests," *Science,* 132: 712-21.

BROEGGER, A. W.
1926: *Kulturgeschichte des norwegischen Altertums.* Leipzig: Harrassowitz. (Translated by V. H. Günther.)

BROOKS, C. E. P.
1949. *Climate Through the Ages* (2d ed.). London: E. Benn.

BROTHWELL, D. R.
1961. "The People of Mt. Carmel," *Proc. Prehist. Soc.,* 27: 155-59.

BROTHWELL, D. R., and E. S. HIGGS (eds.)
1963. *Science in Archeology.* London: Thames and Hudson.

BROWN, C. A.
1960. *Palynological Techniques.* Baton Rouge: private print.

BROWN, R. J. E.
1960. "The Distribution of Permafrost and Its Relation to Air Temperature in Canada and the U.S.S.R.," *Arctic,* 13: 163-77.

BRUNNACKER, K.
1958. "Zur Parallelisierung des Jungpleistozäns in den Periglazialgebieten Bayerns und seiner östlichen Nachbarlander," *Geol. Jahrb.,* 76: 129-50.
1960. "Zur Kenntnis des Spät—und Postglazials in Bayern," *Geologica Bavarica,* 43: 74-150.

BRYAN, K.
1941. "Pre-Columbian Agriculture in the Southwest as Conditioned by Periods of Alluviation," *Ann. Assoc. Amer. Geog.,* 31: 219-42.

BRYAN, K., and L. L. RAY
1940. "Geologic Antiquity of the Lindenmeier Site in Colorado," *Smithsonian Misc. Coll.,* Vol. 99, No. 2.

BRYSON, R. A., and J. A. DUTTON
1961. "Some Aspects of the Variance Spectra of Tree Rings and Varves," *Ann. New York Acad. Sci.,* 95: 580-604.

BÜDEL, J.
1944. "Die morphologischen Wirkungen des Eiszeitklimas im gletscherfreien Gebiet," *Geol. Rundschau,* 34: 482-519.
1950a. "Das System der klimatischen Morphologie," *Abh. deut. Geographentags* (München, 1948), München: Amt für Deutsche Landeskunde, pp. 65-100.
1950b. "Die Klimaphasen der Würmeiszeit," *Naturwiss.* 37: 438-49.

1951a. "Die Klimazonen des Eiszeitalters," *Eiszeitalter und Gegenw.,* 1: 16-26.

1951b. "Klima-morphologische Beobachtungen in Süditalien," *Erdkunde,* 5: 73-76.

1952. "Bericht über klimamorphologische und Eiszeitforschungen in Niederafrika," *ibid.,* 6: 104-32.

1953. "Die "periglazial"—morphologische Wirkungen des Eiszeitklimas auf der ganzen Erde," *ibid.,* 7: 249-66.

1954. "Klima-morphologische Arbeiten in Äthiopien im Frühjahr 1953," *ibid.,* 8: 139-56.

1958. "Die Flächenbildung in den feuchten Tropen und die Rolle fossiler solcher Flächen in anderen Klimazonen," *Abh. deut. Geographentags* (Würzburg, 1957), Wiesbaden: F. Steiner, pp. 89-121.

1960. "Die Frostschutt-Zone Südost-Spitzbergens," *Colloquium Geographicum* (Bonn), Vol. 6.

1961. "Die Abtragungsvoränge auf Spitzbergen im Umkreis der Barentsinsel auf Grund der Stauferland-Expedition 1959/60," *Abh. deut. Geographentags* (Cologne, 1961), Wiesbaden: F. Steiner, pp. 337-75.

1963. "Klima-genetische Geomorphologie," *Geographische Rundschau,* 15: 269-86.

BUTTLER, W.

1938. "Der donauländische und der westische Kulturkreis der jüngeren Steinzeit." In *Handbuch der Urgeschichte Deutschlands,* Berlin: W. de Gruyter, Vol. 2.

BUTZER, K. W.

1957. "Mediterranean Pluvials and the General Circulation of the Pleistocene," *Geografiska Ann.,* 37: 48-53.

1958a. "Quaternary Stratigraphy and Climate in the Near East," *Bonner Geogr. Abhl.,* 24: 1-157.

1958b. "Das ökologische Problem der neolitischen Felsbilder der östlichen Sahara," *Abhl. Akad. Wiss. Lit.* (Mainz), *Math.-Naturw. Kl.,* 1: 20-49.

1958c. "Russian Climate and the Hydrological Budget of the Caspian Sea," *Rév. canadienne de Géog.,* 12: 129-39.

1959a. "Contributions to the Pleistocene Geology of the Nile Valley," *Erdkunde,* 13: 46-67.

1959b. "Die Naturlandschaft Ägyptens während der Vorgeschichte und dem dynastichen Zeitalter," *Abhl. Akad. Wiss. Lit.* (Mainz), *Math.-Naturw. Kl.,* 2: 1-80.

1960a. "On the Pleistocene Shorelines of Arabs' Gulf, Egypt," *Jour. Geol.,* 68: 626-37.

1960b. "Archeology and Geology in Ancient Egypt," *Science,* 132: 1617-24.

1960c. "Dynamic Climatology of Large-Scale European Circulation Patterns in the Mediterranean Area," *Meteor. Rundschau,* 13: 97-105.

1961a. "Climatic Change in Arid Regions since the Pliocene," *Arid Zone Research* (UNESCO), 17: 31-56.

1961b. "Archäologische Fundstellen Ober- und Mittelägyptens in ihrer geologischen Landschaft," *Mitt. Deut. Archäol. Inst., Abt. Kairo,* 17: 54-68.

1961c. "Remarks on Soil Erosion in Spain (Abstract)," *Ann. Assoc. Amer. Geog.,* 52: 405.

1962. "Coastal Geomorphology of Majorca," *ibid.,* pp. 191-212.

1963a. "The Last "Pluvial" Phase of the Eurafrican Subtropics," *Arid Zone Research* (UNESCO), 20: 211-21.

1963b. "Climatic-Geomorphologic Interpretation of Pleistocene Sediments in the Eurafrican Subtropics," *Viking Fund Publ. Anthropol.*, 36: 1-27.

1963c. "Observaciones preliminares sobre la geologia y paleografia de los yacimientos acheulenses de Torralba y Ambrona (Soria)," *Excavaciones arqueologicas en España* (Madrid), 10: 8-19.

1964a. "Pleistocene Geomorphology and Stratigraphy of the Costa Brava Region, Catalonia," *Abhl. Akad. Wiss. Lit.* (·Mainz), *Math.-Naturw. Kl.*, 1: 1-51.

1964b. "Pleistocene Cold-Climate Phenomena of the Island of Mallorca," *Zeitschr. Geomorph.*, 9:7-31.

BUTZER, K. W., and J. CUERDA
1962a. "Coastal Stratigraphy of Southern Mallorca and Its Implications for the Pleistocene Chronology of the Mediterranean Sea," *Jour. Geol.*, 70: 398-416.

1962b. "Nuevos yacimientos marinos cuaternarios de las Baleares," *Notas y Comm. Inst. geol. y minero de España*, 67: 25-70.

BUTZER, K. W., and O. FRÄNZLE
1959. "Observations on Pre-Würm Glaciations of the Iberian Peninsula," *Zeitschr. Geomorph.*, 3: 85-97.

BUTZER, K. W., and C. L. HANSEN
1965. "Upper Pleistocene Stratigraphy of Egyptian Nubia and the Kom Ombo Plain," unpublished manuscript.

CAHEN, L.
1954. *Géologie du Congo Belge*. Liège: H. Vaillant-Carmanne.

CAILLEUX, A.
1942. "Les Actions éoliennes periglaciaires in Europe," *Mém. Soc. Géol. France* (N.S.), Vol. 21, No. 46.

CAILLEUX, A., and J. TRICART
1955. *Introduction à la géomorphologie climatique*. Paris: Centre de Documentation Universitaire (mimeographed).

1963. *Initiation a l'étude des sables et des galets*. Paris: Centre de Documentation Universitaire. Vol. I (text; preceded by Volumes II and III of tabular data, Paris, 1959.)

CAIN, S. A.
1944. *Foundations of Plant Geography*. New York: Harper.

CARPENTER, E. F.
1955. "Astronomical Aspects of Geochronology." In T. L. Smiley (ed.), "Geochronology," *Univ. Ariz. Phys. Sci. Bull.*, 2: 29-74.

CASTANY, G., and F. OTTMANN
1957. "Le Quaternaire marin de la Méditérranée occidentale," *Rev. Géog. phys. Géol. dyn.* (2d ser.), 1: 46-55.

CATON-THOMPSON, G., and E. W. GARDNER
1929. "Recent Work on the Problem of Lake Moeris," *Geog. Jour.*, 73: 20-60.

1932. "The Prehistoric Geography of the Kharga Oasis," *ibid.*, 80: 269-409.

1934. *The Desert Fayum*. London: Roy. Anthropol. Soc., 2 vol.

1939. "Climate, irrigation and early man in the Hadhramaut," *Geogr. Jour.*, 93: 18-38.

CHANEY, R. W.
1940. "Tertiary Forests and Continental History," *Bull. Geol. Soc. Amer.*, 51: 469-88.

CHANG, K. C.
1962. "China," *Viking Fund Publ. Anthropol.*, 32: 177-92.

CHARD, C. S.
  1960. "Routes to Bering Strait," *Amer. Antiquity*, 26: 283-85.
  1963a. "Wurzeln der amerikanischen Frühkulturen," *Saeculum*, 14: 170-78.
  1963b. "Implications of Early Human Migrations from Africa to Europe," *Man*, 152: 124-25.
CHARLESWORTH, J. K.
  1957. *The Quaternary Era*. London: E. Arnold, 2 vol.
CHAVAILLON, J.
  1960. "Précisions apportées à la chronologie quaternaire du Sahara nord occidental," *C. R. Somm. Soc. Géol. France*, 7: 182-83.
CHILDE, V. G.
  1925. *The Dawn of European Civilization* (7th ed., 1957). London: Routledge and Kegan Paul.
  1929. *The Most Ancient East* (4th ed., 1954). London: Routledge and Kegan Paul.
  1958. *The Prehistory of European Society*. Harmondsworth: Pelican.
CHOUBERT, G.
  1948a. "Sur l'âge des limons rouges superficiels du Maroc," *C. R. Acad. Sci.*, 227: 558-60.
  1948b. "Sur la nature des limons rouges superficiels du Maroc," *ibid.*, 639-41.
  1957. "L'étage moghrébien dans le Maroc occidentale," *Actos V. Cong. Int. INQUA* (Madrid-Barcelona, 1957), in press.
  1962. "Réflexion sur les parallelismes probables des formations quaternaires atlantiques du Maroc avec celles de la Méditérranée," *Quaternaria*, 6: 137-75.
CLARK, A. H.
  1954. "Historical Geography." In P. E. James and C. F. Jones (eds.), *American Geography, Inventory and Prospect*, Syracuse: Syracuse University Press (for the Assoc. Amer. Geog.), pp. 70-105.
CLARK, J. D.
  1954. *The Prehistoric Cultures of the Horn of Africa*. Cambridge: Cambridge University Press.
  1960. "Human Ecology During the Pleistocene and Later Times in Africa South of the Sahara," *Current Anthropology*, 1: 307-24.
  1963. "Prehistoric Cultures of Northeast Angola and Their Significance for Tropical Africa" (with an appendix on pollen samples by E. M. van Zinderen Bakker), *Museu do Dundo, Publ. Culturais*, No. 62, 2 vol.
CLARK, J. G. D.
  1945. "Farmers and Forests in Neolithic Europe," *Antiquity*, 19: 57-71.
  1952. *Prehistoric Europe: the Economic Basis*. London: Methuen.
  1953. "The Economic Approach to Prehistory," *Proc. Brit. Acad.*, 39: 215-38.
  1954. *Excavations at Star Carr: an Early Mesolithic Site at Seamer, near Scarborough, Yorkshire* (with palynological contributions by D. Walker and H. Godwin). Cambridge: Cambridge University Press.
  1957. *Archaeology and Society* (2d. ed.). London: Methuen.
CLUTTON-BROCK, J.
  1963. "The Origins of the Dog." In BROTHWELL and HIGGS, 1963, pp. 269-74.
COOK, S. F.
  1951. "The Fossilization of Human Bone: calcium phosphate, and carbonate," *Univ. Calif. Publ. Amer. Arch. Ethnol*, 40: 263-80.
  1960. "Dating Prehistoric Bone by Chemical Analyses," *Viking Fund Publ. Anthropol.*, 28: 223-45.

Cook, S. F., S. T. Brooks, and H. E. Ezra-Cohn
1962. "Histological Studies on Fossil Bone," *Jour. Paleontol.*, 36: 483-94.

Cook, S. F., and R. F. Heizer
1952. "The Fossilization of Human Bone: Organic Components and Water," *Univ. Calif. Arch. Survey Dept.*, No. 17.

Cooke, H. B. S.
1946. "Development of the Vaal River and Its Deposits," *Trans. Geol. Soc. South Africa*, 41: 243-59.
1958. "Observations relating to Quaternary Environments in East and South Africa," *Geol. Soc. South Africa*, Annexure to Vol. 40.
1962. "The Pleistocene Environment in Southern Africa." In D. H. S. Davis (ed.), *Ecology in South Africa*, Amsterdam: W. Junk.
1963. "Pleistocene Mammalian Faunas of Africa, with Particular Reference to Southern Africa," *Viking Fund Publ. Anthropol.*, 36: 65-116.

Coon, C. S.
1939. *The Races of Europe*. New York: Macmillan.
1962. *The Origin of Races*. New York: A. A. Knopf.

Corbel, J.
1961. "Morphologie périglaciaire dans l'arctique," *Ann. de Géog.*, 70: 1-24.

Cornwall, I. W.
1956. *Bones for the Archaeologist*. London: Phoenix House.
1958. *Soils for the Archaeologist*. London: Phoenix House.

Cotton, C. A.
1942. *Climatic Accidents in Landscape Making*. London: Whitcombe and Tombs.
1945. "The Significance of Terraces due to Climate Oscillations," *Geol. Mag.* 82: 10-16.
1949. *Geomorphology*. New York: J. Wiley.
1961. "The Theory of Savanna Planation," *Geography*, 46: 89-101.

Crusafont Pairó, M.
1960. "Le quaternaire espagnol et sa faune de mammifères—essai et synthèse," *Mammalia Pleistocaenica* (Brno), 1: 55-64.

Cuerda, J.
1957. "Fauna marina del Tirreniense de la Bahia de Palma," *Bol. Soc. Hist. Nat. de Baleares*, 3: 1-76.

Dahlberg, A. A.
1960. "The Dentition of the First Agriculturists (Jarmo, Iraq)," *Amer. Jour. Phys. Anthropol.*, 18: 243-56.

Dahlberg, A. A., and V. M. Carbonell
1961. "The Dentition of the Magdalenian Female from Cap Blanc, France," *Man*, 49-50.

Darby, H. C.
1956. "The Clearing of the Woodland in Europe." In Thomas, 1956, pp. 183-216.

Darlington, P. J.
1957. *Zoogeography, the Geographical Distribution of Animals*. New York: J. Wiley.

Davis, W. M.
1930. "Origin of Limestone Caverns," *Bull. Geol. Soc. Amer.*, 4: 475-628.

Dawson, E. W.
1963. "Bird Remains in Archaeology." In Brothwell and Higgs, 1963, pp. 279-93.

DEEVEY, E. S., M. S. GROSS, G. E. HUTCHINSON, and H. L. KRAYBILL
1954. "The Natural C¹⁴ Contents of Materials from Hard-Water Lakes," *Proc. Nat. Acad. Sci.* (Washington), 40: 285-88.

DEFFONTAINES, P.
1930. "Essai de géographie préhistorique de la Tchéchoslovaquie," *Anthropologie,* 40: 275-83.
1933. "Essai de géographie préhistorique du Limoussin et son pourtour sédimentaire," *Ann. de géog.,* 42: 461-76.

DE GEER, G.
1912. "A Geochronology of the Last 12,000 Years," *Proc. 11th Int. Geol. Congr.* (Stockholm, 1912), 1: 241-58.
1934. "Equatorial Palaeolithic Varves in East Africa," *Geografiska Ann.,* 16: 75-96.
1940. "Geochronologia Suecica principles," *K. Svenska Vetensk. Handl.* (ser. 3), Vol. 18, No. 6.

DEGERBOEL, M., and H. KROG
1959. "The Reindeer in Denmark: Zoological and Geological Investigations of the Discoveries in Danish Pleistocene Deposits," *Biol. Skrifter Danske Videnskabernes Selskab* (Copenhagen), Vol. 10, No. 4.

DÉLIBRIAS, G., H. HUGOT, and P. QUÉZEL
1959. "Trois datations de sédiments sahariens récents par le radiocarbone," *Libyca,* 5: 267-70.

DELPORTE, H.
1955. "L'industrie de Chatelperron et son extension géographique," *Congrès Préhist. de France* (Strasbourg-Metz, 1953) pp. 233-49.

DENEVAN, W. M.
1964. "The Aboriginal Settlement of the Llanos de Mojos, a Seasonally Inundated Savanna in Northeastern Bolivia," *Univ. Calif. Publ. Geog.,* in press.

DEVORE, I., and S. L. WASHBURN
1962. "Baboon Ecology and Human Evolution," *Viking Fund Publ. Anthropol.,* 36: 335-67.

DE VRIES, H., G. W. BARENDSEN, and H. T. WATERBOLK
1958. "Groningen Radiocarbon Dates II," *Science,* 127: 129-37.

DE VRIES, H., and A. DREIMANIS
1960. "Finite Radiocarbon Dates of the Port Talbot Interstadial Deposits in Southern Ontario," *Science,* 131: 1738.

DE VRIES, H., F. FLORSCHÜTZ, and J. MENÉNDEZ-AMOR
1960. "Un diagramme pollinique simplifié d'une couche de "gytjja" située à Poueyferré près de Lourdes," *K. Nederlandse Akad. Wetenschappen* (ser. B), 63: 498-500.

DIKAIOS, P.
1953. *Khirokitia.* London: Oxford University Press.

DONN, W. L., W. R. FARRAND, and M. E. EWING
1962. "Pleistocene Ice Volumes and Sea-Level Lowering," *Jour. Geol.,* 70: 206-14.

DONNER, J. J.
1963. "The zoning of the post-glacial pollen diagrams in Finland and the main changes in forest composition," *Acta Botanica Fennica,* No. 65.

DONNER, J. J., and B. KURTÉN
1958. "The Floral and Faunal Succession of Cueva del Toll, Spain," *Eiszeitalter und Gegenw.,* 9: 72-82.

DORF, E.
1955. "Plants and the Geologic Time Scale," *Geol. Soc. Amer., Spec. Paper* 62: 575-92.

DUBIEF, J.
1952. "Le vent et le déplacement du sable au Sahara," *Trav. Inst. Réch. Sahar.* (Algiers), 8: 1-44.

DUBOIS, C., and P. ZANGHERI
1957. "Palynologie de quelques sédiments tourbeux de le basse plaine du Po," *Bull. Serv. Carte Géol. (Alsace-Lorraine)*, 10: 145-50.

DÜCKER, A.
1937. "Über Strukturböden im Riesengebirge. Ein Beitrag zum Bodenfrost- und Lössproblem," *Zeit. deut. Geol. Ges.*, 89: 113-29.
1951. "Über die Entstehung von Frostspalten," *Schriften Naturw. Ver. Schleswig-Holstein*, 25: 58-64.

DUIGAN, S. L., with B. W. SPARKS
1963. "Pollen analyses of the Cromer Forest Bed series in East Anglia," *Phil. Trans. Roy. Soc. London,* (series B), 246: 149-202.

DURAND, J. H.
1959. "Les sols rouges et les croûtes en Algerie," *Serv. des Études Scient.* (Alger-Birmandreis).

DURHAM, J. W.
1950. "Cenozoic Marine Climates of the Pacific Coast," *Bull. Geol. Soc. Amer.*, 61: 1243-64.

DURY, G. H.
1959. *The Face of the Earth.* Harmondsworth: Penguin.

DYLIK, J.
1952. "The Concept of the Periglacial Cycle in Middle Poland," *Bull. Soc. Sci. Letters of Lodz, Cl. III., Sci. Math. Nat.*, 3: 1-29.
1956. "Coup d'oeil sur la Pologne périglaciaire," *Biuletyn Peryglacjalny*, 4: 195-238.

EISELEY, L. C.
1955. "The Paleo Indians: Their Survival and Diffusion." In "New Interpretations of Aboriginal American Culture History," *75. Anniv. Vol. Anthropol. Soc. Washington,* pp. 1-11.

ELISSÉEFF, V.
1960. "Das Paläolithikum Nordostasiens." In A. Varagnac (ed.), *Der Mensch der Urzeit,* Dusseldorf and Cologne: E. Diederichs, pp. 116-40.

ELTON, C.
1946. The Ecology of Animals (2d ed.). London: Methuen.

EMILIANI, C.
1954. "Temperatures of Pacific Bottom Waters and Polar Superficial Waters during the Tertiary," *Science,* 119: 853-55.
1955a. "Pleistocene Temperatures," *Jour. Geol.*, 63: 538-78.
1955b. "Pleistocene Temperature Variations in the Mediterranean," *Quaternaria,* 2: 87-98.
1956. "Oligocene and Miocene Temperatures of the Equatorial and Subtropical Atlantic Ocean," *Jour. Geol.*, 64: 281-88.
1958. "Paleotemperature Analysis of the Core 280 and Pleistocene Correlations," *ibid.*, 66: 264-75.
1961. "Cenozoic Climatic Changes as Indicated by the Stratigraphy and Chronology of Deep-Sea Cores of Globigerina-Ooze Facies," *Ann. New York Acad. Sci.*, 95: 521-36.

EMILIANI, C., and J. GEISS
1957. "On Glaciations and Their Causes," *Geol. Rundschau,* 47: 576-601.
ERDTMANN, G.
1954. *An Introduction to Pollen Analysis.* Waltham: Chronica Botanica.
ERICSON, D. B.
1959. "Coiling Direction of *Globigerina Pachyderma* as Climatic Index," *Science,* 130: 219-20.
1961. "Pleistocene Climatic Record in Some Deep-Sea Sediment Cores," *Ann. New York Acad. Sci.,* 95: 537-41.
ERICSON, D. B., M. EWING, G. WOLLIN, and B. C. HEEZEN
1961. "Atlantic Deep-Sea Sediment Cores," *Bull. Geol. Soc. Amer.,* 72: 193-286.
EVERNDEN, J. F., and G. H. CURTIS
1964. "The Potassium-Argon Dating of Late Cenozoic Rocks in East Africa and Italy," *Bull. Geol. Soc. Amer.,* 75: in press.
EVERNDEN, J. F., G. H. CURTIS, and R. KISTLER
1957a. "Potassium-Argon Dating of Pleistocene Volcanics," *Quaternaria,* 4: 13-17.
EVERNDEN, J. F., G. H. CURTIS, and J. LIPSON
1957b. "Potassium-Argon Dating of Igneous Rocks," *Bull. Amer. Assoc. Petrol. Geol.,* 41: 2120-27.
EYRE, S. R.
1963. *Vegetation and Soils: a World Picture.* London: E. Arnold.
FAEGRI, K., and J. IVERSEN
1964. *Textbook of Modern Pollen Analysis* (2d ed.). Copenhagen: E. Munksgaard.
FAIRBRIDGE, R. W.
1961. "Eustatic Changes in Sea Level," *Physics and Chemistry of the Earth,* 4: 99-185.
1962. "New Radiocarbon Dates of Nile Sediments," *Nature,* 196: 108-10.
FELIX, C. J.
1961. "Palynology." In H. N. Andrews (ed.), *Studies in Paleobotany,* New York: J. Wiley, pp. 436-62.
FINK, J.
1959. "Geologische Problemstellung." In F. Felgenhauer, J. Fink, and H. de Vries, "Studien zur absoluten and relativen Chronologie der fossilen Böden Österreichs. I.," *Archaeologica Austriaca,* 25: 35-73.
1960. "Leitlinien einer österreichischen Quartärstratigraphie," *Mitt. Geol. Ges. Wien,* 53: 249-66.
1962. "Die Gliederung des Jungpleistozäns in Österreich," *ibid,* 54: 1-25.
FIRBAS, F.
1937. "Der pollenanalytische Nachweis des Getreidebaus," *Zeitschr. Botanik,* 31: 447-78.
1949-52. *Spät-und nacheiszeitliche Waldgeschichte Mitteleuropas nördlich der Alpen.* Jena: G. Fischer, 2 vol.
1950. "The Late-Glacial Vegetation of Central Europe," *New Phytologist,* 49: 163-73.
FIRBAS, F., and B. FRENZEL
1960. "Floren-und Vegetationsgeschichte seit dem Ende des Tertiärs," *Fortschr. der Botanik,* 22: 87-111.
FIRBAS, F., and P. ZANGHERI
1954. "Über neue Funde pflanzenführender Ablagerungen in der südlichen Po-Ebene bei Forli," *Nachr. Akad. Wiss. Gottingen,* pp. 11-18.

FITZPATRICK, E. A.
1956. "Progress Report on the Observation of Periglacial Phenomena in the British Isles," *Biuletyn Peryglacjalny,* 4: 99-115.

FLINT, R. F.
1957. *Glacial and Pleistocene Geology* (1st ed., 1947). New York: J. Wiley.
1959. "Pleistocene Climates in Eastern and Southern Africa," *Bull. Geol. Soc. Amer.,* 70: 343-74.

FLOHN, H.
1952. "Allgemeine atmosphärische Zirkulation und Paläoklimatologie," *Geol. Rundschau,* 40: 153-78.
1953. "Studien über die atmosphärische Zirkulation in der letzten Eiszeit," *Erdkunde,* 7: 266-75.

FLORSCHÜTZ, F., and A. M. H. VAN SOMEREN
1950. "The Paleo-Botanical Boundary Pliocene-Pleistocene in the Netherlands," *Proc. 18th Int. Geol. Congr.* (London, 1948), scc. 9: 40-46.

FORDE, C. D.
1934. *Habitat, Economy and Society.* New York: E. P. Dutton.

FRAGA TORREJON, E. DE
1958. "Catalogo bibliografico de la fauna cuaternaria asturiana," *Monograf. Geol., Inst. Geol. Aplicada,* (Oviedo), No. 8.

FRANZ, H.
1960. *Feldbodenkunde als Grundlage der Standortsbeurteilung und Bodenwirtschaft.* Vienna and Munich: G. Fromme.

FRÄNZLE, O.
1959a. "Glaziale und periglaziale Formbildung im östlichen Kastilischen Scheidegebirge," *Bonner Geogr. Abhl.,* Vol. 26.
1959b. "Untersuchungen über Ablagerungen und Boden im eiszeitlichen Gletschergebiet Norditaliens," *Erdkunde,* 13: 289-97.

FRENZEL, B.
1959-60. "Die Vegetations-und Landschaftszonen Nord-Eurasiens während der letzten Eiszeit und während der postglazialen Wärmezeit," *Abhl. Akad. Wiss. Lit.* (Mainz), *Math.-Naturw. Kl.,* 1959, Nr. 13; 1960, Nr. 6.

FRENZEL, B., and C. TROLL
1952. "Die Vegetationszonen des nördlichen Eurasiens während der letzten Eiszeit," *Eiszeitalter und Gegenw.,* 2: 154-67.

FRIES, M.
1963. "Vad myren berättar," *Sartryck Sveriges Naturs Arsbok,* pp. 91-107.

FRIES, M., H. E. WRIGHT, and M. RUBIN
1961. "A Late-Wisconsin Buried Peat near North Branch, Minnesota," *Amer. Jour. Sci.,* 259: 679-93.

FRITTS, H. C.
1963. "Recent Advances in Dendrochronology in America with Reference to the Significance of Climatic Change," *Arid Zone Research* (UNESCO), 20: 255-63.

FRYE, J. E.
1962. "Comparison between Pleistocene Deep-Sea Temperatures and Glacial and Interglacial Episodes," *Bull. Geol. Soc. Amer.,* 73: 263-66.

GAILLARD, C.
1934. "Contribution à l'étude de la faune préhistorique de l'Égypte," *Arch. Mus. Hist. Nat. Lyon,* 14: 1-125.

GAMS, H.
1950. "Die Allerödschwankung im Spätglazial," *Zeitschr. Gletscherkunde* (N.S.), 1: 162-71.

GANSSEN, R.
　　1957. *Bodengeographie.* Stuttgart: K. F. Köhler.
GARDNER, E. W.
　　1932. "Some Lacustrine Mollusca from the Faiyum Depression: a Study in Variation," *Mém. Inst. d' Égypte,* 18: 1-123.
　　1935. "The Pleistocene Fauna and Flora of Kharga Oasis, Egypt," *Quart. Jour. Geol. Soc.,* 91: 479-518.
GARROD, D. A. E.
　　1958. "The Natufian Culture: the Life and Economy of a Mesolithic People in the Near East," *Proc. Brit. Acad.,* 43: 211-27.
GARROD, D. A. E., and D. M. A. BATE
　　1937. *The Stone Age of Mt. Carmel, Vol. I., Excavations at the Wady el-Mughara.* Oxford: Clarendon Press.
GARROD, D. A. E., *et al.*
　　1928. "Excavation of a Mousterian Rock-Shelter at Devil's Tower (Gibraltar)," *Jour. Roy. Anthropol. Soc.,* 58: 33-113.
GENTNER, W., and H. J. LIPPOLT
　　1963. "The Potassium-Argon Dating of Upper Tertiary and Pleistocene Deposits." In BROTHWELL and HIGGS, 1963, pp. 72-84.
GEORGE, W.
　　1962. *Animal Geography.* London: Heinemann.
GERMAIN, L.
　　1923. "Les climats des temps quaternaires d'après les mollusques terrestres et fluviatiles," *Anthropologie,* 33: 301-22.
GIDDINGS, J. L.
　　1954. "Tree Ring Dating in the American Arctic," *Tree Ring Bull.,* 20: 23-25.
GIGOUT, M.
　　1960. "Nouvelles récherches sur le Quaternaire marocain et comparisons avec l'Europe," *Trav. Labor. Géol. Fac. Sci. Lyon* (N. S.), No. 6.
　　1962. "Sur le Tyrrhénien de la Méditérranée occidentale," *Quaternaria,* 6: 209-28.
GLINKA, K. D.
　　1927. *The Great Soil Groups of the World and Their Development.* Translated by C. F. Marbut. Ann Arbor: Edwards Bros. (mimeographed).
GODWIN, H.
　　1944. "Neolithic Forest Clearance," *Nature,* 153: 511-14.
　　1956. *The History of the British Flora.* Cambridge: Cambridge University Press.
GODWIN, H., D. WALKER, and E. H. WILLIS
　　1957. "Radiocarbon Dating and Post-glacial Vegetational History," *Proc. Roy. Soc. London* (series B.), 147: 352-66.
GODWIN, H., and E. H. WILLIS
　　1959. "Radiocarbon Dating of the Late Glacial Period in Britain," *Proc. Royal Soc. London* (series B), 150: 199-215.
GRADMANN, R.
　　1906. "Beziehungen zwischen Pflanzengeographie und Siedlungsgeschichte," *Geog. Zeit.,* 12: 305-25.
　　1933. "Die Steppenheide-theorie," *ibid.,* 39: 265-78.
　　1936. "Vorgeschichtliche Landwirtschaft und Besiedlung," *ibid.,* 42: 378-86.
GRAHMANN, R.
　　1932. "Der Lösz in Europa," *Mitt. Ges. Erdkunde Leipzig,* 51: 5-24.
　　1937. "Form und Entwässerung des nord-europaischen Inlandeises," *ibid.,* 54: 48-70.

1955. "The Lower Palaeolithic Site of Markkleeberg and Other Comparable Localities near Leipzig," *Trans. Amer. Phil. Soc.*, 45: 507-687.

GRAUL, H.
1955. "Bemerkungen zu einer geologischen Übersichtskarte des Iller-Riss-Gebietes," *Zeit. Deut. Geol. Ges.*, 105: 517-24.

GROSS, H.
1958. "Die bisherigen Ergebnisse von C-14 Messungen und paläolithischen Untersuchungen für die Gliederung und Chronologie des Jungpleistozäns in Mitteleuropa und den Nachbahrgebieten," *Eiszeitalter und Gegenw.*, 9: 155-87.

GROVE, A. T.
1958. "The Ancient Erg of Hausaland and Similar Formations on the South Side of the Sahara," *Geog. Jour.*, 124: 528-33.

GROVE, A. T. and R. A. PULLAN
1963. "Some Aspects of the Pleistocene Paleogeography of the Chad Basin," *Viking Fund Publ. Anthropol.*, 36: 230-45.

GRUND, A.
1903. "Die Karsthydrographie, Studien aus Westbosnien," *Pencks geog. Abhandl.*, 7: 103-200.

GUENTHER, E. W.
1961. *Sedimentpetrographische Untersuchungen von Lössen* (Part I) Cologne: Böhlau.

GUILCHER, A.
1954. *Morphologie littorale et sous-marine.* Paris: Presses Universitaires de France.

GUTENBERG, B.
1941. "Changes in Sea Level, Postglacial Uplift, and Mobility of the Earth's Interior," *Bull. Geol. Soc. Amer.*, 52: 721-72.

HAAG, W. G.
1962. "The Bering Strait Land Bridge," *Scientific American*, 206: 112-23.

HAEKEL, J. (ed.)
1961. *Theorie und Praxis der Zusammenarbeit zwischen den anthropologischen Disziplinen.* (Bericht über das 2. österreichische Symposion auf Burg Wartenstein, 1959.) Horn: F. Berger.

HAMMEN, T. VAN DER
1952. "Dating and Correlation of Periglacial Deposits in Middle and Western Europe," *Geol. en Mijnbouw*, 14: 328-36.
1957a. The Stratigraphy of the Late-Glacial," *ibid.*, 19: 250-54.
1957b. "The Age of the Usselo Culture," *ibid.*, pp. 396-97.

HANSEN, S.
1940. "Varvity in Danish and Scanian Late-Glacial Deposits, with Special Reference to the System of Ice-Lakes at Egernsund," *Danmarks Geol. Undersoegelse*, Vol. 2, No. 63.

HARE, F. K.
1954. "The Boreal Conifer Zone," *Geographical Studies* (Birbeck College, London), 1: 1-19.

HARING, A., A. E. DE VRIES, and H. DE VRIES
1958. "Radiocarbon Dating up to 70,000 Years by Isotopic Enrichment," *Science*, 128: 472-73.

HARTSHORNE, R.
1959. *Perspective on the Nature of Geography* (Assoc. of Amer. Geographers, Monograph Series, No. 1.) Chicago: Rand McNally.

HASTENRATH, S.
    1960. "Klimatische Voraussetzungen und grossräumige Verteilung der Frost-
    strukturböden," *Zeitschr. Geomorph.*, 4: 69-73.
HAY, R. L.
    1963. "Stratigraphy of Beds I through IV, Olduvai Gorge, Tanganyika,"
    Science, 139: 829-33.
HEICHELHEIM, F. M.
    1956. "Effects of Classical Antiquity on the Land." In THOMAS, 1956, pp.
    165-82.
HEINZELIN, J. DE
    1963. "Paleoecological Conditions of the Lake Albert-Lake Edward Rift,"
    Viking Fund Publ. Anthropol., 36: 276-84; discussion, pp. 602-3.
HEIZER, R. F.
    1955. "Primitive Man as an Ecologic Factor," *Kroeber Anthropol. Papers*, 13:
    1-31.
    1960. "Physical Analysis of Habitation Residues," *Viking Fund Publ. Anthro-
    pol.*, 28: 93-157.
HEIZER, R. F., (ed.)
    1958. *A Guide to Archaeological Field Methods* (3d ed.). Palo Alto:
    National Press.
HELBAEK, H.
    1959. "Domestication of Food Plants in the Old World," *Science*, 130:
    365-73.
    1960a. "The paleoethnobotany of the Near East and Europe." In BRAIDWOOD,
    HOWE, *et al.*, 1960, pp. 98-118.
    1960b. "Ecological Effects of Irrigation in Ancient Mesopotamia," *Iraq*, 22:
    186-96.
HESCHELER, K., and E. KÜHN
    1949. "Die Tierwelt der prähistorischen Siedlungen der Schweiz." In O.
    Tschumi, *Urgeschichte der Schweiz*, Frauenfeld, Vol. 1, p. 121-368.
HESS, P., and H. BREZOWSKY
    1952. "Katalog der Grosswetterlagen Europas," *Ber. Deut. Wetterdienstes
    US-Zone*, No. 33.
HEY, R. W.
    1957. "The Landsnails of Haua Fteah (N. Cyrenaica)," *Abstracts V. Congr.
    Int. INQUA* (Madrid-Barcelona, 1957), p. 79.
    1962. "The Quaternary and Palaeolithic of Northern Libya," *Quaternaria*,
    6: 435-49.
    1963. "Pleistocene Screes in Cyrenaica (Libya)," *Eiszeitalter und Gegenw.*,
    14: 77-84.
HIERNAUX, J.
    1963. "Some Ecological Factors Effecting Human Populations in Sub-Saharan
    Africa," *Viking Fund Publ. Anthropol.*, 36: 534-46.
HIGGS, E. S.
    1961. "Some Pleistocene Faunas of the Mediterranean Coastal Areas," *Proc.
    Prehist. Soc.*, 27: 144-54.
HIJSZELER, C. W. W. J.
    1957. "Late-glacial Human Cultures in the Netherlands," *Geol. en Mijnbouw*,
    19: 288-302.
HOLE, F., and K. V. FLANNERY
    1962. "Excavations at Ali Kosh, Iran, 1961," *Iranica Antiqua*, 2: 97-148.

HOOIJER, D. A.
1961. "The Fossil Vertebrates of Ksar Akil, a Paleolithic Rock Shelter in the Lebanon," *Zoologische Verhandelingen* (Leiden), No. 49.

HOPKINS, D. M.
1959. "Cenozoic history of the Bering land bridge," *Science*, 129: 1519-28.

HOPKINS, D. M., T. N. V. KARLSTROM, *et al.*
1955. "Permafrost and Groundwater in Alaska," *U. S. Geol. Survey Prof. Paper* 264 f: 113-46.

HOPKINS, D. M., and F. S. SIGAFOS
1950. "Frost Action and Vegetation Patterns on Seward Penninsula, Alaska," *U. S. Geol. Survey Bull.* 974-C: 51-101.

HORTON, R. E.
1945. "Erosional development of streams and their drainage basins," *Bull. Geol. Soc. Amer.*, 56: 275-370.

HÖVERMANN, J.
1954. "Über glaziale und 'periglaziale' Erscheinungen in Erithrea und Nord-abessinien," *Abhl. Akad. Raumforsch. Landesplan.* (Bremen), 28 (Mortensen Festschrift): 87-111.

HOWELL, F. C.
1958. "Upper Pleistocene Men of the Southwest Asian Mousterian." In *Neanderthal Centenary,* Utrecht: Kemink, pp. 185-98.
1959a. "Upper Pleistocene Stratigraphy and Early Man in the Levant," *Proc. Amer. Philos. Soc.*, 103: 1-65.
1959b. "The Villafranchian and Human Origins," *Science*, 130: 831-44.
1960. "European and Northwest African Middle Pleistocene Hominids," *Current Anthropology*, 1: 195-232.
1961. "More on Middle Pleistocene Hominids: a Reply," *ibid.*, 2: 118-20.
1962. "Ambrona/Torralba: Acheulian Open-Air Occupation Sites in Northern Spain." Paper presented at the annual meeting of the Amer. Anthropol. Soc., Chicago, No. 15-18, 1962. 13 pp., mimeo.
1964. *The Emergence of Man.* In press.

HOWELL, F. C., E. AGUIRRE, and K. W. BUTZER
1963. "Noticia preliminar sobre el emplazamiento acheulense de Torralba (Soria)," *Excavaciones arqueologicas en España* (Madrid), No. 10.

HOWELL, F. C., and J. D. CLARK
1963. "Acheulian Hunter-Gatherers of Sub-Saharan Africa," *Viking Fund Publ. Anthropol.*, 36: 458-533.

HOWELL, F. C., G. H. COLE, and M. R. KLEINDIENST
1962. "Isimila, an Acheulian Occupation Site in the Iringa Highlands, Southern Highlands Province, Tanganyika," *Actes IV Congr. Pan-Africain `de Préhistoire et de l'Étude du Quaternaire, Musée Royal de l'Afrique Centrale Ann.* (Tervuren), 40: 42-80. (Geological section after E. G. Haldemann, pp. 45-60.)

HÜCKRIEDE, R.
1962. "Jung-Quartär und End-Mesolithikum in der Provinz Kerman (Iran)," *Eiszeitalter und Gegenw.* 12: 25-42.

IVERSEN, J.
1949. "The Influence of Prehistoric Man on Vegetation," *Danmarks Geol. Undersoegelse,* Series IV, Vol. 3, No. 6.
1954. "The Late-Glacial Flora of Denmark and Its Relation to Climate and Soil," *ibid.*, Series II, 80: 87-119.

490   *Bibliography*

1960. "Problems of the Early Post-Glacial Forest Development in Denmark," *ibid.*, Series IV, Vol. 4, No. 3.

JACKSON, M. L.
1958. *Soil Chemical Analysis.* Englewood Cliffs: Prentice Hall.

JÁNOSSY, D.
1961. "Die Entwicklung der Kleinsäugerfauna Europas im Pleistozän (Insectivora, Rodentia, Lagomorpha)," *Zeitschr. Säugetierkunde,* 26: 1-11.

JÄTZOLD, R.
1960. "Aride und humide Jahreszeiten in Nordamerika," *Stuttgarter Geog. Studien,* 71.

JOHNSSON, G.
1960. "Cryoturbations at Zaragoza, northern Spain," *Zeitschr. Geomorph.,* 4: 74-80.

JUDSON, S.
1949. "The Pleistocene Stratigraphy of Boston, Massachusetts." In E. S. Barghoorn, *et al., "The Boylston Street Fishweir II,* Peabody Found. Archaeol. Papers, Vol. 4, 1: 7-48.
1950. "Depressions of the Northern Portion of the Southern High Plains of Eastern New Mexico," *Bull. Geol. Soc. Amer.,* 61: 253-74.
1953a. "Geology of the San Jon Site, eastern New Mexico," *Smithsonian Misc. Coll.,* Vol. 121.
1953b. "Geology of the Hodges Site, Quay County, New Mexico," *Bull. Bureau Amer. Ethnol.,* 154: 285-302.

KAISER, K. H.
1960. "Klimazeugen des periglazialen Dauerfrostbodens in Mittel- und Westeuropa," *Eiszeitalter und Gegenw.,* 11: 121-41.

KAISER, W.
1961. "Bericht über eine archäologisch-geologische Felduntersuchung in Ober-und Mittelägypten," *Mitt. deut. archäol. Inst., Abt. Kairo,* 17: 1-53.

KELLOGG, C. E.
1941. "Climate and Soil," *Yearbook of Agriculture, 1941* (U. S. Dept. of Agriculture): 265-91.

KENNEDY, G., and L. KNOPFF
1960. "Dating by Thermoluminescence," *Archaeology,* 13: 147-48.

KENYON, K. M.
1959. "Earliest Jericho," *Antiquity,* 33: 5-9.

KEREKES, J.
1951. "Zur periglazialen Sedimentbildung in mitteleuropaischen Höhlen," *Quartär* 5: 41-49.

KILMER, V. J., and L. T. ALEXANDER
1949. "Methods of Making Mechanical Analysis of Soils," *Soil Science,* 68: 15-24.

KING, L. C.
1961. "The Palaeoclimatology of Gondwanaland During the Palaeozoic and Mesozoic Eras." In NAIRN, 1961, pp. 307-31.

KING, W. B. R.
1955. "The Pleistocene Epoch in England," *Quart. Jour. Geol. Soc.,* 111: 187-208.

KLAER, W.
1956. "Verwitterungsformen im Granit auf Korsika," *Peterm. Mitt. Ergzh.,* 261.
1960. "Studien zum Pleistozän im Libanon, im Sinaigebirge, und im Toros

Dagh," *Abhdl. deut. Geographentags* (Berlin, 1959), Wiesbaden: F. Steiner, pp. 204-10.

1963. "Untersuchungen zur klimagenetischen Geomorphologie in den Hochgebirgen Vorderasiens," *Heidelberger Geog. Arb.*, No. 11.

KLEBELSBERG, R. VON

1948-49. *Handbuch der Gletscherkunde und Glazialgeologie.* Vienna: Springer, 2 vol.

KLEIN, A.

1953. "Die Niederschläge in Europa im Maximum der letzten Eiszeit," *Peterm. Geog. Mitt.*, 97: 98-104.

KLÍMA, B.

1954. "Palaeolithic Huts at Dolní Věstonice, Czechoslavakia," *Antiquity*, 109: 4-14.

1962. "The First Ground-Plan of an Upper Paleolithic Loess Settlement in Middle Europe and Its Meaning," *Viking Fund Publ. Anthropol.*, 32: 193-210.

KLIMASZEWSKII, M., W. SZAFER, B. SZAFRAN, and M. URBANSKI

1950. "The Dryas Flora of Kroschienko on the River Dunajic," *Bull. Serv. Geol. de Pologne*, Vol. 24, No. 2.

KLINGE, H.

1958. "Eine Stellungnahme zur Altersfrage von Terra-Rossa-Vorkommen," *Zeitschr. Pflanzenernährung, Düngung, Bodenkunde*, 81: 56-63.

1960. "Beiträge zur Kenntnis tropischer Boden (II)," *ibid*, 89: 211-16.

KLUTE, F.

1928. "Die Bedeutung der Depression der Schneegrenze für eiszeitliche Probleme," *Zeitschr. Gletscherkunde*, 16: 70-93.

KNETSCH, G.

1960. "Über aride Verwitterung unter besonderer Berücksichtigung natürlicher und künstlicher Wande in Ägypten," *Zeitschr. Geomorph.*, Suppl. Vol. 1 (1961): 190-205.

KNETSCH, G., *et al.*

1963. "Untersuchungen an pluvialen Wassern der Ost-Sahara," *Geol. Rundschau*, 52: 587-610.

KOENIGSWALD, G. H. R. VON

1940. "Neue *Pithecanthropus*-Funde 1936-1938. Ein Beitrag zur Kenntnis der Praehominiden," *Nederlandsch-Indie Mijnbouw Dienst, Wetenschap. Mededeel.*, No. 28.

1957. "*Meganthropus* and the Australopithecinae," *Proc. 3rd Pan-African Congr. Prehist.* (Livingstone, 1955): 158-60.

KOEPPEN, W.

1920. "Die Lufttemperatur an der Schneegrenze," *Peterm. Mitt.*, 66: 78-80.

KRUMBEIN, W. C.

1941. "Measurement and Geologic Significance of Shape and Roundness of Sedimentary Particles," *Jour. Sedimentary Petrol.*, 11: 64-72.

KUBIENA, W. L.

1938. *Micropedology.* Ames: Collegiate Press.

1953. *The Soils of Europe.* London: T. Murby.

1954a. "Genesis and Micromorphology of Laterite Formation in Rio Muni," *Proc. 5th Int. Soil Science Congr.* (Léopoldville), 4: 77-84.

1954b. "Über Reliktboden in Spanien," *Aichinger Festschrift*, 1 (Mitt. Inst. f. angewandte Vegetationskunde, Vienna): 213-24.

1955. "Über die Braunlehmrelikte des Atakor (Zentral-Sahara)," *Erdkunde,* 9: 115-32.

1957. "Neue Beiträge zur Kenntnis des planetarischen und hypsometrischen Formenwandels der Böden Africas," *Stuttgarter Geog. Studien* (Lautensach Festschrift), 69: 50-64.

1963. "Paleosols as Indicators of Paleoclimates," *Arid Zone Research* (UNESCO), 20: 207-9.

KUBITZKI, K., and K. O. MÜNNICH

1960. "Neue C-14 Datierungen zur nacheiszeitlichen Waldgeschichte Nordwestdeutschlands," *Ber. deut. botan. Ges.,* 73: 137-45.

KÜHN, H.

1929. *Kunst und Kultur der Vorzeit Europas: das Paläolithikum.* Berlin and Leipzig: de Gruyter.

KUENEN, P. H. and W. G. PERDOK

1962. "Frosting and Defrosting of Quartz Grains (Experimental Abrasion, 5)," *Jour. Geol.,* 70: 648-58.

KULP, J. L., and H. L. VOLCHOK

1953. "Constancy of Cosmic-Ray Flux over the Past 30,000 Years," *Phys. Rev.,* 90: 713-14.

KURTÉN, B.

1957. "The Bears and Hyenas of the Interglacials," *Quaternaria,* 4: 69-81.

1959a. "On the Longevity of Mammalian Species in the Tertiary," *Commentationes Biol. Soc. Sci. Fennica,* Vol. 21, No. 4.

1959b. "On the Bears of the Holsteinian Interglacial," *Stockholm Contrib. in Geol.,* 2: 73-102.

1960a. "Chronology and Faunal Evolution of the Earlier European Glaciations," *Commentationes Biol. Soc. Sci. Fennica,* Vol. 21, No. 5.

1960b. "Faunal Turnover Dates for the Pleistocene and Late Pliocene," *ibid.,* Vol. 22, No. 5.

KURTÉN, B., and Y. VASARI

1960. "On the Date of Peking Man," *Commentationes Biol. Soc. Sci. Fennica,* Vol. 23, No. 7.

LAATSCH, W.

(1957). *Dynamik der mitteleuropaischen Mineralboden* (4th ed.). Dresden and Leipzig: T. Steinkopff.

LAIS, R.

1932. "Die postglazialen Sedimente einer Höhle am Isteiner Klotz in Baden," *Fortschr. der Geol. und Paläont.* (Berlin), Vol. 11, No. 36.

1941. "Über Höhlensedimente," *Quartär,* 3: 56-108.

LAMING, A. (ed.)

1952. *La découverte du passé. Progrès récents et techniques nouvelles en préhistoire et en archéologie.* Paris: A. and J. Picard.

LANG, G.

1963. "Probleme der spätzeitlichen Vegetationsentwicklung in Südwestdeutschland und im französischen Zentralmassiv," *Pollen et Spores,* 5: 129-42.

LAUER, W.

1952. "Humide und aride Jahreszeiten in Afrika und Südamerika and ihre Beziehung zu den Vegetationsgürteln," *Bonner Geogr. Abhl.,* 9: 15-98.

LAUGHLIN, W. S., and W. G. REEDER

1962. "Rationale for the Collaborative Investigation of Aleut-Konyag Prehistory and Ecology," *Arctic Anthropology,* 1: 104-8.

LEAKEY, L. S. B.

1953. *Adam's Ancestors* (3rd ed.). London: Methuen.

1963. "Very Early East African *Hominidae* and Their Ecological Setting," *Viking Fund Fubl. Anthropol.*, 36: 448-57.

LEAKEY, L. S. B., and M. D. LEAKEY

1964. "Recent discoveries of fossil hominids in Tanganyika and Olduvai and near Lake Natron," *Nature*, 202: 5-7.

LEAKEY, L. S. B., P. V. TOBIAS, and J. R. NAPIER

1964. "A new species of the genus *Homo* from Olduvai Gorge," *Nature*, 202: 7-9.

LEES, G. M., and N. L. FALCON

1952. "The Geographical History of the Mesopotamian Plain," *Geogr. Jour.*, 118: 24-39.

LEFFINGWELL, E. DE K.

1919. "The Canning River Region Northern Alaska," *U. S. Geol. Survey Prof. Paper*, No. 109.

LE GROS CLARK, W. E.

1955. *The Fossil Evidence for Human Evolution.* Chicago: University of Chicago Press.

LEMÉE, G.

1954. "Observations nouvelles sur la vegetation au dernier interglaciaire et au tardiglaciaire en France d'après l'analyse pollinique," *Rapports et Comm. 8. Congr. Int. Botanique* (Paris, 1954), sec. 6: 263-64.

LEOPOLD, L. B., M. G. WOLMAN, and J. P. MILLER

1964. *Fluvial processes in geomorphology.* San Francisco: W. H. Freeman.

LEVERENZ, J. M.

1960. "Mammalian Fauna Depicted by Cave Drawings of Southwest Europe with Ecological Implications," Unpubl. research paper, Dept. of Geography, Univ. of Wisconsin, Madison.

LHOTE, H.

1959. *The search for the Tassili frescoes.* New York: Dutton.

LIBBY, W. F.

1955. *Radiocarbon Dating* (2nd ed.). Chicago: University of Chicago Press.

LLOPÍS, LLADO, N.

1957. In F. Hernandez-Pacheco, *et al.*, "Livret guide de l'excusion N₂ Le Quaternaire de la région cantabrique," *5th. Int. Congr. INQUA* (Oviedo).

LORTET, V., and C. GAILLARD

1903. "La faune mommifiee de l'ancienne Egypte," *Arch. Mus. Hist. Nat. Lyon*, Mém. 8.

LOUIS, H.

1934. "Glazialmorphologische Studien in den Gebirgen der Britischen Inseln," *Berliner Geog. Arb.*, No. 6.

1960. *Allgemeine Geomorphologie.* Berlin: de Gruyter.

LOŽEK, V.

1955. "Mollusken des tschechoslowakischen Quartärs," *Rozpravy Ustredn. Ustavu Geol.* (Prague), Vol. 17.

LÜDI, W.

1955. "Die Vegetationsentwicklung seit dem Rückzug der Gletscher in den mittleren Alpen und ihrem nördlichen Vorland," *Ber. Geobotan. Forschungsinst. Rübel* (Zürich), 1954: 36-38.

LÜTTIG, G.

1956. "Eine neue, einfache geröllmorphometrische Methode," *Eiszeitalter und Gegenw.*, 7: 13-20.

1959. "Eiszeit-Stadium-Phase-Staffel. Eine nomenklatorische Betrachtung," *Geol. Jahrb.*, 76: 235-68.

1962. "The Shape of Pebbles in the Continental, Fluviatile and Marine Facies," *Int. Assoc. Sci. Hydrol.*, Publ. 59: 253-58.

LYNCH, T. F., P. BIBERSON, and K. W. BUTZER
1964. "Nota preliminar sobre el yacimiento acheulense de Ambrona (Soria)," *Excavaciones in España*, No. 11 (in press).

MAARLEVELD, G. C.
1951. "De Asymmetrie van de kleine Dalen op net noordelijk Halfrand," *Tijdschr. kon. Nederl. Aardrijkskundig Genootschap*, 68: 297-312.

MCBURNEY, C. B. M., and R. W. HEY
1955. *Prehistory and Pleistocene Geology in Cyrenaican Libya*. Cambridge: Cambridge University Press.

MCFARLAN, E.
1961. "Radiocarbon dating of late Quaternary deposits, South Louisiana," *Bull. Geol. Soc. Amer.*, 72: 129-58.

MACKAY, J. R., W. H. MATTHEWS, and R. S. MACNEISH
1961. "Geology of the Engigstciak Archaeological Site, Yukon Territory," *Arctic*, 14: 25-52.

MACKIN, J. H.
1948. "Concept of the Graded River," *Bull. Geol. Soc. Amer.*, 59: 463-512.

MÄDLER, K.
1939. "Die pliozäne Flora von Frankfurt am Main," *Abhl. Senckenberg. Naturf. Ges.*, 446: 1-36.

MANLEY, G.
1951. "The Range and Variation of the British Climate," *Geog. Jour.*, 117: 43-68.
1955. "A Climatological Survey of the Retreat of the Laurentide Ice-Sheet," *Amer. Jour. Sci.*, 253: 256-73.

MARBUT, C. F.
1936. "Soils of the United States." In *Atlas of American Agriculture* (U. S. Dept. of Agriculture, Washington, D.C.), Pt. 3.

MARÉCHAL, R., and G. C. MAARLEVELD
1956. "L'extension des phénomenes périglaciaires en Belgique et aux Pays Bas," *Med. Geol. Sticht* (Haarlem) (N. S.), 8: 77-86.

MARTIN, P. S.
1963. *The Last 10,000 Years*. Tucson: Univ. of Arizona Press.

MARTIN, P. S., B. E. SABELS, and D. SHUTLER
1961. "Rampart Cave Coprolite and Ecology of the Shasta Ground Sloth," *Amer. Jour. Sci.*, 259: 102-27.

MARX, H., and C. A. REED
1957. "Observations on the Burrowing Rodent *Spalax* in Iraq," *Jour. Mammology*, 39: 386-89.

MASON, H. L.
1936. "The Principles of Geographic Distribution as Applied to Floral Analysis," *Madrono*, 3: 181-90.

MASON, R. J.
1961. "The Earliest Tool-Makers in South Africa," *South Afr. Jour. Sci.*, 57: 13-16.

MASON, RONALD J.
1962. "The Paleo-Indian Tradition in Eastern North America," *Current Anthropology*, 3: 227-78.

MATTHES, F. E., and A. D. BELMONT
1950. "The Glacial Anticyclone Theory Examined in the Light of Recent Meteorological Data from Greenland," *Trans. Amer. Geophys. Union*, 31: 174-82.

MAUNY, R.
1956. "Préhistoire et zoologie: la grande 'faune éthiopienne' du Nord-Quest africaine du paléolithique a nos jours," *Bull. Inst. Franç. d'Afrique Noire* (series A), 18: 246-79.

MEIGS, P.
1952. "Distribution of arid homoclimates," U.N. Maps No. 392 and 393. Paris: UNESCO.

MELLAART, J.
1961. "Excavations at Haçilar, 4th preliminary report," *Anatolian Studies* (London), 11: 159-84.

MENÉNDEZ-AMOR, J., and F. FLORSCHÜTZ
1961. "Contribucion al conocimiento de la historia de la vegetation en España durante el Quaternario," *Estudios geológicos,* 17: 83-99.

MENSCHING, H.
1955a. "Das Quartär in den Gebirgen Marokkos," *Peterm. Mitt. Ergzh.,* Vol. 256.
1955b. "Karst und Terra rossa auf Mallorca," *Erdkunde,* 9: 188-96.

MILANKOVITCH, M.
1941. "Kanon der Erbdestrahlung und seine Anwendung auf das Eiszeitproblem," *Acad. Roy. Serv. Éd. Spéc.,* Vol. 133.

MILLER, D. H.
1955. "Snow Cover and Climate in the Sierra Nevada," *Univ. Calif. Publ. Geog.,* Vol. 11.

MILOJČIC, V.
1958. In H. Bengtson, and V. Milojčić, *Grosser historischer Weltatlas,* Part I, (3d ed.), Munich: Bayerischer Schulbuch-Verlag.
1959. "Zur Chronologie der jüngeren Stein-und Bronzezeit Südost-und Mitteleuropas," *Germania,* 37: 65-84.

MOHR, E. C. J., and F. A. VAN BAREN
1954. *Tropical Soils.* The Hague: Van Hoeve.

MONOD, T.
1963. "The Late Tertiary and Pleistocene in the Sahara and Adjacent Southerly Regions," *Viking Fund Publ. Anthropol.,* 36: 117-229.

MOREAU, R. E.
1933. "Pleistocene Climatic Changes and the Distribution of Life in East Africa," *Jour. Ecology,* 211: 415-35.
1963. "The Distribution of Tropical African Birds in Relation to Past Climatic Changes," *Viking Fund Publ. Anthropol.,* 36: 28-42.

MORI, F., and A. ASCENZI
1959. "La mummia infantile di Uan Muhuggiag," *Riv. di Antropol.,* 46: 125-48.

MORISON, C. G. T., A. C. HOYLE, and J. F. HOPE-SIMPSON
1948. "Tropical Soil-Vegetation Catenas and Mosaics: a Study in the Southwestern Part of the Anglo-Egyptian Sudan," *Jour. Ecology,* 34: 1-84.

MORTENSEN, H.
1952. "Heutiger Firnrückgang und Eiszeitklima," *Erdkunde,* 6: 145-60.
1957. "Temperaturgradient und Eiszeitklima am Beispiel der pleistozänen Schneegrenzdepression in den Rand- und Subtropen," *Zeitschr. Geomorph.* 1: 44-56.

MOVIUS, H. L.
1943. "The Stone Age of Burma," *Trans. Amer. Phil. Soc.,* 32: 341-93.
1949. "Villafranchian Stratigraphy in Southern and Southwestern Europe," *Jour. Geol.,* 57: 380-412.

1955. "Palaeolithic Archaeology in Southern and Eastern Asia, Exclusive of India," *Jour. World History*, 2: 257-82, 520-53.

1960. "Radiocarbon Dates and Upper Paleolithic Archeology in Central and Western Europe," *Current Anthropology*, 1: 355-91.

MOVIUS, H. L., and S. JUDSON

1956. "The Rock-Shelter of La Colombière. Archaeological and Geological Investigation of an Upper Perigordian Site, near Poncin, Ain," *Bull. Amer. School Prehist. Research*, No. 19.

MÜCKENHAUSEN, E.

1960. "Eine besondere Art von Pingos am Hohen Venn (Eifel)," *Eiszeitalter und Gegenw.*, 11: 5-11.

MÜLLER-BECK, H.

1957. "Paläolithische Kulturen und Pleistozäne Stratigraphie in Suddeutschland," *Eiszeitalter und Gegenw.*, 8: 116-40.

MÜLLER-WILLE, W.

1954. "Arten der menschlischen Siedlung," *Abhl. Akad. Raumforsch. Landesplan.* (Bremen), 28 (Mortensen Festschrift): 141-63.

MÜNNICH, K. O.

1957. "Erfahrungen mit der C-14 Datierung verschiedener Arten von Sedimenten," *Veröff. Geobotan. Inst. Rübel* (Zürich), 34: 109-17.

MÜNNICH, K. O., and J. C. VOGEL

1959. "C-14-Altersbestimmung von Suesswasser-Kalkablagerungen," *Naturwiss.*, 46: 168-69.

MULVANEY, D. J.

1961. "The Stone Age of Australia," *Proc. Prehist. Soc.*, 27: 56-107.

MURRAY, G. W.

1951. "The Egyptian Climate: an Historical Outline," *Geogr. Jour.*, 117: 422-34.

NAMIAS, J.

1963. "Surface-Atmosphere Interactions as Fundamental Causes of Drought and Other Climatic Fluctuations," *Arid Zone Research* (UNESCO), 20: 345-60.

NANGERONI, G.

1952. "I fenomeni di morfologia periglaciale in Italia," *Proc. 17th Int. Geogr. Congr., Comm. on Periglacial Morph.* (Washington, D. C.): 7-14.

NAIRN, A. E. M. (ed.)

1961. *Descriptive Palaeoclimatology*. New York: Interscience.

NAIRN, A. E. M., and N. THORLEY

1961. "The Application of Geophysics to Palaeoclimatology." In NAIRN, 1961, pp. 156-82.

NARR, K. J.

1956. "Early Food-Producing Populations." In THOMAS, 1956, pp. 134-51.

1961. *Urgeschichte der Kultur*. Stuttgart: A. Kroner.

1963. *Kultur, Umwelt und Leiblichkeit des Eiszeitmenschens*. Stuttgart: G. Fischer.

NEUVILLE, R.

1951. "Le Paléolithique et le Mésolithique de Désert de Judée," *Arch. Inst. Paléontol. Humaine* (Paris), No. 24.

NIETSCH, H.

1939. *Wald und Siedlung im vorgeschichtlichen Mitteleuropa*. Leipzig: Mannus-Bücherei, Vol. 64.

NIKIFOROFF, C. C.

1941. "Morphological Classification of Soil Structure," *Soil Science*, 52: 193-212.

NILSSON, E.
  1931. "Quaternary Glaciations and Pluvial Lakes in British East Africa," *Geografiska Ann.*, 13: 249-349.
  1940. "Ancient Changes of Climate in British East Africa and Abyssinia," *ibid*, 22: 1-79.

NISKANEN, E.
  1943. "On the Deformation of the Earth's Crust Under the Weight of a Glacial Ice Load and Related Phenomena," *Ann. Acad. Sci. Fennicae*, (series A III), No. 7.

NORDENSKJÖLD, O., and L. MECKING
  1928. "The Geography of the Polar Regions," *Amer. Geogr. Soc.*, Spec. Pub. 8.

NUSSBAUM, F.
  1928. "Die diluviale Vergletscherung der östlichen Pyrenäen," *Geogr. Zeit.*, 34: 385-401.

NUSSBAUM, F., and F. GYGAX
  1952. "Glazialmorphologische Untersuchungen im Kantabrischen Gebirge (Nord-Spanien)," *Jahresber. Geogr. Ges.* (Bern, 1951-52): 54-79.

NYE, P. H., and D. J. GREENLAND
  1960. *The Soil under Shifting Cultivation*, Farnham Royal: Commonwealth Agr. Bur.

OAKLEY, K. P.
  1958. *Man the Tool-Maker* (4th ed.). London: British Mus. Nat. Hist.
  1961. "On Man's Use of Fire, With Comments on Toolmaking and Hunting," *Viking Fund Publ. Anthropol.*, 31: 176-93.
  1963. "Analytical Methods of Dating Bones." In BROTHWELL and HIGGS, 1963, pp. 24-34.

OAKLEY, K. P., *et al.*
  1950. "The Pliocene-Pleistocene Boundary," *Report 18th Int. Geol. Congr.* (London), Pt. 9.

OLAUSSON, E.
  1961a. "Remarks on Some Cenozoic Core Sequences from the Central Pacific," *Medd. Oceanografiska Inst. Goeteborg*, No. 29.
  1961b. "Sediment Cores from the Mediterranean Sea and the Red Sea IV. Studies of Deep-sea Cores." In H. Pettersson (ed.), *Reports of the Swedish Deep-Sea Expedition 1947-1948*, Goeteborg: Elanders, pp. 337-91.

OLDFIELD, F.
  1961. "The Full and Late-glacial Period in South-West France," *Proc. Linn. Soc. London*, 172: 49-53.

OLLIER, C. D., and A. J. THOMASSON
  1957. "Asymmetrical Valleys of the Chiltern Hills," *Geogr. Jour.* 83: 71-80.

OPDYKE, N. D., and S. K. RUNCORN
  1959. "Palaeomagnetism and Ancient Wind Directions," *Endeavour*, 18: 26-34.

OSBORN, H. F.
  1934-42. *The Proboscidea*. New York: Amer. Mus. Nat. Hist., 2 vol.

OVERBECK, F.
  1950. *Die Moore, Geologie und Lagerstätten Niedersachsens III* (2d ed.). Bremen: Niedersachsisches Amt. f. Landesplanung, Series Ac, Abh. 4.

PAAS, W.
  1962. "Rezente und fossile Boden auf niederrheinischen Terrassen und deren Deckschichten," *Eiszeitalter und Gegenw.*, 12: 165-230.

PANNEKOEK, A. J. (ed.)
1956. *Geological History of the Netherlands*. The Hague: Govt. Printing and Publ. Office.

PASCHINGER, H.
1954. "Würmvereisung und Spätglazial in der Sierra Nevada," *Zeitschr. Gletscherkunde*, 3: 55-67.
1961. "Quartäre Formenwelt im Fussgebiet der Sierra Nevada Spaniens," *Erdkunde*, 15: 201-9.

PASSARGE, S.
1940. "Die Urlandschaft Ägyptens und die Lokalisierung der Wiege der Altägyptischen Kultur," *Nova Acta Leopoldina*, 9: 77-152.

PATERSON, S. S.
1956. *The forest area of the world and its potential productivity*. Göteborg: Royal University of Göteborg, 2 vol.

PAVLOVSKY, E. N.
1956. "Quelques considérations sur les conditions écologiques de l'existence du mammouth," *Proc. 14. Int. Congr. Zool.* (Copenhagen, 1953): 61-63.

PEAKE, H. J., and H. FLEURE
1927-36. *The Corridors of Time*. Oxford: The University Press, 6 vols. (*Peasants and Potters*, Vol. III, 1927).

PEEL, R. F.
1960. "Some Aspects of Desert Geomorphology," *Geography*, 45: 241-62.

PELTIER, L. C.
1949. "Pleistocene Terraces of the Susquehanna River, Pennsylvania," *Penn. Geol. Survey*, (4th Series), Bull. G 23.
1950. "The Geographic Cycle in Periglacial Regions as It Is Related to Climatic Geomorphology," *Ann. Assoc. Amer. Geog.*, 40: 214-36.

PENCK, A.
1914. "The Shifting of the Climatic Belts," *Scottish Geog. Mag.*, 30: 281-93.

PERKINS, D.
1964. "The prehistoric fauna from Shanidar, Iraq." *Science*, Vol. 145: in press.

PERROT, J.
1957. "Le mésolithique de Palestine et les recentes découvertes à Eynan (Ain Mallaha)," *Antiquity and Survival*, 2: 91-110.
1960. "Excavations at Eynan (Ain Mallaha)," *Israel Exploration Jour.*, 10: 14-22.
1962. "Palestine-Syria-Cilicia," *Viking Fund Publ. Anthropol.*, 32: 147-64.

PETTIJOHN, F. J.
1957. *Sedimentary Rocks* (2d ed.) New York: Harper.

PÉWÉ, T. L.
1951. "An Observation of Wind-Blown Silt," *Jour. Geol.*, 59: 399-410.

PFANNENSTIEL, M.
1944. "Die diluviale Entwicklungsstadien und die Urgeschichte von Dardanellen, Marmarameer, und Bosporous," *Geol. Rundschau*, 34: 342-434.
1954. "Die Entstehung der ägyptischen Oasendepressionen. Das Quartär der Levante II," *Abhl. Akad. Wiss. Lit.* (Mainz), *Math.-Naturw. Kl.*, 1953, No. 7.

PFIZENMAYER, E. W.
1939. *Siberian man and mammoth*. London: Blackie.

PHILIPS, C. W.
1951. "The Fenland Research Committee, Its Past Achievements and Future Prospects." In W. F. Grimes (ed.), *Aspects of Archaeology in Britain and Beyond: Essays presented to O. G. S. Crawford*, London, pp. 258-73.

Pittioni, R.
1961. "Über die Zusammenarbeit der "anthropologischen Disziplinen" vom Standpunkt der Urgeschichte." In Haekel, 1961, pp. 10-36.

Polutoff, N.
1955. "Das Mammut von Taimyr. Neue Erkenntnisse zur Ökologie des sibirischen Mammuts," *Eiszeitalter und Gegenw.*, 6: 153-58.

Pons, A., and P. Quézel
1957. "Première étude palynologique de quelques paléosols sahariens," *Trav. Inst. Réch. Sahar.* (Algiers), 15: 15-40.
1958. "Premières remarques sur l'étude palynologique d'un guano fossile du Hoggar," *C. R. Acad. Sci.*, 246: 2290-92.

Pop, E.
1957. "Les recherches pollenanalytiques en Roumanie et leurs résultats" (Russian with French summary), *Botaniueskii Jurnal, Akad. Nauk SSSR*, 42: 363-76.

Popov, A. I.
1955. Materialy k osnovam ucenija o merzlych zonach zemoj kory ("The origin and development of massive fossil ice)," *Akad. Nauk. SSSR.* 2: 5-24.

Poser, H.
1948. "Boden und Klimaverhältnisse in Mittel- und Westeuropa während der Würmeiszeit," *Erdkunde*, 2: 53-68.
1950. "Zur Rekonstruktion der Spätglazialen Luftdruckverhältnisse in Mittel- und Westeuropa auf Grund der vorzeitlichen Dünen," *ibid*, 4: 81-88.
1957. "Klimamorphologische Probleme auf Kreta," *Zeitschr. Geomorph.*, 1: 113-42.

Prošek, F., and V. Ložek
1957. "Stratigraphische Übersicht des tschechoslowakischen Quartärs," *Eiszeitalter und Gegenw.*, 8: 37-90.

Pumpelly, R.
1908. "Explorations in Turkestan: Expedition of 1904: Prehistoric Civilizations of Anau," *Publ. Carnegie Inst.* (Washington), No. 73, 2 vol.

Quézel, P., and C. Martinez
1958. "Étude palynologique de deux diatomites du Borkou," *Bull. Soc. Hist. Nat. Afrique Nord*, 49: 230-44
1961. "Le dernier interpluvial au Sahara Central. Essai de chronologie palynologique et paléoclimatique," *Libyca*, 6/7: 211-27.

Quézel, P., and J. Y. Thébault
1959. "Palynologie et datation du volcanisme récent de l'Ahaggar," *Bull. Scien. Econ. Bur. Rech. Min. Algèrie*, No. 6: 59-64.

Ralph, E. K.
1955. "University of Pennsylvania Radiocarbon dates I," *Science*, 121: 150-52.
1959. "University of Pennsylvania Radiocarbon dates IV," *Amer. Jour. Sci.*, *Radiocarbon Supplement* 1: 45-53.

Ralph, E. K., and R. Stuckenrath
1960. "Carbon—14 Measurements of Known Age Samples," *Nature*, 188: 185-87.

Rattray, J. M.
1960. *The grass cover of Africa.* Rome: FAO.

Raynal, R.
1956. "Les phénomènes périglaciaires au Maroc et leur place dans l'évolution morphologique," *Biuletyn Peryglacjalny*, 4: 143-62.
1960a. "Les ébo: s ordonnés au Maroc," *ibid.*, 8: 21-30.

1960b. "Quelques apercus sur l'existence et l'importance des phénomènes periglaciaires préwurmiens au Maroc," *ibid.*, 9: 109-22.

REED, C. A.

1959. "Animal Domestication in the Prehistoric Near East," *Science*, 130: 1629-39.

1960. "A Review of the Archeological Evidence on Animal Domestication in the Prehistoric Near East." In BRAIDWOOD, HOWE, *et al.*, 1960, pp. 119-46.

1961. "Osteological Evidences for Prehistoric Domestication in Southwestern Asia," *Zeitschr. Tierzüchtung und Züchtungsbiologie,* 76: 31-38.

REID, E. M.

1921. "A Comparative Review of Pliocene Floras, Based on the Study of Fossil Seeds," *Quart. Jour. Geol. Soc.,* 76: 145-59.

REIFF, W.

1955. "Über den pleistozanen Sauerwasserkalk von Stuttgart-Münster-Bad Cannstadt," *Jahresber. u. Mitt. oberrhein. geol. Ver.* (N. S.), 37: 1-16.

REIFENBERG, A.

1947. *The Soils of Palestine.* London: T. Murby.

REMY, H.

1958. "Zur Flora und Fauna der Villafranca-Schichten von Villárroya, Prov. Logroño/Spanien," *Eiszeitalter und Gegenw.,* 9: 83-103.

RHOTERT, H.

1952. *Libysche Felsbilder.* Darmstadt: L. C. Wittich.

RICHARDS, H. G.

1962. "Studies on the marine Pleistocene," *Trans. Amer. Phil. Soc.,* Vol. 52, Pt. 3.

RICHARDS, R. W.

1952. *The Tropical Rainforest: an Ecological Study.* Cambridge: Cambridge University Press.

RICHTER, K.

1956. "Klimatische Verschiedenartigkert glazialer Vorstossphasen in Norddeutschland," *Actes IV. Congr. Int. INQUA* (Rome, 1953).

1958. "Fluorteste quartärer Knochen in ihrer Bedeutung für die absolute Chronologie des Pleistozäns," *Eiszeitalter und Gegenw.,* 9: 18-27.

ROBINSON, J. T.

1963. "Adaptive radiation in the australopithecines and the origin of man," *Viking Fund Publ. Anthropol.,* 36: 385-416.

RODE, A. A.

1961. *The soil forming process and soil evolution.* Jerusalem: Israel Program for Scientific Translations.

ROSHOLT, J. N., C. EMILIANI, H. GEISS, F. F. KOCZY, and P. J. WANGERSKY

1961. "Absolute Dating of Deep Sea cores by the Pa^{231}/Th^{230} Method," *Jour. Geol.,* 69: 162-85.

RUBIN, M.

1963. "Simultaneity of Glacial and Pluvial Episodes from C-14 Chronology of the Wisconsin Glaciation," *Arid Zone Research* (UNESCO), 20: 223-28.

RUBIN, M., R. C. LIKINS, and E. G. BERRY

1963. "On the Validity of Radiocarbon Dates from Snail Shells," *Jour. Geol.,* 71: 84-89.

RUETIMEYER, L.

1862. "Die Fauna der Pfahlbauten der Schweiz," *Neue Denkschr. Schweiz. Ges. Naturw.* (Zürich), Vol. 19.

RUST, A.

1937. *Das altsteinzeitliche Rentierjägerlager Meiendorf* (with sections on geology by K. Gripp, paleontology by W. Krause, palynology by R. Schütrumpf). Neumünster: K. Wachholtz.

1943. *Die alt-und mittelsteinzeitlichen Funde von Stellmoor* (with sections on paleontology by K. Gripp and W. Kollau, palynology by R. Schütrumpf, geology by K. Gripp). Neumünster: K. Wachholtz.

1950. *Die Höhlenfunde von Jabrud (Syrien)*. Neumünster: K. Wachholtz.

1958. *Die jungpaläolitischen Zeltanlagen von Ahrensburg* (with section on palynology by R. Schütrumpf). Neumünster: K. Wachholtz.

1962. *Vor 20,000 Jahren* (2d ed.). Neumünster: K. Wachholtz.

RUXTON, B. P., and L. BERRY

1960. "Weathering Profiles and Geomorphic Position on Granite in Two Tropical Regions," *Rév. Géomorphologie Dynam.*, 12: 16-31.

RYDER, M. L.

1963. "Remains of Fishes and Other Aquatic Animals." In BROTHWELL and HIGGS, 1963, pp. 294-312.

SABBAGH, M. E.

1962. "A Preliminary Regional Dynamic Climatology of the Antarctic Continent," *Erdkunde*, 16: 94-111.

SABELS, B. E.

1960. "Trace Element Studies on Cave Sediments," *Nev. State Mus. Anthropol. Papers*, 3: 17-23.

SANDFORD, K. S.

1934. "Paleolithic Man and the Nile Valley in Upper and Middle Egypt," *Univ. Chicago Oriental Inst. Publ.*, Vol. 18.

SANKALIA, H. D.

1962. "India," *Viking Fund Publ. Anthropol.*, 32: 60-83.

SAUER, C. O.

1927. "Recent Developments in Cultural Geography." In E. C. Hayes, (ed.), *Recent Developments in the Social Sciences*, Philadelphia, pp. 154-212.

1944. "A Geographic Sketch of Early Man in America," *Geog. Rev.*, 34: 529-573.

1947. "Early Relations of Man to Plants," *ibid.*, 37: 1-25.

1952. *Agricultural Origins and Dispersals*. New York: Amer. Geog. Soc.

SAURAMO, M.

1929. "The Quaternary Geology of Finland," *Bull. Comm. Géol. de Finlande*, No. 86.

SCHAEFER, I.

1950. "Die diluviale Erosion und Akkumulation," *Forsch. z. deut. Landeskunde*, 49.

SCHALLER, G. B., and J. T. EMLEN

1963. "Observations of the Ecology and Social Behavior of the Mountain Gorilla," *Viking Fund Publ. Anthropol.*, 36: 368-84.

SCHANFIELD, S.

1962. "The Middle Pleistocene of the western and central Sahara." Unpublished Ph.D. dissertation, Department of Anthropology, University of Chicago.

SCHEFFER, F., and P. SCHACHTSCHABEL

1960. *Bodenkunde* (5th ed.). Stuttgart: F. Enke.

SCHENK, E.

1955. "Die Mechanik der periglazialen Strukturboden," *Abhl. Hessischen Landesamtes f. Bodenforschung*, Vol. 13.

SCHERY, R. W.

1952. *Plants for Man*. Englewood Cliffs: Prentice-Hall.

502 *Bibliography*

SCHMID, E.
1958. "Höhlenforschung und Sedimentanalyse," *Schriften Inst. Ur-und Früh-geschichte der Schweiz* (Basel), No. 13.
1963. "Cave Sediments and Prehistory." In BROTHWELL and HIGGS, 1963, 123-38.
SCHMIDT, W. F.
1948. "Die Steppenschluchten Sudrusslands," *Erdkunde*, 2: 213-29.
SCHÖNHALS, E.
1951. "Über fossile Böden im nichtvereisten Gebiet," *Eiszeitalter und Gegenw.*, 1: 109-30.
1953. "Gesetzmässigkeiten im Feinaufbau von Talrandlössen mit Bemerkungen über die Entstehung des Lösses," *ibid.*, 3: 19-36.
SCHOTT, C.
1931. "Die Blockmeere in den deutschen Mittelgebirgen," *Forsch. deut. Landes- und Volkskunde*, 29: 1-78.
1939. "Die vorgeschichtliche Kulturlandschaft Mitteleuropas," *Zeitschr. Erdkunde*, 8: 641-50.
SCHOTT, W.
1935. "Die Foraminiferen in dem äquatorialen Teil des atlantischen Ozeans," *Wiss. Ergebnisse der deut. Atlantik Exped. Meteor 1925-1927*, Vol. 3, Pt. 3: 43-134.
SCHOVE, D. J., A. E. M. NAIRN, and N. D. OPDYKE
1958. "The Climatic Geography of the Permian," *Geografiska Ann.*, 40: 216-31.
SCHULMAN, E.
1956. "Dendroclimatic Changes in Semiarid America," Geochronological Lab., Univ. of Arizona.
SCHÜTRUMPF, R.
1936. "Paläobotanisch-pollenanalytische Untersuchungen der paläolithischen Rentierjägerfundstätte von Meiendorf bei Hamburg," *Veröff. des archäolog. Reichsinst.*, 1: 1-54.
1938. "Stratigraphisch-pollenanalytische Mooruntersuchungen im Dienste der Vorgeschichtsforschung," *Prähist. Zeit.*, 28/29: 158-83.
1955. "Das Spätglazial," *Eiszeitalter und Gegenw.*, 6: 41-51.
SCHWARZ, G.
1961. *Allgemeine Siedlungsgeographie* (2d ed.). Berlin: de Gruyter.
SCHWARZBACH, M.
1961. *Das Klima der Vorzeit* (2d ed.). Stuttgart: F. Enke.
SCHWEITZER, H. J.
1958. "Entstehung und Flora des Trasses im nördlichen Laachersee-Gebiet," *Eiszeitalter und Gegenw.*, 9: 28-48.
SEKYRA, J.
1960. "Pusobeni mrazu na pudu: Kryopedologie se Zvlast nim zretelem k CSR," *Geotechnica* (Prague), 27: 1-164.
SELLI, R.
1962. "Le Quaternaire marin du versant Adriatique-Ionien de la péninsule italienne," *Quaternaria*, 6: 391-413.
SERČELJ, A.
1963. "Die Entwicklung der Würm und der Holozänwaldvegetation in Slowenien" (Yugoslav with German summary), *Dissertationes Acad. Scient. Art. Slovenica*, Class IV: 361-418.
SERRA RAFOLS, J., J. F. DE VILLALTA and J. M. THOMAS
1957. "Livret Guide des Excursions B₂-B₃ (Alentours de Barcelone et Moia)," *5th Int. Congr. INQUA* (Madrid-Barcelona).

SHEPARD, F. P., and R. YOUNG
1961. "Distinguishing Between Beach and Dune Sands," *Jour. Sedimentary Petrol.*, 31: 196-214.

SHOSTAKOVITCH, V. B.
1936. "Geschichtete Bodenablagerungen der Seen als Klima-Annalen," *Meteor. Zeitschr.*, 53: 176-82.

SIMONSON, R. W.
1954. "Identification and interpretation of buried soils," *Amer. Jour. Sci.*, 252: 705-22.

SIRÉN, G.
1961. "Skogsgränstallen som indikator for klimafluktuationerna i norra Fennoskandien under historisk tid," *Communicationes Inst. Forestalis Fenniae*, Vol. 54, No. 2.

SMITH, G. D., and SOIL SURVEY STAFF
1961. *Soil Classification, a Comprehensive System* (7th Approximation). Washington, D.C.: U.S. Dept. of Agriculture.

SMITH, H. T. U.
1949. "Physical Effects of Pleistocene Climatic Changes in Non-Glaciated Areas—Eolian Phenomena, Frost Action and Stream Terracing," *Bull. Geol. Soc. Amer.*, 60: 1485-1516.
1954. "Coast dunes," *Coastal Geog. Congr., Office of Naval Research*, (Washington, Feb. 1954), pp. 51-56.

SMOLLA, G.
1960. "Neolithische Kulturerscheinungen: Studien zur Frage ihrer Herausbildungen," *Antiquitas* (Bonn: R. Habelt) (Series 2), 3: 1-180.

SOERGEL, W.
1921. *Die Ursachen der diluvialen Aufschotterung, und Erosion.* Berlin: Borntraeger.
1922. *Die Jagd der Vorzeit.* Jena: G. Fischer.
1937. *Die Vereisungskurve.* Berlin: Borntraeger.
1940. "Der Klimacharakter des Mammuts," *Paläontol. Zeitschr.*, 22: 29-55.
1941. "Rentiere des deutschen Alt-und Mitteldiluviums," *ibid.*, 22: 387-420.
1942. "Die Verbreitung des diluvialen Moschusochsen in Mitteleuropa," *Beiträge zur Geol. Thüringens* (Jena), 7: 75-95.
1943. "Der Klimacharakter der als nordisch geltenden Säugetiere des Eiszeitalters," *Sitz-Ber. Heidelberger Akad. Wiss., math.-naturw. Kl.* (1941), No. 4.

SOKOLOFF, V. P., and G. F. CARTER
1952. "Time and Trace Metals in Archaeological Sites," *Science*, 116: 1-5.

SOLÉ SABARÍS *et al.*
1957. "Livret Guide de l'Excursion N_1 (Pyrenees)," *5th Int. Congr. INQUA*, (Madrid-Barcelona).

SOLECKI, R. S., and M. RUBIN
1958. "Dating of Zawi Chemi, an Early Village Site at Shanidar, Northern Iraq," *Science*, 127: 1446.

SOLECKI, R., and A. LEROI-GOURHAN
1961. "Paleoclimatology and Archaeology in the Near East," *Ann. New York Acad. Sci.*, 95: 729-39.

SONNENFELD, J.
1962. "Prehistoric Technology: Functional Interpretations and Geographical Implications," *Professional Geographer*, Vol. 14, No.2: 4-8.

SPARKS, B. W.
1960. *Geomorphology.* London: Longmans.

1963. "Non-marine mollusca and archaeology." In Brothwell and Higgs, 1960, pp. 313-24.

Sparks, B. W., and A. T. Grove

1961. "Some Quaternary Fossil Non-Marine Mollusca from the Central Sahara," *Jour. Linnaean Soc. London, Zoology,* 44: 355-64.

Steeger, A.

1944. "Diluviale Bodenfrosterscheinungen am Niederrhein," *Geol. Rundschau,* 34: 520-38.

Steensburg, A.

1957. "Some Recent Danish Experiments in Neolithic Agriculture," *Agr. Hist. Rev.,* 5: 66-73.

Stewart, O. C.

1956. "Fire as the First Great Force Employed by Man." In Thomas, 1956, pp. 115-31.

Strahler, A. N.

1960. *Physical Geography* (2d ed.). New York: J. Wiley.

Suess, H. E.

1955. "Radiocarbon Concentration in Modern Wood," *Science,* 122: 415-17.

Suggate, R. P., R. G. West, and B. W. Sparks

1959. "On the Extent of the Last Glaciation in Eastern England," *Proc. Roy. Soc.* (series B), 150: 263-83.

Suslov, S. P.

1961. *Physical Geography of Asiatic Russia.* San Francisco: W. H. Freeman.

Sutcliffe, R. C.

1963. "Theories of Recent Changes of Climate," *Arid Zone Research* (UNESCO), 20: 277-80.

Szafer, W.

1953. "Pleistocene Stratigraphy of Poland from the Floristical Point of View" (in Polish), *Ann. Soc. Geol. Pologne,* 22: 1-99.

1954. "Pliocene Flora from the Vicinity of Czorsztyn (West Carpathians) and Its Relationship to the Pleistocene," *Prace Inst. Geol.* (Warsaw), No. 11.

Taber, S. S.

1943. "Perennially Frozen Ground in Alaska: Its Origin and History," *Bull. Geol. Soc. Amer.,* 54: 1433-1584.

Tator, B. A.

1952. "Pediment characteristics and terminology," *Ann. Assoc. Amer. Geog.,* 42: 293-317.

Tedrow, J. C. F., and H. Harries

1960. "Tundra Soil in Relation to Vegetation, Permafrost and Glaciation," *Oikos,* 11: 237-49.

Teilhard de Chardin, P.

1941. "Early Man in China," *Inst. de Géo-Biologie* (Peking), No. 7.

Te Punga, M. T.

1957. "Periglaciation in Southern England." In J. B. L. Hol (ed.), *The Earth, Its Crust and Its Atmosphere,* Leiden: E. J. Brill, pp. 186-98.

Terra, H. de, and H. L. Movius

1943. "Research on Early Man in Burma," *Trans. Amer. Phil. Soc.,* 32: 265-464.

Terra, H. de, and T. T. Patterson

1939. "Studies on the Ice Age in India and Associated Human Cultures," *Publ. Carnegie Inst.* (Washington), No. 493.

Thenius, E.

1961a. "Über die Bedeutung der Paläokologie fur die Anthropologie und Urgeschichte." In Haekel, 1961, pp. 80-103.

1961b. "Paläozoologie und Prähistorie," *Mitt. Urgeschichtl. und Anthropol. Ges.* (Vienna), 12, 3/4: 39-61.

1962. "Die Grossäugetiere des Pleistozäns von Mitteleuropa," *Zeitschr. Säugetierkunde,* 27: 65-83.

THIEL, E. C.

1962. "The Amount of Ice on Planet Earth," *Antarctic Research, Amer. Geophys. Union:* 172-175.

THOMAS, W. L. (ed.)

1956. *Man's Role in Changing the Face of the Earth.* Chicago: University of Chicago Press.

THOMÉ, K. N.

1958. "Die Begegnung des nordischen Inlandeises mit dem Rhein," *Geol. Jahrb.* (Hannover), 76: 261-308.

THORNBURY, W. D.

1954. *Principles of Geomorphology.* New York: J. Wiley.

THORNTHWAITE, C. W.

1948. "An Approach Toward a Rational Classification of Climates," *Geogr. Rev.,* 38: 55-94.

1956. "Modification of Rural Microclimate." In THOMAS, 1956, pp. 567-83.

THUN, R., R. HERRMANN, and E. KNICKMAN

1955. *Die Untersuchung von Böden* (3d ed.). Radebeul and Berlin: Neumann.

TISCHLER, W.

1955. *Synökologie der Landtiere.* Stuttgart: G. Fischer.

TODE, A.

1954. *Mammutjäger vor 100,000 Jahren.* Braunschweig: E. Appelhans.

TODE, A. F. PREUL, K. RICHTER, A. KLEINSCHMIDT, *et al.*

1953. "Die Untersuchung der paläolithischen Freilandstation von Salzgitter-Lebenstedt," *Eiszeitalter und Gegenw.,* 3: 144-220.

TONGIORGI, E.

1938. "Vegetation und Klima der letzten Eiszeit und des Postglazials in Mittelitalien," *Proc. 3rd. Int. Congr. INQUA* (Vienna, 1936), pp. 280-83.

TOTHILL, J. D.

1946. "The Origin of the Sudan Gezira Clay Plain," *Sudan Notes and Records,* 27: 153-83.

1948. "Origins of Soils of the Sudan." In J. D. Tothill (ed.), *Agriculture in the Sudan,* London: Oxford University Press, pp. 129-43.

TOYNBEE, A. J.

1935. *A Study of History* (2d ed.). London: Oxford University Press, Vols. 1 and 3.

TREWARTHA, G. T., A. H. ROBINSON, and E. H. HAMMOND

1961. *Fundamentals of Physical Geography.* New York: McGraw-Hill.

TRICART, J.

1956a. "France," *Biuletyn Peryglacjalny,* 4: 117-38.

1956b. *Cartes des phénomènes périglaciaires quaternaires en France.* Paris: Imprimerie Nationale.

1958. "Division morphoclimatique du Brésil atlantique central," *Rev. Geomorph. Dyn,* 9: 1-22.

1961. "Notice explicative de la carte géomorphologique du delta du Sénégal," *Mém. Bur. Rech. Géol. Min.,* No. 8.

1963. *Géomorphologie des régions froides.* Paris: Presses Universitaires de France.

TRICART, J., and A. CAILLEUX
 1956. "Action du froid Quaternaire en Italie Péninsulaire," *Actes IV. Congr. Int. Quaternaire* (Rome, 1953).
 1960-61. *Le modèle des régions sèches*. Paris: Centre de Documentation Universitaire, 2 vol. (mimeographed).

TRICART, J., and J. SCHAEFFER
 1950. "L'indice d'émousse des galets. Moyen d'étude des systèmes d'érosion," *Rev. Géomorph. Dynam.*, 4: 151-79.

TROELS-SMITH, J.
 1960. "Ivy, Mistletoe and Elm. Climate Indicators—Fodder Plants," *Danmarks Geol. Undersoegelse*, series IV, Vol. 4, No. 4.

TROLL, C.
 1944. "Strukturböden, Solifluktion, und Frostklimate der Erde," *Geol. Rundschau*, 34: 545-964. (Also in H. E. Wright (trans.), "Structure Soils, Solifluction, and Frost Climates of the Earth," *U.S. Army Snow, Ice and Permafrost Research Establishment* [Wilmette, Ill.], Translation 43, October, 1958.)
 1947. "Die Formen der Solifluktion und die periglaziale Bodenabtragung," *Erdkunde*, 1: 162-75.
 1948. "Der subnivale oder periglaziale Zyklus der Denudation," *ibid.*, 2: 1-21.
 1950. "Die geographische Landschaft und ihre Erforschung," *Studium generale*, 3: 163-81.
 1956. "Die Klimatypen an der Schneegrenze," *Actes IV. Congr. Int. INQUA* (Rome, 1953), pp. 820-30.

TROMBE, F.
 1952. *Traité de Spéléologie*. Paris: Payot.

VALENTIN, H.
 1952. *Die Kusten der Erde*. Petermanns Mitt.: Ergänzungs-Heft 246.
 1957. "Die Grenze der letzten Vereisung im Nordseeraum," *Abhl. deut. Geographentags* (Hamburg, 1955), Wiesbaden: F. Steiner, pp. 359-72.

VALLOIS, H. V.
 1961. "The Social Life of Early Man: the Evidence of Skeletons," *Viking Fund Publ. Anthropol.*, 31: 214-35.

VAN CAMPO, M.
 1964. "Quelques pollens pleistocènes nouveaux pour le Hoggar," *C. R. Acad. Sci.*, 258: 1297-99.

VAN CAMPO, M., and J. BOUCHUD
 1962. "Flore accompagnent le squélette d'enfant moustérien découvert au Roc de Marsal, commune du Bugue (Dordogne) et première étude de la faune du gisement," *C. R. Acad. Sci.*, 254: 897-99.

VAN CAMPO, M., and R. COQUE
 1960. "Palynologie et géomorphologie dans le sud tunésien," *Pollen et Spores*, 2: 275-84.

VAUFREY, R.
 1928. "Le Paléolithique italien," *Arch. Inst. Paléont. Humaine* (Paris), Mém. 3.
 1929. "Les éléphants nains des iles méditerranéennes," *Arch. Inst. Paléontol. Humaine* (Paris), Mém. 6.

VENZO, S.
 1955. "Le attuali conoscenze sul Pleistocene Lombardo con particolare riguardo al Bergamasco," *Atti Soc. Ital. Sci. Nat.*, 94: 155-200.

VÉRTES, L.
   1959. "Untersuchungen an Höhlensedimenten, Methoden und Ergebnisse," *Régészeti Füzetek* (Budapest) (series 2), No. 7.
VIETE, G.
   1951. "Zum Klima der Vorzeit," *Zeitschr. Meteor.*, 5: 102-10.
VILLALTA, J. F. DE
   1952. "Contribución al conocimiento de la fauna de mamíferos fósiles del Plioceno de Villarroya (Logroño)," *Bol. Inst. Geol. Min. España*, 44.
VIRET, J.
   1954. "Le loess à bancs durcis de Saint-Vallier (Drôme) et sa faune de mammifères villafranchiens," *Nouv. Arch. Mus. Hist. Nat. Lyon*, No. 4.
VIRGILI, C., and I. ZAMARREÑO
   1957. In "Livret Guide de l'Excursion B, (Environs de Barcelona et Montserrat)," *5th Int. Congr. INQUA* (Madrid-Barcelona), pp. 7-16.
VLERK, I. M. VAN DER, and F. FLORSCHÜTZ,
   1953. "The Palaeontological Base of the Subdivision of the Pleistocene in the Netherlands," *Verh. Kon. Nederlandse Akad. Wetenschappen, Naturkunde* (series 1), P. 20, No. 2.
WADELL, H.
   1932. "Volume, Shape and Roundness of Rock Particles," *Jour. Geol.*, 40: 443-51.
WAGNER, P. L., and M. W. MIKESELL (eds.)
   1962. *Readings in Cultural Geography*. Chicago: University of Chicago Press.
WALLÉN, C. C.
   1953. "The Variability of Summer-Temperature in Sweden and Its Connection with Changes in the General Circulation," *Tellus*, 5: 157-78.
   1963. "Aims and Methods in Studies of Climatic Fluctuations," *Arid Zone Research* (UNESCO), 20: 469-75.
WALTER, H.
   1954. *Grundlagen der Pflanzenverbreitung II. Arealkunde*. Stuttgart: E. Ulmer.
   1960. *Grundlagen der Pflanzenverbreitung I. Standortslehre* (2d ed.). Stuttgart: E. Ulmer.
WASHBURN, A. L.
   1956. "Classification of Patterned Ground and Review of Suggested Origins," *Bull. Geol. Soc. Amer.*, 67: 823-66.
WATTERS, R. F.
   1960. "The Nature of Shifting Cultivation, a Review of Recent Research," *Pacific Viewpoint*, 1: 59-99.
WEBER, H.
   1958. *Die Oberflächenformen des festen Landes*. Leipzig: B. G. Teubner.
WEERTMEN, J.
   1961. "Equilibrium Profiles of Ice Caps," *Jour. Glaciol.*, Vol. 3: 953-64.
WEISCHET, W.
   1954. "Die gegenwärtige Kenntnis vom Klima in Mitteleuropa beim Maximum der letzten Vereisung," *Mitt. Geog. Ges. München*, 39: 95-116.
WELTEN, M.
   1954. "Pollenniederschlagstypen aus höhern Lagen Spaniens und ihre subrezenten Veränderungen," *Veröff. Geobotan. Inst. Rübel* (Zürich), 31: 199-216.
WENTWORTH, C. K.
   1922. "A Scale of Grade and Class Terms for Clastic Sediments," *Jour. Geol.*, 30: 277-92.

WERDECKER, J.
    1955. "Beobachtungen in den Hochländern Äthiopiens auf einer Forschungs-
    reise 1953/54," *Erdkunde,* 9: 305-17.
WEST, R. G.
    1955. "The Glaciations and Interglacials of East Anglia," *Quaternaria,* 2:
    45-52.
    1956. "The Quaternary Deposits at Hoxne, Suffolk," *Phil. Trans. Roy. Soc.
    London* (series B), 239: 265-356.
    1961. "Interglacial and Interstadial Vegetation in England," *Proc. Linn. Soc.
    London,* 175: 81-90.
WEST, R. G., and J. J. DONNER
    1956. "The Glaciations of East Anglia and the East Midlands, a Dif-
    ferentiation Based on Stone-Orientation Measurements of the Tills," *Quart.
    Jour. Geol. Soc.,* 112: 69-91.
WEST, R. G., and C. B. M. McBURNEY
    1954. "The Quaternary Deposits at Hoxne, Suffolk, and Their Archaeology,"
    Proc. Prehist. Soc., 20: 131-54.
WHITTOW, J. B., *et al.*
    1963. "Observations on the Glaciers of the Ruwenzori," *Jour. Glaciol.,* 4:
    581-616.
WICHE, K.
    1961. "Beiträge zur Formenentwicklung der Sierren am unteren Segura
    (Südostspanien)," *Mitt. Österr. Geogr. Ges.,* 103: 125-57.
WILHEMY, H.
    1950. "Das Alter der Schwarzerde und die Steppen Mittel-und Osteuropas,"
    Erdkunde, 4: 5-34.
    1958. *Klimamorphologie der Massengesteine.* Braunschweig: G. Westermann.
WILLETT, H. C.
    1949. "Long-Period Fluctuations of the General Circulation of the At-
    mosphere," *Jour. Meteor.,* 6: 34-50.
WILLETT, H. C., and F. SANDERS
    1959. *Descriptive Meteorology.* New York: Academic Press.
WILLIAMS, P. J.
    1961. "Climatic Factors Controlling the Distribution of Certain Frozen
    Ground Phenomena," *Geografiska Ann.,* 43: 339-47.
WILLIS, E. H., H. TAUBER, K. O. MÜNNICH
    1960. "Variations in the Atmospheric Radiocarbon Concentration over the
    Past 1300 Years," *Amer. Jour. Sci., Radiocarbon Supplement,* 2: 1-4.
WISEMAN, J. D. H.
    1954. "The Determination and Significance of Past Temperature Changes in
    the Upper Layer of the Equatorial Atlantic Ocean," *Proc. Roy. Soc.* (series
    A), 222: 296-323.
    1961. Unpublished paper given *in absèntia* at W.M.O.-UNESCO Symposium
    on "Changes of Climate," Rome, Oct. 1-7, 1961.
WISSMANN, H. VON
    1938. "Über Lössbildung und Würmeiszeit in China," *Geog. Zeit.,* 44:
    201-20.
    1957. "Ursprung und Ausbreitungswege von Pflanzen- und Tierzucht und
    ihre Abhängigkeit von der Klimageschichte," *Erdkunde,* 11: 81-94, 175-93.
WITTFOGEL, K. A.
    1956. "The Hydraulic Civilizations." In THOMAS, 1956, pp. 152-64.
WOERKOM, A. J. J. VAN
    1953. "The Astronomical Theory of Climatic Changes." In H. Shapley (ed.),
    Climatic change, Cambridge: Harvard University Press, pp. 147-57.

WOLDSTEDT, P.

1929. *Das Eiszeitalter. Grundlinien einer Geologie des Diluviums.* Stuttgart: F. Enke.

1952. "Probleme der Terrassenbildung," *Eiszeitalter und Gegenw.,* 2: 36-44.

1954. *Die allgemeinen Erscheinungen des Eiszeitalters* (Vol. 1 of *Das Eiszeitalter*). Stuttgart: F. Enke.

1958. *Europa, Vorderasien und Nordafrika im Eiszeitalter* (Vol. 2 of *Das Eiszeitalter*). Stuttgart: F. Enke.

1960a. "Mississippi und Rhein: ein geologischer Vergleich," *Eiszeitalter und Gegenw.,* 11: 31-38.

1960b. "Alte Quartäre Strandlinien in Nordamerika und Europa," *ibid.,* 11: 12-19.

1962a. "Interglaziale marine Stände in Australien," *ibid.,* 12: 60-65.

1962b. "Uber die Gliederung des Quartärs und Pleistozäns," *ibid.,* 13: 115-24.

WORTMANN, H.

1956. "Ein erstes sicheres Vorkommen von periglazialen Steinnetzböden im norddeutschen Flachland," *Eiszeitalter und Gegenw.,* 7: 119-26.

WRIGHT, H. E.

1951. "Geologic Setting of Ksar Akil, a Palaeolithic Site in Lebanon," *Jour. Near Eastern Studies,* 10: 115-19.

1952. "The Geological Setting of Four Prehistoric Sites in Northeastern Iraq," *Bull. Amer. Schools Oriental Research,* 128: 11-24.

1957. "Geology." In *The Identification of Non-Artifactual Archaeological Materials,* Washington, D.C.: Nat. Acad. Sci.—Nat. Res. Council, Publ. 565, pp. 50-51.

1961. "Late Pleistocene Climate of Europe: a Review," *Bull. Geol. Soc. Amer.,* 72: 933-84.

1962a. "Late Pleistocene Geology of Coastal Lebanon," *Quaternaria,* 6: 525-40.

1962b. "Pleistocene Glaciation in Kurdistan," *Eiszeitalter und Gegenw.,* 12: 131-64.

WUNDT, W.

1933. Änderungen der Erdalbedo während der Eiszeit," *Meteor. Zeitschr.,* 50: 241-48.

1944. "Die Mitwirkung der Erdbahnelemente bei der Entstehung der Eiszeiten," *Geol. Rundschau,* 34: 713-47.

ZAGWIJN, W. H.

1960. "Aspects of the Pliocene and Early Pleistocene Vegetation in the Netherlands," *Proefschr. Leiden* (Maastricht).

ZEIST, W. VAN, and H. E. WRIGHT

1963. "Preliminary Pollen Studies at Lake Zeribar, Zagros Mtns., Southwestern Iran," *Science,* 140: 65-67.

ZEUNER, F. E.

1932. "Die Schotteranalyse," *Geol. Rundschau,* 24: 66-104.

1934. "Die Beziehung zwischen Schädelform und Lebensweise bei den rezenten und fossilen Nashörnern," *Ber. Naturforsch. Ges. Freiburg,* 34: 21-80.

1952. "Pleistocene Shore-Lines," *Geol. Rundschau,* 40: 39-50.

1958. *Dating the Past. An Introduction to Geochronology* (1st ed., 1946). London: Methuen.

1959. *The Pleistocene Period. Its Climate, Chronology and Faunal Successions* (2d ed.). London: Hutchinson.

1961. "Criteria for the Determination of Mean Sea-Level for Pleistocene Shoreline Features," *Quaternaria,* 5: 143-47.

1963. *A History of Domesticated Animals.* London: Hutchinson.

ZINDEREN BAKKER, E. M. VAN

1962a. "Botanical Evidence for Quaternary Climates in Africa," *Ann. Cape Provincial Museums,* 2: 16-31.

1962b. "A Pollen Diagram from Equatorial Africa (Cherangani, Kenya)," *Nature,* 194: 201-3.

ZÓLYOMI, B.

1953. "Die Entwicklungsgeschichte der Vegetation Ungarns seit dem letzten Interglacial," *Acta Biol. Acad. Sci. Hung.* (Budapest), 4: 367-430.

ZOTZ, L. F.

1951. *Altsteinzeitkunde Mitteleuropas.* Stuttgart: F. Enke.

1955. *Das Paläolithikum in den Weinberghöhlen bei Mauern* (with sections on geology by G. Freund and palynology by E. Hofman). Bonn: Quartär Bibliothek, L. Röhrscheid, Vol. 2.

1956. "Das Campignien in Süddeutschland," *Forschungen und Fortschritte* (Berlin), 30: 331-35.

Index